These safety symbols are used in laboratory and field investigations in this book to indicate possible hazards. Learn the meaning of each symbol and refer to this page often. *Remember to wash your hands thoroughly after completing lab procedures.*

PROTECTIVE EQUIPMENT   Do not begin any lab without the proper protection equipment.

 GOGGLES Proper eye protection must be worn when performing or observing science activities that involve items or conditions as listed below.

 APRON Wear an approved apron when using substances that could stain, wet, or destroy cloth.

 SOAP Wash hands with soap and water before removing goggles and after all lab activities.

 GLOVES Wear gloves when working with biological materials, chemicals, animals, or materials that can stain or irritate hands.

LABORATORY HAZARDS

Symbols	Potential Hazards	Precaution	Response
DISPOSAL	contamination of classroom or environment due to improper disposal of materials such as chemicals and live specimens	• DO NOT dispose of hazardous materials in the sink or trash can. • Dispose of wastes as directed by your teacher.	• If hazardous materials are disposed of improperly, notify your teacher immediately.
EXTREME TEMPERATURE	skin burns due to extremely hot or cold materials such as hot glass, liquids, or metals; liquid nitrogen; dry ice	• Use proper protective equipment, such as hot mitts and/or tongs, when handling objects with extreme temperatures.	• If injury occurs, notify your teacher immediately.
SHARP OBJECTS	punctures or cuts from sharp objects such as razor blades, pins, scalpels, and broken glass	• Handle glassware carefully to avoid breakage. • Walk with sharp objects pointed downward, away from you and others.	• If broken glass or injury occurs, notify your teacher immediately.
ELECTRICAL	electric shock or skin burn due to improper grounding, short circuits, liquid spills, or exposed wires	• Check condition of wires and apparatus for fraying or uninsulated wires, and broken or cracked equipment. • Use only GFCI-protected outlets	• DO NOT attempt to fix electrical problems. Notify your teacher immediately.
CHEMICAL	skin irritation or burns, breathing difficulty, and/or poisoning due to touching, swallowing, or inhalation of chemicals such as acids, bases, bleach, metal compounds, iodine, poinsettias, pollen, ammonia, acetone, nail polish remover, heated chemicals, mothballs, and any other chemicals labeled or known to be dangerous	• Wear proper protective equipment such as goggles, apron, and gloves when using chemicals. • Ensure proper room ventilation or use a fume hood when using materials that produce fumes. • NEVER smell fumes directly. • NEVER taste or eat any material in the laboratory.	• If contact occurs, immediately flush affected area with water and notify your teacher. • If a spill occurs, leave the area immediately and notify your teacher.
FLAMMABLE	unexpected fire due to liquids or gases that ignite easily such as rubbing alcohol	• Avoid open flames, sparks, or heat when flammable liquids are present.	• If a fire occurs, leave the area immediately and notify your teacher.
OPEN FLAME	burns or fire due to open flame from matches, Bunsen burners, or burning materials	• Tie back loose hair and clothing. • Keep flame away from all materials. • Follow teacher instructions when lighting and extinguishing flames. • Use proper protection, such as hot mitts or tongs, when handling hot objects.	• If a fire occurs, leave the area immediately and notify your teacher.
ANIMAL SAFETY	injury to or from laboratory animals	• Wear proper protective equipment such as gloves, apron, and goggles when working with animals. • Wash hands after handling animals.	• If injury occurs, notify your teacher immediately.
BIOLOGICAL	infection or adverse reaction due to contact with organisms such as bacteria, fungi, and biological materials such as blood, animal or plant materials	• Wear proper protective equipment such as gloves, goggles, and apron when working with biological materials. • Avoid skin contact with an organism or any part of the organism. • Wash hands after handling organisms.	• If contact occurs, wash the affected area and notify your teacher immediately.
FUME	breathing difficulties from inhalation of fumes from substances such as ammonia, acetone, nail polish remover, heated chemicals, and mothballs	• Wear goggles, apron, and gloves. • Ensure proper room ventilation or use when using substances that produce • NEVER smell fumes directly.	• If a spill occurs, leave area ... your teacher
IRRITANT	irritation of skin, mucous membranes, or respiratory tract due to materials such as acids, bases, bleach, pollen, mothballs, steel wool, and potassium permanganate	• Wear goggles, apron, and gloves. • Wear a dust mask to protect agains	
RADIOACTIVE	excessive exposure from alpha, beta, and gamma particles	• Remove gloves and wash hands with soap and water before removing remainder of protective equipment.	• If cracks or holes ... in the container, notify your teacher immediately.

INTEGRATED iSCIENCE

GLENCOE

GRADE 8

Mc
Graw
Hill
Education

COVER: Zdenka Darula/shutterstock

mheducation.com/prek-12

Send all inquiries to:
McGraw-Hill Education
8787 Orion Place
Columbus, OH 43240

ISBN: 978-0-07-898600-0
MHID: 0-07-898600-1

Printed in the United States of America.

2 3 4 5 6 7 QVS 21 20 19 18 17

Contents in Brief

Nature of Science .... NOS 2

Unit 1

Properties of Matter 2
Chapter 1 Foundations of Chemistry 6
Chapter 2 Understanding the Atom 48
Chapter 3 The Periodic Table............................. 80
Chapter 4 Elements and Chemical Bonds 116
Chapter 5 Chemical Reactions and Equations 150

Unit 2

Earth's Systems **184**
Chapter 6 Weather...................................... 188
Chapter 7 Climate...................................... 224
Chapter 8 Earth's Water................................ 260
Chapter 9 Environmental Impacts 296

Unit 3

Exploring Life **338**
Chapter 10 Life's Classification and Structure 342
Chapter 11 Reproduction of Organisms 370
Chapter 12 Genetics..................................... 402
Chapter 13 The Environment and Change Over Time........ 442
Chapter 14 Bacteria and Viruses......................... 480

Authors and Contributors

Authors

American Museum of Natural History
New York, NY

Michelle Anderson, MS
Lecturer
The Ohio State University
Columbus, OH

Juli Berwald, PhD
Science Writer
Austin, TX

John F. Bolzan, PhD
Science Writer
Columbus, OH

Rachel Clark, MS
Science Writer
Moscow, ID

Patricia Craig, MS
Science Writer
Bozeman, MT

Randall Frost, PhD
Science Writer
Pleasanton, CA

Lisa S. Gardiner, PhD
Science Writer
Denver, CO

Jennifer Gonya, PhD
The Ohio State University
Columbus, OH

Mary Ann Grobbel, MD
Science Writer
Grand Rapids, MI

Whitney Crispen Hagins, MA, MAT
Biology Teacher
Lexington High School
Lexington, MA

Carole Holmberg, BS
Planetarium Director
Calusa Nature Center and Planetarium, Inc.
Fort Myers, FL

Tina C. Hopper
Science Writer
Rockwall, TX

Jonathan D. W. Kahl, PhD
Professor of Atmospheric Science
University of Wisconsin-Milwaukee
Milwaukee, WI

Nanette Kalis
Science Writer
Athens, OH

S. Page Keeley, MEd
Maine Mathematics and Science Alliance
Augusta, ME

Cindy Klevickis, PhD
Professor of Integrated Science and Technology
James Madison University
Harrisonburg, VA

Kimberly Fekany Lee, PhD
Science Writer
La Grange, IL

Michael Manga, PhD
Professor
University of California, Berkeley
Berkeley, CA

Devi Ried Mathieu
Science Writer
Sebastopol, CA

Elizabeth A. Nagy-Shadman, PhD
Geology Professor
Pasadena City College
Pasadena, CA

William D. Rogers, DA
Professor of Biology
Ball State University
Muncie, IN

Donna L. Ross, PhD
Associate Professor
San Diego State University
San Diego, CA

Marion B. Sewer, PhD
Assistant Professor
School of Biology
Georgia Institute of Technology
Atlanta, GA

Julia Meyer Sheets, PhD
Lecturer
School of Earth Sciences
The Ohio State University
Columbus, OH

Michael J. Singer, PhD
Professor of Soil Science
Department of Land, Air and Water Resources
University of California
Davis, CA

Karen S. Sottosanti, MA
Science Writer
Pickerington, Ohio

Paul K. Strode, PhD
I.B. Biology Teacher
Fairview High School
Boulder, CO

Jan M. Vermilye, PhD
Research Geologist
Seismo-Tectonic Reservoir Monitoring (STRM)
Boulder, CO

Judith A. Yero, MA
Director
Teacher's Mind Resources
Hamilton, MT

Dinah Zike, MEd
Author, Consultant, Inventor of Foldables
Dinah Zike Academy; Dinah-Might Adventures, LP
San Antonio, TX

Margaret Zorn, MS
Science Writer
Yorktown, VA

Consulting Authors

Alton L. Biggs
Biggs Educational Consulting
Commerce, TX

Ralph M. Feather, Jr., PhD
Assistant Professor
Department of Educational Studies
and Secondary Education
Bloomsburg University
Bloomsburg, PA

Douglas Fisher, PhD
Professor of Teacher Education
San Diego State University
San Diego, CA

Edward P. Ortleb
Science/Safety Consultant
St. Louis, MO

Series Consultants

Science

Solomon Bililign, PhD
Professor
Department of Physics
North Carolina Agricultural and
Technical State University
Greensboro, NC

John Choinski
Professor
Department of Biology
University of Central Arkansas
Conway, AR

Anastasia Chopelas, PhD
Research Professor
Department of Earth and Space
Sciences
UCLA
Los Angeles, CA

David T. Crowther, PhD
Professor of Science Education
University of Nevada, Reno
Reno, NV

A. John Gatz
Professor of Zoology
Ohio Wesleyan University
Delaware, OH

Sarah Gille, PhD
Professor
University of California San Diego
La Jolla, CA

David G. Haase, PhD
Professor of Physics
North Carolina State University
Raleigh, NC

Janet S. Herman, PhD
Professor
Department of Environmental Sciences
University of Virginia
Charlottesville, VA

David T. Ho, PhD
Associate Professor
Department of Oceanography
University of Hawaii
Honolulu, HI

Ruth Howes, PhD
Professor of Physics
Marquette University
Milwaukee, WI

Jose Miguel Hurtado, Jr., PhD
Associate Professor
Department of Geological Sciences
University of Texas at El Paso
El Paso, TX

Monika Kress, PhD
Assistant Professor
San Jose State University
San Jose, CA

Mark E. Lee, PhD
Associate Chair & Assistant Professor
Department of Biology
Spelman College
Atlanta, GA

Linda Lundgren
Science writer
Lakewood, CO

Keith O. Mann, PhD
Ohio Wesleyan University
Delaware, OH

Charles W. McLaughlin, PhD
Adjunct Professor of Chemistry
Montana State University
Bozeman, MT

Katharina Pahnke, PhD
Research Professor
Department of Geology and Geophysics
University of Hawaii
Honolulu, HI

Jesús Pando, PhD
Associate Professor
DePaul University
Chicago, IL

Hay-Oak Park, PhD
Associate Professor
Department of Molecular Genetics
Ohio State University
Columbus, OH

David A. Rubin, PhD
Associate Professor of Physiology
School of Biological Sciences
Illinois State University
Normal, IL

Toni D. Sauncy
Assistant Professor of Physics
Department of Physics
Angelo State University
San Angelo, TX

Series Consultants, continued

Malathi Srivatsan, PhD
Associate Professor of Neurobiology
College of Sciences and
Mathematics
Arkansas State University
Jonesboro, AR

Cheryl Wistrom, PhD
Associate Professor of Chemistry
Saint Joseph's College
Rensselaer, IN

Reading

ReLeah Cossett Lent
Author/Educational Consultant
Blue Ridge, GA

Math

Vik Hovsepian
Professor of Mathematics
Rio Hondo College
Whittier, CA

Series Reviewers

Thad Boggs
Mandarin High School
Jacksonville, FL

Catherine Butcher
Webster Junior High School
Minden, LA

Erin Darichuk
West Frederick Middle School
Frederick, MD

Joanne Hedrick Davis
Murphy High School
Murphy, NC

Anthony J. DiSipio, Jr.
Octorara Middle School
Atglen, PA

Adrienne Elder
Tulsa Public Schools
Tulsa, OK

Carolyn Elliott
Iredell-Statesville Schools
Statesville, NC

Christine M. Jacobs
Ranger Middle School
Murphy, NC

Jason O. L. Johnson
Thurmont Middle School
Thurmont, MD

Felecia Joiner
Stony Point Ninth Grade Center
Round Rock, TX

Joseph L. Kowalski, MS
Lamar Academy
McAllen, TX

Brian McClain
Amos P. Godby High School
Tallahassee, FL

Von W. Mosser
Thurmont Middle School
Thurmont, MD

Ashlea Peterson
Heritage Intermediate Grade
Center
Coweta, OK

Nicole Lenihan Rhoades
Walkersville Middle School
Walkersvillle, MD

Maria A. Rozenberg
Indian Ridge Middle School
Davie, FL

Barb Seymour
Westridge Middle School
Overland Park, KS

Ginger Shirley
Our Lady of Providence Junior-
Senior High School
Clarksville, IN

Curtis Smith
Elmwood Middle School
Rogers, AR

Sheila Smith
Jackson Public School
Jackson, MS

Sabra Soileau
Moss Bluff Middle School
Lake Charles, LA

Tony Spoores
Switzerland County Middle
School
Vevay, IN

Nancy A. Stearns
Switzerland County Middle
School
Vevay, IN

Kari Vogel
Princeton Middle School
Princeton, MN

Alison Welch
Wm. D. Slider Middle School
El Paso, TX

Linda Workman
Parkway Northeast Middle
School
Creve Coeur, MO

 **Indiana Reviewers**

Each reviewer provided valuable feedback and suggestions regarding the effectiveness of the science instruction. We thank them for their feedback.

LaTheresa King
Secondary Curriculum Coordinator
Fort Wayne Community Schools

Deborah Watson
Secondary Curriculum Coordinator
East Allen County Schools

Rosie Easterday
Math Department Chair
DeKalb County Eastern

Ginger Shirley
Secondary Science
Education Specialist
New Albany High School

Jill Swango
Secondary Science
Education Specialist
Brownsburg East Middle School

Jane Buckingham
Secondary Science
Education Specialist
Secondary Administrator
Indianapolis Public Schools

Teacher Advisory Board

The Teacher Advisory Board gave the authors, editorial staff, and design team feedback on the content and design of the Student Edition. They provided valuable input in the development of *Glencoe Integrated iScience.*

Frances J. Baldridge
Department Chair
Ferguson Middle School
Beavercreek, OH

Jane E. M. Buckingham
Teacher
Crispus Attucks Medical Magnet
High School
Indianapolis, IN

Elizabeth Falls
Teacher
Blalack Middle School
Carrollton, TX

Nelson Farrier
Teacher
Hamlin Middle School
Springfield, OR

Michelle R. Foster
Department Chair
Wayland Union Middle School
Wayland, MI

Rebecca Goodell
Teacher
Reedy Creek Middle School
Cary, NC

Mary Gromko
Science Supervisor K–12
Colorado Springs District 11
Colorado Springs, CO

Randy Mousley
Department Chair
Dean Ray Stucky Middle School
Wichita, KS

David Rodriguez
Teacher
Swift Creek Middle School
Tallahassee, FL

Derek Shook
Teacher
Floyd Middle Magnet School
Montgomery, AL

Karen Stratton
Science Coordinator
Lexington School District One
Lexington, SC

Stephanie Wood
Science Curriculum Specialist, K–12
Granite School District
Salt Lake City, UT

Welcome to

iSCIENCE

We are your partner in learning by meeting your diverse 21st century needs. Designed for today's tech-savvy middle school students, the McGraw-Hill Education Indiana *iScience* program offers hands-on investigations, rigorous science content, and engaging, real-world applications to make science fun, exciting, and stimulating.

Quick Start Guide
Indiana iScience | Student Center

Login information

(1) Go to **connected.mcgraw-hill.com.**

(2) Enter your registered Username and Password.

(3) For **new users** click here to create a new account.

(4) Get **ConnectED Help** for creating accounts, verifying master codes, and more.

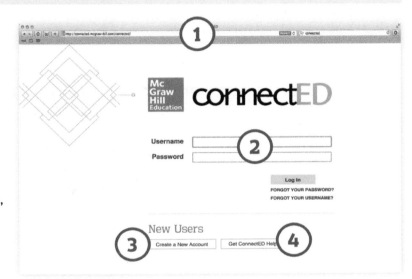

Your ConnectED Center

(5) Scroll down to find the program from which you would like to work.

Quick Start Guide
Indiana iScience | Student Center

1 The Menu allows you to easily jump to anywhere you need to be.

2 Click the **program icon** at the top left to **return to the main page** from any screen.

3 **Select a Chapter and Lesson** Use the drop down boxes to quickly jump to any lesson in any chapter.

4 Return to your **My Home** page for all your **ConnectED** content.

5 The **Help** icon will guide you to online help. It will also allow for a quick logout.

6 The **Search Bar** allows you to search content by topic or standard.

7 **Access the eBook** **Use** the **Student Edition** to see content.

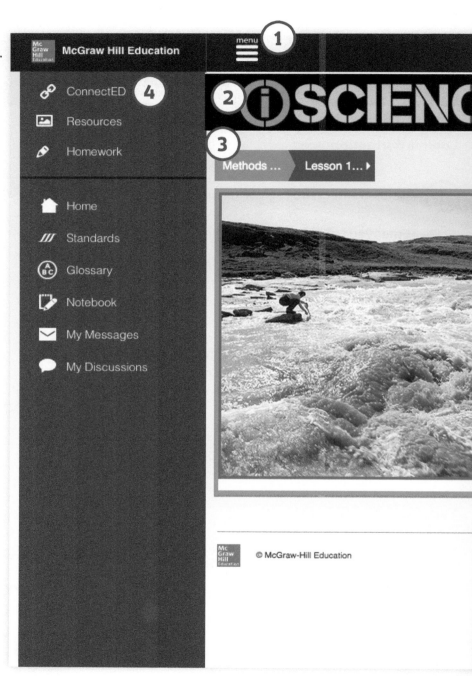

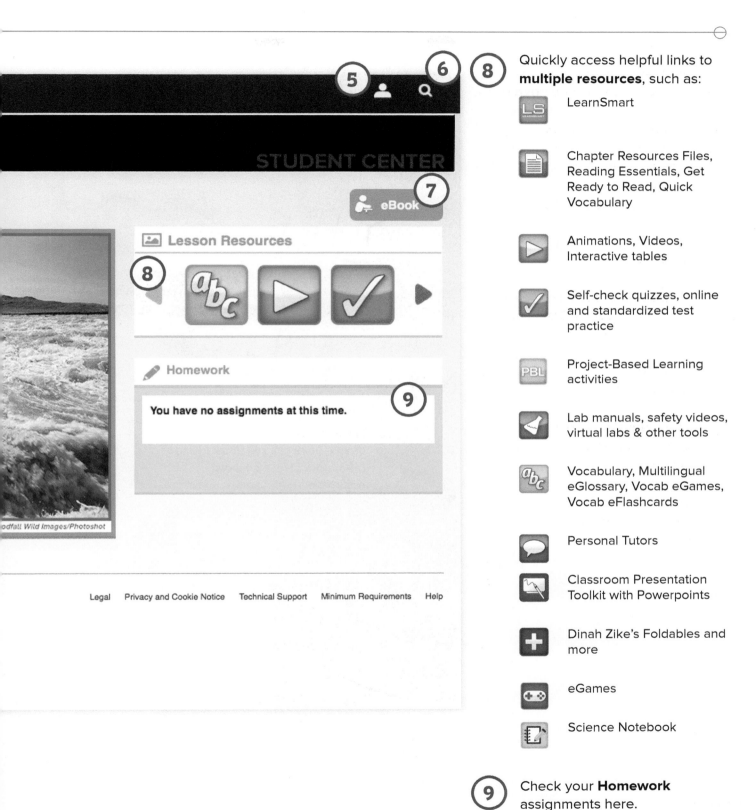

5

6

8 Quickly access helpful links to **multiple resources**, such as:

LearnSmart

Chapter Resources Files, Reading Essentials, Get Ready to Read, Quick Vocabulary

Animations, Videos, Interactive tables

Self-check quizzes, online and standardized test practice

Project-Based Learning activities

Lab manuals, safety videos, virtual labs & other tools

Vocabulary, Multilingual eGlossary, Vocab eGames, Vocab eFlashcards

Personal Tutors

Classroom Presentation Toolkit with Powerpoints

Dinah Zike's Foldables and more

eGames

Science Notebook

STUDENT CENTER

7 eBook

🖼 **Lesson Resources**

8 *abc* ▶ ✓ ▶

✏ **Homework**

You have no assignments at this time. **9**

odfall Wild Images/Photoshot

Legal   Privacy and Cookie Notice   Technical Support   Minimum Requirements   Help

9 Check your **Homework** assignments here.

connected.mcgraw-hill.com

Treasure Hunt

Your science book has many features that will aid you in your learning. Some of these features are listed below. You can use the activity at the right to help you find these and other special features in the book.

- **BIG IDEA** can be found at the start of each chapter.
- The Reading Guide at the start of each lesson lists 🔑 **Key Concepts,** vocabulary terms, and online supplements to the content.
- **connectED** icons direct you to online resources such as animations, personal tutors, math practices, and quizzes.
- **Inquiry** Labs and Skill Practices are in each chapter.
- Your **FOLDABLES** help organize your notes.

1 What four margin items can help you build your vocabulary?

2 On what page does the glossary begin? What glossary is online?

3 In which Student Resource at the back of your book can you find a listing of Laboratory Safety Symbols?

4 Suppose you want to find a list of all the Launch Labs, MiniLabs, Skill Practices, and Labs, where do you look?

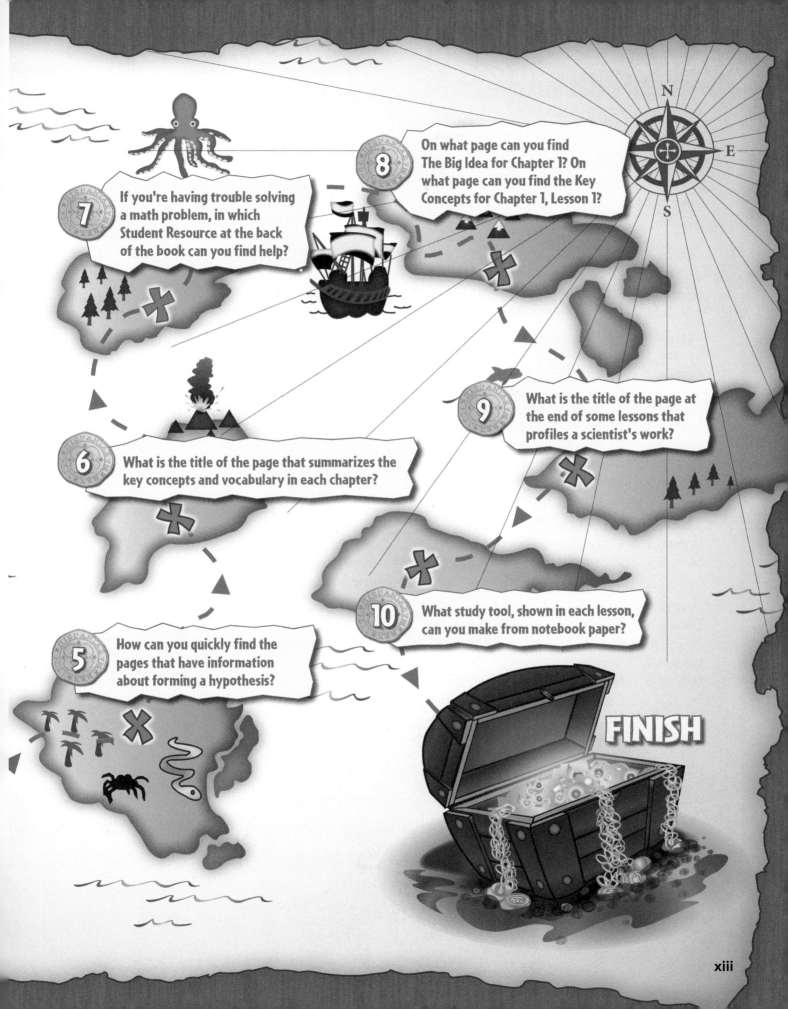

7 If you're having trouble solving a math problem, in which Student Resource at the back of the book can you find help?

8 On what page can you find The Big Idea for Chapter 1? On what page can you find the Key Concepts for Chapter 1, Lesson 1?

9 What is the title of the page at the end of some lessons that profiles a scientist's work?

6 What is the title of the page that summarizes the key concepts and vocabulary in each chapter?

10 What study tool, shown in each lesson, can you make from notebook paper?

5 How can you quickly find the pages that have information about forming a hypothesis?

FINISH

Table of Contents

Scientific Problem Solving . . . . .NOS 2
Lesson 1   Scientific Inquiry. . . . . .NOS 4
Lesson 2   Measurement and Scientific Tools . . . . .NOS 18
             ☑ **Lab: Skill Practice** How do geometric shapes differ
             in strength? . . . . NOS 19
Lesson 3   Case Study . . . . NOS 26
             ☑ **Lab** Build and Test a Bridge . . . . .NOS 34

Unit 1   **Properties of Matter**. 2

Chapter 1   **Foundations of Chemistry**. 6
Lesson 1   Classifying Matter. 8
Lesson 2   Physical Properties 17
             ☑ **Lab: Skill Practice** How can following a procedure help you
             solve a crime?. 25
Lesson 3   Physical Changes. 26
             ☑ **Lab: Skill Practice** How can known substances help you
             identify unknown substances?. 32
Lesson 4   Chemical Properties and Changes. 33
             ☑ **Lab** Design an Experiment to Solve a Crime. 40

Chapter 2   **Understanding the Atom**. 48
Lesson 1   Discovering Parts of the Atom. 50
Lesson 2   Protons, Neutrons, and Electrons—How Atoms Differ 63
             ☑ **Lab** Communicate Your Knowledge About the Atom. 72

Chapter 3   **The Periodic Table** 80
Lesson 1   Using the Periodic Table. 82
             ☑ **Lab: Skill Practice** How is the periodic table arranged?. 91
Lesson 2   Metals. 92
Lesson 3   Nonmetals and Metalloids 100
             ☑ **Lab** Alien Insect Periodic Table 108

Chapter 4 **Elements and Chemical Bonds** **116**
Lesson 1 Electrons and Energy Levels 118
Lesson 2 Compounds, Chemical Formulas, and Covalent Bonds 127
  Lab: Skill Practice How can you model compounds? 134
Lesson 3 Ionic and Metallic Bonds. 135
  Lab Ions in Solution 142

Chapter 5 **Chemical Reactions and Equations** **150**
Lesson 1 Understanding Chemical Reactions 152
  Lab: Skill Practice What can you learn from an experiment? 162
Lesson 2 Types of Chemical Reactions. 163
Lesson 3 Energy Changes and Chemical Reactions 169
  Lab Design an Experiment to Test Advertising Claims 176

Unit 2 **Earth's Systems** **184**

Chapter 6 **Weather** **188**
Lesson 1 Describing Weather. 190
Lesson 2 Weather Patterns 198
  Skill Practice Why does the weather change? 209
Lesson 3 Weather Forecasts. 210
  Lab Can you predict the weather? 216

Chapter 7 **Climate** **224**
Lesson 1 Climates of Earth 226
  Skill Practice Can reflection of the Sun's rays change the climate? 234
Lesson 2 Climate Cycles 235
Lesson 3 Recent Climate Change 244
  Lab The greenhouse effect is a gas!. 252

Chapter 8 **Earth's Water** **260**
Lesson 1 The Water Planet 262
Lesson 2 The Properties of Water 272
  Skill Practice Why is liquid water denser than ice? 280
Lesson 3 Water Quality 281
  Lab Temperature and Water's Density 288

TABLE OF CONTENTS

xv

Table of Contents

Chapter 9 **Environmental Impacts** **296**
Lesson 1 People and the Environment 298
    Skill Practice What amount of Earth's resources do
    you use in a day? 303
Lesson 2 Impacts on the Land 304
    Skill Practice How will you design an environmentally
    safe landfill? 313
Lesson 3 Impacts on Water 314
Lesson 4 Impacts on the Atmosphere 322
    Lab Design a Green City 330

Unit 3 **Exploring Life** **338**

Chapter 10 **Life's Classification and Structure** **342**
Lesson 1 Classifying Living Things 344
Lesson 2 Cells 354
    Lab How can living things be classified? 362

Chapter 11 **Reproduction of Organisms** **370**
Lesson 1 Sexual Reproduction and Meiosis 372
Lesson 2 Asexual Reproduction 384
    Lab Mitosis and Meiosis 394

Chapter 12 **Genetics** **402**
Lesson 1 Mendel and His Peas 404
Lesson 2 Understanding Inheritance 414
    Skill Practice How can you use Punnett squares to model inheritance? . . . 424
Lesson 3 DNA and Genetics 425
    Lab Gummy Bear Genetics 434

TABLE OF CONTENTS

Chapter 13 The Environment and Change Over Time **442**
Lesson 1   Fossil Evidence of Evolution 444
            ◿ **Skill Practice** Can you observe changes through time
            in collections of everyday objects? 453
Lesson 2   Theory of Evolution by Natural Selection 454
Lesson 3   Biological Evidence of Evolution. 464
            ◿ **Lab** Model Adaptations in an Organism. 472

Chapter 14 Bacteria and Viruses **480**
Lesson 1   What are bacteria?. 482
Lesson 2   Bacteria in Nature 490
            ◿ **Skill Practice** How do lab techniques affect an investigation? 497
Lesson 3   What are viruses?. 498
            ◿ **Lab** Bacterial Growth and Disinfectants 506

Table of Contents

Student Resources

Science Skill Handbook **SR-2**
Scientific Methods SR-2
Safety Symbols SR-11
Safety in the Science Laboratory SR-12

Math Skill Handbook **SR-14**
Math Review SR-14
Science Applications SR-24

Foldables Handbook **SR-29**

Reference Handbook **SR-40**
Periodic Table of the Elements SR-40
Topographic Map Symbols SR-42
Rocks SR-43
Minerals SR-44
Weather Map Symbols SR-46

Glossary **G-2**

Index **I-2**

TABLE OF CONTENTS

Inquiry

Launch Labs

1-1 How do you classify matter?. 9

1-2 Can you follow the clues?. 18

1-3 Where did it go? .27

1-4 What can colors tell you? 34

2-1 What's in there?. .51

2-2 How many different things can you make? 64

3-1 How can objects be organized? 83

3-2 What properties make metals useful?. . . . 93

3-3 What are some properties of nonmetals? 101

4-1 How is the periodic table organized?. . 119

4-2 How is a compound different from its elements? 128

4-3 How can atoms form compounds by gaining and losing electrons?. 136

5-1 Where did it come from? 153

5-2 What combines with what?. 164

5-3 Where's the heat?. 170

6-1 Can you make clouds in a bag?. 191

6-2 How can temperature affect pressure? 199

6-3 Can you understand the weather report? 211

7-1 How do climates compare?. 227

7-2 How does Earth's tilted axis affect climate?. 236

7-3 What changes climates? 245

8-1 Which heats faster? 263

8-2 How many drops can fit on a penny? 273

8-3 How can you test the cloudiness of water?. 282

9-1 What happens as populations increase in size? 299

9-2 How can items be reused?. 305

9-3 Which water filter is the most effective? 315

9-4 Where's the air? 323

10-1 How can you tell if it is alive?. 345

10-2 Are all cells alive?. 355

11-1 Why do offspring look different? 373

11-2 How do yeast reproduce?. 385

12-1 What makes you unique? 405

12-2 What is the span of your hand?. 415

12-3 How are codes used to determine traits?. 426

13-1 How do fossils form? 445

13-2 Are there variations within your class? 455

13-3 How is the structure of a spoon related to its function?. 465

14-1 How small are bacteria? 483

14-2 How do bacteria affect the environment?. 491

14-3 How quickly do viruses replicate?. . . . 499

TABLE OF CONTENTS

Inquiry

MiniLabs

1-1 How can you model an atom? 10

1-2 Can the weight of an object change? 20

1-3 Can you make ice without a freezer? 29

1-4 Can you spot the clues for chemical change? 36

2-1 How can you gather information about what you can't see? 58

2-2 How many penny isotopes do you have? 67

3-1 How does atom size change across a period? 89

3-2 How well do materials conduct thermal energy? 97

3-3 Which insulates better? 106

4-1 How does an electron's energy relate to its position in an atom? 124

4-2 How do compounds form? 132

4-3 How many ionic compounds can you make? 139

5-1 How does an equation represent a reaction? 157

5-3 Can you speed up a reaction? 174

6-1 When will dew form? 193

6-2 How can you observe air pressure? 201

6-3 How is weather represented on a map? 214

7-1 Where are microclimates found? 232

7-2 How do climates vary? 241

7-3 How much CO_2 do vehicles emit? 249

8-1 What happens to temperature during a change of state? 267

8-2 Is every substance less dense in its solid state? 277

8-3 How do oxygen levels affect marine life? 284

9-2 What happens when you mine? 307

9-3 What's in well water? 318

9-4 What's in the air? 327

10-1 Whose shoe is it? 351

10-2 What can you see in a cell? 358

11-1 How does one cell produce four cells? 375

11-2 What parts of plants can grow? 389

12-1 Which is the dominant trait? 411

12-2 Can you infer genotype? 417

12-3 How can you model DNA? 428

13-1 How do species change over time? . . .451

13-2 Who survives? 461

13-3 How related are organisms? 469

14-1 How does a slime layer work? 485

14-2 Can decomposition happen without oxygen? 492

14-3 How do antibodies work? 504

✦ Skill Practice

NOS 2 How do geometric shapes differ in strength? . . . . NOS 25

1-2 How can following a procedure help you solve a crime? 25

1-3 How can known substances help you identify unknown substances? 32

3-1 How is the periodic table arranged? 91

4-2 How can you model compounds? 134

5-1 What can you learn from an experiment? 162

6-2 Why does the weather change? 209

7-1 Can reflection of the Sun's rays change the climate? 234

8-2 Why is liquid water denser than ice? 280

9-1 What amount of Earth's resources do you use in a day? 303

9-2 How will you design an environmentally safe landfill? 313

12-2 How can you use Punnett squares to model inheritance? 424

13-1 Can you observe changes through time in collections of everyday objects? . . . 453

14-2 How do lab techniques affect an investigation? 497

Inquiry

 **Labs**

NOS 3 Build and Test a Bridge . . . . .NOS 28

1-4 Design an Experiment to Solve a
Crime. 40

2-2 Communicate Your Knowledge
about the Atom 72

3-3 Alien Insect Periodic Table 108

4-3 Ions in Solution .142

5-3 Design an Experiment to Test
Advertising Claims 176

6-3 Can you predict the weather? 216

7-3 The greenhouse effect is a gas! 252

8-3 Temperature and Water's Density 288

9-4 Design a Green City. 330

10-2 How can living things
be classified?. 362

11-2 Mitosis and Meiosis 394

12-3 Gummy Bear Genetics. 434

13-3 Model Adaptations in an Organism. . . 472

14-3 Bacterial Growth and Disinfectants . . . 506

TABLE OF CONTENTS

Features

HOW NATURE WORKS

14-1 Cooking Bacteria!. 489

HOW IT WORKS

1-1 U.S. Mint. 16
5-2 How does a light stick work?. 168

GREEN SCIENCE

4-1 New Green Airships. 126
9-3 Dead Zones. 321

SCIENCE & SOCIETY

2-1 Subatomic Particles 62
3-2 Fireworks. 99
6-1 Is there a link between hurricanes
and global warming? 197

12-1 Pioneering the Science
of Genetics 413

CAREERS in SCIENCE

7-2 Frozen in Time 243
8-1 Oceans on the Rise—Again 271
10-1 On a Quest for Leeches 353

11-1 The Spider Mating Dance. 383
13-2 Peter and Rosemary Grant 463

Nature of Science

SEPS.1, SEPS.2, SEPS.3, SEPS.4, SEPS.5, SEPS.6, SEPS.8, 6-8.E.1, 6-8.E.2, 6-8.E.3, 6-8.E.4, 6-8.LST.4.2

Scientific Problem Solving

THE BIG IDEA What is scientific inquiry?

Inquiry Sci-Fi Movie Scene?

This might look like a weird spaceship docking in a science-fiction movie. However, it is actually the back of an airplane engine being tested in a huge wind tunnel. An experiment is an important part of scientific investigations.

- Why is an experiment important?

- Does experimentation occur in all branches of science?

- What is scientific inquiry?

photo by John Kaplan, NASA

Nature of SCIENCE

This chapter begins your study of the nature of science, but there is even more information about the nature of science in this book. Each unit begins by exploring an important topic that is fundamental to scientific study. As you read these topics, you will learn even more about the nature of science.

Patterns	**Unit 1**
Models	**Unit 2**
History	**Unit 3**

connectED

Your one-stop online resource
connectED.mcgraw-hill.com

 LearnSmart®

 Chapter Resources Files, Reading Essentials, Get Ready to Read, Quick Vocabulary

 Animations, Videos, Interactive Tables

 Self-checks, Quizzes, Tests

 Project-Based Learning Activities

 Lab Manuals, Safety Videos, Virtual Labs & Other Tools

 Vocabulary, Multilingual eGlossary, Vocab eGames, Vocab eFlashcards

 Personal Tutors

Scientific Inquiry

Reading Guide

Key Concepts
ESSENTIAL QUESTIONS

- What are some steps used during scientific inquiry?

- What are the results of scientific inquiry?

- What is critical thinking?

Vocabulary

science p. NOS 4

observation p. NOS 6

inference p. NOS 6

hypothesis p. NOS 6

prediction p. NOS 6

scientific theory p. NOS 8

scientific law p. NOS 8

technology p. NOS 9

critical thinking p. NOS 10

 Multilingual eGlossary

BrainPOP®
Science Video

 SEPS.1, SEPS.2, SEPS.3, SEPS.4, SEPS.8, 6-8.E.1, 6-8.E.2, 6-8.E.3, 6-8.E.4, 6-8.LST.4.2

Understanding Science

A clear night sky is one of the most beautiful sights on Earth. The stars seem to shine like a handful of diamonds scattered on black velvet. Why do stars seem to shine more brightly some nights than others?

Did you know that when you ask questions, such as the one above, you are practicing science? **Science** *is the investigation and exploration of natural events and of the new information that results from those investigations.* Like a scientist, you can help shape the future by accumulating knowledge, developing new technologies, and sharing ideas with others.

Throughout history, people of many different backgrounds, interests, and talents have made scientific contributions. Sometimes they overcame a limited educational background and excelled in science. One example is Marie Curie, shown in **Figure 1.** She was a scientist who won two Nobel prizes in the early 1900s for her work with radioactivity. As a young student, Curie was not allowed to study at the University of Warsaw in Poland because she was a woman. Despite this obstacle, she made significant contributions to science.

Figure 1 Modern medical procedures such as X-rays, radioactive cancer treatments, and nuclear-power generation are some of the technologies made possible because of the pioneering work of Marie Curie and her associates.

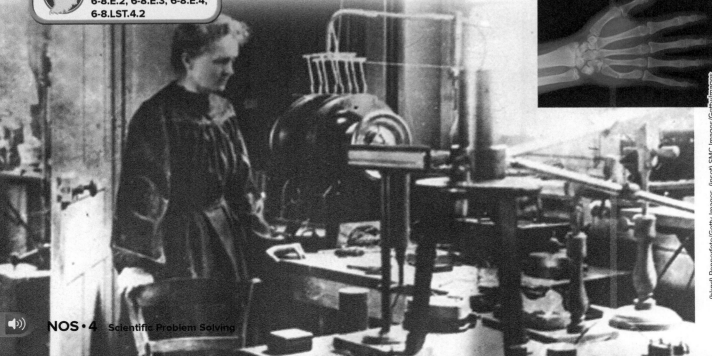

(bkgd) Popperfoto/Getty Images, (inset) SMC Images/Getty Images

Branches of Science

Scientific study is organized into several branches, or parts. The three branches that you will study in middle school are physical science, Earth science, and life science. Each branch focuses on a different part of the natural world.

WORD ORIGIN

science
from Latin scientia, means "knowledge" or "to know"

Physical Science

Physical science, or physics and chemistry, is the study of matter and energy. The physicist shown here is adjusting an instrument that measures radiation from the Big Bang. Physical scientists ask questions such as

- What happens to energy during chemical reactions?
- How does gravity affect roller coasters?
- What makes up protons, neutrons, and electrons?

Earth Science

Earth scientists study the many processes that occur on Earth and deep within Earth. This scientist is collecting a water sample in southern Mexico.

Earth scientists ask questions such as

- What are the properties of minerals?
- How is energy transferred on Earth?
- How do volcanoes form?

Life Science

Life scientists study all organisms and the many processes that occur in them. The life scientist shown is studying the avian flu virus.

Life scientists ask questions such as

- How do plant cells and animal cells differ?
- How do animals survive in the desert?
- How do organisms in a community interact?

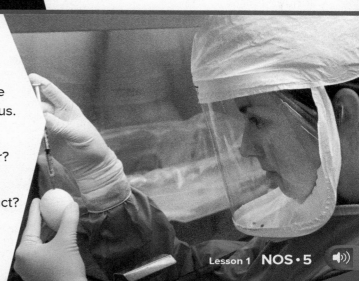

What is Scientific Inquiry?

When scientists conduct investigations, they often want to answer questions about the natural world. To do this, they use scientific inquiry–a process that uses a variety of skills and tools to answer questions or to test ideas. You might have heard these steps called "the scientific method." However, there is no one scientific method. In fact, the skills that scientists use to conduct an investigation can be used in any order. One possible sequence is shown in **Figure 2**. Like a scientist, you perform scientific investigations every day, and you will do investigations throughout this course.

 Reading Check What is scientific inquiry?

Ask Questions

Imagine warming yourself near a fireplace or a campfire? As you throw twigs and logs onto the fire, you see that fire releases smoke and light. You also feel the warmth of the thermal energy being released. These are **observations**–*the results of using one or more of your senses to gather information and taking note of what occurs.* Observations often lead to questions. You ask yourself, "When logs burn, what happens to the wood? Do the logs disappear? Do they change in some way?"

When observing the fire, you might recall from an earlier science course that matter can change form, but it cannot be created or destroyed. Therefore, you infer that the logs do not just disappear. They must undergo some type of change. An **inference** *is a logical explanation of an observation that is drawn from prior knowledge or experience.*

Hypothesize and Predict

After making observations and inferences, you decide to investigate further. Like a scientist, you might develop a **hypothesis**–*a possible explanation for an observation that can be tested by scientific investigations.* Your hypothesis about what happens to the logs might be: When logs burn, new substances form because matter cannot be destroyed.

When scientists state a hypothesis, they often use it to make predictions to help test their hypothesis. *A* **prediction** *is a statement of what will happen next in a sequence of events.* Scientists make predictions based on what information they think they will find when testing their hypothesis. For instance, based on your hypothesis, you might predict that if logs burn, then the substances that make up the logs change into other substances.

Figure 2 There are many possible steps in the process of scientific inquiry, and they can be performed in a variety of different sequences.

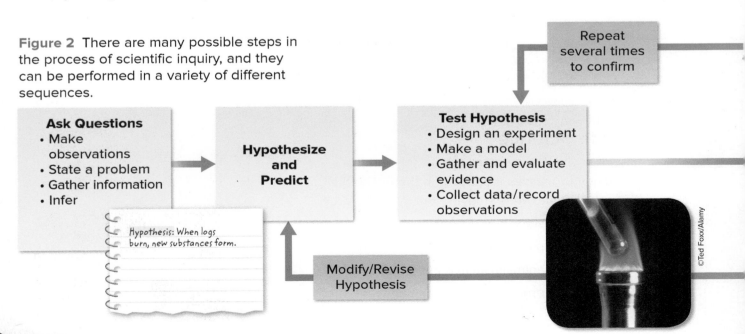

Ask Questions
- Make observations
- State a problem
- Gather information
- Infer

Hypothesis: When logs burn, new substances form.

Hypothesize and Predict

Test Hypothesis
- Design an experiment
- Make a model
- Gather and evaluate evidence
- Collect data/record observations

Repeat several times to confirm

Modify/Revise Hypothesis

©Ted Foxx/Alamy

Test Hypothesis and Analyze Results

How could you test your hypothesis? When you test a hypothesis, you often test your predictions. If a prediction is confirmed, then it supports your hypothesis. If your prediction is not confirmed, you might modify your hypothesis and retest it.

To test your predictions and hypothesis, you could design an experiment to find out what substances make up wood. Then you could determine what makes up the ash, the smoke, and other products that formed after the burning process. You also could research this topic and possibly find answers on reliable science Web sites or in science books.

After doing an experiment or research, you need to analyze your results and findings. You might make additional inferences after reviewing your data. If you find that new substances actually do form when wood burns, your hypothesis is supported. If new products do not form, your hypothesis is not supported. Some methods of testing a hypothesis and analyzing results are shown in **Figure 2.**

Draw Conclusions

After analyzing your results, you can begin to draw conclusions about your investigation. A conclusion is a summary of the information gained from testing a hypothesis. Like a scientist does, you should test and retest your hypothesis several times to make sure the results are consistent.

Communicate Results

Sharing the results of a scientific inquiry is an important part of science. By exchanging information, scientists can evaluate and test others' work and make faster progress in their own research. Exchanging information is one way of making scientific advances as quickly as possible and keeping scientific information accurate. During your investigation, if you do research on the Internet or in science books, you use information that someone else communicated. Scientists exchange information in many ways, as shown below in **Figure 2.**

Key Concept Check What are some steps used during scientific inquiry?

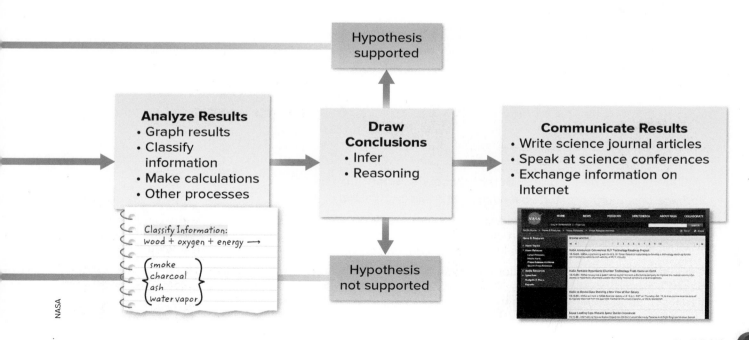

Analyze Results
- Graph results
- Classify information
- Make calculations
- Other processes

Classify Information:
wood + oxygen + energy ⟶
{ smoke, charcoal, ash, water vapor }

Draw Conclusions
- Infer
- Reasoning

Hypothesis supported

Hypothesis not supported

Communicate Results
- Write science journal articles
- Speak at science conferences
- Exchange information on Internet

NASA

Unsupported or Supported Hypotheses

What happens if a hypothesis is not supported by an investigation? Was the scientific investigation a failure and a waste of time? Absolutely not! Even when a hypothesis is not supported, you gain valuable information. You can revise your hypothesis and test it again. Each time you test a hypothesis, you learn more about the topic you are studying.

Scientific Theory

When a hypothesis (or a group of closely related hypotheses) is supported through many tests over many years, a scientific theory can develop. A **scientific theory** *is an explanation of observations or events that is based on knowledge gained from many observations and investigations.*

A scientific theory does not develop from just one hypothesis, but from many hypotheses that are connected by a common idea. The kinetic molecular theory described below is the result of the investigations of many scientists.

Scientific Law

A scientific law is different from a societal law, which is an agreement on a set of behaviors. A **scientific law** *is a rule that describes a repeatable pattern in nature.* A scientific law does not explain why or how the pattern happens, it only states that it will happen. For example, if you drop a ball, it will fall towards the ground every time. This is a repeated pattern that relates to the law of universal gravitation. The law of conservation of energy, described below, is also a scientific law.

Kinetic Molecular Theory

The kinetic molecular theory explains how particles that make up a gas move in constant, random motions. A particle moves in a straight line until it collides with another particle or with the wall of its container.

The kinetic molecular theory also assumes that the collisions of particles in a gas are elastic collisions. An elastic collision is a collision in which no kinetic energy is lost. Therefore, kinetic energy among gas particles is conserved.

Law of Conservation of Energy

The law of conservation of energy states that in any chemical reaction or physical change, energy is neither created nor destroyed. The total energy of particles before and after collisions is the same.

However, this scientific law, like all scientific laws, does not explain *why* energy is conserved. It simply states that energy *is* conserved.

Scientific Law v. Scientific Theory

Both are based on repeated observations and can be rejected or modified.

A scientific law states that an event *will* occur. For example, energy will be conserved when particles collide. It does not explain why an event will occur or how it will occur. Scientific laws work under specific conditions in nature. A law stands true until an observation is made that does not follow the law.

A scientific theory is an explanation of *why* or *how* an event occurred. For example, collisions of particles of a gas are elastic collisions. Therefore, no kinetic energy is lost. A theory can be rejected or modified if someone observes an event that disproves the theory. A theory will never become a law.

Results of Scientific Inquiry

Why do you and others ask questions and investigate the natural world? Just as scientific questions vary, so do the results of science. Most often, the purpose of a scientific investigation is to develop new materials and technology, discover new objects, or find answers to questions, as shown below.

 Key Concept Check What are the results of scientific inquiry?

New Materials and Technology

Every year, corporations and governments spend millions of dollars on research and design of new materials and technologies. **Technology** *is the practical use of scientific knowledge, especially for industrial or commercial use.* For example, scientists hypothesize and predict how new materials will make bicycles and cycling gear lighter, more durable, and more aerodynamic. Using wind tunnels, scientists test these new materials to see whether they improve the cyclist's performance. If the cyclist's performance improves, their hypotheses are supported. If the performance does not improve or it doesn't improve enough, scientists will revise their hypotheses and conduct more tests.

New Objects or Events

Scientific investigations also lead to newly discovered objects or events. For example, NASA's *Hubble Space Telescope* captured this image of two colliding galaxies. They have been nicknamed the mice, because of their long tails. The tails are composed of gases and young, hot blue stars. If computer models are correct, these galaxies will combine in the future and form one large galaxy.

Answers to Questions

Often scientific investigations are launched to answer *who, what, when, where,* or *how* questions. For example, research chemists investigate new substances, such as substances found in mushrooms and bacteria, as shown on the right. New drug treatments for cancer, HIV, and other diseases might be found using new substances. Other scientists look for clues about what causes diseases, whether they can be passed from person to person, and when the disease first appeared.

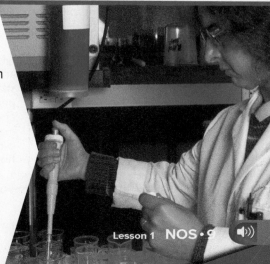

Evaluating Scientific Information

Do you ever you read advertisements, articles, or books that claim to contain scientifically proven information? Are you able to determine if the information is actually true and scientific instead of pseudoscientific (information incorrectly represented as scientific)? Whether you are reading printed media or watching commercials on TV, it is important that you are skeptical, identify facts and opinions, and think critically about the information. **Critical thinking** *is comparing what you already know with the information you are given in order to decide whether you agree with it.*

Key Concept Check What is critical thinking?

FOLDABLES

Create a two-tab book and label it as shown. Use it to discuss the importance of evaluating scientific information.

Why is it important to...

...be scientifically literate?	...use critical thinking?

Skepticism
Have you heard the saying, if it sounds too good to be true, it probably is? To be skeptical is to doubt the truthfulness of something. A scientifically literate person can read information and know that it misrepresents the facts. Science often is self-correcting because someone usually challenges inaccurate information and tests scientific results for accuracy.

Critical Thinking
Use critical thinking skills to compare what you know with the new information given to you. If the information does not sound reliable, either research and find more information about the topic or dismiss the information as unreliable.

Be A Rock Star!
Do you dream of being a rock star?

Sing, dance, and play guitar like a rock star with the new Rocker-rific Spotlight. A new scientific process developed by Rising Star Laboratories allows you to overcome your lack of musical talent and enables you to perform like a real rock star.

This amazing new light actually changes your voice quality and enhances your brain chemistry so that you can sing, dance, and play a guitar like a professional rock star. Now, there is no need to practice or pay for expensive lessons. The Rocker-rific Spotlight does the work for you.

Dr. Sammy Truelove says, "Before lack of talent might have stopped someone from achieving his or her dreams of being a rock star. This scientific breakthrough transforms people with absolutely no talent into amazing rock stars in just minutes. Of the many patients that I have tested with this product, no one has failed to achieve his or her dreams."

Disclaimer: This product was tested on laboratory rats and might not work for everyone.

Identifying Facts and Misleading Information
Misleading information often is worded to sound like scientific facts. A scientifically literate person can recognize fake claims and quickly determine when information is false.

Identify Opinions
An opinion is a personal view, feeling, or claim about a topic. Opinions cannot be proven true or false. And, an opinion might contain inaccurate information.

Josie Clyde/Alamy

Science cannot answer all questions.

It might seem that scientific inquiry is the best way to answer all questions. But there are some questions that science cannot answer. Questions that deal with beliefs, values, personal opinions, and feelings cannot be answered scientifically. This is because it is impossible to collect scientific data on these topics.

Science cannot answer questions such as

• Which video game is the most fun to play?

• Are people kind to others most of the time?

• Is there such a thing as good luck?

Safety in Science

Scientists know that using safe procedures is important in any scientific investigation. When you begin a scientific investigation, you should always wear protective equipment, as shown in **Figure 3.** You also should learn the meaning of safety symbols, listen to your teacher's instructions, and learn to recognize potential hazards. For more information, consult the Science Skills Handbook at the back of this book.

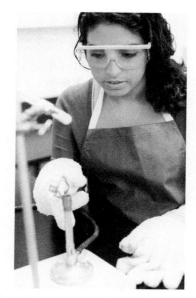

Figure 3 Always follow safety procedures when doing scientific investigations. If you have questions, ask your teacher.

Lesson 1 Review

✓ Online Quiz

◀ Virtual Lab

Use Vocabulary

1 Define *technology* in your own words.

2 Use the term *observation* in a sentence.

Understand Key Concepts 🔑

3 Which action is NOT a way to test a hypothesis?
  A. analyze results **C.** make a model
  B. design an experiment **D.** gather and evaluate evidence

4 Describe three examples of the results of scientific inquiry.

5 Give an example of a time when you practiced critical thinking.

Interpret Graphics

6 Compare Copy and fill in the graphic organizer below. List some examples of how to communicate the results of scientific inquiry.

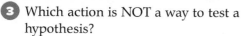

Critical Thinking

7 Summarize Your classmate writes the following as a hypothesis:

Red is a beautiful color.

Write a brief explanation to your classmate explaining why this is not a hypothesis.

Purestock/SuperStock

Science & Engineering

The Design Process

Create a Solution

Scientists and engineers do some of the same things. They both collect data, analyze it, and then draw conclusions from it. How do scientists and engineers differ? Recall that scientists investigate and explore natural events. Engineers, on the other hand, investigate and explore things that do not occur naturally. They also design, construct, and maintain human-made things. All the roads, buildings, computers, cars, and phones around you are the result of engineering. Another difference between scientists and engineers is the processes that they use. Science involves using scientific inquiry, but engineering also includes the design process—a set of methods used to find and create a solution to a problem or need.

The Steps

Identify a Problem or Need

- Determine a problem or a need.
- Document all questions, research, and procedures throughout the process.

↓

Research the Problem & Brainstorm Solutions

- Research any existing solutions that address the problem or need.
- Brainstorm all possible solutions.

↓

Design Solutions

- Suggest limitations of the solutions.
- Look at all solutions and select the best one.
- Create a design of the solution.

↓

Redesign the Solution

- Redesign and modify solution, as needed.
- Construct final solution.

Construct a Prototype

- Estimate materials, costs, resources, and time to develop the solution.
- Construct a prototype.

Test & Evaluate the Solution

- Use models to test the solutions.
- Use graphs, charts, and tables to evaluate results.
- Analyze and evaluate strengths and weaknesses of the solution.

↓

Communicate the Results

- Communicate your designed solution and results to others.

Identify a Problem

Rollercoasters offer riders a chance to experience engineering in action. They swoop through the air without injury because of how they are designed. Suppose a team of engineers has been assigned the task of creating the tallest roller coaster that can run without hurting the people on it. What is the next step that an engineering team will take to create a solution to this problem?

Science & Engineering

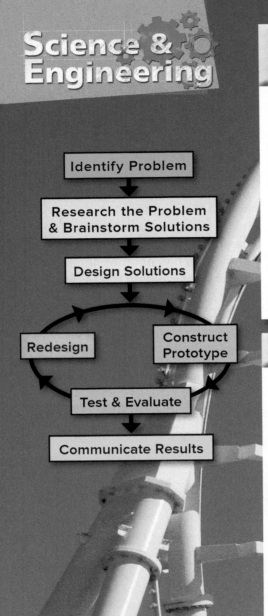

Identify Problem

Research the Problem & Brainstorm Solutions

Design Solutions

Redesign

Construct Prototype

Test & Evaluate

Communicate Results

Research the Problem & Brainstorm Solutions

The next step should be to gather research and then brainstorm solutions. It is important to gather background information before proceeding in the design process. Researching solutions that have been tried is critical in determining if the problem statement is still accurate. For example, other engineers might have discovered that a certain type of seat belt does not work efficiently on drops above a certain height. If the original problem has already been solved, it will need to be redefined. After the research is completed the team will brainstorm multiple solutions to the problem. Brainstorming involves a lot of creativity and can result in unique solutions to problems.

Design Solutions

After potential solutions have been identified, the best one must be selected for further development. Part of choosing the best design involves looking at its constraints. Constraints are limitations put on the product from outside factors. These factors can include cost, ethical issues such as animal testing, environmental impacts, or attractiveness. Other constraints such as political and social issues or product safety can limit choices for product design. The materials required for the solution may also present some constraints. For example, it would not make sense to use a metal which rusts easily for the roller coaster frame because the coaster will be exposed to moisture for many years. This is one way in which the chemical, physical, and mechanical properties of a material can be constraints. Engineers must also make sure that all the materials used in a design do not interact in a negative way.

Construct a Prototype

Before the design goes into mass production, a prototype is produced. This is the first example of the design which is tested under real conditions. A prototype is sometimes also called a model. Models are used to think about processes that happen too slowly, too quickly, or on too small a scale to observe directly, as well as ones that are potentially dangerous or too large to otherwise study. Engineers might model the same design in several different ways to gather the most information about the design. Models that can be seen and touched are called physical models. Engineers also develop mathematical models and computer simulations.

Limitations of Models

Engineers use all the information that they currently have when constructing a model. Models do not show all the characteristics of a design. They might not always work the way that the real item might. This is why it can be important to model the same design several different ways.

Mathematical Model

When designing a roller coaster, engineers use mathematical models to calculate the heights of hills, the angles of loops and turns, and the forces that affect the ride. Each tested characteristic will have its own model. These models use numerical data and equations to model the ride. With mathematical models, engineers can input data and apply constraints to the equations and evaluate how the output data changes.

98 ft

55°

Computer Simulation

After mathematical models are developed and tested, computer simulations might be created. Computer simulations can contain thousands of complex mathematical models. They combine large amounts of data with computer graphics and animation programs. As engineers change variables in mathematical models, they use computer simulations to view the effects of the change

Physical Model

Once the design solution has been created, engineers will build a physical model. A physical model is a model that you can see and touch. It shows how parts relate to one another, how the roller coaster is built, or how complex objects work together. These models are often built to scale allowing engineers to see the design from all sides. A scale model is not the same size as the actual object but it has the same proportions. During testing of the prototype, engineers may change the physical model many times.

Identify Problem

Research the Problem & Brainstorm Solutions

Design Solutions

Redesign

Construct Prototype

Test & Evaluate

Communicate Results

Test & Evaluate

Analyzing the design and gathering data from the prototype is part of testing and evaluating the design. This allows engineers to find and correct problems. Tests can include running computer programs to identify errors, putting the physical model through many trials, and having many people look at the design. It is important to test the design many times to make sure there will be no unexpected problems.

Redesign

Occasionally, the results of testing might mean that the design must be changed. For example, testing a physical model could show that the roller coaster sways in the wind at the top of the hill. This might result in making the hill shorter or adding braces to the track so it does not sway. Engineers redesign the solution and test it again. One solution is chosen after testing and evaluation has been completed.

Communicate Results

After examining possible solutions, then testing and evaluating them, one is chosen for development. This information is shared with other engineers and scientists. It might be researched further by other engineers and scientists, or combined with information gathered by other teams. Engineers might go through the design process many times before developing a model that meets their needs. Once they do, it is sent to manufacturing for production.

It's Your Turn

Design a Pollution Solution

The design team you just read about used the design process to design a tall but safe roller coaster for park customers. Using the same process, you can be an engineer and solve a different problem.

You are a water-pollution specialist working for Pollution Solutions, Inc. For your job, you travel all over the world, examine various water-pollution problems, and design and engineer devices to solve water-pollution crises. You have just received an urgent call to analyze and solve a water crisis.

☐ Identify the Problem

You know that clean water is essential for life on Earth and that polluted water can cause harm. What is the source of your water crisis? What type of pollution is present? Is it thermal or industrial pollution? Or is it sewage, acid rain, litter, nuclear waste, eutrophication, or underground storage tanks? How can the solution treat the pollution, restore clean water, and protect humans and the environment? How can future pollution be avoided? Record in your Science Journal your problem and questions with possible solutions.

☐ Research Existing Solutions

Begin answering your questions by researching types of water pollution, the sources, and the solutions. Choose one type of water pollution to address in this crisis. Note any limitations to possible solutions, such as cost, size, materials, location, time, or other restraints.

☐ Brainstorm Possible Solutions

Record ideas to develop solutions to water pollution in varying environments and locations. Note materials and equipment necessary for clean water devices. Also include the estimated cost and time of development and construction. Because this has been identified as a crisis, time is very short for developing a solution and constructing an antipollution device.

☐ Construct a Prototype

Draw several plans to address your problem. Use simple materials to construct a scale model of your water-pollution solution. Check the scale of the dimensions of each element for accuracy to guarantee a viable water-pollution solution.

☐ Test & Evaluate Solutions

Test your model to help guarantee an effective and safe solution. Use graphs, charts, and tables to record and evaluate the process and identify strengths and weaknesses in your solutions.

☐ Redesign Your Pollution Solution & ☐ Communicate Your Results

Communicate your design process and solution to peers using visual displays and models. Discuss and critique your working pollution solution. Do further research and testing, if necessary. Redesign and modify your solution to meet design objectives. Then, construct a model of your final water-pollution solution.

Measurement and Scientific Tools

Reading Guide

Key Concepts
ESSENTIAL QUESTIONS

* Why did scientists create the International System of Units (SI)?

* Why is scientific notation a useful tool for scientists?

* How can tools, such as graduated cylinders and triple-beam balances, assist physical scientists?

Vocabulary

description p. NOS 18

explanation p. NOS 18

International System of Units (SI) p. NOS 18

scientific notation p. NOS 21

percent error p. NOS 21

 Multilingual eGlossary

SEPS.2, SEPS.5, SEPS.6

Description and Explanation

Suppose you work for a company that tests cars to see how they perform during accidents, as shown in **Figure 4.** You might use various scientific tools to measure the acceleration of cars as they crash into other objects.

A **description** *is a spoken or written summary of observations.* The measurements you record are descriptions of the results of the crash tests. Later, your supervisor asks you to write a report that interprets the measurements you took during the crash tests. An **explanation** *is an interpretation of observations.* As you write your explanation, you make inferences about why the crashes damaged the vehicles in specific ways.

Notice that there is a difference between a description and an explanation. When you describe something, you report your observations. When you explain something, you interpret your observations.

The International System of Units

Different parts of the world use different systems of measurements. This can cause confusion when people who use different systems communicate their measurements. This confusion was eliminated in 1960 when a new system of measurement was adopted. *The internationally accepted system of measurement is the* **International System of Units (SI).**

 Key Concept Check Why did scientists create the International System of Units?

Figure 4 A description of an event details what you observed. An explanation explains why or how the event occurred.

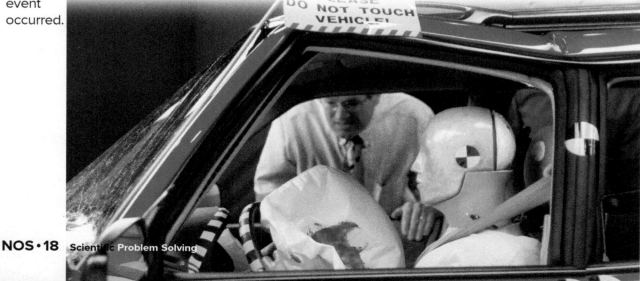

©Tim Wright/Corbis

SI Base Units

When you take measurements during scientific investigations and labs in this course, you will use the SI system. The SI system uses standards of measurement, called base units, as shown in Table 1. Other units used in the SI system that are not base units are derived from the base units. For example, the liter, used to measure volume, was derived from the base unit for length.

SI Unit Prefixes

In older systems of measurement, there usually was no common factor that related one unit to another. The SI system eliminated this problem.

The SI system is based on multiples of ten. Any SI unit can be converted to another by multiplying by a power of ten. Factors of ten are represented by prefixes, as shown in Table 2. For example, the prefix *milli-* means 0.001 or 10^{-3}. So, a milliliter is 0.001 L, or 1/1,000 L. Another way to say this is: 1 L is 1,000 times greater than 1 mL.

Converting Among SI Units

It is easy to convert from one SI unit to another. You either multiply or divide by a factor of ten. You also can use proportion calculations to make conversions. An example of how to convert between SI units is shown in Figure 5.

▶ Interactive Concept Map

Table 1 SI Base Units

Quantity Measured	Unit (symbol)
Length	meter (m)
Mass	kilogram (kg)
Time	second (s)
Electric current	ampere (A)
Temperature	kelvin (K)
Substance amount	mole (mol)
Light intensity	candela (cd)

Table 2 Prefixes

Prefix	Meaning
Mega- (M)	1,000,000 or (10^6)
Kilo- (k)	1,000 or (10^3)
Hecto- (h)	100 or (10^2)
Deka- (da)	10 or (10^1)
Deci- (d)	0.1 or $\left(\frac{1}{10}\right)$ or (10^{-1})
Centi- (c)	0.01 or $\left(\frac{1}{100}\right)$ or (10^{-2})
Milli- (m)	0.001 or $\left(\frac{1}{1,000}\right)$ or (10^{-3})
Micro- (μ)	0.000001 or $\left(\frac{1}{1,000,000}\right)$ or (10^{-6})

Figure 5 The rock in the photograph has a mass of 17.5 grams. Convert that measurement to kilograms. ▼

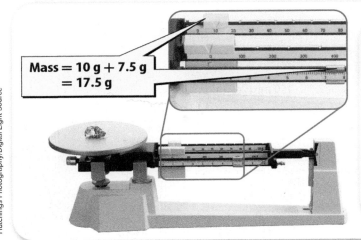

Mass = 10 g + 7.5 g
= 17.5 g

1. Determine the correct relationship between grams and kilograms. There are 1,000 g in 1 kg.

$$\frac{1 \text{ kg}}{1,000 \text{ g}}$$

$$\frac{x}{17.5 \text{ g}} = \frac{1 \text{ kg}}{1,000 \text{ g}}$$

$$x = \frac{(17.5 \text{ g})(1 \text{ kg})}{1,000 \text{ g}}; x = 0.0175 \text{ kg}$$

2. Check your units. The unit *grams* is cancelled out in the equation, so the answer is 0.0175 kg.

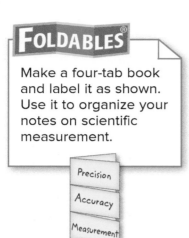

FOLDABLES®

Make a four-tab book and label it as shown. Use it to organize your notes on scientific measurement.

Precision
Accuracy
Measurement
Uncertainty

Table 3 Student Density and Error Data
(Accepted value: Density of sodium chloride, 21.7 g/cm³)

	Student A	Student B	Student C
	Density	**Density**	**Density**
Trial 1	23.4 g/cm³	18.9 g/cm³	21.9 g/cm³
Trial 2	23.5 g/cm³	27.2 g/cm³	21.4 g/cm³
Trial 3	23.4 g/cm³	29.1 g/cm³	21.3 g/cm³
Mean	23.4 g/cm³	25.1 g/cm³	21.5 g/cm³

Measurement and Uncertainty

You might be familiar with the terms *precision* and *accuracy.* In science, these terms have different meanings. Precision is a description of how similar or close repeated measurements are to each other. Accuracy is a description of how close a measurement is to an accepted value.

The difference between precision and accuracy is illustrated in **Table 3.** Students were asked to find the density of sodium chloride (NaCl). In three trials, each student measured the volume and the mass of NaCl. Then, they calculated the density for each trial and calculated the mean, or average. Student A's measurements are the most precise because they are closest to each other. Student C's measurements are the most accurate because they are closest to the scientifically accepted value. Student B's measurements are neither precise nor accurate. They are not close to each other or to the accepted value.

Tools and Accuracy

No measuring tool provides a perfect measurement. All measurements have some degree of uncertainty. Some tools or instruments produce more accurate measurements, as shown in **Figure 6.**

WORD ORIGIN ············

notation
from Latin *notationem,* means
"a marking or explanation"

Figure 6 The graduated cylinder is graduated in 0.5-mL increments. The beaker is graduated in, or divided into, 25-mL increments. Liquid measurements taken with the graduated cylinder have greater accuracy.

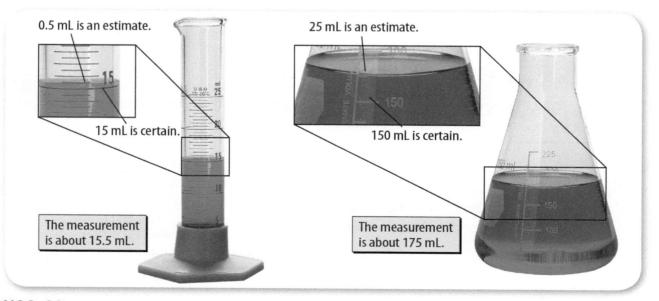

0.5 mL is an estimate.

15 mL is certain.

The measurement is about 15.5 mL.

25 mL is an estimate.

150 mL is certain.

The measurement is about 175 mL.

Hutchings Photography/Digital Light Source

Scientific Notation

Suppose you are writing a report that includes Earth's distance from the Sun—149,600,000 km—and the density of the Sun's lower atmosphere—0.000000028 g/cm³. These numerals take up too much space and might be difficult to read, so you use **scientific notation**—*a method of writing or displaying very small or very large values in a short form.* To write the numerals in scientific notation, use the steps shown to the right.

 Key Concept Check Why is scientific notation a useful tool for scientists?

Percent Error

The densities recorded in Table 3 are experimental values because they were calculated during an experiment. Each of these values has some error because the accepted value for table salt density is 21.65 g/cm³. Percent error can help you determine the size of your experimental error. **Percent error** *is the expression of error as a percentage of the accepted value.*

How to Write in Scientific Notation

1. Write the original number.
   - A. 149,600,000
   - B. 0.000000028

2. Move the decimal point to the right or the left to make the number between 1 and 10. Count the number of decimal places moved and note the direction.
   - A. 1.49600000 = 8 places to the left
   - B. 00000002.8 = 8 places to the right

3. Rewrite the number deleting all extra zeros to the right or to the left of the decimal point.
   - A. 1.496
   - B. 2.8

4. Write a multiplication symbol and the number *10* with an exponent. The exponent should equal the number of places that you moved the decimal point in step 2. If you moved the decimal point to the left, the exponent is positive. If you moved the decimal point to the right, the exponent is negative.
   - A. 1.496×10^8
   - B. 2.8×10^{-8}

Math Skills

Percent Error

Solve for Percent Error A student in the laboratory measures the boiling point of water at 97.5°C. If the accepted value for the boiling point of water is 100.0°C, what is the percent error?

1. This is what you know:
   experimental value = 97.5°C
   accepted value = 100.0°C

2. This is what you need to find: percent error

3. Use this formula:
   $$\text{percent error} = \frac{|\text{experimental value} - \text{accepted value}|}{\text{accepted value}} \times 100\%$$

4. Substitute the known values into the equation and perform the calculations
   $$\text{percent error} = \frac{|97.5° - 100.0°|}{100.0°} \times 100\% = 2.50\%$$

 Math Practice

Personal Tutor

Practice

Calculate the percent error if the experimental value of the density of gold is 18.7 g/cm³ and the accepted value is 19.3 g/cm³.

Scientific Tools

As you conduct scientific investigations, you will use tools to make measurements. The tools listed here are some of the tools commonly used in science. For more information about the correct use and safety procedures for these tools, see the Science Skills Handbook at the back of this book.

◄ Science Journal

Use a science journal to record observations, write questions and hypotheses, collect data, and analyze the results of scientific inquiry. All scientists record the information they learn while conducting investigations. Your journal can be a spiral-bound notebook, a loose-leaf binder, or even just a pad of paper.

Balances ►

A balance is used to measure the mass of an object. Units often used for mass are grams (g), kilograms (kg), and milligrams (mg). Two common types of balances are the electronic balance and the triple-beam balance. In order to get the most accurate measurements when using a balance, it is important to calibrate the balance often.

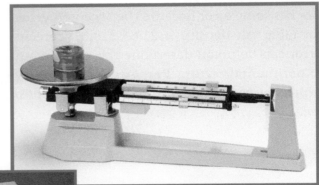

◄ Glassware

Laboratory glassware is used to hold or measure the volume of liquids. Flasks, beakers, test tubes, and graduated cylinders are just some of the different types of glassware available. Volume usually is measured in liters (L) and milliliters (mL).

(tl)Matt Meadows, (tr)ASP/YPP/age fotostock, (c)Louis Rosenstock/McGraw-Hill Education, (b)Steve Allen/Brand X Pictures

Thermometers ▶

A thermometer is used to measure the temperature of substances. Although Kelvin is the SI unit of measurement for temperature, in the science classroom, you often measure temperature in degrees Celsius (°C). Never stir a substance with a thermometer because it might break. If a thermometer does break, tell your teacher immediately. Do not touch the broken glass or the liquid inside the thermometer.

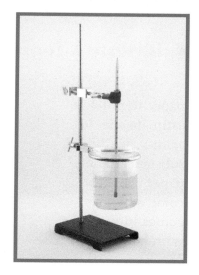

◀ Calculators

A hand-held calculator is a scientific tool that you might use in math class. But you also can use it in the lab and in the field (real situation outside the lab) to make quick calculations using your data.

Computers ▼

For today's students, it is difficult to think of a time when scientists—or anyone—did not use computers in their work. Scientists can collect, compile, and analyze data more quickly using a computer. Scientists use computers to prepare research reports and to share their data and ideas with investigators worldwide.

Hardware refers to the physical components of a computer, such as the monitor and the mouse. Computer software refers to the programs that are run on computers, such as word processing, spreadsheet, and presentation programs.

Electronic probes can be attached to computers and handheld calculators to record measurements. There are probes for collecting different kinds of information, such as temperature and the speed of objects.

 Key Concept Check How can scientific tools, such as graduated cylinders and triple-beam balances, assist scientists?

Additional Tools Used by Physical Scientists

You can use pH paper to quickly estimate the acidity of a liquid substance. The paper changes color when it comes into contact with an acid or a base.

Scientists use stopwatches to measure the time it takes for an event to occur. The SI unit for time is seconds (s). However, for longer events, the units *minutes (min)* and *hours (h)* can be used.

A hot plate is a small heating device that can be placed on a table or desk. Hot plates are used to heat substances in the laboratory.

You use a spring scale to measure the weight or the amount of force applied to an object. The SI unit for weight is the newton (N).

Lesson 2 Review

✓ Online Quiz

Use Vocabulary

1. A spoken or written summary of observations is a(n) _____, while a(n) _____ is an interpretation of observations.

Understand Key Concepts 🔑

2. Which type of glassware would you use to measure the volume of a liquid?
   A. beaker
   B. flask
   C. graduated cylinder
   D. test tube

3. **Summarize** why a scientist measuring the diameter of an atom or the distance to the Moon would use scientific notation.

4. **Explain** why scientists use the International System of Units (SI).

Interpret Graphics

5. **Identify** Copy and fill in the graphic organizer below listing some scientific tools that you could use to collect data.

Scientific tools

Critical Thinking

6. **Explain** why precision and accuracy should be reported in a scientific investigation.

Math Skills ✕➗ | ✓ Math Practice

7. Calculate the percent error if the experimental value for the density of zinc is 9.95 g/cm³. The accepted value is 7.13 g/cm³.

Materials

plastic straws

scissors

ruler

string

Safety

How do geometric shapes differ in strength?

If you look at a bridge, a building crane, or the framework of a tall building, you will notice that various geometric shapes make up the structure. In this activity, you will observe the strength of several geometric shapes in terms of their rigidity, or resistance to changing their shape.

Learn It

When scientists make a hypothesis, they often then **predict** that an event will occur based on their hypothesis.

Try It

1. Read and complete a lab safety form.

2. You are going to construct a triangle and a square using straws. Predict which shape will be more resistant to changing shape and write your prediction in your Science Journal.

3. Measure and cut the straws into seven segments, each 6 cm long.

4. Measure and cut one 20-cm and one 30-cm length of string.

5. Thread the 30-cm length of string through four straw segments. Bend the corners to form a square. Tie the ends of the string together in a double knot to complete the square.

6. Thread the 20-cm string through three of the straw segments. Bend to form a triangle. Tie the ends of the string together to complete the triangle.

7. Test the strength of the square by gently trying to change its shape. Repeat with the triangle. Record your observations.

8. Propose several ways to make the weaker shape stronger. Draw diagrams showing how to modify the shape to make it more rigid.

9. Test your hypothesis. If necessary, refine your hypothesis and retest it. Repeat this step until you make the shape stronger.

Apply It

10. Look at the photograph at to the left. Which of your tested shapes is used the most? Based on your observations, why is this shape used?

11. What modifications made your shape stronger? Why?

12. 🔑 **Key Concept** How might a scientist use a model to test a hypothesis?

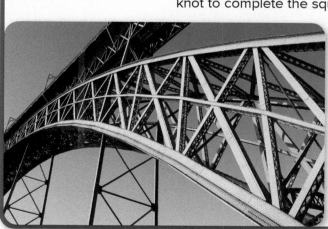

Case Study

Reading Guide

Key Concepts
ESSENTIAL QUESTIONS

- Why are evaluation and testing important in the design process?
- How is scientific inquiry used in a real-life scientific investigation?

Vocabulary

variable p. NOS 27

constant p. NOS 27

independent variable p. NOS 27

dependent variable p. NOS 27

experimental group p. NOS 27

control group p. NOS 27

qualitative data p. NOS 30

quantitative data p. NOS 30

 Multilingual eGlossary

Science Video

 SEPS.2, SEPS.3, SEPS.4, SEPS.8

The Minneapolis Bridge Failure

On August 1, 2007, the center section of the Interstate-35W (I-35W) bridge in Minneapolis, Minnesota, suddenly collapsed. A major portion of the bridge fell more than 30 m into the Mississippi River, as shown in **Figure 7**. There were more than 100 cars and trucks on the bridge at the time, including a school bus carrying over 50 students.

The failure of this 8-lane, 581-m long interstate bridge came as a surprise to almost everyone. Drivers do not expect a bridge to drop out from underneath them. The design and engineering processes that bridges undergo are supposed to ensure that bridge failures do not happen.

Controlled Experiments

After the 2007 bridge collapse, investigators had to determine why the bridge failed. To do this, they needed to use scientific inquiry, which you read about in Lesson 1. The investigators designed controlled experiments to help them answer questions and test their hypotheses. A controlled experiment is a scientific investigation that tests how one factor affects another. You might conduct controlled experiments to help discover answers to questions, to test a hypotheses, or to collect data.

Figure 7 A portion of the Interstate-35W bridge in Minneapolis, Minnesota, collapsed in August 2007. Several people were killed, and many more were injured.

MANDEL NGAN/AFP/Getty Images

Identifying Variables and Constants

When conducting an experiment, you must identify factors that can affect the experiment's outcome. A **variable** *is any factor that can have more than one value.* In controlled experiments, there are two kinds of variables. The **independent variable** *is the factor that you want to test. It is changed by the investigator to observe how it affects a dependent variable.* The **dependent variable** *is the factor you observe or measure during an experiment.* **Constants** *are the factors in an experiment that do not change.*

Experimental Groups

A controlled experiment usually has at least two groups. The **experimental group** *is used to study how a change in the independent variable changes the dependent variable.* The **control group** *contains the same factors as the experimental group, but the independent variable is not changed.* Without a control, it is impossible to know whether your experimental observations result from the variable you are testing or some other factor.

This case study will explore how the investigators used scientific inquiry to determine why the bridge collapsed. Notebooks in the margin identify what a scientist might write in a science journal. The blue boxes contain additional helpful information that you might use.

You can change the independent variable to observe how it affects the dependent variable. Without constants, two independent variables could change at the same time, and you would not know which variable affected the dependent variable.

Simple Beam Bridges

Before you read about the bridge-collapse investigation, think about the structure of bridges. The simplest type of bridge is a beam bridge, as shown in **Figure 8.** This type of bridge has one horizontal beam across two supports. A beam bridge often is constructed across small creeks. A disadvantage of beam bridges is that they tend to sag in the middle if they are too long.

Figure 8 Simple beam bridges span short distances, such as small creeks.

Brian Stevenson/Getty Images

Figure 9 Truss bridges can span long distances and are strengthened by a series of interconnecting triangles called trusses. ▶

Truss Bridges

A truss bridge, shown in **Figure 9,** often spans long distances. This type of bridge is supported only at its two ends, but an assembly of interconnected triangles, or trusses, strengthens it. The I-35W bridge, shown in **Figure 10,** was a truss bridge designed in the early 1960s. The I-35W bridge was designed with straight beams connected to triangular and vertical supports. These supports held up the deck of the bridge, or the roadway. The beams in the bridge's deck and the supports came together at structures known as gusset plates, shown below on the right. These steel plates joined the triangular and vertical truss elements to the overhead roadway beams. These beams ran along the deck of the bridge. This area, where the truss structure connects to the roadway portion of the bridge at a gusset plate, also is called a node.

Reading Check What are the gusset plates of a bridge?

Figure 10 Trusses were a major structural element of the I-35W bridge. The gusset plates at each node in the bridge, shown on the right, are critical pieces that hold the bridge together. ▼

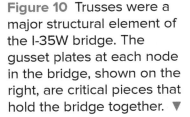

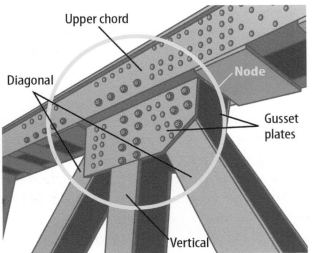

Upper chord

Diagonal

Node

Gusset plates

Vertical

(t)Hisham Ibrahim/Getty Images, (b)John Weeks III/AP Images

Scientists often observe and gather information about an object or an event before proposing a hypothesis. This information is recorded or filed for the investigation.

Observations:
• Recovered parts of the collapsed bridge

• A video showing the sequence of events as the bridge fails and falls into the river

Bridge Failure Observations

After the I-35W bridge collapsed, shown in **Figure 11,** the local sheriff's department handled the initial recovery of the collapsed bridge structure. Finding, freeing, and identifying victims was a high priority, and unintentional damage to the collapsed bridge occurred in the process. However, investigators eventually recovered the entire structure.

The investigators labeled each part with the location where it was found. They also noted the date when they removed each piece. Investigators then moved the pieces to a nearby park. There, they placed the pieces in their relative original positions. Examining the reassembled structure, investigators found physical evidence they needed to determine where the breaks in each section occurred.

The investigators found more clues in a video. A motion-activated security camera recorded the bridge collapse. The video showed about 10 seconds of the collapse, which revealed the sequence of events that destroyed the bridge. Investigators used this video to help pinpoint where the collapse began.

Asking Questions

One or more factors could have caused the bridge to fail. Was the original bridge design faulty? Were bridge maintenance and repair poor or lacking? Was there too much weight on the bridge at the time of the collapse? Each of these questions was studied to determine why the bridge collapsed. Did one or a combination of these factors cause the bridge to fail?

Asking questions and seeking answers to those questions is a way that scientists formulate hypotheses.

Lawrence Sawyer/Getty Images

When gathering information or collecting data, scientists might perform an experiment, create a model, gather and evaluate evidence, or make calculations.

Qualitative data:
A thicker layer of concrete was added to the bridge to protect rods.

Quantitative data:
• The concrete increased the load on the bridge by 13.4 percent.

• The modifications in 1998 increased the load on the bridge by 6.1 percent.

• At the time of the collapse in 2007, the load on the bridge increased by another 20 percent.

A hypothesis is a possible explanation for an observation that can be tested by scientific investigations.

Hypothesis:
The bridge failed because it was overloaded.

Gathering Information and Data

Investigators reviewed the modifications made to the bridge since it opened in 1967. In 1977, engineers noticed that salt used to deice the bridge during winter weather was causing the reinforcement rods in the roadway to weaken. To protect the rods, engineers applied a thicker layer of concrete to the surface of the bridge roadway. Analysis after the collapse revealed that this extra concrete increased the dead load on the bridge by about 13.4 percent. A load can be a force applied to the structure from the structure itself (dead load) or from temporary loads such as traffic, wind gusts, or earthquakes (live load). Investigators recorded this qualitative and quantitative data. **Qualitative data** *uses words to describe what is observed.* **Quantitative data** *uses numbers to describe what is observed.*

In 1998, additional modifications were made to the bridge. The bridge that was built in the 1960s did not meet current safety standards. Analysis showed that the changes made to the bridge during this renovation further increased the dead load on the bridge by about 6.1 percent.

An Early Hypothesis

At the time of the collapse in 2007, the bridge was undergoing additional renovations. Four piles of sand, four piles of gravel, a water tanker filled with over 11,000 L of water, a cement tanker, a concrete mixer, and other equipment, supplies, and workers were assembled on the bridge. This caused the load on the bridge to increase by about 20 percent. In addition to these renovation materials, normal vehicle traffic was on the bridge. Did the renovation equipment and traffic overload the bridge, causing the center section to collapse as shown in **Figure 12**? Only a thorough analysis could answer this question.

Figure 12 The center section of the bridge broke away and fell into the river.

US Navy Photo/Alamy

Plus Pix/age fotostock

Figure 13 Engineers used computer models to study the structure and loads on the bridge.

Computer Modeling

The analysis of the bridge was conducted using computer-modeling software, as shown in **Figure 13.** Using computer software, investigators entered data from the Minnesota bridge into a computer. The computer performed numerous mathematical calculations. After thorough modeling and analysis, it was determined that the bridge was not overloaded.

Revising the Hypothesis

Evaluations conducted in 1999 and 2003 provided additional clues as to why the bridge failed. As part of the study, investigators took numerous pictures of the bridge structure. The photos revealed bowing of the gusset plates at the eleventh node from the south end of the bridge. Investigators labeled this node *U10.* Gusset plates are designed to be stronger than the structural parts they connect. It is possible that the bowing of the plates indicated a problem with the gusset plate design. Previous inspectors and engineers missed this warning sign.

The accident investigators found that some recovered gusset plates were fractured, while others were not damaged. If the bridge had been properly constructed, none of the plates should have failed. But inspection showed that some of the plates failed very early in the collapse.

After evaluating the evidence, the accident investigators formulated the hypothesis that the gusset plates failed, which lead to the bridge collapse. Now investigators had to test this hypothesis.

Hypothesis:
1. ~~The bridge failed because it was overloaded.~~
2. The bridge collapsed because the gusset plates failed.
Prediction:
If a gusset plate is not properly designed, then a heavy load on a bridge will cause a gusset plate to fail.

Test the Hypothesis:

- Compare the load on the bridge when it collapsed with the load limits of the bridge at each of the main gusset plates.
- Determine the demand-to-capacity ratios for the main gusset plates.
- Calculate the appropriate thicknesses of the U10 gusset plates.

Independent Variables: actual load on bridge and load bridge was designed to handle

Dependent Variable: demand-to-capacity ratio

Testing the Hypothesis

The investigators knew the load limits of the bridge. To calculate the load on the bridge when it collapsed, they estimated the combined weight of the bridge and the traffic on the bridge. The investigators divided the load on the bridge when it collapsed by the load limits of the bridge to find the demand-to-capacity ratio. The demand-to-capacity ratio provides a measure of a structure's safety.

Analyzing Results

As investigators calculated the demand-to-capacity ratios for each of the main gusset plates, like those shown in **Figure 14,** they found that the ratios were particularly high for the U10 node. The U10 plate failed earliest in the bridge collapse. **Table 4** shows the demand-to-capacity ratios for a few of the gusset plates at some nodes. A value greater than 1 means the structure is unsafe. Notice how high the ratios are for the U10 gusset plate compared to the other plates.

Further calculations showed that the U10 plates were not thick enough to support the loads they were supposed to handle. They were about half the thickness they should have been.

 Key Concept Check Why are evaluation and testing important in the design process?

Figure 14 The steel plates, or gusset plates, at the U10 node were too thin for the loads the bridge carried.

Table 4 Node-Gusset Plate Analysis

Gusset Plate	Thick-ness (cm)	Demand-to-Capacity Ratios for the Upper-Node Gusset Plates					
		Horizontal loads			Vertical loads		
U8	3.5	0.05	0.03	0.07	0.31	0.46	0.20
U10	1.3	1.81	1.54	1.83	1.70	1.46	1.69
U12	2.5	0.11	0.11	0.10	0.71	0.37	1.15

Jim Mone/AP Images

Drawing Conclusions

Over the years, modifications to the I-35W bridge added more load to the bridge. On the day of the accident, traffic and the concentration of construction vehicles and materials added still more load. Investigators concluded that if the U10 gusset plates were properly designed, they would have supported the added load. When the investigators examined the original records for the bridge, they were unable to find any detailed gusset plate specifications. They could not determine whether undersized plates were used because of a mistaken calculation or some other error in the design process. The only thing that they could conclude with certainty was that undersized gusset plates could not reliably hold up the bridge.

The Federal Highway Administration and the National Transportation Safety Board published the results of their investigations. These published reports now provide scientists and engineers with valuable information they can use in future bridge designs. These reports are good examples of why it is important for scientists and engineers to publish their results and to share information.

Analyzing Results: The U10 gusset plates should have been twice as thick as they were to support the bridge.

Conclusions: The bridge failed because the gusset plates were not properly designed and they could not carry the load that they were supposed to carry.

 Key Concept Check Give three examples of the scientific inquiry process that was used in this investigation.

Lesson 3 Review

 Online Quiz

Use Vocabulary

1 **Distinguish** between qualitative data and quantitative data.

2 **Contrast** *variable, independent variable,* and *dependent variable.*

Understand Key Concepts

3 Constants are necessary in a controlled experiment because, without constants, you would not know which variable affected the
   A. control group.
   B. experimental group.
   C. dependent variable.
   D. independent variable.

4 **Give an example** of a situation in your life in which you depend on adequate testing and evaluation in a product design to keep you safe.

Interpret Graphics

5 **Summarize** Copy and fill in the flow chart below and summarize the sequence of scientific inquiry steps that was used in one part of the case study.

Critical Thinking

6 **Analyze** how the scientific inquiry process differs when engineers design a product, such as a bridge, and when they investigate design failure.

7 **Evaluate** why the gusset plates were such a critical piece in the bridge design.

8 **Recommend** ways that bridge designers and inspectors can prevent future bridge collapses.

 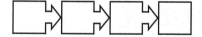

Build and Test a Bridge

Materials

plastic straws

ruler

scissors

cotton string

cardboard

Also needed:
notebook paper, books or other masses, balance (with a capacity of at least 2 kg)

Safety

In the Skill lab, you observed the relative strengths of two different geometric shapes. In the case study about the bridge collapse, you learned how scientists used scientific inquiry to determine the cause of the bridge collapse. In this investigation, you will combine geometric shapes to build model bridge supports. Then you will use scientific inquiry to determine the maximum load that your bridge will hold.

Ask a Question

What placement of supports produces the strongest bridge?

Make Observations

1 Read and complete a lab safety form.

2 Cut the straws into 24 6-cm segments.

3 Thread three straw segments onto a 1-m piece of string. Slide the segments toward one end of the string. Double knot the string to form a triangle. There should be very little string showing between the segments.

4 Thread the long end of the remaining string through two more straw segments. Double knot the string to one unattached corner to form another triangle. Cut off the remaining string, leaving at least a 1 cm after the knot. Use the string and one more straw segment to form a tetrahedron, as shown below.

5 Use the remaining string and straw segments to build three more tetrahedrons.

6 Set the four tetrahedrons on a piece of paper. They will serve as supports for your bridge deck, a 20-cm x 30-cm piece of cardboard.

7 With your teammates, decide where you will place the tetrahedrons on the paper to best support a load placed on the bridge deck.

Form a Hypothesis

8 Form a hypothesis about where you will place your tetrahedrons and why that placement will support the most weight. Recall that a hypothesis is an explanation of an observation.

Test Your Hypothesis

9 Test your hypothesis by placing the tetrahedrons in your chosen locations on the paper. Lay the cardboard "bridge deck" over the top.

10 Use a balance to find the mass of a textbook. Record the mass in your Science Journal.

11 Gently place the textbook on the bridge deck. Continue to add massed objects until your bridge collapses. Record the total mass that collapsed the bridge.

12 Examine the deck and supports. Look for possible causes of bridge failure.

Analyze and Conclude

13 **Analyze** Was your hypothesis supported? How do you know?

14 **Compare and Contrast** Study the pictures of bridges in Lesson 3. How does the failure of your bridge compare to the failure of the I-35W bridge?

15 **The Big Idea** What steps of scientific inquiry did you use in this activity? What would you do next to figure out how to make a stronger bridge?

Communicate Your Results

Compare your results with those of several other teams. Discuss the placement of your supports and any other factors that may cause your bridge to fail.

Inquiry Extension

Try building your supports with straw segments that are shorter (4 cm long) and longer (8 cm long). Test your bridges in the same way with each size of support.

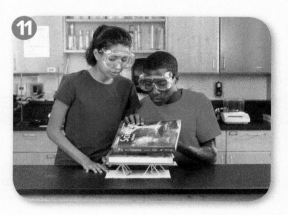

11

Lab Tips

☑ When building your tetrahedrons, make sure to double knot all connections and pull them tight. When you are finished, test each tetrahedron by pressing lightly on the top point.

☑ When adding the books to the bridge deck, place the books gently on top of the pile. Do not drop them.

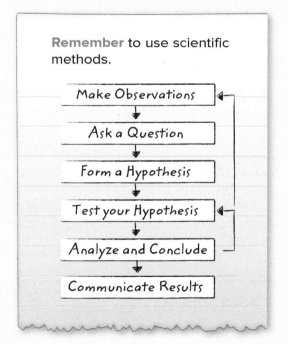

Remember to use scientific methods.

Make Observations
↓
Ask a Question
↓
Form a Hypothesis
↓
Test your Hypothesis
↓
Analyze and Conclude
↓
Communicate Results

Study Guide and Review

 THE BIG IDEA Scientific inquiry is a collection of methods that scientists use in different combinations to perform scientific investigations.

Key Concepts Summary

Key Concepts Summary	Vocabulary
Lesson 1: Scientific Inquiry • Some steps used during scientific inquiry are making **observations** and **inferences**, developing a **hypothesis**, analyzing results, and drawing conclusions. These steps, among others, can be performed in any order. • There are many results of scientific inquiry, and a few possible outcomes are the development of new materials and new technology, the discovery of new objects and events, and answers to basic questions. • **Critical thinking** is comparing what you already know about something to new information and deciding whether or not you agree with the new information.	**science** p. NOS 4 **observation** p. NOS 6 **inference** p. NOS 6 **hypothesis** p. NOS 6 **prediction** p. NOS 6 **scientific theory** p. NOS 8 **scientific law** p. NOS 8 **technology** p. NOS 9 **critical thinking** p. NOS 10
Lesson 2: Measurement and Scientific Tools • Scientists developed one universal system of units, the **International System of Units (SI),** to improve communication among scientists. • **Scientific notation** is a useful tool for writing large and small numbers in a shorter form. • Tools such as graduated cylinders and triple-beam balances make scientific investigation easier, more accurate, and repeatable.	**description** p. NOS 18 **explanation** p. NOS 18 **International System of Units (SI)** p. NOS 18 **scientific notation** p. NOS 21 **percent error** p. NOS 21
Lesson 3: Case Study—The Minneapolis Bridge Failure • Evaluation and testing are important in the design process for the safety of the consumer and to keep costs of building or manufacturing the product at a reasonable level. • Scientific inquiry was used throughout the process of determining why the bridge collapsed, including hypothesizing potential reasons for the bridge failure and testing those hypotheses.	**variable** p. NOS 27 **independent variable** p. NOS 27 **dependent variable** p. NOS 27 **constants** p. NOS 27 **qualitative data** p. NOS 27 **quantitative data** p. NOS 27 **experimental group** p. NOS 30 **control group** p. NOS 30

Use Vocabulary

1 The _____ contains the same factors as the experimental group, but the independent variable is not changed.

2 The expression of error as a percentage of the accepted value is _____.

3 The process of studying nature at all levels and the collection of information that is accumulated is _____.

4 The _____ are the factors in the experiment that stay the same.

Understand Key Concepts 🔑

5 Which is NOT an SI base unit?

A. kilogram

B. liter

C. meter

D. second

6 While analyzing results from an investigation, a scientist calculates a very small number that he or she wants to make easier to use. Which does the scientist use to record the number?

A. explanation

B. inference

C. scientific notation

D. scientific theory

7 Which is NOT true of a scientific law?

A. It can be modified or rejected.

B. It states that an event will occur.

C. It explains why an event will occur.

D. It is based on repeated observations.

8 Which tool would a scientist use to find the mass of a small steel rod?

A. balance

B. computer

C. hot plate

D. thermometer

Critical Thinking

9 Write a brief description of the activity shown in the photo.

Writing in Science ✏️

10 Write a five-sentence paragraph that gives examples of how critical thinking, skepticism, and identifying facts and opinions can help you in your everyday life. Be sure to include a topic sentence and concluding sentence in your paragraph.

REVIEW THE BIG IDEA

11 What is scientific inquiry? Explain why it is a constantly changing process.

12 Which part of scientific inquiry does this photo demonstrate?

Math Skills ✖️➗ ✔️ Math Practice

13 The accepted scientific value for the density of sucrose is 1.59 g/cm³. You perform three trials to measure the density of sucrose, and your data is shown in the table below. Calculate the percent error for each trial.

Trial	Density	Percent Error
Trial 1	1.55 g/cm³	
Trial 2	1.60 g/cm³	
Trial 3	1.58 g/cm³	

Properties of Matter

1000 B.C.
Chemistry is considered more of an art than a science. Chemical arts include the smelting of metals and the making of drugs, dyes, iron, and bronze.

1661
A clear distinction is made between chemistry and alchemy when *The Sceptical Chymist* is published by Robert Boyle. Modern chemistry begins to emerge.

1789
Antoine Lavoisier, the "father of modern chemistry," clearly outlines the law of conservation of mass.

1803
John Dalton publishes his atomic theory, which states that all matter is composed of atoms, which are small and indivisible and can join together to form chemical compounds. Dalton is considered the originator of modern atomic theory.

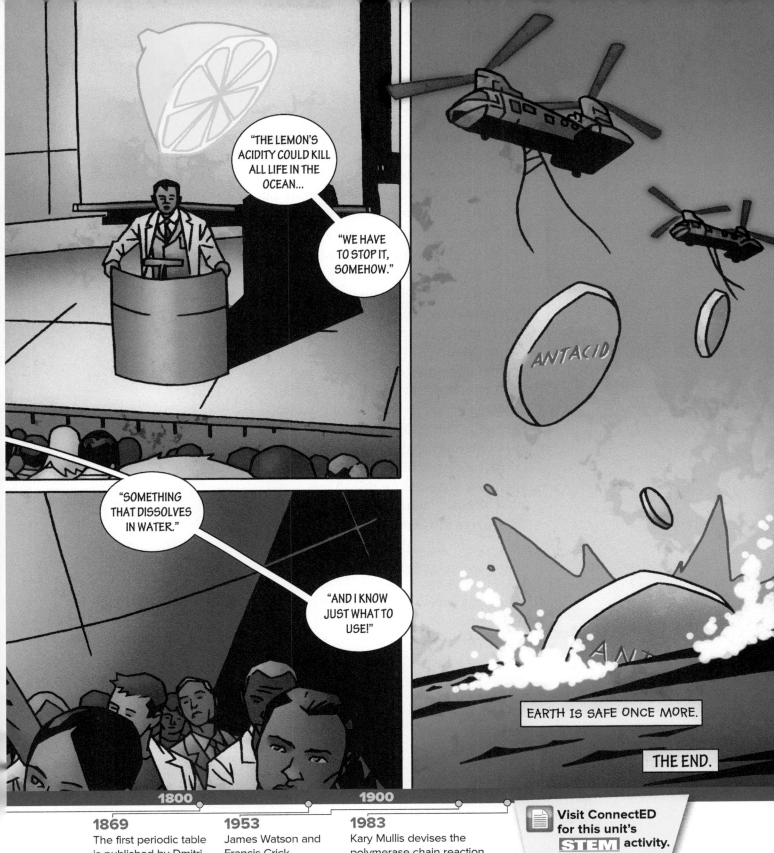

1869
The first periodic table is published by Dmitri Mendeleev. The table arranges elements into vertical columns and horizontal rows and is arranged by atomic number.

1953
James Watson and Francis Crick develop the double-helix model of DNA. This discovery leads to a spike in research of the biochemistry of life.

1983
Kary Mullis devises the polymerase chain reaction (PCR), a technique for copying a small portion of DNA in a lab environment. PCR can be used to synthesize specific pieces of DNA and makes the sequencing of DNA of organisms possible.

Visit ConnectED for this unit's **STEM** activity.

Patterns

It's a bird! It's a plane! No, it's Venus! Besides the Sun, Venus is brighter than any other star or planet in the sky. It is often seen from Earth without the aid of a telescope, as shown in **Figure 1**. At certain times of the year, Venus can be seen in the early evening. At other times of the year, Venus is best seen in the morning or even during daylight hours.

Astronomers study the patterns of each planet's orbit and rotation. A pattern is a consistent plan or model used as a guide for understanding and predicting things. Studying the orbital patterns of planets allows scientists to predict the future position of each planet. By studying the pattern of Venus's orbit, astronomers can predict when Venus will be most visible from Earth. Astronomers also can predict when Venus will travel between Earth and the Sun, and be visible from Earth, as shown in **Figure 2**. This event is so rare that it has only occurred seven or eight times since the mid-1600s. Using patterns, scientists are able to predict the date when you will be able to see this event in the future.

▲ **Figure 1** Venus is often so bright in the morning sky that it has been nicknamed the morning star.

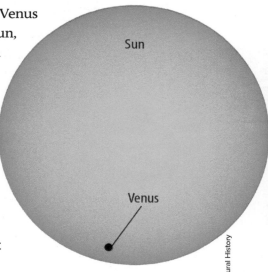

Figure 2 On June 5 and 6, 2012 observers around the world watched Venus pass in front of the Sun. This was the last time this event will take place until 2117. ▶

Types of Patterns

Physical Patterns

A pattern that you can see and touch is a physical pattern. The crystalline structures of minerals are examples of physical patterns. When atoms form crystals, they produce structural, or physical, patterns. The crystal structure of the Star of India sapphire creates a pattern that reflects light in a stunning star shape.

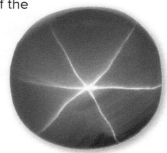

Cyclic Patterns

An event that repeats many times again in a predictable order has a cyclic pattern. Since Earth's axis is tilted, the angle of the Sun's rays on your location on Earth changes as Earth orbits the Sun. This causes the seasons—winter, spring, summer, and fall—to occur in the same pattern every year.

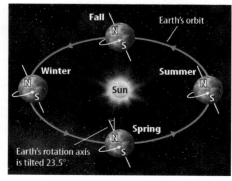

(t) Azem Ramadani/Getty Images, (c) Ian Waldie/Getty Images, (b)American Museum of Natural History

Patterns in Engineering

Engineers study patterns for many reasons, including to understand the physical properties of materials or to optimize the performance of their designs. Have you ever seen bricks with a pattern of holes through them? Clay bricks used in construction are fired, or baked, to make them stronger. Ceramic engineers understand that a regular pattern of holes in a brick assures that the brick is evenly fired and will not easily break.

Maybe you have seen a bridge constructed with a repeating pattern of large, steel triangles. Civil engineers, who design roads and bridges, know that the triangle is one of the strongest shapes in geometry. Engineers often use patterns of triangles in the structure of bridges to make them withstand heavy traffic and high winds.

Patterns in Physical Science

Scientists use patterns to explain past events or predict future events. At one time, only a few chemical elements were known. Chemists arranged the information they knew about these elements in a pattern according to the elements' properties. Scientists predicted the atomic numbers and the properties of elements that had yet to be discovered. These predictions made the discovery of new elements easier because scientists knew what properties to look for.

Look around. There are patterns everywhere—in art and nature, in the motion of the universe, in vehicles traveling on the roads, and in the processes of plant and animal growth. Analyzing patterns helps to understand the universe.

Patterns in Graphs

Scientists often graph their data to help identify patterns. For example, scientists might plot data from experiments on parachute nylon in graphs, such as the one below. Analyzing patterns on graphs then gives engineers information about how to design the strongest parachutes.

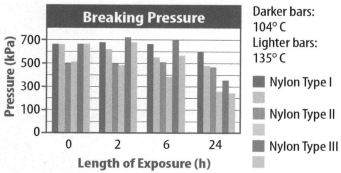

8.PS.1, 8.PS.2, 8.PS.3, 8.PS.5, 8.PS.6,
8.PS.7, SEPS.2, SEPS.3, SEPS.4, SEPS.5,
SEPS.6, SEPS.7, SEPS.8, 6-8.LST.7.1

Foundations of Chemistry

THE BIG IDEA What is matter, and how does it change?

 Why does it glow?

This siphonophore (si FAW nuh fawr) lives in the Arctic Ocean. Its tentacles have a very powerful sting. However, the most obvious characteristic of this organism is the way it glows.

- What might cause the siphonophore to glow?

- How do you think its glow helps the siphonophore survive?

- What changes happen in the matter that makes up the organism?

Gregory G. Dimijian/Science Source

Get Ready to Read

What do you think?

Before you read, decide if you agree or disagree with each of these statements. As you read this chapter, see if you change your mind about any of the statements.

1 The atoms in all objects are the same.

2 You cannot always tell by an object's appearance whether it is made of more than one type of atom.

3 The weight of a material never changes, regardless of where it is.

4 Boiling is one method used to separate parts of a mixture.

5 Heating a material decreases the energy of its particles.

6 When you stir sugar into water, the sugar and water evenly mix.

7 When wood burns, new materials form.

8 Temperature can affect the rate at which chemical changes occur.

Mc Graw Hill Education connectED

Your one-stop online resource
connectED.mcgraw-hill.com

 LS LearnSmart®

 Chapter Resources Files, Reading Essentials, Get Ready to Read, Quick Vocabulary

 Animations, Videos, Interactive Tables

 Self-checks, Quizzes, Tests

 PBL Project-Based Learning Activities

 Lab Manuals, Safety Videos, Virtual Labs & Other Tools

 Vocabulary, Multilingual eGlossary, Vocab eGames, Vocab eFlashcards

 Personal Tutors

Lesson 1

Reading Guide

Key Concepts 🗝️
ESSENTIAL QUESTIONS

- What is a substance?
- How do atoms of different elements differ?
- How do mixtures differ from substances?
- How can you classify matter?

Vocabulary

matter p. 9

atom p. 9

substance p. 11

element p. 11

compound p. 12

mixture p. 13

heterogeneous mixture p. 13

homogeneous mixture p. 13

dissolve p. 13

 Multilingual eGlossary

 BrainPOP®
Science Video
What's Science Got to do With It?

 8.PS.1, 8.PS.2, 8.PS.3, SEPS.2, SEPS.8, 6-8.LST.7.1

Classifying Matter

Magdevski/Getty Images

Inquiry Making Green?

You probably have mixed paints together. Maybe you wanted green paint and had only yellow paint and blue paint. Perhaps you watched an artist mixing several tints get the color he or she needed. In all these instances, the final color came from mixing colors together and not from changing the color of a paint.

How do you classify matter?

An object made of paper bound together might be classified as a book. Pointed metal objects might be classified as nails or needles. How can you classify an item based on its description?

1. Read and complete a lab safety form.
2. Place the **objects** on a table. Discuss how you might separate the objects into groups with these characteristics:
   a. Every object is the same and has only one part.
   b. Every object is the same but is made of more than one part.
   c. Individual objects are different. Some have one part, and others have more than one part.
3. Identify the objects that meet the requirements for group *a*, and record them in your Science Journal. Repeat with groups *b* and *c*. Any object can be in more than one group.

Think About This

1. Does any object from the bag belong in all three of the groups (*a, b,* and *c*)? Explain.

2. What objects in your classroom would fit into group *b*?

3. 🔑 **Key Concept** What descriptions would you use to classify items around you?

Understanding Matter

Have you ever seen a rock like the one in **Figure 1**? Why are different parts of the rock different in color? Why might some parts of the rock feel harder than other parts? The parts of the rock look and feel different because they are made of different types of matter. **Matter** *is anything that has mass and takes up space.* If you look around, you will see many types of matter. If you are in a classroom, you might see things made of metal, wood, or plastic. If you go to a park, you might see trees, soil, or water in a pond. If you look up at the sky, you might see clouds and the Sun. All of these things are made of matter.

Everything you can see is matter. However, some things you cannot see also are matter. Air, for example, is matter because it has mass and takes up space. Sound and light are not matter. Forces and energy also are not matter. To decide whether something is matter, ask yourself if it has mass and takes up space.

An **atom** *is a small particle that is a building block of matter.* In this lesson, you will explore the parts of an atom and read how atoms can differ. You will also read how different arrangements of atoms make up the many types of matter.

WORD ORIGIN ··········

matter
from Latin materia, meaning "material, stuff"

Figure 1 You can see different types of matter in this rock.

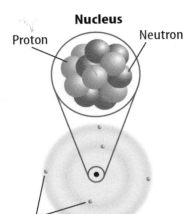

Nucleus

Proton   Neutron

Electrons

Figure 2 An atom has electrons moving in an area outside a nucleus. Protons and neutrons make up the nucleus.

 Personal Tutor

Atoms

To understand why there are so many types of matter, it helps if you first learn about the parts of an atom. Look at the diagram of an atom in **Figure 2.** At the center of an atom is a nucleus. Protons, which have a positive charge, and neutrons, which have a neutral charge, make up the nucleus. Negatively charged particles, or electrons, move quickly throughout an area around the nucleus called the electron cloud.

✓ **Reading Check** What are the parts of an atom?

Not all atoms have the same number of protons, neutrons, and electrons. Atoms that have different numbers of protons differ in their properties. You will read more about the differences in atoms on the next page.

An atom is almost too small to imagine. Think about how thin a human hair is. The diameter of a human hair is about a million times greater than the diameter of an atom. In addition, an atom is about 10,000 times wider than its nucleus! Even though atoms are so tiny, they determine the properties of the matter they compose.

◀ MiniLab   20 minutes

How can you model an atom?

How can you model an atom out of its three basic parts?

1 Read and complete a lab safety form.

2 Twist the ends of a piece of **florist wire** together to form a ring. Attach two **wires** across the ring to form an *X*.

3 Use **double-sided tape** to join the **large pom-poms** (protons and neutrons), forming a nucleus. Hang the nucleus from the center of the *X* with **fishing line.**

4 Use fishing line to suspend each **small pom-pom** (electron) from the ring so they surround the nucleus.

5 Suspend your model as instructed by your teacher.

Analyze and Conclude

1. **Infer** Based on your model, what can you infer about the relative sizes of protons, neutrons, and electrons?

2. **Model** Why is it difficult to model the location of electrons?

3. 🔑 **Key Concept** Compare your atom with those of other groups. How do they differ?

Substances

You can see that atoms make up most of the matter on Earth. Atoms can combine and arrange in millions of different ways. In fact, these different combinations and arrangements of atoms are what makes up the various types of matter. There are two main classifications of matter—substances and mixtures.

A **substance** *is matter with a composition that is always the same.* This means that a given substance is always made up of the same combination(s) of atoms. Aluminum, oxygen, water, and sugar are examples of substances. Any sample of aluminum is always made up of the same type of atoms, just as samples of oxygen, sugar, and water each are always made of the same combinations of atoms. To gain a better understanding of what makes up substances, let's take a look at the two types of substances—elements and compounds.

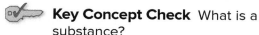 **Key Concept Check** What is a substance?

Elements

Look at the periodic table of elements on the inside back cover of this book. The substances oxygen and aluminum are on the table. They are both elements. *An* **element** *is a substance that consists of just one type of atom.* Because there are 118 known elements, there are 118 different types of atoms. Each type of atom contains a different number of protons in its nucleus. For example, each aluminum atom has 13 protons in its nucleus. The number of protons in an atom is the atomic number of the element. Therefore, the atomic number of aluminum is 13, as shown in **Figure 3.**

The atoms of most elements exist as individual atoms. For example, a roll of pure aluminum foil consists of trillions of individual aluminum atoms. However, the atoms of some elements usually exist in groups. For example, the oxygen atoms in air exist in pairs. Whether the atoms of an element exist individually or in groups, each element contains only one type of atom. Therefore, its composition is always the same.

 Key Concept Check How do atoms of different elements differ?

Figure 3 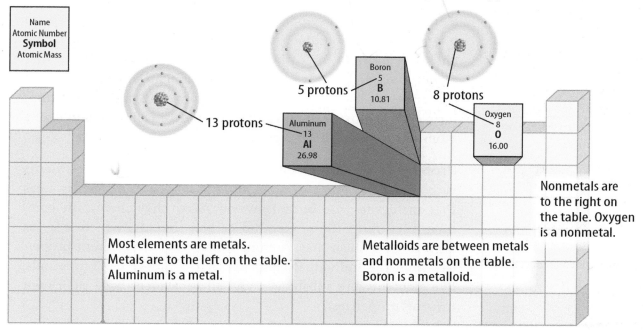 Each element on the periodic table consists of just one type of atom.

Name
Atomic Number
Symbol
Atomic Mass

5 protons

Boron
5
B
10.81

8 protons

13 protons — Aluminum
13
Al
26.98

Oxygen
8
O
16.00

Nonmetals are to the right on the table. Oxygen is a nonmetal.

Most elements are metals. Metals are to the left on the table. Aluminum is a metal.

Metalloids are between metals and nonmetals on the table. Boron is a metalloid.

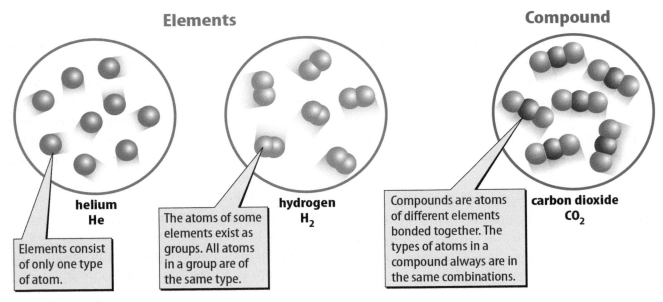

Elements   **Compound**

helium
He

Elements consist
of only one type
of atom.

The atoms of some
elements exist as
groups. All atoms
in a group are of
the same type.

hydrogen
H₂

Compounds are atoms
of different elements
bonded together. The
types of atoms in a
compound always are in
the same combinations.

carbon dioxide
CO₂

▲ Figure 4 If a substance contains only one type of atom, it is an element.
If it contains more than one type of atom, it is a compound.

Personal Tutor

Figure 5 Carbon dioxide
is a compound composed
of carbon and oxygen
atoms. ▼

This subscript means there
are two oxygen atoms
bonded to one carbon atom.

ACADEMIC VOCABULARY

unique
(*adjective*) having nothing else
like it

Compounds

Water is a substance, but it is not an element. It is a compound.
A **compound** *is a type of substance containing atoms of two or more
different elements chemically bonded together.* As shown in **Figure 4**,
carbon dioxide (CO_2) is also a compound. It consists of atoms of
two different elements, carbon (C) and oxygen (O), bonded together.
Carbon dioxide is a substance because the C and the O atoms are
always combined in the same way.

Chemical Formulas The combination of symbols and numbers
that represents a compound is called a chemical formula. Chemical
formulas show the different atoms that make up a compound,
using their element symbols. Chemical formulas also help explain
how the atoms combine. As illustrated in **Figure 5**, CO_2 is the
chemical formula for carbon dioxide. The formula shows that
carbon dioxide is made of C and O atoms. The small *2* is called a
subscript. It means that two oxygen atoms and one carbon atom
form carbon dioxide. If no subscript is written after a symbol, one
atom of that element is present in the chemical formula.

Properties of Compounds Think again about the elements
carbon and oxygen. Carbon is a black solid, and oxygen is a gas
that enables fuels to burn. However, when they chemically combine, they form the compound carbon dioxide, which is a gas
used to extinguish fires. A compound often has different properties from the individual elements that compose it. Compounds,
like elements, are substances, and all substances have their own
unique properties.

Mixtures

Another classification of matter is mixtures. *A* **mixture** *is matter that can vary in composition.* Mixtures are combinations of two or more substances that are physically blended together. The amounts of the substances can vary in different parts of a mixture and from mixture to mixture. Think about sand mixed with water at the beach. The sand and the water do not bond together. Instead, they form a mixture. The substances in a mixture do not combine chemically. Therefore, they can be separated by physical methods, such as filtering.

Heterogeneous Mixtures

Mixtures can differ depending on how well the substances that make them up are mixed. Sand and water at the beach form a mixture, but the sand is not evenly mixed throughout the water. Therefore, sand and water form a heterogeneous mixture. *A* **heterogeneous mixture** *is a type of mixture in which the individual substances are not evenly mixed.* Because the substances in a heterogeneous mixture are not evenly mixed, two samples of the same mixture can have different amounts of the substances, as shown in **Figure 6.** For example, if you fill two buckets with sand and water at the beach, one bucket might have more sand in it than the other.

Homogeneous Mixtures

Unlike a mixture of water and sand, the substances in mixtures such as apple juice, air, or salt water are evenly mixed. *A* **homogeneous mixture** *is a type of mixture in which the individual substances are evenly mixed.* In a homogeneous mixture, the particles of individual substances are so small and well-mixed that they are not visible, even with most high-powered microscopes.

A homogeneous mixture also is known as a solution. In a solution, the substance present in the largest amount is called the solvent. All other substances in a solution are called solutes. The solutes dissolve in the solvent. *To* **dissolve** *means to form a solution by mixing evenly.* Because the substances in a solution, or homogeneous mixture, are evenly mixed, two samples from a solution will have the same amounts of each substance. For example, imagine pouring two glasses of apple juice from the same container. Each glass will contain the same substances (water, sugar, and other substances) in the same amounts. However, because apple juice is a mixture, the amounts of the substances from one container of apple juice to another might vary.

 Key Concept Check How do mixtures differ from substances?

Figure 6 Types of mixtures differ in how evenly their substances are mixed.

Heterogeneous Mixture	Homogeneous Mixture
• The individual substances are not evenly mixed. • Different samples of a given heterogeneous mixture can have different combinations of the same substances.	• The individual substances are evenly mixed. • Different samples of a given homogeneous mixture will have the same combinations of the same substances.

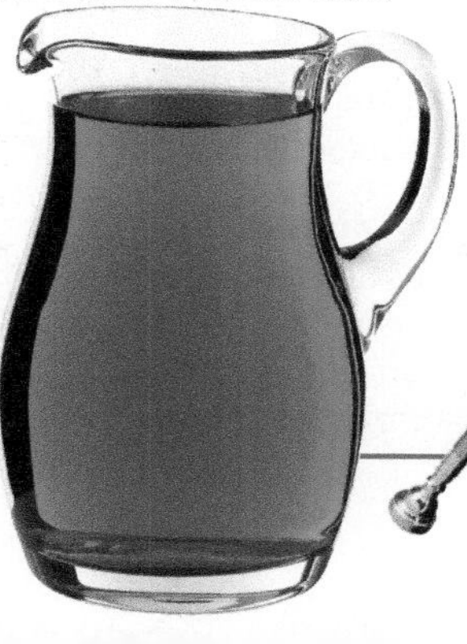

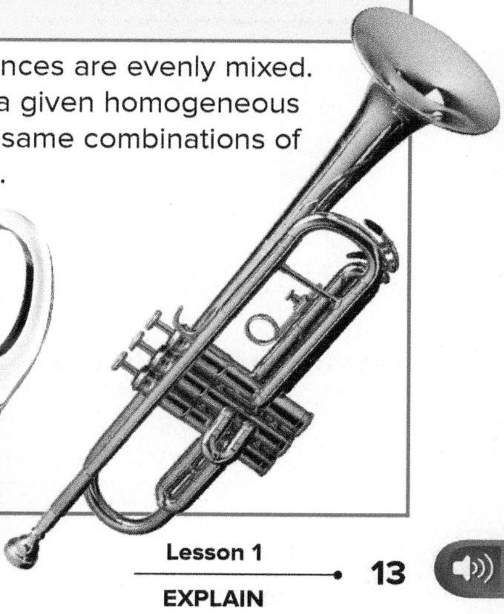

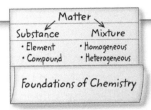

FOLDABLES®

Use three sheets of copy paper to make a layered Foldable. Cut and label the tabs as illustrated. Use this Foldable to summarize the lesson.

Compounds v. Solutions

If you have a glass of pure water and a glass of salt water, can you tell which is which just by looking at them? You cannot. Both the compound (water) and the solution (salt water) appear identical. How do compounds and solutions differ?

Because water is a compound, its composition does not vary. Pure water is always made up of the same atoms in the same combinations. Therefore, a chemical formula can be used to describe the atoms that make up water (H_2O). Salt water is a homogeneous mixture, or solution. The solute (NaCl) and the solvent (H_2O) are evenly mixed but are not bonded together. Adding more salt or more water only changes the relative amounts of the substances. In other words, the composition varies. Because composition can vary in a mixture, a chemical formula cannot be used to describe mixtures.

Summarizing Matter

You have read in this lesson about classifying matter by the arrangement of its atoms. **Figure 7** is a summary of this classification system.

 Key Concept Check How can you classify matter?

Figure 7 Scientists classify matter according to the arrangement of the atoms that make up the matter.

Classifying Matter

Matter
- Anything that has mass and takes up space
- Matter on Earth is made up of atoms.
- Two classifications of matter: substances and mixtures

Substances
- Matter with a composition that is always the same
- Two types of substances: elements and compounds

Element
- Consists of just one type of atom
- Organized on the periodic table
- Each element has a chemical symbol.

Compound
- Two or more types of atoms bonded together
- Properties are different from the properties of the elements that make it up
- Each compound has a chemical formula.

Substances physically combine to form mixtures.

Mixtures can be separated into substances by physical methods.

Mixtures
- Matter that can vary in composition
- Substances are not bonded together.
- Two types of mixtures: heterogeneous and homogeneous

Heterogeneous Mixture
- Two or more substances unevenly mixed
- Different substances are visible by an unaided eye or a microscope.

Homogeneous Mixture—Solution
- Two or more substances evenly mixed
- Different substances cannot be seen even by a microscope.

Lesson 1 Review

Visual Summary

A substance has the same composition throughout. A substance is either an element or a compound.

An atom is the smallest part of an element that has its properties. Atoms contain protons, neutrons, and electrons.

The substances in a mixture are not chemically combined. Mixtures can be either heterogeneous or homogeneous.

FOLDABLES

Use your lesson Foldable to review the lesson. Save your Foldable for the project at the end of the chapter.

What do you think NOW?

You first read the statements below at the beginning of the chapter.

1. The atoms in all objects are the same.

2. You cannot always tell by an object's appearance whether it is made of more than one type of atom.

Did you change your mind about whether you agree or disagree with the statements? Rewrite any false statements to make them true.

Use Vocabulary

1 Substances and mixtures are two types of _____.

2 Use the term *atom* in a complete sentence.

3 Define *dissolve* in your own words.

Understand Key Concepts

4 **Explain** why aluminum is a substance.

5 The number of _____ always differs in atoms of different elements.
   A. electrons   C. neutrons
   B. protons   D. nuclei

6 **Distinguish** between a heterogeneous mixture and a homogeneous mixture.

7 **Classify** Which term describes matter that is a substance made of different kinds of atoms bonded together?

Interpret Graphics

8 **Describe** what each letter and number means in the chemical formula below.

$$C_6H_{12}O_6$$

9 **Organize Information** Copy and fill in the graphic organizer below to classify matter by the arrangement of its atoms.

Type of Matter	Description

Critical Thinking

10 **Reorder** the elements aluminum, oxygen, fluorine, calcium, and hydrogen from the least to the greatest number of protons. Use the periodic table if needed.

11 **Evaluate** this statement: Substances are made of two or more types of elements.

U.S. Mint

How Coins are Made

In 1793, the U.S. Mint produced more than 11,000 copper pennies and put them into circulation. Soon after, gold and silver coins were introduced as well. Early pennies were made of 95 percent copper and 5 percent zinc. Today's penny contains much more zinc than copper and is much less expensive to produce. Quarters, dimes, and nickels, once made of silver, are now made of copper-nickel alloy.

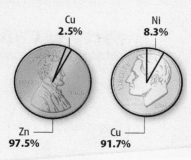

Cu 2.5%
Zn 97.5%
Ni 8.3%
Cu 91.7%

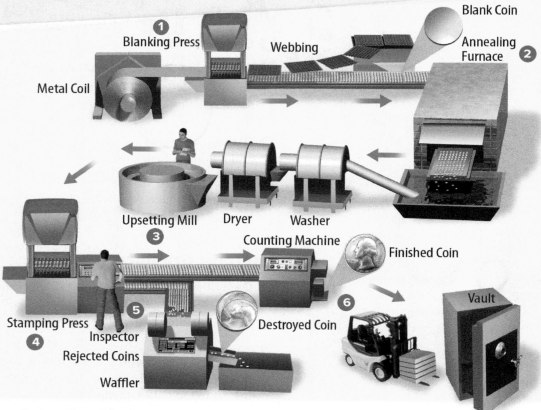

Blanking Press
Webbing
Blank Coin
Annealing Furnace
Metal Coil
Upsetting Mill   Dryer   Washer
Counting Machine
Finished Coin
Stamping Press
Inspector
Rejected Coins
Waffler
Destroyed Coin
Vault

How Coins Are Made

1 Blanking For nickels, dimes, quarters, half-dollars, and coin dollars, a strip of 13-inch-wide metal is fed through a blanking press, which punches out round discs called blanks. The leftover webbing strip is saved for recycling. Ready-made blanks are purchased for making the penny.

2 Annealing, Washing, Drying Blanks are softened in an annealing furnace, which makes the metal less brittle. The blanks are then run through a washer and a dryer.

3 Upsetting Usable blanks are put through an upsetting mill, which creates a rim around the edges of each blank.

4 Striking The blanks then go to the stamping press, where they are imprinted with designs and inscriptions.

5 Inspection Once blanks leave the stamping press, inspectors check a few coins from each batch. Coins that are defective go to the waffler in preparation for recycling.

6 Counting and Bagging A machine counts the finished coins then drops them into large bags that are sealed shut. The coins are then taken to storage before being shipped to Federal Reserve Banks and then to your local bank.

It's Your Turn

COMPARE Collect a variety of coins that includes both older and current coins. Observe and compare their properties. Using the dates of the coins' production, utilize library or Internet sources to research the composition of metals used.

Don Farrall/Getty Images

Lesson 2

Physical Properties

Reading Guide

Key Concepts

ESSENTIAL QUESTIONS

- What are some physical properties of matter?
- How are physical properties used to separate mixtures?

Vocabulary

physical property p. 18

mass p. 20

density p. 21

solubility p. 22

 Multilingual eGlossary

 Science Video

8.PS.5, SEPS.2, SEPS.5

Inquiry Panning by Properties?

The man lowers his pan into the waters of a river and scoops up a mixture of water, sediment, and hopefully gold. As he moves the pan in a circle, water sloshes out of it. If he is careful, gold will remain in the pan after the water and sediment are gone. What properties of water, sediment, and gold enable this man to separate this mixture?

Fuse/Getty Images (inset)Mike Perry/Alamy

Can you follow the clues?

Clues are bits of information that help you solve a mystery. In this activity, you will use clues to help identify an object in the classroom.

1. Read and complete a lab safety form.

2. Select one **object** in the room. Write a different clue about the object on each of five **index cards.** Clues might include one or two words that describe the object's color, size, texture, shape, or any property you can observe with your senses.

3. Stack your cards face down. Have your partner turn over one card and try to identify the object. Respond either "yes" or "no."

4. Continue turning over cards until your partner identifies your object or runs out of cards. Repeat for your partner's object.

Think About This

1. What kind of clues are the most helpful in identifying an object?

2. How would your clues change if you were describing a substance, such as iron or water, rather than an object?

3. 🔑 **Key Concept** How do you think you use similar clues in your daily life?

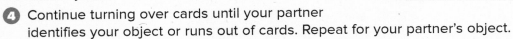
Physical Properties

As you read in Lesson 1, the arrangement of atoms determines whether matter is a substance or a mixture. The arrangement of atoms also determines the properties of different types of matter. Each element and compound has a unique set of properties. When substances mix together and form mixtures, the properties of the substances that make up the mixture are still present.

You can observe some properties of matter, and other properties can be measured. For example, you can see that gold is shiny, and you can find the mass of a sample of iron. Think about how you might describe the different substances and mixtures in the photo on the previous page. Could you describe some of the matter in the photo as a solid or a liquid? Why do the water and the rocks leave the pan before the gold does? Could you describe the mass of the various items in the photo? Each of these questions asks about the physical properties of matter. *A **physical property** is a characteristic of matter that you can observe or measure without changing the identity of the matter.* There are many types of physical properties, and you will read about some of them in this lesson.

REVIEW VOCABULARY

property
a characteristic used to describe something

🔵 **Applying Practices**

Does the density of a substance change? Go online to investigate density, a physical property, and gather evidence about whether properties of a substance change.

Hutchings Photography/Digital Light Source

States of Matter

How do aluminum, water, and air differ? Recall that aluminum is an element, water is a compound, and air is a mixture. How else do these three types of matter differ? At room temperature, aluminum is a solid, water is a liquid, and air is a gas. Solids, liquids, and gases are called states of matter. The state of matter is a physical property of matter. Substances and mixtures can be solids, liquids, or gases. For example, water in the ocean is a liquid, but water in an iceberg is a solid. In addition, water vapor in the air above the ocean is a gas.

Did you know that the particles, or atoms and groups of atoms, that make up all matter are constantly moving and are attracted to each other? Look at your pencil. It is made up of trillions of moving particles. Every solid, liquid, and gas around you is made up of moving particles that attract one another. What makes some matter a solid and other matter a liquid or a gas? It depends on how close the particles in the matter are to one another and how fast they move, as shown in **Figure 8.**

✅ **Reading Check** How do solids, liquids, and gases differ?

Figure 8 The three common states of matter on Earth are solid, liquid, and gas.

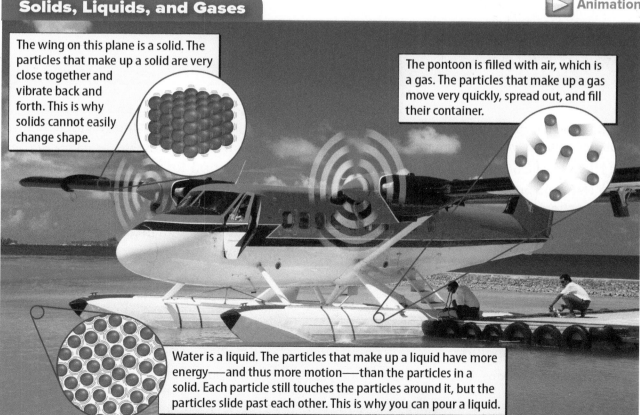

Solids, Liquids, and Gases

▶ Animation

The wing on this plane is a solid. The particles that make up a solid are very close together and vibrate back and forth. This is why solids cannot easily change shape.

The pontoon is filled with air, which is a gas. The particles that make up a gas move very quickly, spread out, and fill their container.

Water is a liquid. The particles that make up a liquid have more energy—and thus more motion—than the particles in a solid. Each particle still touches the particles around it, but the particles slide past each other. This is why you can pour a liquid.

✅ **Visual Check** Which state of matter flows, keeps the same volume, and takes the shape of its container?

Rob Rae/age fotostock

Figure 9 The larger dumbbells have greater mass than the smaller dumbbells because they contain more matter.

Size-Dependent Properties

State is only one of many physical properties that you can use to describe matter. Some physical properties, such as mass and volume, depend on the size or amount of matter. Measurements of these properties vary depending on how much matter is in a sample.

Mass Imagine holding a small dumbbell in one hand and a larger one in your other hand. What do you notice? The larger dumbbell is heavier. The larger dumbbell has more mass than the smaller one. **Mass** *is the amount of matter in an object.* Both small dumbbells shown in **Figure 9** have the same mass because they both contain the same amount of matter. Mass is a size-dependent property of a given substance because its value depends on the size of a sample.

Mass sometimes is confused with weight, but they are not the same. Mass is the amount of matter in something. Weight is the pull of gravity on that matter. Weight changes with location, but mass does not. Suppose one of the dumbbells in the figure was on the Moon. The dumbbell would have the same mass on the Moon that it has on Earth. However, the Moon's gravity is much less than Earth's gravity, so the weight of the dumbbell would be less on the Moon.

MiniLab

20 minutes

Can the weight of an object change?

When people go on a diet, both their mass and weight might change. Can the weight of an object change without changing its mass? Let's find out.

1. Read and complete a lab safety form.
2. Use a **balance** to find the mass of five **metal washers.** Record the mass in grams in your Science Journal.
3. Hang the washers from the hook on a **spring scale.** Record the weight in newtons.
4. Lower just the washers into a **500-mL beaker** containing approximately 300 mL water. Record the weight in newtons.

Analyze and Conclude

1. **Draw Conclusions** Did the weight of the washers change during the experiment? How do you know?

2. **Predict** In what other ways might you change the weight of the washers?

3. **Key Concept** What factors affect the weight of an object, but not its mass?

Volume Another physical property that depends on the size or the amount of a substance is volume. A unit often used to measure volume is the milliliter (mL). Volume is the amount of space something takes up. Suppose a full bottle of water contains 400 mL of water. If you pour exactly half of the water out, the bottle contains half of the original volume, or 200 mL, of water.

 Reading Check What is a common unit for volume?

Size-Independent Properties

Unlike mass, weight, and volume, some physical properties of a substance do not depend on the amount of matter present. These properties are the same for both small samples and large samples. They are called size-independent properties. Examples of size-independent properties are melting point, boiling point, density, electrical conductivity, and solubility.

Melting Point and Boiling Point The temperature at which a substance changes from a solid to a liquid is its melting point. The temperature at which a substance changes from a liquid to a gas is its boiling point. Different substances have different boiling points and melting points. The boiling point for water is 100°C at sea level. Notice in **Figure 10** that this temperature does not depend on how much water is in the container.

Density Imagine holding a bowling ball in one hand and a foam ball of the same size in the other. The bowling ball is heavier because the density of the material that makes up the bowling ball is greater than the density of foam. **Density** *is the mass per unit volume of a substance.* Like melting point and boiling point, density is a size-independent property.

Math Skills

Use Ratios
When you compare two numbers by division, you are using a ratio. Density can be written as a ratio of mass and volume. What is the density of a substance if a 5-mL sample has a mass of 25 g?

1. Set up a ratio.
$$\frac{mass}{volume} = \frac{25 \text{ g}}{5 \text{ mL}}$$

2. Divide the numerator by the denominator to get the mass (in g) of 1 mL.
$$\frac{25 \text{ g}}{5 \text{ mL}} = \frac{5 \text{ g}}{1 \text{ mL}}$$

3. The density is 5 g/mL.

Practice
A sample of wood has a mass of 12 g and a volume of 16 mL. What is the density of the wood?

✓ **Math Practice**

💬 **Personal Tutor**

WORD ORIGIN ··············

density
from Latin *densus*, means "compact"; and Greek *dasys*, means "thick"

Figure 10 The boiling point of water is 100°C at sea level. The boiling point does not change for different volumes of water.

Conductivity Another property that is independent of the sample size is conductivity. Electrical conductivity is the ability of matter to conduct, or carry along, an electric current. Copper often is used for electrical wiring because it has high electrical conductivity. Thermal conductivity is the ability of a material to conduct thermal energy. Metals tend to have high electrical and thermal conductivity. Stainless steel, for example, often is used to make cooking pots because of its high thermal conductivity. However, the handles on the pan probably are made out of wood, plastic, or some other substance that has low thermal conductivity.

✓ **Reading Check** What are two types of conductivity?

Solubility Have you ever made lemonade by stirring a powdered drink mix into water? As you stir, the powder mixes evenly in the water. In other words, the powder dissolves in the water.

What do you think would happen if you tried to dissolve sand in water? No matter how much you stir, the sand does not dissolve. **Solubility** *is the ability of one substance to dissolve in another.* The powdered drink mix is soluble in water, but sand is not. Table 1 explains how physical properties such as conductivity and solubility can be used to identify objects and separate mixtures.

Key Concept Check What are five different physical properties of matter?

Table 1 This table contains the descriptions of several physical properties. It also shows examples of how physical properties can be used to separate mixtures.

✓ **Visual Check** How might you separate a mixture of iron filings and salt?

Table 1 Physical Properties of Matter

	Property		
	Mass	**Conductivity**	**Volume**
Description of property	The amount of matter in an object	The ability of matter to conduct, or carry along, electricity or heat	The amount of space something occupies
Size-dependent or size-independent	Size-dependent	Size-independent	Size-dependent
How the property is used to separate a mixture (example)	Mass typically is not used to separate a mixture.	Conductivity typically is not used to separate a mixture.	Volume could be used to separate mixtures whose parts can be separated by filtration.

(l)©Lawrence Manning/Corbis, (c)Getty Images, (r)ULTRA.F/Getty Images

Separating Mixtures

In Lesson 1, you read about different types of mixtures. Recall that the substances that make up mixtures are not held together by chemical **bonds.** When substances form a mixture, the properties of the individual substances do not change. One way that a mixture and a compound differ is that the parts of a mixture often can be separated by physical properties. For example, when salt and water form a solution, the salt and the water do not lose any of their individual properties. Therefore, you can separate the salt from the water by using differences in their physical properties. Water has a lower boiling point than salt. If you boil salt water, the water will boil away, and the salt will be left behind. Other physical properties that can be used to separate different mixtures are described in Table 1.

Physical properties cannot be used to separate a compound into the elements it contains. The atoms that make up a compound are bonded together and cannot be separated by physical means. For example, you cannot separate the hydrogen atoms from the oxygen atoms in water by boiling water.

 Key Concept Check How are physical properties used to separate mixtures?

 Interactive Table

		Property		
Boiling/Melting Points	**State of matter**	**Density**	**Solubility**	**Magnetism**
The temperature at which a material changes state	Whether something is a solid, a liquid, or a gas	The amount of mass per unit of volume	The ability of one substance to dissolve in another	Attractive force for some metals, especially iron
Size-independent	Size-independent	Size-independent	Size-independent	Size-independent
Each part of a mixture will boil or melt at a different temperature.	A liquid can be poured off a solid.	Objects with greater density sink in objects with less density.	Dissolve a soluble material to separate it from a material with less solubility.	Attract iron from a mixture of materials.

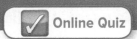
Visual Summary

A physical property is a characteristic of matter that can be observed or measured without changing the identity of the matter.

Examples of physical properties include mass, density, volume, melting point, boiling point, state of matter, and solubility.

Many physical properties can be used to separate the components of a mixture.

FOLDABLES

Use your lesson Foldable to review the lesson. Save your Foldable for the project at the end of the chapter.

What do you think NOW?

You first read the statements below at the beginning of the chapter.

3. The weight of a material never changes, regardless of where it is.

4. Boiling is one method used to separate parts of a mixture.

Did you change your mind about whether you agree or disagree with the statements? Rewrite any false statements to make them true.

Use Vocabulary

1. **Distinguish** between mass and weight.

2. **Use the term** *solubility* in a sentence.

3. An object's _____ is the amount of mass per a certain unit of volume.

Understand Key Concepts

4. **Explain** how to separate a mixture of sand and pebbles.

5. Which physical property is NOT commonly used to separate mixtures?
   - **A.** magnetism
   - **C.** density
   - **B.** conductivity
   - **D.** solubility

6. **Analyze** Name two size-dependent properties and two size-independent properties of an iron nail.

Interpret Graphics

7. **Sequence** Draw a graphic organizer like the one below to show the steps in separating a mixture of sand, iron filings, and salt.

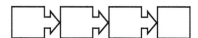

Critical Thinking

8. **Examine** the diagram below.

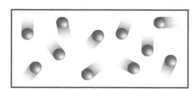

How can you identify the state of matter represented by the diagram?

Math Skills   Math Practice

9. A piece of copper has a volume of 100.0 cm^3. If the mass of the copper is 890 g, what is the density of copper?

(t)Hutchings Photography/Digital Light Source, (b)Crawford/Dorling Kindersley/Getty Images

How can following a procedure help you solve a crime?

Materials

Plastic
sealable bag

triple-beam
balance

50-mL
graduated
cylinder

paper towels

Also needed:

Crime Scene
Objects

Safety

Imagine that you are investigating a crime scene. You find several pieces of metal and broken pieces of plastic that look as if they came from a car's tail light. You also have similar objects collected from the suspect. How can you figure out if they are parts of the same objects?

Learn It

To be sure you do the same tests on each object, it is helpful to **follow a procedure.** A procedure tells you how to use the materials and what steps to take.

Try It

1. Read and complete a lab safety form.

2. Copy the table below into your Science Journal.

3. Use the balance to find the mass of an object from the crime scene. Record the mass in your table.

4. Place about 25 mL of water in a graduated cylinder. Read and record the exact volume. Call this volume V_1.

5. Carefully tilt the cylinder, and allow one of the objects to slide into the water. Read and record the volume. Call this volume V_2.

6. Repeat steps 3–5 for each of the other objects.

Apply It

7. Complete the table by calculating the volume and the density of each object.

8. What conclusions can you draw about the objects collected from the crime scene and those collected from the suspect?

9. **Key Concept** How could you use this procedure to help identify and compare various objects?

Object	Mass (M) (g)	V_1 (mL)	V_2 (mL)	Volume of Object (V) ($V_2 - V_1$) (mL)	Density of Object M/V (g/mL)
1					
2					
3					
4					
5					
6					

Physical Changes

Reading Guide

Key Concepts
ESSENTIAL QUESTIONS

- How can a change in energy affect the state of matter?
- What happens when something dissolves?
- What is meant by conservation of mass?

Vocabulary
physical change p. 27

 Multilingual eGlossary

8.PS.6, SEPS.2, SEPS.4, SEPS.5

Inquiry Change by Chipping?

This artist is changing a piece of wood into an instrument that will make beautiful music. He planned and chipped, measured and shaped. Chips of wood flew, and rough edges became smooth. Although the wood changed shape, it remained wood. Its identity did not change, just its form.

Where did it go?

When you dissolve sugar in water, where does the sugar go? One way to find out is to measure the mass of the water and the sugar before and after mixing.

1. Read and complete a lab safety form.

2. Add **sugar** to a **small paper cup** until the cup is approximately half full. Bend the cup's opening, and pour the sugar into a **balloon.**

3. With the balloon hanging over the side, stretch the neck of the balloon over a **flask** half full of **water.**

4. Use a **balance** to find the mass of the flask-and-balloon assembly. Record the mass in your Science Journal.

5. Lift the end of the balloon, and empty the sugar into the flask. Swirl until the sugar dissolves. Measure and record the mass of the flask-and-balloon assembly again.

Think About This

1. Is the sugar still present after it dissolves? How do you know?

2. 🔑 **Key Concept** Based on your observations, what do you think happens to the mass of objects when they dissolve? Explain.

Physical Changes

How would you describe water? If you think about water in a stream, you might say that it is a cool liquid. If you think about water as ice, you might describe it as a cold solid. How would you describe the change from ice to water? As ice melts, some of its properties change, such as the state of matter, the shape, and the temperature, but it is still water. In Lesson 2, you read that substances and mixtures can be solids, liquids, or gases. In addition, substances and mixtures can change from one state to another. *A* **physical change** *is a change in size, shape, form, or state of matter in which the matter's identity stays the same.* During a physical change, the matter does not become something different even though physical properties change.

Change in Shape and Size

Think about changes in the shapes and the sizes of substances and mixtures you experience each day. When you chew food, you are breaking it into smaller pieces. This change in size helps make food easier to digest. When you pour juice from a bottle into a glass, you are changing the shape of the juice. If you fold clothes to fit them into a drawer, you are changing their shapes. Changes in shape and size are physical changes. The identity of the matter has not changed.

Hutchings Photography/Digital Light Source

WORD ORIGIN · · · · · · · · · ·

physical
from Greek *physika*, means "natural things"

change
from Latin *cambire*, means "to exchange"

FOLDABLES

Make a vertical two-tab book. Label the tabs as illustrated. Record specific examples illustrating how adding or releasing thermal energy results in physical change.

Increasing Thermal Energy

Decreasing Thermal Energy

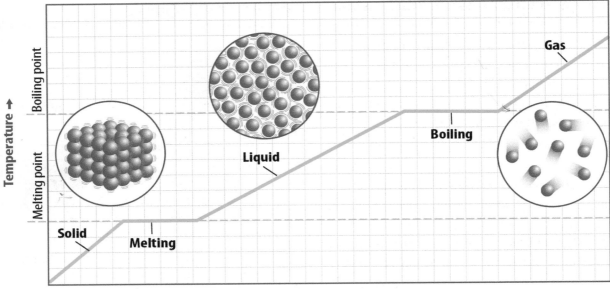

Temperature →

Boiling point

Melting point

Gas

Boiling

Liquid

Solid

Melting

Adding thermal energy →

▲ Figure 11 🗝 As thermal energy is added to a material, temperature increases when the state of the material is not changing. Temperature stays the same during a change of state.

▶ Animation

Figure 12 Solid iodine undergoes sublimation. It changes from a solid to a gas without becoming a liquid. ▼

Change in State of Matter

Why does ice melt in your hand? Or, why does water turn to ice in the freezer? Matter, such as water, can change state. Recall from Lesson 2 how the particles in a solid, a liquid, and a gas behave. To change the state of matter, the movement of the particles has to change. In order to change the movement of particles, thermal energy must be either added or removed.

Adding Thermal Energy When thermal energy is added to a solid, the particles in the solid move faster and faster, and the temperature increases. As the particles move faster, they are more likely to overcome the attractive forces that hold them tightly together. When the particles are moving too fast for attractive forces to hold them tightly together, the solid reaches its melting point. The melting point is the temperature at which a solid changes to a liquid.

After all the solid has melted, adding more thermal energy causes the particles to move even faster. The temperature of the liquid increases. When the particles are moving so fast that attractive forces cannot hold them close together, the liquid is at its boiling point. The boiling point is the temperature at which a liquid changes into a gas and the particles spread out. Figure 11 shows how temperature and change of state relate to each other when thermal energy is added to a material.

Some solids change directly to a gas without first becoming a liquid. This process is called sublimation. An example of sublimation is shown in Figure 12. You saw another example of sublimation in Figure 5 in Lesson 1.

Perennou Nuridsany/Photo Researchers, Inc.

Removing Thermal Energy When thermal energy is removed from a gas, such as water vapor, particles in the gas move more slowly and the temperature decreases. Condensation occurs when the particles are moving slowly enough for attractive forces to pull the particles close together. Recall that condensation is the process that occurs when a gas becomes a liquid.

After the gas has completely changed to a liquid, removing more thermal energy from the liquid causes particles to move even more slowly. As the motion between the particles slows, the temperature decreases. Freezing occurs when the particles are moving so slowly that attractive forces between the particles hold them tightly together. Now the particles only can vibrate in place. Recall that freezing is the process that occurs when a liquid becomes a solid.

Freezing and melting are reverse processes, and they occur at the same temperature. The same is true of boiling and condensation. Another change of state is deposition. Deposition is the change from a gas directly to a solid, as shown in **Figure 13.** It is the process that is the opposite of sublimation.

 Key Concept Check How can removing thermal energy affect the state of matter?

Figure 13 When enough thermal energy is removed, one of several processes occurs.

Freezing

Condensation

Deposition

(l)Digital Vision/Getty Images, (c)©BananaStock/PunchStock, (r)IT Stock/age fotostock

Dissolving

Have you ever owned a saltwater aquarium, such as the one shown in **Figure 14?** If you have, you probably had to add certain salts to the water before you added the fish. Can you see the salt in the water? As you added the salt to the water, it gradually disappeared. It was still there, but it dissolved, or mixed evenly, in the water. Because the identities of the substances–water and salt–are not changed, dissolving is a physical change.

Like many physical changes, dissolving is usually easy to reverse. If you boil the salt water, the liquid water will change to water vapor, leaving the salt behind. You once again can see the salt because the particles that make up the substances do not change identity during a physical change.

 Key Concept Check What happens when something dissolves?

▲ **Figure 14** Salt dissolves when it is added to the water in this aquarium.

Conservation of Mass

During a physical change, the physical properties of matter change. The particles in matter that are present before a physical change are the same as those present after the physical change. Because the particles are the same both before and after a physical change, the total mass before and after the change is also the same, as shown in **Figure 15.** This is known as the law of conservation of mass. You will read in Lesson 4 that mass also is conserved during another type of change–a chemical change.

 Key Concept Check What is meant by conservation of mass?

Figure 15 Mass is conserved during a physical change. ▼

Conservation of Mass

5.0 grams + **150.0** grams = **155.0** grams

✓ **Visual Check** If a sample of water has a mass of 200 g and the final solution has a mass of 230 g, how much solute dissolved in the water?

GK Hart/Vikki Hart/Getty Images

Lesson 3 Review

Visual Summary

During a physical change, matter can change form, shape, size, or state, but the identity of the matter does not change.

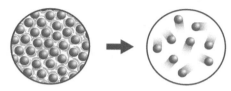

 Matter either changes temperature or changes state when enough thermal energy is added or removed.

 Mass is conserved during physical changes, which means that mass is the same before and after the changes occur.

FOLDABLES

Use your lesson Foldable to review the lesson. Save your Foldable for the project at the end of the chapter.

What do you think NOW?

You first read the statements below at the beginning of the chapter.

5. Heating a material decreases the energy of its particles.

6. When you stir sugar into water, the sugar and water evenly mix.

Did you change your mind about whether you agree or disagree with the statements? Rewrite any false statements to make them true.

IT Stock/age fotostock

Use Vocabulary

1 **Use the term** *physical change* in a sentence.

Understand Key Concepts

2 **Describe** how a change in energy can change ice into liquid water.

3 Which never changes during a physical change?
   A. state of matter   C. total mass
   B. temperature   D. volume

4 **Relate** What happens when something dissolves?

Interpret Graphics

5 **Examine** the graph below of temperature over time as a substance changes from solid to liquid to gas. Explain why the graph has horizontal lines.

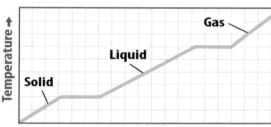
Adding Thermal Energy →

6 **Take Notes** Copy the graphic organizer below. For each heading, summarize the main idea described in the lesson.

Heading	Main Idea
Physical Changes	
Change in State of Matter	
Conservation of Mass	

Critical Thinking

7 **Design** a demonstration that shows that temperature remains unchanged during a change of state.

How can known substances help you identify unknown substances?

Materials

plastic spoons

magnifying lens

stirring rod

Also needed: known substances (baking soda, ascorbic acid, sugar, cornstarch) test tubes, test tube rack, watch glass, dropper bottles containing water, iodine, vinegar, and red cabbage indicator

Safety

While investigating a crime scene, you find several packets of white powder. Are they illegal drugs or just harmless packets of candy? Here's one way to find out.

Learn It

A **control** is something that stays the same. If you determine how a known substance reacts with other substances, you can use it as a control. Unknown substances are **variables.** They might or might not react in the same way.

Try It

1. Read and complete a lab safety form.

2. Copy the data table below into your Science Journal.

3. Use a magnifying lens to observe the appearance of each known substance.

4. Test small samples of each known substance for their reaction with a drop or two of water, vinegar, and iodine solution.

5. Mix each substance with water, and add the red cabbage indicator.

6. After you complete your observations, ask your teacher for a mystery powder. Repeat steps 3–6 using the mystery powder. Use the data you collect to identify the powder.

Apply It

7. What test suggests that a substance might be cornstarch?

8. Why should you test the reactions of the substances with many different things?

9. 🔑 **Key Concept** How did you use the properties of the controls to identify your variable?

Substance	Appearance	Texture	Reaction to Water	Reaction to Iodine	Reaction to Vinegar	Red Cabbage Indicator
Baking soda						
Sugar						
Ascorbic acid						
Cornstarch						
Mystery powder						

Reading Guide

Key Concepts 🔑

ESSENTIAL QUESTIONS

- What is a chemical property?
- What are some signs of chemical change?
- Why are chemical equations useful?
- What are some factors that affect the rate of chemical reactions?

Vocabulary

chemical property p. 34

chemical change p. 35

concentration p. 38

 Multilingual eGlossary

 BrainPOP®
What's Science
Got to do With It?

 8.PS.1, 8.PS.6, 8.PS.7, SEPS.2, SEPS.3, SEPS.4, SEPS.6, SEPS.7, SEPS.8, 6-8.LST.7.1

Chemical Properties and Changes

 PBL Go to the resource tab in ConnectED to find the PBL *A Tale of Two Changes*

Inquiry A Burning Issue?

As this car burns, some materials change to ashes and gases. The metal might change form or state if the fire is hot enough, but it probably won't burn. Why do fabric, leather, and paint burn? Why do many metals not burn? The properties of matter determine how matter behaves when it undergoes a change.

Luis Calabor/Getty Images

What can colors tell you?

You mix red and blue paint to get purple paint. Iron changes color when it rusts. Are color changes physical changes?

1. Read and complete a lab safety form.

2. Divide a **paper towel** into thirds. Label one section *RCJ*, the second section *A*, and the third section *B*.

3. Dip one end of three **cotton swabs** into **red cabbage juice** (RCJ). Observe the color, and set the swabs on the paper towel, one in each of the three sections.

4. Add one drop of **substance A** to the swab in the *A* section. Observe any changes, and record observations in your Science Journal.

5. Repeat step 4 with **substance B** and the swab in the *B* section.

6. Observe **substances C** and **D** in their **test tubes.** Then pour C into D. Rock the tube gently to mix. Record your observations.

Think About This

1. What happened to the color of the red cabbage juice when substances A and B were added?

2. 🔑 **Key Concept** Which of the changes you observed do you think was a physical change? Explain your reasoning.

Chemical Properties

Recall that a physical property is a characteristic of matter that you can observe or measure without changing the identity of the matter. However, matter has other properties that can be observed only when the matter changes from one substance to another. *A* **chemical property** *is a characteristic of matter that can be observed as it changes to a different type of matter.* For example, what are some chemical properties of a piece of paper? Can you tell by just looking at it that it will burn easily? The only way to know that paper burns is to bring a flame near the paper and watch it burn. When paper burns, it changes into different types of matter. The ability of a substance to burn is a chemical property. The ability to rust is another chemical property.

Comparing Properties

You now have read about physical properties and chemical properties. All matter can be described using both types of properties. For example, a wood log is solid, rounded, heavy, and rough. These are physical properties that you can observe with your senses. The log also has mass, volume, and density, which are physical properties that can be measured. The ability of wood to burn is a chemical property. This property is obvious only when you burn the wood. It also will rot, another chemical property you can observe when the log decomposes, becoming other substances. When you describe matter, you need to consider both its physical and its chemical properties.

🔑 **Key Concept Check** What are some chemical properties of matter?

Hutchings Photography/Digital Light Source

Chemical Changes

Recall that during a physical change, the identity of matter does not change. However, *a* **chemical change** *is a change in matter in which the substances that make up the matter change into other substances with new physical and chemical properties.* For example, when iron undergoes a chemical change with oxygen, rust forms. The substances that undergo a change no longer have the same properties because they no longer have the same identity.

 Reading Check What is the difference between a physical change and a chemical change?

Signs of Chemical Change

How do you know when a chemical change occurs? What signs show you that new types of matter form? As shown in **Figure 16,** signs of chemical changes include the formation of bubbles or a change in energy, odor, or color.

It is important to remember that these signs do not always mean a chemical change occurred. Think about what happens when you heat water on a stove. Bubbles form as the water boils. In this case, bubbles show that the water is changing state, which is a physical change. The evidence of chemical change shown in **Figure 16** means that a chemical change might have occurred. However, the only proof of chemical change is the formation of a new substance.

 Key Concept Check What are signs of a chemical change?

FOLDABLES

Use a sheet of paper to make a chart with four columns. Use the chart throughout this lesson to explain how the identity of matter changes during a chemical change.

Action/ Matter	Signs of Chemical Change	Explain the Chemical Reaction	What affects the reaction rate?

WORD ORIGIN

chemical
from Greek *chemeia,* means "cast together"

Project-Based Learning Activity

A Tale of Two Changes Go online to write a story that contrasts physical and chemical changes.

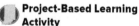
Some Signs of Chemical Change

Figure 16 Sometimes you can observe clues that a chemical change has occurred.

Bubbles

Energy change

Odor change

Color change

 Visual Check What signs show that a chemical change takes place when fireworks explode?

(l)©Brand X Pictures/Punchstock, (cl)IMAGEMORE Co.,Ltd./Getty Images, (cr)Martin Hospach/Getty Images, (r)Siede Preis/Getty Images

MiniLab  20 minutes

Can you spot the clues for chemical change?

What are some clues that let you know a chemical change might have taken place?

1. Read and complete a lab safety form.

2. Add about 25 mL of room-temperature water to a **self-sealing plastic bag.** Add two **dropperfuls** of **red cabbage juice.**

3. Add one **measuring scoop** of **calcium chloride** to the bag. Seal the bag. Tilt the bag to mix the contents until the solid disappears. Feel the bottom of the bag. Record your observations in your Science Journal.

4. Open the bag, and add one measuring scoop of **baking soda.** Quickly press the air from the bag and reseal it. Tilt the bag to mix the contents. Observe for several minutes. Record your observations.

Analyze and Conclude

1. **Observe** What changes did you observe?

2. **Infer** Which of the changes suggested that a new substance formed? Explain.

3. 🔑 **Key Concept** Are changes in energy always a sign of a chemical change? Explain.

Explaining Chemical Reactions

You might wonder why chemical changes produce new substances. Recall that particles in matter are in constant motion. As particles move, they collide with each other. If the particles collide with enough force, the bonded atoms that make up the particles can break apart. These atoms then rearrange and bond with other atoms. When atoms bond together in new combinations, new substances form. This process is called a reaction. Chemical changes often are called chemical reactions.

✔ **Reading Check** What does it mean to say that atoms rearrange during a chemical change?

Using Chemical Formulas

A useful way to understand what happens during a chemical reaction is to write a chemical equation. A chemical equation shows the chemical formula of each substance in the reaction. The formulas to the left of the arrow represent the reactants. Reactants are the substances present before the reaction takes place. The formulas to the right of the arrow represent the products. Products are the new substances present after the reaction. The arrow indicates that a reaction has taken place.

🔑 **Key Concept Check** Why are chemical equations useful?

Figure 17 Chemical formulas and other symbols are parts of a chemical equation.

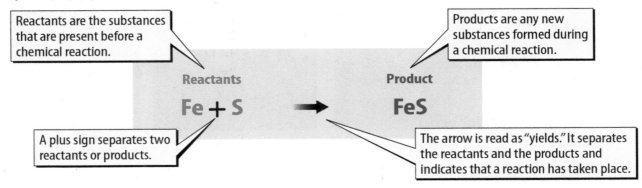

Reactants are the substances that are present before a chemical reaction.

Products are any new substances formed during a chemical reaction.

Reactants

$$Fe + S$$

Product

$$FeS$$

A plus sign separates two reactants or products.

The arrow is read as "yields." It separates the reactants and the products and indicates that a reaction has taken place.

Hutchings Photography/Digital Light Source

Balancing Chemical Equations

Look at the equation in **Figure 17**. Notice that there is one iron (Fe) atom on the reactants side and one iron atom on the product side. This is also true for the sulfur (S) atoms. Recall that during both physical and chemical changes, mass is conserved. This means that the total mass before and after a change must be equal. Therefore, in a chemical equation, the number of atoms of each element before a reaction must equal the number of atoms of each element after the reaction. This is called a balanced chemical equation, and it illustrates the law of conservation of mass. **Figure 18** explains how to write and balance a chemical equation.

When balancing an equation, you cannot change the chemical formula of any reactants or products. Changing a formula changes the identity of the substance. Instead, you can place coefficients, or multipliers, in front of formulas. Coefficients change the amount of the reactants and products present. For example, an H_2O molecule has two H atoms and one O atom. Placing the coefficient 2 before H_2O ($2H_2O$) means that you double the number of H atoms and O atoms present:

> 2×2 H atoms $= 4$ H atoms
> 2×1 O atom $= 2$ O atoms

Note that $2H_2O$ is still water. However, it describes two water particles instead of one.

Figure 18 Equations must be balanced because mass is conserved during a chemical reaction.

Balancing Chemical Equations

Personal Tutor

Balancing Chemical Equations Example

When methane (CH_4)—a gas burned in furnaces—reacts with oxygen (O_2) in the air, the reaction produces carbon dioxide (CO_2) and water (H_2O). Write and balance a chemical equation for this reaction.

1 **Write the equation, and check to see if it is balanced.**

a. Write the chemical formulas with the reactants on the left side of the arrow and the products on the right side.	**a.** $CH_4 + O_2 \rightarrow CO_2 + H_2O$ not balanced
b. Count the atoms of each element in the reactants and in the products. ■ Note which elements have a balanced number of atoms on each side of the equation. ■ If all elements are balanced, the overall equation is balanced. If not, go to step 2.	**b.** reactants $\rightarrow$ products C=1 C=1 **balanced** H=4 H=2 **not balanced** O=2 O=3 **not balanced**

2 **Add coefficients to the chemical formulas to balance the equation.**

a. Pick an element in the equation whose atoms are not balanced, such as hydrogen. Write a coefficient in front of a reactant or a product that will balance the atoms of the chosen element in the equation. **b.** Recount the atoms of each element in the reactants and the products, and note which are balanced on each side of the equation. **c.** Repeat steps 2a and 2b until all atoms of each element in the reactants equal those in the products.	**a.** $CH_4 + O_2 \rightarrow CO_2 + 2H_2O$ not balanced **b.** reactants $\rightarrow$ products C=1 C=1 **balanced** H=4 H=4 **balanced** O=2 O=4 **not balanced** **c.** $CH_4 + 2O_2 \rightarrow CO_2 + 2H_2O$ **balanced** C=1 C=1 **balanced** H=4 H=4 **balanced** O=4 O=4 **balanced**

3 **Write the balanced equation that includes the coefficients:** $CH_4 + 2O_2 \rightarrow CO_2 + 2H_2O$

Figure 19 The rate of most chemical reactions increases with an increase in temperature, concentration, or surface area.

1 **Temperature**

Chemical reactions that occur during cooking happen at a faster rate when temperature increases.

2 **Concentration**

Acid rain contains a higher concentration of acid than normal rain does. As a result, a statue exposed to acid rain is damaged more quickly than a statue exposed to normal rain.

3 **Surface Area**

When an antacid tablet is broken into pieces, the pieces have more total surface area than the whole tablet does. The pieces react more rapidly with water because more of the broken tablet is in contact with the water.

The Rate of Chemical Reactions

Recall that the particles that make up matter are constantly moving and colliding with one another. Different factors can make these particles move faster and collide harder and more frequently. These factors increase the rate of a chemical reaction, as shown in Figure 19.

1 A higher temperature usually increases the rate of reaction. When the temperature is higher, the particles move faster. Therefore, the particles collide with greater force and more frequently.

2 **Concentration** is the *amount of substance in a certain volume.* A reaction occurs faster if the concentration of at least one reactant increases. When concentration increases, there are more particles available to bump into each other and react.

3 Surface area also affects reaction rate if at least one reactant is a solid. If you drop a whole effervescent antacid tablet into water, the tablet reacts with the water. However, if you break the tablet into several pieces and then add them to the water, the reaction occurs more quickly. Smaller pieces have more total surface area, so more space is available for reactants to collide.

 Key Concept Check List three factors that affect the rate of a chemical reaction.

Chemistry

To understand chemistry, you need to understand matter. You need to know how the arrangement of atoms results in different types of matter. You also need to be able to distinguish physical properties from chemical properties and describe ways these properties can change. In later chemistry chapters and courses, you will examine each of these topics closely to gain a better understanding of matter.

Visual Summary

A chemical property is observed only as a material undergoes chemical change and changes identity.

Signs of possible chemical change include bubbles, energy change, and change in odor or color.

Chemical equations show the reactants and products of a chemical reaction and that mass is conserved.

Reactants		Product
Fe + S	→	FeS

FOLDABLES®

Use your lesson Foldable to review the lesson. Save your Foldable for the project at the end of the chapter.

What do you think NOW?

You first read the statements below at the beginning of the chapter.

7. When wood burns, new materials form.

8. Temperature can affect the rate at which chemical changes occur.

Did you change your mind about whether you agree or disagree with the statements? Rewrite any false statements to make them true.

Use Vocabulary

1 The amount of substance in a certain volume is its _____.

2 **Use the term** *chemical change* in a complete sentence.

Understand Key Concepts

3 **List** some signs of chemical change.

4 Which property of matter changes during a chemical change but does NOT change during a physical change?
   A. energy   C. mass
   B. identity   D. volume

5 **State** why chemical equations are useful.

6 **Analyze** What affects the rate at which acid rain reacts with a statue?

Interpret Graphics

7 **Examine** Explain how the diagram below shows conservation of mass.

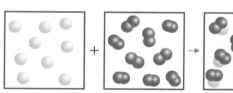

8 **Compare and Contrast** Copy and fill in the graphic organizer to compare and contrast physical and chemical changes.

Physical and Chemical Changes	
Alike	
Different	

Critical Thinking

9 **Compile** a list of three physical changes and three chemical changes you have observed recently.

10 **Recommend** How could you increase the rate at which the chemical reaction between vinegar and baking soda occurs?

(t)Slede Preis/Getty Images, (b)©Brand X Pictures/Punchstock

Materials

triple-beam
balance

50-mL
graduated
cylinder

magnifying
lens

bar magnet

Also needed:
crime scene
evidence,
unknown
substances,
dropper
bottles
containing
water, iodine,
cornstarch,
and red
cabbage
indicator,
test tubes,
test tube rack,
stirring rod

Safety

Design an Experiment to Solve a Crime

Recall how you can use properties to identify and compare substances. You now will apply those ideas to solving a crime. You will be given evidence collected from the crime scene and from the suspect's house. As the investigator, decide whether evidence from the crime scene matches evidence from the suspect. What tests will you use? What does the evidence tell you?

Question

Determine which factors about the evidence you would like to investigate further. Consider how you can describe and compare the properties of each piece of evidence. Evaluate the properties you will observe and measure, and decide whether it would be an advantage to classify them as physical properties or chemical properties. Will the changes that the evidence will undergo be helpful to you? Think about controls, variables, and the equipment you have available. Is there any way to match samples exactly?

Procedure

1. Read and complete a lab safety form.

2. In your Science Journal, write the procedures you will use to answer your question. Include the materials and steps you will use to test each piece of evidence. By the appropriate step in the procedure, list any safety procedures you should observe while performing the investigation. Organize your steps by putting them in a graphic organizer, such as the one below. Have your teacher approve your procedures.

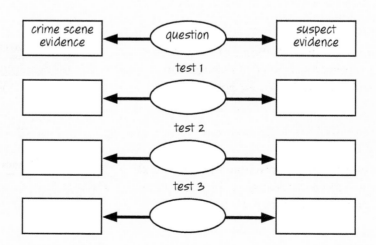

(t to b, 2–3)Hutchings Photography/Digital Light Source, (4)Jacques Cornell/McGraw-Hill Education

3 Begin by observing and recording your observations on each piece of evidence. What can you learn by comparing physical properties? Are any of the samples made of several parts?

4 Use the available materials to test the evidence. Accurately record all observations and data for each piece of evidence.

5 Add any additional tests you think you need to answer your questions.

Analyze and Conclude

6 **Examine** the data you have collected. What does the evidence tell you about whether the crime scene and the suspect are related?

7 **Formulate** Write your conclusions in your Science Journal. Be thorough because these are the notes you would use if you had to testify in court about the case.

8 **Analyze** Which data suggest that evidence from the crime scene was or wasn't connected to the suspect?

9 **Draw Conclusions** If you were to testify in court, what conclusions would you be able to state confidently based on your findings?

10 **The Big Idea** How does understanding physical and chemical properties of matter help you to solve problems?

Communicate Your Results

Compare your results with those of other teams. Discuss the kinds of evidence that might be strong enough to convict a suspect.

Inquiry Extension

Research the difference between individual and class evidence used in forensics. Decide which class of evidence your tests provided.

Lab Tips

☑ Don't overlook simple ideas such as matching the edges of pieces.

☑ Can you separate any of the samples into other parts?

☑ Always get your teacher's approval before trying any new test.

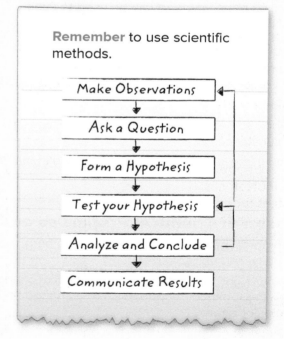

Remember to use scientific methods.

Make Observations

Ask a Question

Form a Hypothesis

Test your Hypothesis

Analyze and Conclude

Communicate Results

Chapter 1 Study Guide

THE BIG IDEA — Matter is anything that has mass and takes up space. Its physical properties and its chemical properties can change.

Key Concepts Summary 🔑

	Vocabulary

Lesson 1: Classifying Matter

- A **substance** is a type of **matter** that always is made of atoms in the same combinations.
- **Atoms** of different elements have different numbers of protons.
- The composition of a substance cannot vary. The composition of a **mixture** can vary.
- Matter can be classified as either a substance or a mixture.

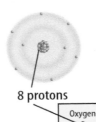

8 protons

Oxygen
8
O
16.00

Vocabulary

matter p. 9
atom p. 9
substance p. 11
element p. 11
compound p. 12
mixture p. 13
heterogeneous mixture p. 13
homogeneous mixture p. 13
dissolve p. 13

Lesson 2: Physical Properties

- **Physical properties** of matter include size, shape, texture, and state.
- Physical properties such as **density,** melting point, boiling point, and size can be used to separate mixtures.

physical property p. 18
mass p. 20
density p. 21
solubility p. 22

Lesson 3: Physical Changes

- A change in energy can change the state of matter.
- When something dissolves, it mixes evenly in a substance.
- The masses before and after a change in matter are equal.

physical change p. 27

Lesson 4: Chemical Properties and Changes

- **Chemical properties** include ability to burn, acidity, and ability to rust.
- Some signs that might indicate **chemical changes** are the formation of bubbles and a change in odor, color, or energy.
- Chemical equations are useful because they show what happens during a chemical reaction.
- Some factors that affect the rate of chemical reactions are temperature, **concentration,** and surface area.

chemical property p. 34
chemical change p. 35
concentration p. 38

Vocabulary eFlashcards
Vocabulary eGames

Personal Tutor

FOLDABLES®

Chapter Project

Assemble your lesson Foldables as shown to make a Chapter Project. Use the project to review what you have learned in this chapter. Fasten the Foldable from Lesson 4 on the back of the board.

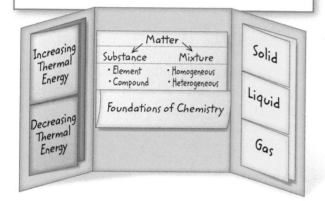

Use Vocabulary

Give two examples of each of the following.

1 element

2 compound

3 homogeneous mixture

4 heterogeneous mixture

5 physical property

6 chemical property

7 physical change

8 chemical change

Link Vocabulary and Key Concepts

Interactive Concept Map

Copy this concept map, and then use vocabulary terms from the previous page to complete the concept map.

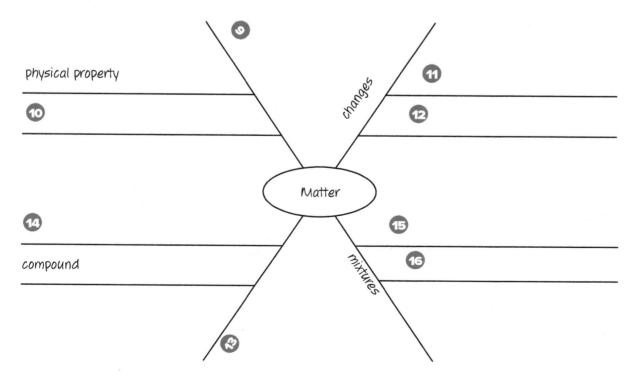

Chapter 1 Review

Understand Key Concepts

1 The formula $AgNO_3$ represents a compound made of which atoms?

    A. 1 Ag, 1 N, 1 O
    B. 1 Ag, 1 N, 3 O
    C. 1 Ag, 3 N, 3 O
    D. 3 Ag, 3 N, 3 O

2 Which is an example of an element?

    A. air
    B. water
    C. sodium
    D. sugar

3 Which property explains why copper often is used in electrical wiring?

    A. conductivity
    B. density
    C. magnetism
    D. solubility

4 The table below shows densities for different substances.

Substance	Density (g/cm³)
1	1.58
2	0.32
3	1.52
4	1.62

For which substance would a 4.90-g sample have a volume of 3.10 cm³?

    A. substance 1
    B. substance 2
    C. substance 3
    D. substance 4

5 Which would decrease the rate of a chemical reaction?

    A. increase in concentration
    B. increase in temperature
    C. decrease in surface area
    D. increase in both surface area and concentration

6 Which physical change is represented by the diagram below?

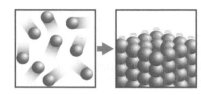

    A. condensation
    B. deposition
    C. evaporation
    D. sublimation

7 Which chemical equation is unbalanced?

    A. $2KClO_3 \rightarrow 2KCl + 3O_2$
    B. $CH_4 + 2O_2 \rightarrow CO_2 + 2H_2O$
    C. $Fe_2O_3 + CO \rightarrow 2Fe + 2CO_2$
    D. $H_2CO_3 \rightarrow H_2O + CO_2$

8 Which is a size-dependent property?

    A. boiling point
    B. conductivity
    C. density
    D. mass

9 Why is the following chemical equation said to be balanced?

$$O_2 + 2PCl_3 \rightarrow 2POCl_3$$

    A. There are more reactants than products.
    B. There are more products than reactants.
    C. The atoms are the same on both sides of the equation.
    D. The coefficients are the same on both sides of the equation.

10 The elements sodium (Na) and chlorine (Cl) react and form the compound sodium chloride (NaCl). Which is true about the properties of these substances?

    A. Na and Cl have the same properties.
    B. NaCl has the properties of Na and Cl.
    C. All the substances have the same properties.
    D. The properties of NaCl are different from the properties of Na and Cl.

Critical Thinking

11 **Compile** a list of ten materials in your home. Classify each material as an element, a compound, or a mixture. Then, describe how the 118 currently known elements relate to the composition of these materials.

12 **Evaluate** Would a periodic table based on the number of electrons in an atom be as effective as the one shown in the back of this book? Why or why not?

13 **Develop** a demonstration to show how weight is not the same thing as mass.

14 **Construct** an explanation for how the temperature and energy of a material changes during the physical changes represented by the diagram below.

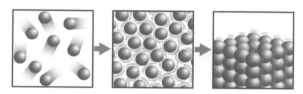

15 **Revise** the definition of physical change given in this chapter so it mentions the type and arrangement of atoms.

16 **Find an example** of a physical change in your home or school. Describe the changes in physical properties that occur during the change. Then explain how you know the change is not a chemical change.

17 **Develop** a list of five chemical reactions you observe each day. For each, describe one way that you could either increase or decrease the rate of the reaction.

Writing in Science

18 **Write** a poem at least five lines long to describe the organization of matter by the arrangement of its atoms. Be sure to include both the names of the different types of matter as well as their meanings.

REVIEW **THE BIG IDEA**

19 Explain how you are made of matter that undergoes changes. Provide specific examples in your explanation.

20 How does the photo below show an example of a physical change, a chemical change, a physical property, and a chemical property?

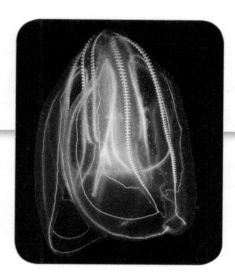

Math Skills ✕∻ ✓ Math Practice

Use Ratios

21 A sample of ice at 0°C has a mass of 23 g and a volume of 25 cm³. Why does ice float on water? (The density of water is 1.00 g/cm³.)

22 The table below shows the masses and the volumes for samples of two different elements.

Element	Mass (g)	Volume (cm³)
Gold	386	20
Lead	22.7	2.0

Which element sample in the table has greater density?

Standardized Test Practice

Record your answers on the answer sheet provided by your teacher or on a sheet of paper.

Multiple Choice

1 Which describes how mixtures differ from substances?

   A Mixtures are homogeneous.

   B Mixtures are liquids.

   C Mixtures can be separated physically.

   D Mixtures contain only one kind of atom.

Use the figure below to answer question 2.

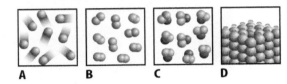

2 Which image in the figure above is a model for a compound?

   A A

   B B

   C C

   D D

3 Which is a chemical property?

   A the ability to be compressed

   B the ability to be stretched into thin wire

   C the ability to melt at low temperature

   D the ability to react with oxygen

4 You drop a sugar cube into a cup of hot tea. What causes the sugar to disappear in the tea?

   A It breaks into elements.

   B It evaporates.

   C It melts.

   D It mixes evenly.

5 Which is an example of a substance?

   A air

   B lemonade

   C soil

   D water

Use the figure below to answer question 6.

6 The figure above is a model of atoms in a sample at room temperature. Which physical property does this sample have?

   A It can be poured.

   B It can expand to fill its container.

   C It cannot easily change shape.

   D It has a low boiling point.

7 Which observation is a sign of a chemical change?

   A bubbles escaping from a carbonated drink

   B iron filings sticking to a magnet

   C lights flashing from fireworks

   D water turning to ice in a freezer

8 Zinc, a solid metal, reacts with a hydrochloric acid solution. Which will increase the reaction rate?

A cutting the zinc into smaller pieces

B decreasing the concentration of the acid

C lowering the temperature of the zinc

D pouring the acid into a larger container

Use the figure below to answer question 9.

9 In the figure above, what will be the mass of the final solution if the solid dissolves in the water?

A 5 g

B 145 g

C 150 g

D 155 g

10 Which is NOT represented in a chemical equation?

A chemical formula

B product

C conservation of mass

D reaction rate

Constructed Response

Use the graph below to answer questions 11 and 12.

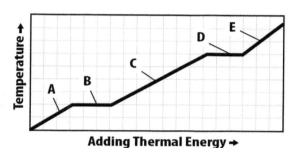

11 Use the graph above to explain why ice will keep water cold on a hot day.

12 Use two sections of the graph to explain what happens when you put a pot of cold water on a stove to boil. Specify which two sections you used.

13 Describe how you would separate a mixture of sugar, sand, and water.

14 The reaction of zinc metal with hydrochloric acid produces zinc chloride and hydrogen gas. A student writes the following to represent the reaction.

$$Zn + HCl \rightarrow ZnCl_2 + H_2$$

Is the equation correct? Use conservation of mass to support your answer.

NEED EXTRA HELP?														
If You Missed Question...	1	2	3	4	5	6	7	8	9	10	11	12	13	14
Go to Lesson...	1	1	4	3	1	2	4	4	3	4	3	3	2	4

Chapter 2

Understanding the Atom

THE BIG IDEA

What are atoms, and what are they made of?

Inquiry All This to Study Tiny Particles?

This huge machine is called the Large Hadron Collider (LHC). It's like a circular racetrack for particles and is about 27 km long. The LHC accelerates particle beams to high speeds and then smashes them into each other. The longer the tunnel, the faster the beams move and the harder they smash together. Scientists study the tiny particles produced in the crash.

- How might scientists have studied matter before colliders were invented?

- What do you think are the smallest parts of matter?

- What are atoms, and what are they made of?

xenotar/Getty Images. (Inset) ©Frederic Pitchal/Sygma/Corbis

What do you think?

Before you read, decide if you agree or disagree with each of these statements. As you read this chapter, see if you change your mind about any of the statements.

1 The earliest model of an atom contained only protons and electrons.

2 Air fills most of an atom.

3 In the present-day model of the atom, the nucleus of the atom is at the center of an electron cloud.

4 All atoms of the same element have the same number of protons.

5 Atoms of one element cannot be changed into atoms of another element.

6 Ions form when atoms lose or gain electrons.

Discovering Parts of an Atom

Reading Guide

Key Concepts 🔑

ESSENTIAL QUESTIONS

- What is an atom?
- How would you describe the size of an atom?
- How has the atomic model changed over time?

Vocabulary

atom p. 53

electron p. 55

nucleus p. 58

proton p. 58

neutron p. 59

electron cloud p. 60

 Multilingual eGlossary

 BrainPOP®

 8.PS.1, SEPS.2, SEPS.4, SEPS.8, 6-8.LST.7.1

©Alessandro Della Bella/Keystone/Corbis, (inset)Drs.Ali Yazdani & Daniel J.Hornbaker/Science Source

Inquiry A Microscopic Mountain Range?

This photo shows a glimpse of the tiny particles that make up matter. A special microscope, invented in 1981, made this image. However, scientists knew these tiny particles existed long before they were able to see them. What are these tiny particles? How small do you think they are? How might scientists have learned so much about them before being able to see them?

What's in there?

When you look at a sandy beach from far away, it looks like a solid surface. You can't see the individual grains of sand. What would you see if you zoomed in on one grain of sand?

1 Read and complete a lab safety form.

2 Have your partner hold a **test tube** of **a substance,** filled to a height of 2–3 cm.

3 Observe the test tube from a distance of at least 2 m. Write a description of what you see in your Science Journal.

4 Pour about 1 cm of the substance onto a piece of **waxed paper.** Record your observations.

5 Use a **toothpick** to separate out one particle of the substance. Suppose you could zoom in. What do you think you would see? Record your ideas in your Science Journal.

Think About This

1. Do you think one particle of the substance is made of smaller particles? Why or why not?

2. 🔑 **Key Concept** Do you think you could use a microscope to see what the particles are made of? Why or why not?

Early Ideas About Matter

Look at your hands. What are they made of? You might answer that your hands are made of things such as skin, bone, muscle, and blood. You might recall that each of these is made of even smaller structures called cells. Are cells made of even smaller parts? Imagine dividing something into smaller and smaller parts. What would you end up with?

Greek philosophers discussed and debated questions such as these more than 2,000 years ago. At the time, many thought that all matter is made of only four elements—fire, water, air, and earth, as shown in **Figure 1.** However, they weren't able to test their ideas because scientific tools and methods, such as experimentation, did not exist yet. The ideas proposed by the most influential philosophers usually were accepted over the ideas of less influential philosophers. One philosopher, Democritus (460–370 B.C.), challenged the popular idea of matter.

Figure 1 🔑 Most Greek philosophers believed that all matter is made of only four elements—fire, water, air, and earth.

Democritus

Democritus believed that matter is made of small, solid objects that cannot be divided, created, or destroyed. He called these objects *atomos,* from which the English word *atom* is derived. Democritus proposed that different types of matter are made from different types of atoms. For example, he said that smooth matter is made of smooth atoms. He also proposed that nothing is between these atoms except empty space. Table 1 summarizes Democritus's ideas.

Although Democritus had no way to test his ideas, many of his ideas are similar to the way scientists describe the atom today. Because Democritus's ideas did not conform to the popular opinion and because they could not be tested scientifically, they were open for debate. One philosopher who challenged Democritus's ideas was Aristotle.

 Reading Check According to Democritus, what might atoms of gold look like?

Aristotle

Aristotle (384–322 B.C.) did not believe that empty space exists. Instead, he favored the more popular idea–that all matter is made of fire, water, air, and earth. Because Aristotle was so influential, his ideas were accepted. Democritus's ideas about atoms were not studied again for more than 2,000 years.

Dalton's Atomic Model

In the late 1700s, English schoolteacher and scientist John Dalton (1766–1844) revisited the idea of atoms. Since Democritus's time, advancements had been made in technology and scientific methods. Dalton made careful observations and measurements of chemical reactions. He combined data from his own scientific research with data from the research of other scientists to propose the atomic theory. Table 1 lists ways that Dalton's atomic theory supported some of the ideas of Democritus.

Table 1 Similarities Between Democritus's and Dalton's Ideas

Democritus

1. Atoms are small solid objects that cannot be divided, created, or destroyed.

2. Atoms are constantly moving in empty space.

3. Different types of matter are made of different types of atoms.

4. The properties of the atoms determine the properties of matter.

John Dalton

1. All matter is made of atoms that cannot be divided, created, or destroyed.

2. During a chemical reaction, atoms of one element cannot be converted into atoms of another element.

3. Atoms of one element are identical to each other but different from atoms of another element.

4. Atoms combine in specific ratios.

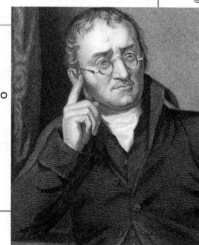

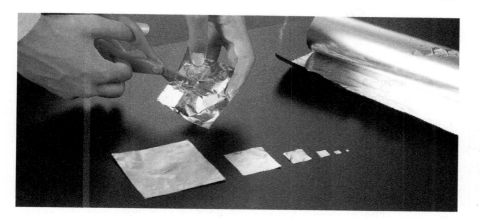

◄ **Figure 2** If you could keep dividing a piece of aluminum, you eventually would have the smallest possible piece of aluminum—an aluminum atom.

The Atom

Today, scientists agree that matter is made of atoms with empty space between and within them. What is an atom? Imagine dividing the piece of aluminum shown in **Figure 2** into smaller and smaller pieces. At first you would be able to cut the pieces with scissors. But eventually you would have a piece that is too small to see–much smaller than the smallest piece you could cut with scissors. This small piece is an aluminum atom. An aluminum atom cannot be divided into smaller aluminum pieces. *An* **atom** *is the smallest piece of an element that still represents that element.*

 Key Concept Check What is a copper atom?

The Size of Atoms

Just how small is an atom? Atoms of different elements are different sizes, but all are very, very small. You cannot see atoms with just your eyes or even with most microscopes. Atoms are so small that about 7.5 trillion carbon atoms could fit into the period at the end of this sentence.

 Key Concept Check How would you describe the size of an atom?

Seeing Atoms

Scientific experiments verified that matter is made of atoms long before scientists were able to see atoms. However, the 1981 invention of a high-powered microscope, called a scanning tunneling microscope (STM), enabled scientists to see individual atoms for the first time. **Figure 3** shows an STM image. An STM uses a tiny, metal tip to trace the surface of a piece of matter. The result is an image of atoms on the surface.

Even today, scientists still cannot see inside an atom. However, scientists have learned that atoms are not the smallest particles of matter. In fact, atoms are made of much smaller particles. What are these particles, and how did scientists discover them if they could not see them?

Figure 3 A scanning tunneling microscope created this image. The yellow sphere is a manganese atom on the surface of gallium arsenide. ▼

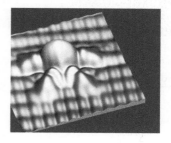

Thomson—Discovering Electrons

Not long after Dalton's findings, another English scientist, named J.J. Thomson (1856-1940), made some important discoveries. Thomson and other scientists of that time worked with cathode ray tubes. Cube-shaped computer monitors and television screens are cathode ray tubes. Flat screens are not. Neon signs are also cathode ray tubes. Thomson's cathode ray tube, shown in Figure 4, was a glass tube with pieces of metal, called electrodes, attached inside the tube. The electrodes were connected to wires, and the wires were connected to a battery. Thomson discovered that if most of the air was removed from the tube and electricity was passed through the wires, greenish-colored rays traveled from one electrode to the other end of the tube. What were these rays made of?

Negative Particles

Scientists called these rays cathode rays. Thomson wanted to know if these rays had an electric charge. To find out, he placed two plates on opposite sides of the tube. One plate was positively charged, and the other plate was negatively charged, as shown in Figure 4. Thomson discovered that these rays bent toward the positively charged plate and away from the negatively charged plate. Recall that opposite charges attract each other, and like charges repel each other. Thomson concluded that cathode rays are negatively charged.

Reading Check If the rays were positively charged, what would Thomson have observed as they passed between the plates?

Figure 4 As the cathode rays passed between the plates, they were bent toward the positive plate. Because opposite charges attract, the rays must be negatively charged.

Thomson's Cathode Ray Tube Experiment

Animation

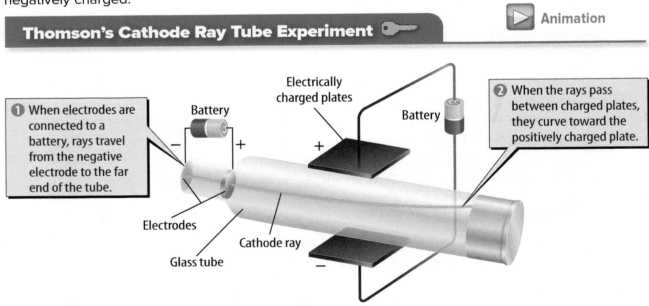

❶ When electrodes are connected to a battery, rays travel from the negative electrode to the far end of the tube.

Battery

Electrically charged plates

Battery

❷ When the rays pass between charged plates, they curve toward the positively charged plate.

Electrodes

Cathode ray

Glass tube

Parts of Atoms

Through more experiments, Thomson learned that these rays were made of particles that had mass. The mass of one of these particles was much smaller than the mass of the smallest atoms. This was surprising information to Thomson. Until then, scientists understood that the smallest particle of matter is an atom. But these rays were made of particles that were even smaller than atoms.

Where did these small, negatively charged particles come from? Thomson proposed that these particles came from the metal atoms in the electrode. Thomson discovered that identical rays were produced regardless of the kind of metal used to make the electrode. Putting these clues together, Thomson concluded that cathode rays were made of small, negatively charged particles. He called these particles electrons. *An **electron** is a particle with one negative charge (1−).* Because atoms are neutral, or not electrically charged, Thomson proposed that atoms also must contain a positive charge that balances the negatively charged electrons.

Thomson's Atomic Model

Thomson used this information to propose a new model of the atom. Instead of a solid, neutral sphere that was the same throughout, Thomson's model of the atom contained both positive and negative charges. He proposed that an atom was a sphere with a positive charge evenly spread throughout. Negatively charged electrons were mixed through the positive charge, similar to the way chocolate chips are mixed in cookie dough. **Figure 5** shows this model.

 Reading Check How did Thomson's atomic model differ from Dalton's atomic model?

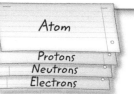
WORD ORIGIN

electron
from Greek *elektron,* means "amber," from *electricity,* the physical force so called because it first was generated by rubbing amber. Amber is a fossilized substance produced by trees.

Thomson's Atomic Model 🔑

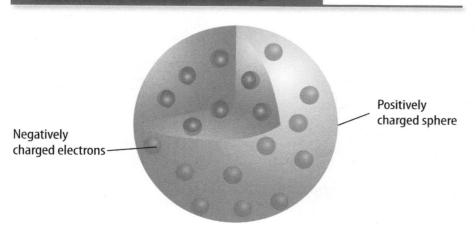

Negatively charged electrons

Positively charged sphere

Figure 5 Thomson's model of the atom contained a positively charged sphere with negatively charged electrons within it.

Rutherford—Discovering the Nucleus

The discovery of electrons stunned scientists. Ernest Rutherford (1871–1937) was a student of Thomson's who eventually had students of his own. Rutherford's students set up experiments to test Thomson's atomic model and to learn more about what atoms contain. They discovered another surprise.

Rutherford's Predicted Result

Imagine throwing a baseball into a pile of table tennis balls. The baseball likely would knock the table tennis balls out of the way and continue moving in a relatively straight line. This is similar to what Rutherford's students expected to see when they shot alpha particles into atoms. Alpha particles are dense and positively charged. Because they are so dense, only another dense particle could deflect the path of an alpha particle. According to Thomson's model, the positive charge of the atom was too spread out and not dense enough to change the path of an alpha particle. Electrons wouldn't affect the path of an alpha particle because electrons didn't have enough mass. The result that Rutherford's students expected is shown in Figure 6.

 Reading Check Explain why Rutherford's students did not think an atom could change the path of an alpha particle.

Figure 6 The Thomson model of the atom did not contain a charge that was dense enough to change the path of an alpha particle. Rutherford expected the positive alpha particles to travel straight through the foil with only small deflections.

Rutherford's Predicted Result 🔑

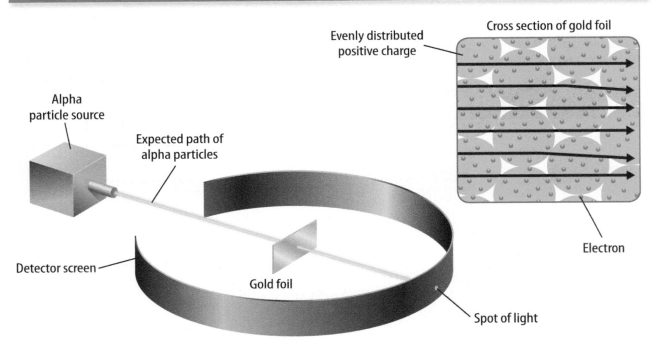

Cross section of gold foil

Evenly distributed positive charge

Electron

Alpha particle source

Expected path of alpha particles

Detector screen

Gold foil

Spot of light

The Gold Foil Experiment

Rutherford's students went to work. They placed a source of alpha particles near a very thin piece of gold foil. Recall that all matter is made of atoms. Therefore, the gold foil was made of gold atoms. A screen surrounded the gold foil. When an alpha particle struck the screen, it created a spot of light. Rutherford's students could determine the path of the alpha particles by observing the spots of light on the screen.

The Surprising Result

Figure 7 shows what the students observed. Most of the particles did indeed travel through the foil in a straight path. However, a few particles struck the foil and bounced off to the side. And one particle in 10,000 bounced straight back! Rutherford later described this surprising result, saying it was almost as incredible as if you had fired a 38-cm shell at a piece of tissue paper and it came back and hit you. The alpha particles must have struck something dense and positively charged inside the nucleus. Thomson's model had to be refined.

 Key Concept Check Given the results of the gold foil experiment, how do you think an actual atom differs from Thomson's model?

 Animation

Figure 7 Some alpha particles traveled in a straight path, as expected. But some changed direction, and some bounced straight back.

Visual Check What do the dots on the screen indicate?

The Surprising Result

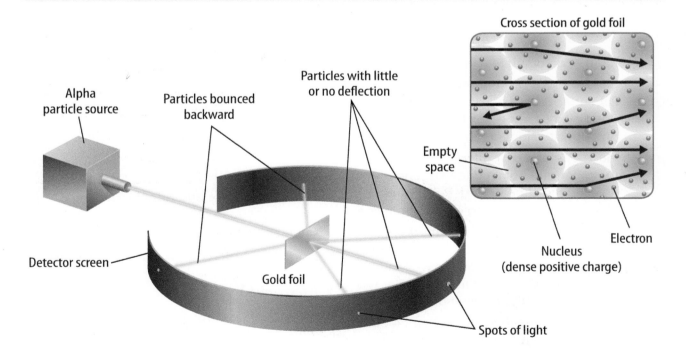

Alpha particle source

Particles bounced backward

Particles with little or no deflection

Detector screen

Gold foil

Spots of light

Cross section of gold foil

Empty space

Electron

Nucleus (dense positive charge)

Rutherford's Atomic Model 🔑

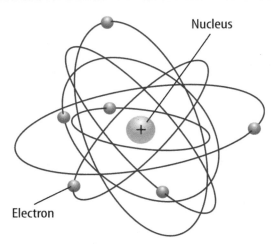

Nucleus

Electron

Figure 8 Rutherford's model contains a small, dense, positive nucleus. Tiny, negatively charged electrons travel in empty space around the nucleus.

Rutherford's Atomic Model

Because most alpha particles traveled through the foil in a straight path, Rutherford concluded that atoms are made mostly of empty space. The alpha particles that bounced backward must have hit a dense, positive mass. Rutherford concluded that *most of an atom's mass and positive charge is concentrated in a small area in the center of the atom called the* **nucleus.** Figure 8 shows Rutherford's atomic model. Additional research showed that the positive charge in the nucleus was made of positively charged particles called protons. *A* **proton** *is an atomic particle that has one positive charge (1+).* Negatively charged electrons move in the empty space surrounding the nucleus.

✓ **Reading Check** How did Rutherford explain the observation that some of the alpha particles bounced directly backward?

🔬 MiniLab

20–30 minutes

How can you gather information about what you can't see? 🖐

Rutherford did his gold foil experiment to learn more about the structure of the atom. What can you learn by doing a similar investigation?

1 Read and complete a lab safety form.

2 Place a piece of white **newsprint** on a flat surface. Your teacher will place an upside-down **shoe box lid** with holes cut on opposite sides on the newsprint.

3 Place one end of a **ruler** on a **book,** with the other end pointing toward one of the holes in the shoe box lid. Roll a **marble** down the ruler and into one of the holes.

4 Team members should use **markers** to draw the path of the marble on the newsprint as it enters and leaves the lid. Predict the path of the marble under the lid. Draw it on the lid. Number the path *1*.

5 Take turns repeating steps 3 and 4 eight to ten times, numbering each path *2, 3, 4,* etc. Move the ruler and aim it in a slightly different direction each time.

Analyze and Conclude

1. **Recognize Cause and Effect** What caused the marble to change its path during some rolls and not during others?

2. **Draw Conclusions** How many objects are under the lid? Where are they located? Draw your answer.

3. 🔑 **Key Concept** If the shoe box lid were an accurate model of the atom, what hypothesis would you make about the atom's structure?

Discovering Neutrons

The modern model of the atom was beginning to take shape. Rutherford's colleague, James Chadwick (1891-1974), also researched atoms and discovered that, in addition to protons, the nucleus also contained neutrons. *A **neutron** is a neutral particle that exists in the nucleus of an atom.*

Bohr's Atomic Model

Rutherford's model explained much of his students' experimental evidence. However, there were several observations that the model could not explain. For example, scientists noticed that if certain elements were heated in a flame, they gave off specific colors of light. Each color of light had a specific amount of energy. Where did this light come from? Niels Bohr (1885-1962), another student of Rutherford's, proposed an answer. Bohr studied hydrogen atoms because they contain only one electron. He experimented with adding electric energy to hydrogen and studying the energy that was released. His experiments led to a revised atomic model.

Electrons in the Bohr Model

Bohr's model is shown in Figure 9. Bohr proposed that electrons move in circular orbits, or energy levels, around the nucleus. Electrons in an energy level have a specific amount of energy. Electrons closer to the nucleus have less energy than electrons farther away from the nucleus. When energy is added to an atom, electrons gain energy and move from a lower energy level to a higher energy level. When the electrons return to the lower energy level, they release a specific amount of energy as light. This is the light that is seen when elements are heated.

Limitations of the Bohr Model

Bohr reasoned that if his model were accurate for atoms with one electron, it would be accurate for atoms with more than one electron. However, this was not the case. More research showed that, although electrons have specific amounts of energy, energy levels are not arranged in circular orbits. How do electrons move in an atom?

 Key Concept Check How did Bohr's atomic model differ from Rutherford's?

 Animation

Figure 9 In Bohr's atomic model, electrons move in circular orbits around the atom. When an electron moves from a higher energy level to a lower energy level, energy is released—sometimes as light. Further research showed that electrons are not arranged in orbits.

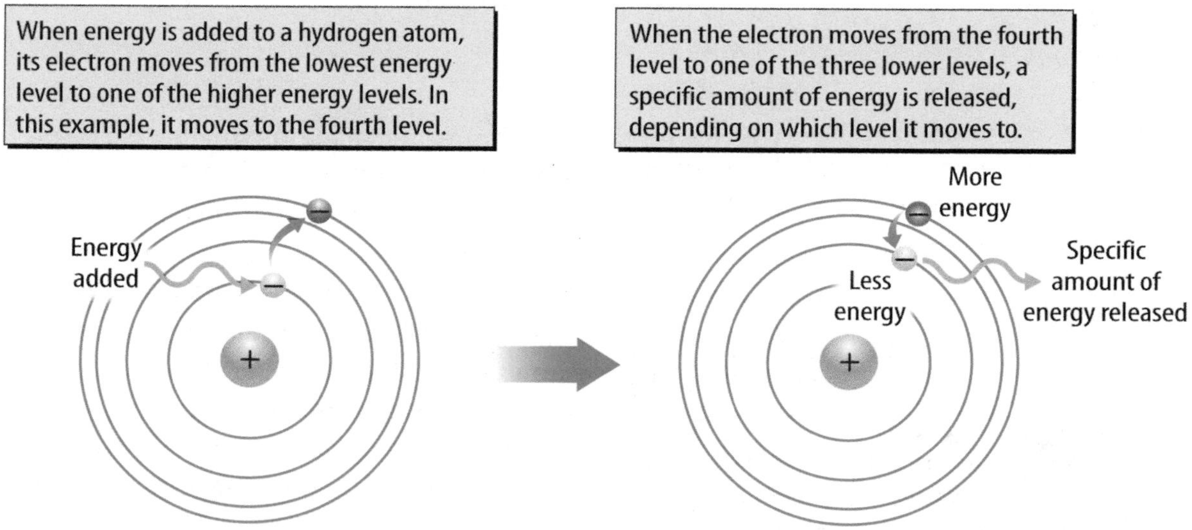

When energy is added to a hydrogen atom, its electron moves from the lowest energy level to one of the higher energy levels. In this example, it moves to the fourth level.

When the electron moves from the fourth level to one of the three lower levels, a specific amount of energy is released, depending on which level it moves to.

Energy added

More energy

Less energy

Specific amount of energy released

Nucleus

Electron cloud

Neutron

Proton

Figure 10 In this model, electrons are more likely to be found closer to the nucleus than farther away.

 Visual Check Why do you think this model of the atom doesn't show the electrons?

The Modern Atomic Model

In the modern atomic model, electrons form an electron cloud. *An **electron cloud** is an area around an atomic nucleus where an electron is most likely to be located.* Imagine taking a time-lapse photograph of bees around a hive. You might see a blurry cloud. The cloud might be denser near the hive than farther away because the bees spend more time near the hive.

In a similar way, electrons constantly move around the nucleus. It is impossible to know both the speed and exact location of an electron at a given moment in time. Instead, scientists only can predict the likelihood that an electron is in a particular location. The electron cloud shown in **Figure 10** is mostly empty space but represents the likelihood of finding an electron in a given area. The darker areas represent areas where electrons are more likely to be.

Key Concept Check How has the model of the atom changed over time?

Quarks

You have read that atoms are made of smaller parts–protons, neutrons, and electrons. Are these particles made of even smaller parts? Scientists have discovered that electrons are not made of smaller parts. However, research has shown that protons and neutrons are made of smaller particles called quarks. Scientists theorize that there are six types of quarks. Protons are made of two up quarks and one down quark. Neutrons are made of two down quarks and one up quark. Just as the model of the atom has changed over time, the current model might also change with the invention of new technology that aids the discovery of new information.

Lesson 1 Review

Visual Summary

If you were to divide an element into smaller and smaller pieces, the smallest piece would be an atom.

Atoms are so small that they can be seen only by using very powerful microscopes.

Scientists now know that atoms contain a dense, positive nucleus surrounded by an electron cloud.

Use your lesson Foldable to review the lesson. Save your Foldable for the project at the end of the chapter.

What do you think NOW?

You first read the statements below at the beginning of the chapter.

1. The earliest model of an atom contained only protons and electrons.

2. Air fills most of an atom.

3. In the present-day model of the atom, the nucleus of the atom is at the center of an electron cloud.

Did you change your mind about whether you agree or disagree with the statements? Rewrite any false statements to make them true.

Use Vocabulary

1 The smallest piece of the element gold is a gold _____.

2 **Write** a sentence that describes the nucleus of an atom.

3 **Define** *electron cloud* in your own words.

Understand Key Concepts

4 What is an atom mostly made of?
- **A.** air
- **B.** empty space
- **C.** neutrons
- **D.** protons

5 Why have scientists only recently been able to see atoms?
- **A.** Atoms are too small to see with ordinary microscopes.
- **B.** Early experiments disproved the idea of atoms.
- **C.** Scientists didn't know atoms existed.
- **D.** Scientists were not looking for atoms.

6 **Draw** Thomson's model of the atom, and label the parts of the drawing.

7 **Explain** how Rutherford's students knew that Thomson's model of the atom needed to change.

Interpret Graphics

8 **Contrast** Copy the graphic organizer below and use it to contrast the locations of electrons in Thomson's, Rutherford's, Bohr's, and the modern models of the atom.

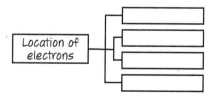

Critical Thinking

9 **Explain** what might have happened in Rutherford's experiment if he had used a thin sheet of copper instead of a thin sheet of gold.

Subatomic Particles

Welcome To The Particle Zoo

QUARKS

BOSONS →

LEPTONS

Much has changed since Democritus and Aristotle studied atoms.

When Democritus and Aristotle developed ideas about matter, they probably never imagined the kinds of research being performed today! From the discovery of electrons, protons, and neutrons to the exploration of quarks and other particles, the atomic model continues to change.

You've learned about quarks, which make up protons and neutrons. But quarks are not the only kind of particles! In fact, some scientists call the collection of particles that have been discovered the particle zoo, because different types of particles have unique characteristics, just like the different kinds of animals in a zoo.

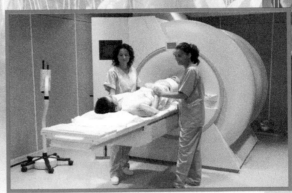

▲ MRIs are just one way in which particle physics technology is applied.

In addition to quarks, scientists have discovered a group of particles called leptons, which includes the electron. Gluons and photons are examples of bosons—particles that carry forces. Some particles, such as the Higgs Boson, have been predicted to exist but have yet to be observed in experiments.

Identifying and understanding the particles that make up matter is important work. However, it might be difficult to understand why time and money are spent to learn more about tiny subatomic particles. How can this research possibly affect everyday life? Research on subatomic particles has changed society in many ways. For example, magnetic resonance imaging (MRI), a tool used to diagnose medical problems, uses technology that was developed to study subatomic particles. Cancer treatments using protons, neutrons, and X-rays are all based on particle physics technology. And, in the 1990s, the need for particle physicists to share information with one another led to the development of the World Wide Web!

It's Your Turn

RESEARCH AND REPORT Learn more about research on subatomic particles. Find out about one recent discovery. Make a poster to share what you learn with your classmates.

Javier Larrea/Pixtal/age fotostock

Lesson 2

Protons, Neutrons, and Electrons—How Atoms Differ

Reading Guide

Key Concepts

ESSENTIAL QUESTIONS

- What happens during nuclear decay?
- How does a neutral atom change when its number of protons, electrons, or neutrons changes?

Vocabulary

atomic number p. 65

isotope p. 66

mass number p. 66

average atomic mass p. 67

radioactive p. 68

nuclear decay p. 69

ion p. 70

 Multilingual eGlossary

 BrainPOP®

8.PS.1, 8.PS.3, SEPS.4, SEPS.5, SEPS.8

Inquiry Is this glass glowing?

Under natural light, this glass vase is yellow. But when exposed to ultraviolet light, it glows green! That's because it is made of uranium glass, which contains small amounts of uranium, a radioactive element. Under ultraviolet light, the glass emits radiation.

Derrick Alderman/Alamy

Launch Lab

How many different things can you make?

Many buildings are made of just a few basic building materials, such as wood, nails, and glass. You can combine those materials in many different ways to make buildings of various shapes and sizes. How many things can you make from three materials?

1. Read and complete a lab safety form.

2. Use **colored building blocks** to make as many different objects as you can with the following properties:

   • Each object must have a different number of red blocks.
   • Each object must have an equal number of red and blue blocks.
   • Each object must have at least as many yellow blocks as red blocks but can have no more than two extra yellow blocks.

3. As you complete each object, record in your Science Journal the number of each color of block used to make it. For example, R = 1; B = 1; Y = 2.

4. When time is called, compare your objects with others in the class.

Think About This

1. How many different objects did you make? How many different objects did the class make?

2. How many objects do you think you could make out of the three types of blocks?

3. 🔑 **Key Concept** In what ways does changing the number of building blocks change the properties of the objects?

Table 2 Properties of Protons, Neutrons, and Electrons			
	Electron	**Proton**	**Neutron**
Symbol	e—	p	n
Charge	1—	1+	0
Location	electron cloud around the nucleus	nucleus	nucleus
Relative mass	1/1,840	1	1

The Parts of the Atom

If you could see inside any atom, you probably would see the same thing—empty space surrounding a very tiny nucleus. A look inside the nucleus would reveal positively charged protons and neutral neutrons. Negatively charged electrons would be whizzing by in the empty space around the nucleus.

Table 2 compares the properties of protons, neutrons, and electrons. Protons and neutrons have about the same mass. The mass of electrons is much smaller than the mass of protons or neutrons. That means most of the mass of an atom is found in the nucleus. In this lesson, you will learn that, while all atoms contain protons, neutrons, and electrons, the numbers of these particles are different for different types of atoms.

Different Elements—Different Numbers of Protons

Look at the periodic table on the inside back cover of this book. Notice that there are more than 115 different elements. Recall that an element is a substance made from atoms that all have the same number of protons. For example, the element carbon is made from atoms that all have six protons. Likewise, all atoms that have six protons are carbon atoms. *The number of protons in an atom of an element is the element's* **atomic number.** The atomic number is the whole number listed with each element on the periodic table.

What makes an atom of one element different from an atom of another element? Atoms of different elements contain different numbers of protons. For example, oxygen atoms contain eight protons; nitrogen atoms contain seven protons. Different elements have different atomic numbers. **Figure 11** shows some common elements and their atomic numbers.

Neutral atoms of different elements also have different numbers of electrons. In a neutral atom, the number of electrons equals the number of protons. Therefore, the number of positive charges equals the number of negative charges.

 Reading Check What two numbers can be used to identify an element?

FOLDABLES

Create a three-tab book and label it as shown. Use it to organize the three ways that atoms can differ.

Different Numbers of:
Protons | Neutrons | Electrons

Applying Practices

How can you model atoms? Go online to create models to represent the arrangement and charges of subatomic particles in atoms.

Figure 11 Atoms of different elements contain different numbers of protons.

Visual Check Explain the difference between an oxygen atom and a carbon atom.

Different Elements 🔑 💬 **Personal Tutor**

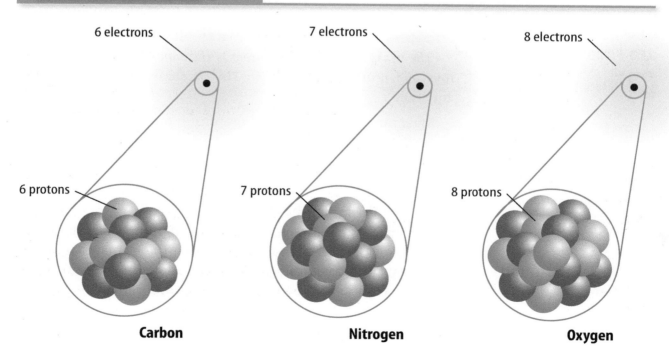

6 electrons

7 electrons

8 electrons

6 protons

7 protons

8 protons

Carbon

Nitrogen

Oxygen

Use Percentages

You can calculate the average atomic mass of an element if you know the percentage of each isotope in the element. Lithium (Li) contains 7.5% Li-6 and 92.5% Li-7. What is the average atomic mass of Li?

1. Divide each percentage by 100 to change to decimal form.
$$\frac{7.5\%}{100} = 0.075$$
$$\frac{92.5\%}{100} = 0.925$$

2. Multiply the mass of each isotope by its decimal percentage.
$6 \times 0.075 = 0.45$
$7 \times 0.925 = 6.475$

3. Add the values together to get the average atomic mass.
$0.45 + 6.475 = 6.93$

Practice
Nitrogen (N) contains 99.63% N-14 and 0.37% N-15. What is the average atomic mass of nitrogen?

 Math Practice

 Personal Tutor

WORD ORIGIN · · · · · · · · · ·

isotope
from Greek *isos*, means "equal"; and *topos*, means "place"

Table 3 Naturally Occurring Isotopes of Carbon			
Isotope	Carbon-12 Nucleus	Carbon-13 Nucleus	Carbon-14 Nucleus
Abundance	98.89%	<1.11%	<0.01%
Protons	6	6	6
Neutrons	+ 6	+ 7	+ 8
Mass Number	12	13	14

Neutrons and Isotopes

You have read that atoms of the same element have the same numbers of protons. However, atoms of the same element can have different numbers of neutrons. For example, carbon atoms all have six protons, but some carbon atoms have six neutrons, some have seven neutrons, and some have eight neutrons. These three different types of carbon atoms, shown in Table 3, are called isotopes. **Isotopes** *are atoms of the same element that have different numbers of neutrons.* Most elements have several isotopes.

Protons, Neutrons, and Mass Number

The **mass number** *of an atom is the sum of the number of protons and neutrons in an atom.* This is shown in the following equation:

Mass number = number of protons + number of neutrons

Any one of these three quantities can be determined if you know the value of the other two quantities. For example, to determine the mass number of an atom, you must know the number of neutrons and the number of protons in the atom.

The mass numbers of the isotopes of carbon are shown in Table 3. An isotope often is written with the element name followed by the mass number. Using this method, the isotopes of carbon are written carbon-12, carbon-13, and carbon-14.

Reading Check How do two different isotopes of the same element differ?

Average Atomic Mass

You might have noticed that the periodic table does not list mass numbers or the numbers of neutrons. This is because a given element can have several isotopes. However, you might notice that there is a decimal number listed with most elements, as shown in **Figure 12**. This decimal number is the average atomic mass of the element. The **average atomic mass** *of an element is the average mass of the element's isotopes, weighted according to the abundance of each isotope.*

Table 3 shows the three isotopes of carbon. The average atomic mass of carbon is 12.01. Why isn't the average atomic mass 13? After all, the average of the mass numbers 12, 13, and 14 is 13. The average atomic mass is weighted based on each isotope's abundance–how much of each isotope is present on Earth. Almost 99 percent of Earth's carbon is carbon-12. That is why the average atomic mass is close to 12.

Reading Check What does the term *weighted average* mean?

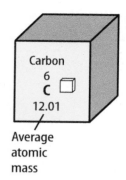

Figure 12 The element carbon has several isotopes. The decimal number 12.01 is the average atomic mass of these isotopes.

◀ MiniLab

20 minutes

How many penny isotopes do you have? 🥽 🧤

All pennies look similar, and all have a value of one cent. But do they have the same mass? Let's find out.

1. Read and complete a lab safety form.

2. Copy the data table into your Science Journal.

3. Use a **balance** to find the mass of **10 pennies minted before 1982.** Record the mass in the data table.

4. Divide the mass by 10 to find the average mass of one penny. Record the answer.

5. Repeat steps 3 and 4 with **10 pennies minted after 1982.**

6. Have a team member combine pre- and post-1982 pennies for a total of 10 pennies. Find the mass of the ten pennies and the average mass of one penny. Record your observations.

Penny Sample	Mass of 10 pennies (g)	Average mass of 1 penny (g)
Pre-1982		
Post-1982		
Unknown mix		

Analyze and Conclude

1. **Compare and Contrast** How did the average mass of pre- and post-1982 pennies compare?

2. **Draw Conclusions** How many pennies of each type were in the 10 pennies assembled by your partner? How do you know?

3. 🔑 **Key Concept** How does this activity relate to the way in which scientists calculate the average atomic mass of an element?

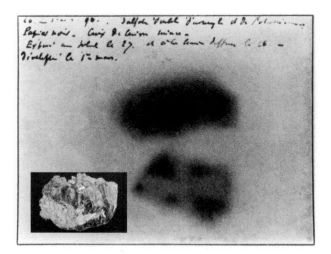

▲ **Figure 13** The black and white photo shows Henri Becquerel's photographic plate. The dark area on the plate was exposed to radiation given off by uranium in the mineral even though the mineral was not exposed to sunlight.

ACADEMIC VOCABULARY

spontaneous
(adjective) occurring without external force or cause

Figure 14 Marie Curie studied radioactivity and discovered two new radioactive elements—polonium and radium. ▼

Radioactivity

More than 1,000 years ago, people tried to change lead into gold by performing chemical reactions. However, none of their reactions were successful. Why not? Today, scientists know that a chemical reaction does not change the number of protons in an atom's nucleus. If the number of protons does not change, the element does not change. But in the late 1800s, scientists discovered that some elements change into other elements spontaneously. How does this happen?

An Accidental Discovery

In 1896, a scientist named Henri Becquerel (1852–1908) studied minerals containing the element uranium. When these minerals were exposed to sunlight, they gave off a type of energy that could pass through paper. If Becquerel covered a photographic plate with black paper, this energy would pass through the paper and expose the film. One day, Becquerel left the mineral next to a wrapped, unexposed plate in a drawer. Later, he opened the drawer, unwrapped the plate, and saw that the plate contained an image of the mineral, as shown in **Figure 13**. The mineral spontaneously emitted energy, even in the dark! Sunlight wasn't required. What was this energy?

Radioactivity

Becquerel shared his discovery with fellow scientists Pierre and Marie Curie. Marie Curie (1867–1934), shown in **Figure 14**, called *elements that spontaneously emit radiation* **radioactive.** Becquerel and the Curies discovered that the radiation released by uranium was made of energy and particles. This radiation came from the nuclei of the uranium atoms. When this happens, the number of protons in one atom of uranium changes. When uranium releases radiation, it changes to a different element!

Types of Decay

Radioactive elements contain unstable nuclei. **Nuclear decay** *is a process that occurs when an unstable atomic nucleus changes into another more stable nucleus by emitting radiation.* Nuclear decay can produce three different types of radiation—alpha particles, beta particles, and gamma rays. Figure 15 compares the three types of nuclear decay.

Alpha Decay An alpha particle is made of two protons and two neutrons. When an atom releases an alpha particle, its atomic number decreases by two. Uranium-238 decays to thorium-234 through the process of alpha decay.

Beta Decay When beta decay occurs, a neutron in an atom changes into a proton and a high-energy electron called a beta particle. The new proton becomes part of the nucleus, and the beta particle is released. In beta decay, the atomic number of an atom increases by one because it has gained a proton.

Gamma Decay Gamma rays do not contain particles, but they do contain a lot of energy. In fact, gamma rays can pass through thin sheets of lead! Because gamma rays do not contain particles, the release of gamma rays does not change one element into another element.

 Key Concept Check What happens during radioactive decay?

Uses of Radioactive Isotopes

The energy released by radioactive decay can be both harmful and beneficial to humans. Too much radiation can damage or destroy living cells, making them unable to function properly. Some organisms contain cells, such as cancer cells, that are harmful to the organism. Radiation therapy can be beneficial to humans by destroying these harmful cells.

 Animation

Figure 15 ⚷ Alpha and beta decay change one element into another element.

✔ **Visual Check** Explain the change in atomic number for each type of decay.

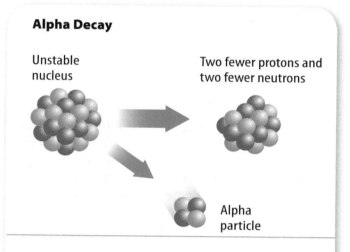

Alpha Decay

Unstable nucleus

Two fewer protons and two fewer neutrons

Alpha particle

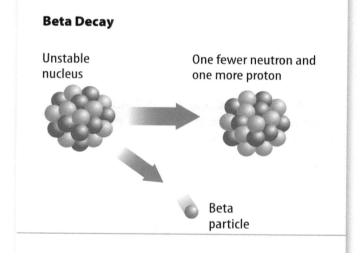

Beta Decay

Unstable nucleus

One fewer neutron and one more proton

Beta particle

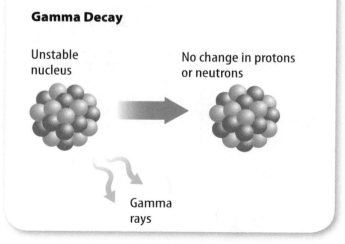

Gamma Decay

Unstable nucleus

No change in protons or neutrons

Gamma rays

Ions—Gaining or Losing Electrons

What happens to a neutral atom if it gains or loses electrons? Recall that a neutral atom has no overall charge. This is because it contains equal numbers of positively charged protons and negatively charged electrons. When electrons are added to or removed from an atom, that atom becomes an ion. *An **ion** is an atom that is no longer neutral because it has gained or lost electrons.* An ion can be positively or negatively charged depending on whether it has lost or gained electrons.

Positive Ions

When a neutral atom loses one or more electrons, it has more protons than electrons. As a result, it has a positive charge. An atom with a positive charge is called a positive ion. A positive ion is represented by the element's symbol followed by a superscript plus sign ($^+$). For example, **Figure 16** shows how sodium (Na) becomes a positive sodium ion (Na^+).

Negative Ions

When a neutral atom gains one or more electrons, it now has more electrons than protons. As a result, the atom has a negative charge. An atom with a negative charge is called a negative ion. A negative ion is represented by the element's symbol followed by a superscript negative sign ($^-$). **Figure 16** shows how fluorine (F) becomes a fluoride ion (F^-).

Figure 16 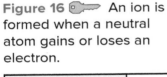 An ion is formed when a neutral atom gains or loses an electron.

 Key Concept Check How does a neutral atom change when its number of protons, electrons, or neutrons changes?

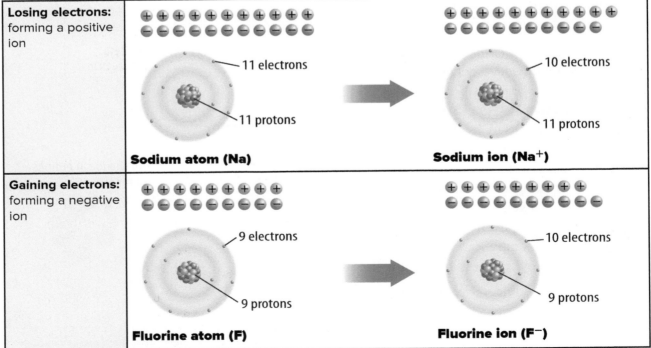

| Losing electrons: forming a positive ion | 11 electrons   11 protons **Sodium atom (Na)** | → | 10 electrons   11 protons **Sodium ion (Na⁺)** |
| Gaining electrons: forming a negative ion | 9 electrons   9 protons **Fluorine atom (F)** | → | 10 electrons   9 protons **Fluorine ion (F⁻)** |

Lesson 2 Review

Visual Summary

Carbon   **Nitrogen**

Different elements contain different numbers of protons.

Isotopes

Two isotopes of a given element contain different numbers of neutrons.

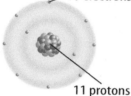

10 electrons

11 protons

Sodium ion (Na⁺)

When a neutral atom gains or loses an electron, it becomes an ion.

 FOLDABLES

Use your lesson Foldable to review the lesson. Save your Foldable for the project at the end of the chapter.

Use Vocabulary

1 The number of protons in an atom of an element is its _____.

2 Nuclear decay occurs when an unstable atomic nucleus changes into another nucleus by emitting _____.

3 **Describe** how two isotopes of nitrogen differ from two nitrogen ions.

Understand Key Concepts

4 An element's average atomic mass is calculated using the masses of its

  A. electrons.   **C.** neutrons.

  B. isotopes.   **D.** protons.

5 **Compare and contrast** oxygen-16 and oxygen-17.

6 **Show** what happens to the electrons of a neutral calcium atom (Ca) when it is changed into a calcium ion (Ca^{2+}).

Interpret Graphics

7 **Contrast** Copy and fill in this graphic organizer to contrast how different elements, isotopes, and ions are produced.

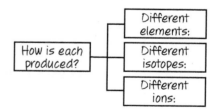

How is each produced? — Different elements: — Different isotopes: — Different ions:

Critical Thinking

8 **Consider** Find two neighboring elements on the periodic table whose positions would be reversed if they were arranged by atomic mass instead of atomic number.

9 **Infer** Can an isotope also be an ion?

Math Skills   Math Practice

10 A sample of copper (Cu) contains 69.17% Cu-63. The remaining copper atoms are Cu-65. What is the average atomic mass of copper?

What do you think NOW?

You first read the statements below at the beginning of the chapter.

4. All atoms of the same element have the same number of protons.

5. Atoms of one element cannot be changed into atoms of another element.

6. Ions form when atoms lose or gain electrons.

Did you change your mind about whether you agree or disagree with the statements? Rewrite any false statements to make them true.

Communicate Your Knowledge About the Atom

Materials

computer

creative building materials

drawing and modeling materials

office supplies

Also needed: recording devices, software, or other equipment for multimedia presentations

In this chapter, you have learned many things about atoms. Suppose that you are asked to take part in an atom fair. Each exhibit in the fair will help visitors understand something new about atoms in an exciting and interesting way. What will your exhibit be like? Will you hold a mock interview with Democritus or Rutherford? Will you model a famous experiment and explain its conclusion? Can visitors assemble or make models of their own atoms? Is there a multimedia presentation? Will your exhibit be aimed at children or adults? The choice is yours!

Question

Which concepts about the atom did you find most interesting? How can you present the information in exciting, creative, and perhaps unexpected ways? Think about whether you will present the information yourself or have visitors interact with the exhibit.

Procedure

1. In your Science Journal, write your ideas about the following questions:

- What specific concepts about the atom do you want your exhibit to teach?

- How will you present the information to your visitors?

- How will you make the information exciting and interesting to keep your visitors' attention?

2. Outline the steps in preparing for your exhibit.

- What materials and equipment will you need?

- How much time will it take to prepare each part of your exhibit?

- Will you involve anyone else? For example, if you are going to interview a scientist about an early model of the atom, who will play the scientist? What questions will you ask?

(t to b, 3-4)McGraw-Hill Education, (2, r)Hutchings Photography/Digital Light Source

3 Have your teacher approve your plan.

4 Follow the steps you outlined, and prepare your exhibit.

5 Ask family members and/or several friends to view your exhibit. Invite them to tell you what they've learned from your exhibit. Compare this with what you had expected to teach in your exhibit.

6 Ask your friends for feedback about what could be more effective in teaching the concepts you intend to teach.

7 Modify your exhibit to make it more effective.

8 If you can, present your exhibit to visitors of various ages, including teachers and students from other classes. Have visitors fill out a comment form.

Analyze and Conclude

9 **Infer** What did visitors to your exhibit find the most and least interesting? How do you know?

10 **Predict** What would you do differently if you had a chance to plan your exhibit again? Why?

11 **BIG IDEA** **The Big Idea** In what ways did your exhibit help visitors understand the current model of the atom?

Communicate Your Results

After the fair is over, discuss the visitors' comments and how you might improve organization or individual experiences if you were to do another fair.

Inquiry Extension

Design and describe an interactive game or activity that would teach the same concept you used for your exhibit. Invite other students to comment on your design.

Lab Tips

☑ For very young visitors, you might draw a picture book about the three parts of the atom and make them into cartoon characters.

☑ Plan your exhibit so visitors spend about 5 minutes there. Don't try to present too much or too little information.

☑ Remember that a picture is worth a thousand words!

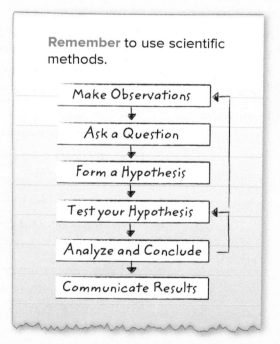

Remember to use scientific methods.

Make Observations

↓

Ask a Question

↓

Form a Hypothesis

↓

Test your Hypothesis

↓

Analyze and Conclude

↓

Communicate Results

Chapter 2 Study Guide

THE BIG IDEA An atom is the smallest unit of an element and is made mostly of empty space. It contains a tiny nucleus surrounded by an electron cloud.

Key Concepts Summary 🗝

Lesson 1: Discovering Parts of the Atom

- If you were to divide an element into smaller and smaller pieces, the smallest piece would be an **atom.**
- Atoms are so small that they can be seen only by powerful scanning microscopes.
- The first model of the atom was a solid sphere. Now, scientists know that an atom contains a dense positive **nucleus** surrounded by an **electron cloud.**

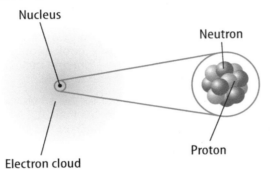

Nucleus

Neutron

Electron cloud

Proton

atom p. 53

electron p. 55

nucleus p. 58

proton p. 58

neutron p. 59

electron cloud p. 60

Lesson 2: Protons, Neutrons, and Electrons—How Atoms Differ

- **Nuclear decay** occurs when an unstable atomic nucleus changes into another more stable nucleus by emitting radiation.
- Different elements contain different numbers of protons. Two **isotopes** of the same element contain different numbers of neutrons. When a neutral atom gains or loses an electron, it becomes an **ion.**

Nuclear Decay

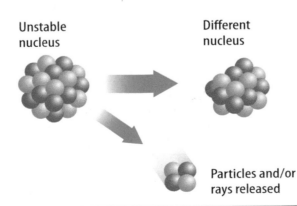

Unstable nucleus

Different nucleus

Particles and/or rays released

atomic number p. 65

isotope p. 66

mass number p. 66

average atomic mass p. 67

radioactive p. 68

nuclear decay p. 69

ion p. 70

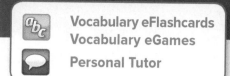
FOLDABLES® Chapter Project

Assemble your lesson Foldables as shown to make a Chapter Project. Use the project to review what you have learned in this chapter.

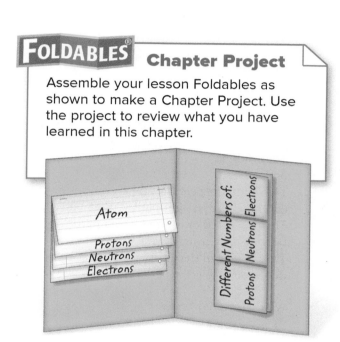

Use Vocabulary

1 A(n) _____ is a very small particle that is the basic unit of matter.

2 Electrons in an atom move throughout the _____ surrounding the nucleus.

3 _____ is the weighted average mass of all of an element's isotopes.

4 All atoms of a given element have the same number of _____.

5 When _____ occurs, one element is changed into another element.

6 Isotopes have the same _____, but different mass numbers.

Link Vocabulary and Key Concepts

 **Interactive Concept Map**

Copy this concept map, and then use vocabulary terms from the previous page to complete the concept map.

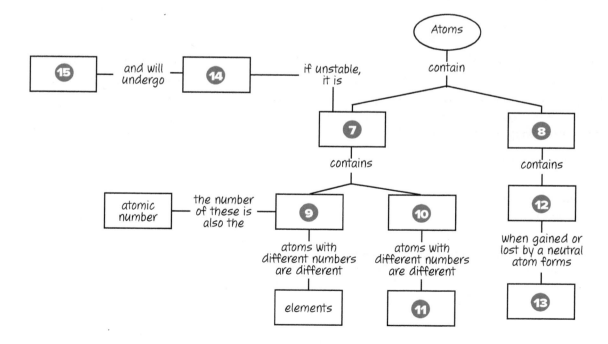

Chapter 2 Review

Understand Key Concepts

1 Which part of an atom makes up most of its volume?

A. its electron cloud
B. its neutrons
C. its nucleus
D. its protons

2 What did Democritus believe an atom was?

A. a solid, indivisible object
B. a tiny particle with a nucleus
C. a nucleus surrounded by an electron cloud
D. a tiny nucleus with electrons surrounding it

3 If an ion contains 10 electrons, 12 protons, and 13 neutrons, what is the ion's charge?

A. 2−
B. 1−
C. 2+
D. 3+

4 J.J. Thomson's experimental setup is shown below.

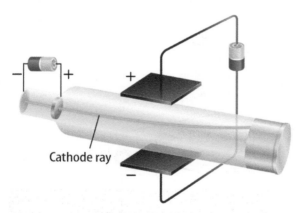

What is happening to the cathode rays?
A. They are attracted to the negative plate.
B. They are attracted to the positive plate.
C. They are stopped by the plates.
D. They are unaffected by either plate.

5 How many neutrons does iron-59 have?

A. 30
B. 33
C. 56
D. 59

6 Why were Rutherford's students surprised by the results of the gold foil experiment?

A. They didn't expect the alpha particles to bounce back from the foil.
B. They didn't expect the alpha particles to continue in a straight path.
C. They expected only a few alpha particles to bounce back from the foil.
D. They expected the alpha particles to be deflected by electrons.

7 Which determines the identity of an element?

A. its mass number
B. the charge of the atom
C. the number of its neutrons
D. the number of its protons

8 The figure below shows which of the following?

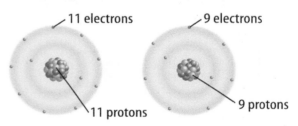

A. two different elements
B. two different ions
C. two different isotopes
D. two different protons

9 How is Bohr's atomic model different from Rutherford's model?

A. Bohr's model has a nucleus.
B. Bohr's model has electrons.
C. Electrons in Bohr's model are located farther from the nucleus.
D. Electrons in Bohr's model are located in circular energy levels.

Critical Thinking

10 **Consider** what would have happened in the gold foil experiment if Dalton's theory had been correct.

11 **Contrast** How does Bohr's model of the atom differ from the present-day atomic model?

12 **Describe** the electron cloud using your own analogy.

13 **Summarize** how radioactive decay can produce new elements.

14 **Hypothesize** What might happen if a negatively charged ion comes into contact with a positively charged ion?

15 **Infer** Why isn't mass number listed with each element on the periodic table?

16 **Explain** How is the average atomic mass calculated?

17 **Infer** Oxygen has three stable isotopes.

Isotope	Average Atomic Mass
Oxygen-16	0.99757
Oxygen-17	0.00038
Oxygen-18	0.00205

What can you determine about the average atomic mass of oxygen without calculating it?

Writing in Science

18 **Write** a newspaper article that describes how the changes in the atomic model provide an example of the scientific process in action.

REVIEW THE BIG IDEA

19 **Describe** the current model of the atom. Explain the size of atoms. Also explain the charge, the location, and the size of protons, neutrons, and electrons.

20 **Summarize** The Large Hadron Collider, shown below, is continuing the study of matter and energy. Use a set of four drawings to summarize how the model of the atom changed from Thomson, to Rutherford, to Bohr, to the modern model.

Math Skills ✓ Math Practice

Use Percentages

Use the information in the table to answer questions 21 and 22.

Magnesium (Mg) Isotope	Percent Found in Nature
Mg-24	78.9%
Mg-25	10.0%
Mg-26	

21 What is the percentage of Mg-26 found in nature?

22 What is the average atomic mass of magnesium?

Standardized Test Practice

Record your answers on the answer sheet provided by your teacher or on a sheet of paper.

Multiple Choice

1 Which best describes an atom?

  A a particle with a single negative charge

  B a particle with a single positive charge

  C the smallest particle that still represents a compound

  D the smallest particle that still represents an element

Use the figure below to answer questions 2 and 3.

Structure X

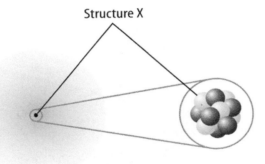

2 What is Structure X?

  A an electron

  B a neutron

  C a nucleus

  D a proton

3 Which best describes Structure X?

  A most of the atom's mass, neutral charge

  B most of the atom's mass, positive charge

  C very small part of the atom's mass, negative charge

  D very small part of the atom's mass, positive charge

4 Which is true about the size of an atom?

  A It can only be seen using a scanning tunneling microscope.

  B It is about the size of the period at the end of this sentence.

  C It is large enough to be seen using a magnifying lens.

  D It is too small to see with any type of microscope.

Use the figure below to answer question 5.

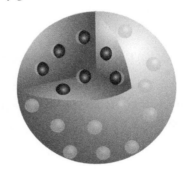

5 Whose model for the atom is shown?

  A Bohr's

  B Dalton's

  C Rutherford's

  D Thomson's

6 What structure did Rutherford discover?

  A the atom

  B the electron

  C the neutron

  D the nucleus

Use the table below to answer questions 7–9.

Particle	Number of Protons	Number of Neutrons	Number of Electrons
1	4	5	2
2	5	5	5
3	5	6	5
4	6	6	6

7 What is atomic number of particle 3?

  A 3

  B 5

  C 6

  D 11

8 Which particles are isotopes of the same element?

  A 1 and 2

  B 2 and 3

  C 2 and 4

  D 3 and 4

9 Which particle is an ion?

  A 1

  B 2

  C 3

  D 4

10 Which reaction starts with a neutron and results in the formation of a proton and a high-energy electron?

  A alpha decay

  B beta decay

  C the formation of positive ion

  D the formation of negative ion

Constructed Response

Use the figure below to answer questions 11 and 12.

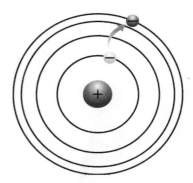

11 Identify the atomic model shown in the figure, and describe its characteristics.

12 How does this atomic model differ from the modern atomic model?

13 Compare two different neutral isotopes of the same element. Then compare two different ions of the same element. What do all of these particles have in common?

14 How does nuclear decay differ from the formation of ions? What parts of the atom are affected in each type of change?

NEED EXTRA HELP?														
If You Missed Question...	1	2	3	4	5	6	7	8	9	10	11	12	13	14
Go to Lesson...	1	1	1	1	1	1	2	2	2	2	1	1	2	2

Chapter 3

The Periodic Table

THE BIG IDEA

How is the periodic table used to classify and provide information about all known elements?

Inquiry What makes this balloon so special?

Things are made out of specific materials for a reason. A weather balloon can rise high in the atmosphere and gather weather information. The plastic that forms this weather balloon and the helium gas that fills it were chosen after scientists researched and studied the properties of these materials.

- What property of helium do you think makes the balloon rise through the air?

- How do you think the periodic table is a useful tool when determining properties of different materials?

Get Ready to Read

What do you think?

Before you read, decide if you agree or disagree with each of these statements. As you read this chapter, see if you change your mind about any of the statements.

1 The elements on the periodic table are arranged in rows in the order they were discovered.

2 The properties of an element are related to the element's location on the periodic table.

3 Fewer than half of the elements are metals.

4 Metals are usually good conductors of electricity.

5 Most of the elements in living things are nonmetals.

6 Even though they look very different, oxygen and sulfur share some similar properties.

connectED

Your one-stop online resource
connectED.mcgraw-hill.com

 LearnSmart®

 Chapter Resources Files, Reading Essentials, Get Ready to Read, Quick Vocabulary

 Animations, Videos, Interactive Tables

 Self-checks, Quizzes, Tests

 Project-Based Learning Activities

 Lab Manuals, Safety Videos, Virtual Labs & Other Tools

 Vocabulary, Multilingual eGlossary, Vocab eGames, Vocab eFlashcards

 Personal Tutors

Reading Guide

Key Concepts 🔑

ESSENTIAL QUESTIONS

- How are elements arranged on the periodic table?
- What can you learn about elements from the periodic table?

Vocabulary

periodic table p. 83

group p. 88

period p. 88

 Multilingual eGlossary

▶ **BrainPOP®**

8.PS.3, 8.PS.4, SEPS.4, SEPS.5

Using the Periodic Table

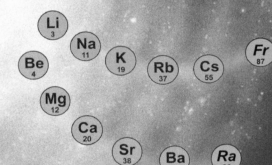
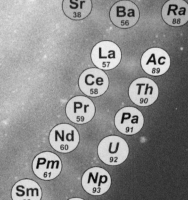
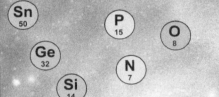

Inquiry Same Information?

You probably have seen a copy of a table that is used to organize the elements. Does it look like this chart? There is no specific shape that a chart of elements must have. However, the relationships among the elements in the chart are important.

P.J. Stewart/Science Source

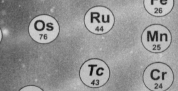

How can objects be organized?

What would it be like to shop at a grocery store where all the products are mixed up on the shelves? Maybe cereal is next to the dish soap and bread is next to the canned tomatoes. It would take a long time to find the groceries that you needed. How does organizing objects help you to find and use what you need?

1 Read and complete a lab safety form.

2 Empty the **interlocking plastic bricks** from the **plastic bag** onto your desk and observe their properties. Think about ways you might group and sequence the bricks so that they are organized.

3 Organize the bricks according to your plan.

4 Compare your pattern of organization with those used by several other students.

Think About This

1. Describe in your Science Journal the way you grouped your bricks. Why did you choose that way of grouping?

2. Describe how you sequenced the bricks.

3. 🔑 **Key Concept** How does organizing things help you to use them more easily?

What is the periodic table?

The "junk drawer" in **Figure 1** is full of pens, notepads, rubber bands, and other supplies. It would be difficult to find a particular item in this messy drawer. How might you organize it? First, you might dump the contents onto the counter. Then you could sort everything into piles. Pens and pencils might go into one pile. Notepads and paper go into another. Organizing the contents of the drawer makes it easier to find the things you need, also shown in **Figure 1.**

Just as sorting helped to organize the objects in the junk drawer, sorting can help scientists organize information about the elements. Recall that there are more than 100 elements, each with a unique set of physical and chemical properties.

Scientists use a table called the periodic (pihr ee AH dihk) table to organize elements. *The **periodic table** is a chart of the elements arranged into rows and columns according to their physical and chemical properties.* It can be used to determine the relationships among the elements.

In this chapter, you will read about how the periodic table was developed. You will also read about how you can use the periodic table to learn about the elements.

Figure 1 Sorting objects by their similarities makes it easier to find what you need.

Hutchings Photography/Digital Light Source

Developing a Periodic Table

In 1869 a Russian chemist and teacher named Dimitri Mendeleev (duh MEE tree • men duh LAY uf) was working on a way to classify elements. At that time, more than 60 elements had been discovered. He studied the physical properties such as density, color, melting point, and atomic mass of each element. Mendeleev also noted chemical properties such as how each element reacted with other elements. Mendeleev arranged the elements in a list using their atomic masses. He noticed that the properties of the elements seemed to repeat in a pattern.

When Mendeleev placed his list of elements into a table, he arranged them in rows of increasing atomic mass. Elements with similar properties were grouped the same column. The columns in his table are like the piles of sorted objects in your junk drawer. Both contain groups of things with similar properties.

 Reading Check What physical property did Mendeleev use to place the elements in rows on the periodic table?

Patterns in Properties

The term *periodic* means "repeating pattern." For example, seasons and months are periodic because they follow a repeating pattern every year. The days of the week are periodic since they repeat every seven days.

What were some of the repeating patterns Mendeleev noticed in his table? Melting point is one property that shows a repeating pattern. Recall that melting point is the temperature at which a solid changes to a liquid. The blue line in Figure 2 represents the melting points of the elements in row 2 of the periodic table. Notice that the melting point of carbon is higher than the melting point of lithium. However, the melting point of fluorine, at the far right of the row, is lower than that of carbon. How do these melting points show a pattern? Look at the red line in Figure 2. This line represents the melting points of the elements in row 3 of the periodic table. The melting points follow the same increasing and then decreasing pattern as the blue line, or row 2. Boiling point and reactivity also follow a periodic pattern.

A Periodic Property

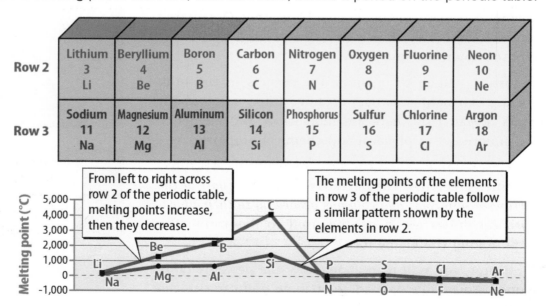

Figure 2 Melting points increase, then decrease, across a period on the periodic table.

Predicting Properties of Undiscovered Elements

When Mendeleev arranged all known elements by increasing atomic mass, there were large gaps between some elements. He predicted that scientists would discover elements that would fit into these spaces. Mendeleev also predicted that the properties of these elements would be similar to the known elements in the same columns. Both of his predictions turned out to be true.

Changes to Mendeleev's Table

Mendeleev's periodic table enabled scientists to relate the properties of the known elements to their position on the table. However, the table had a problem–some elements seemed out of place. Mendeleev believed that the atomic masses of certain elements must be invalid because the elements appeared in the wrong place on the periodic table. For example, Mendeleev placed tellurium before iodine despite the fact that tellurium has a greater atomic mass than iodine. He did so because iodine's properties more closely resemble those of fluorine and chlorine, just as copper's properties are closer to those of silver and gold, as shown in **Figure 3**.

Applying Practices

Where is it? What's it made of? Go online to use information to locate elements on the periodic table and find the numbers of subatomic particles in their atoms.

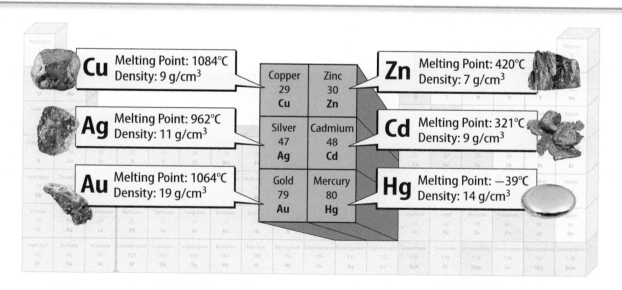

Cu Melting Point: 1084°C Density: 9 g/cm³

Ag Melting Point: 962°C Density: 11 g/cm³

Au Melting Point: 1064°C Density: 19 g/cm³

Copper 29 **Cu**	Zinc 30 **Zn**
Silver 47 **Ag**	Cadmium 48 **Cd**
Gold 79 **Au**	Mercury 80 **Hg**

Zn Melting Point: 420°C Density: 7 g/cm³

Cd Melting Point: 321°C Density: 9 g/cm³

Hg Melting Point: −39°C Density: 14 g/cm³

The Importance of Atomic Number

In the early 1900s, the scientist Henry Moseley solved the problem with Mendeleev's table. Moseley found that if elements were listed according to increasing atomic number instead of increasing atomic mass, columns would contain elements with similar properties. Recall that the atomic number of an element is the number of protons in the nucleus of each of that element's atoms.

 Animation

Figure 3 On today's periodic table, copper is in the same column as silver and gold. Zinc is in the same column as cadmium and mercury.

Key Concept Check What determines where an element is located on the periodic table you use today?

(t)DEA/A.RIZZI/De Agostini Picture Library/Getty Images, (tr)Astrid & Hanns-Frieder Michler/Science Source, (c)Dalgic/iStock/360/Getty Images, (cr)Richard Treptow/Science Source, (b)©Don Mason/Corbis, (br) Andra'Y Cerar/Getty Images

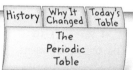

SCIENCE USE V. COMMON USE

period

Science Use the completion of a cycle; a row on the periodic table

Common Use a point used to mark the end of a sentence; a time frame

 Animation

Figure 4 🔑 The periodic table is used to organize elements according to increasing atomic number and properties.

Today's Periodic Table

You can identify many of the properties of an element from its placement on the periodic table. The table, as shown in **Figure 4**, is organized into columns, rows, and blocks, which are based on certain patterns of properties. In the next two lessons, you will learn how an element's position on the periodic table can help you interpret the element's physical and chemical properties.

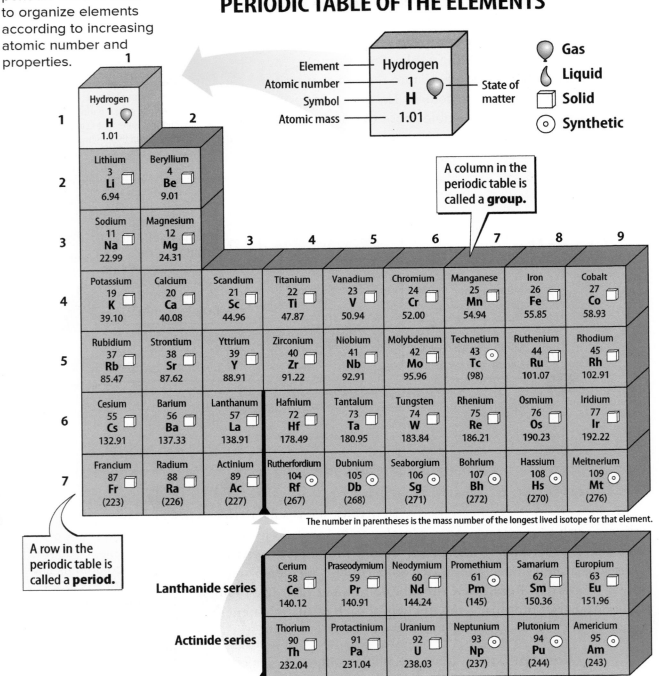

PERIODIC TABLE OF THE ELEMENTS

What is on an element key?

The element key shows an element's chemical symbol, atomic number, and atomic mass. The key also contains a symbol that shows the state of matter at room temperature. Look at the element key for helium in **Figure 5.** Helium is a gas at room temperature. Some versions of the periodic table give additional information, such as density, conductivity, or melting point.

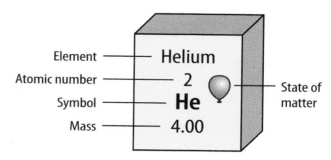

Figure 5 An element key shows important information about each element.

✓ **Visual Check** What does this key tell you about helium?

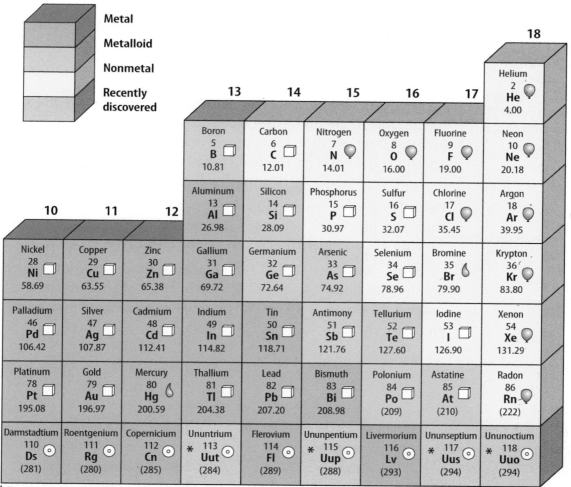

* The names and symbols for elements 113, 115, 117, and 118 are temporary. Final names will be approved by IUPAC (International Union of Pure and Applied Chemistry)

Use Geometry

The distance around a circle is the circumference (C). The distance across the circle, through its center, is the diameter (d). The radius (r) is half of the diameter. The circumference divided by the diameter for any circle is equal to π (pi), or 3.14. The formula for determining the circumference is:

$$C = \pi d \quad \text{or} \quad C = 2\pi r$$

For example, an iron (Fe) atom has a radius of 126 pm (picometers; 1 picometer = one-trillionth of a meter). The circumference of an iron atom is:

$$C = 2 \times 3.14 \times 126 \text{ pm}$$

$$C = 791 \text{ pm}$$

Practice

The radius of a uranium (U) atom is 156 pm. What is its circumference?

✓ **Math Practice**

💬 **Personal Tutor**

Groups

A **group** *is a column on the periodic table.* Elements in the same group have similar chemical properties and react with other elements in similar ways. There are patterns in the physical properties of a group such as density, melting point, and boiling point. The groups are numbered 1–18, as shown in **Figure 4.**

🔑 **Key Concept Check** What can you infer about the properties of two elements in the same group?

Periods

The rows on the periodic table are called **periods.** The atomic number of each element increases by one as you read from left to right across each period. The physical and chemical properties of the elements also change as you move left to right across a period.

Metals, Nonmetals, and Metalloids

Almost three-fourths of the elements on the periodic table are metals. Metals are on the left side and in the middle of the table. Individual metals have some properties that differ, but all metals are shiny and conduct thermal energy and electricity.

With the exception of hydrogen, nonmetals are located on the right side of the periodic table. The properties of nonmetals differ from the properties of metals. Many nonmetals are gases, and they do not conduct thermal energy or electricity.

Between the metals and the nonmetals on the periodic table are the metalloids. Metalloids have properties of both metals and nonmetals. **Figure 6** shows an example of a metal, a metalloid, and a nonmetal.

Figure 6 In period 3, magnesium is a metal, silicon is a metalloid, and sulfur is a nonmetal.

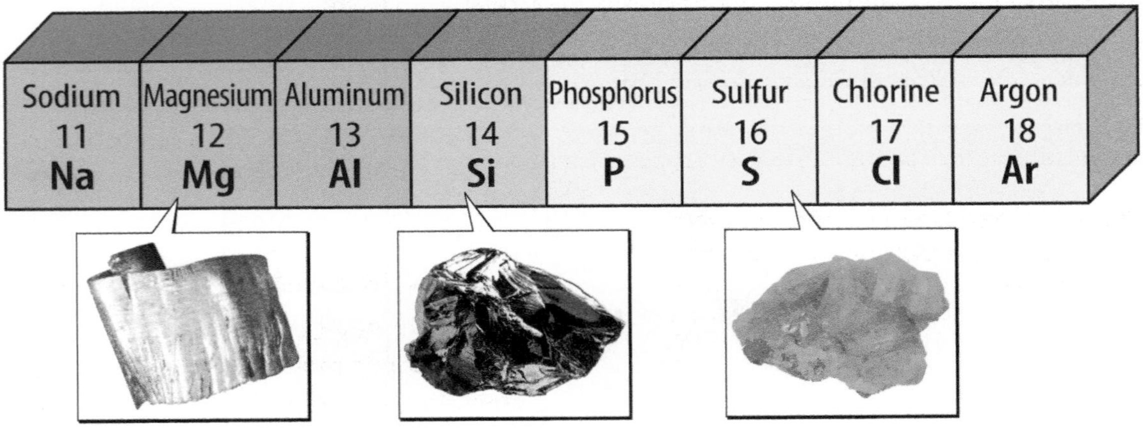

Sodium	Magnesium	Aluminum	Silicon	Phosphorus	Sulfur	Chlorine	Argon
11	12	13	14	15	16	17	18
Na	**Mg**	**Al**	**Si**	**P**	**S**	**Cl**	**Ar**

(l)David J. Green/Alamy, (c)GYRO PHOTOGRAPHY/amanaimagesRF/Getty Images, (r)MarcelC/iStock/360/Getty Images

Glenn T. Seaborg

Niels Bohr

Lise Meitner

Seaborgium	Bohrium	Hassium	Meitnerium
106	107	108	109
Sg	**Bh**	**Hs**	**Mt**

Figure 7 Three of these synthetic elements are named to honor important scientists.

How Scientists Use the Periodic Table

Even today, new elements are created in laboratories, named, and added to the present-day periodic table. Four of these elements are shown in **Figure 7**. These elements are all synthetic, or made by people, and do not occur naturally on Earth. Sometimes scientists can create only a few atoms of a new element. Yet scientists can use the periodic table to predict the properties of new elements they create. Look back at the periodic table in **Figure 4**. What group would you predict to contain element 119? You would probably expect element 119 to be in group 1 and to have similar properties to other elements in that group. Scientists hope to one day synthesize element 119.

The periodic table contains more than 100 elements. Each element has unique properties that differ from the properties of other elements. But each element also shares similar properties with nearby elements. The periodic table shows how elements relate to each other and fit together into one organized chart. Scientists use the periodic table to understand and predict elements' properties. You can, too.

Reading Check How is the periodic table used to predict the properties of an element?

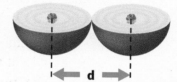

MiniLab   **20 minutes**

How does atom size change across a period?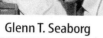

One pattern seen on the periodic table is in the radius of different atoms. The figure below shows how atomic radius is measured.

Atomic radius $= \frac{1}{2}d$

1 Read and complete a lab safety form.

2 Using **scissors** and **card stock paper,** cut seven 2-cm × 4-cm rectangles. Using a **marker,** label each rectangle with the atomic symbol of each of the first seven elements in period 2. Obtain the radius for each atom from your teacher.

3 Using a **ruler,** cut **plastic straws** to the same number of millimeters as each atomic radius given in picometers. For example, if the atomic radius is 145 pm, cut a straw 145 mm long.

4 **Tape** each of the labeled rectangles to the top of its appropriate straw.

5 Insert the straws into **modeling clay** according to increasing atomic number.

Analyze and Conclude

1. **Describe** the pattern you see in your model.

2. **Key Concept** Predict the pattern of atomic radii of the elements in period 4.

Lesson 1 Review

Visual Summary

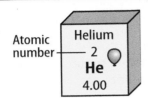

Atomic number

Helium
2
He
4.00

On the periodic table, elements are arranged according to increasing atomic number and similar properties.

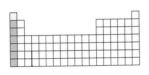

A column of the periodic table is called a group. Elements in the same group have similar properties.

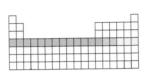

A row of the periodic table is called a period. Properties of elements repeat in the same pattern from left to right across each period.

FOLDABLES

Use your lesson Foldable to review the lesson. Save your Foldable for the project at the end of the chapter.

What do you think NOW?

You first read the statements below at the beginning of the chapter.

1. The elements on the periodic table are arranged in rows in the order they were discovered.

2. The properties of an element are related to the element's location on the periodic table.

Did you change your mind about whether you agree or disagree with the statements? Rewrite any false statements to make them true.

Use Vocabulary

1 **Identify** the scientific term used for rows on the periodic table.

2 **Name** the scientific term used for columns on the periodic table.

Understand Key Concepts

3 The _____ increases by one for each element as you move left to right across a period.

4 What does the decimal number in an element key represent?

A. atomic mass   C. chemical symbol

B. atomic number   D. state of matter

Interpret Graphics

5 **Classify** each marked element, 1 and 2, as a metal, a nonmetal, or a metalloid.

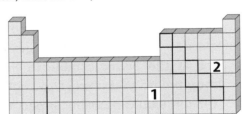

6 **Identify** Copy and fill in the graphic organizer below to identify the color-coded regions of the periodic table.

Critical Thinking

7 **Predict** Look at the perioidic table and predict three elements that have lower melting points than calcium (Ca).

Math Skills ✓ Math Practice

8 Carbon (C) and silicon (Si) are in group 4 of the periodic table. The atomic radius of carbon is 77 pm and sulfur is 103 pm. What is the circumference of each atom?

How is the periodic table arranged?

Materials

20 cards

What would happen if schools did not assign students to grades or classes? How would you know where to go on the first day of school? What if your home did not have an address? How could you tell someone where you live? Life becomes easier with organization. The following activity will help you discover how elements are organized on the periodic table.

Learn It

Patterns help you make sense of the world around you. The days of the week follow a pattern, as do the months of the year. **Identifying a pattern** involves organizing things into similar groups and then sequencing the things in the same way in each group.

Try It

1. Obtain cards from your teacher. Turn the cards over so the sides with numbers are facing up.

2. Separate the cards into three or more piles. All of the cards in a pile should have a characteristic in common.

3. Organize each pile into a pattern. Use all of the cards.

4. Lay out the cards into rows and columns based on their characteristics and patterns.

Apply It

5. Describe in your Science Journal the patterns you used to organize your cards. Do other patterns exist in your arrangement?

6. Are there gaps in your arrangement? Can you describe what a card in one of those gaps would look like?

7. 🔑 **Key Concept** What characteristics of elements might you use to organize them in a similar pattern?

Lesson 2

Reading Guide

Key Concepts
ESSENTIAL QUESTIONS

- What elements are metals?
- What are the properties of metals?

Vocabulary

metal p. 93

luster p. 93

ductility p. 94

malleability p. 94

alkali metal p. 95

alkaline earth metal p. 95

transition element p. 96

 Multilingual eGlossary

8.PS.4, SEPS.7, 6-8.LST.5.1,
6-8.LST.7.1

Metals

Inquiry Where does it strike?

Lightning strikes the top of the Empire State Building approximately 100 times a year. Why does lightning hit the top of this building instead of the city streets or buildings below? Metal lightning rods allow electricity to flow through them more easily than other materials do. Lightning moves through these materials and the building is not harmed.

Clarence Holmes Photography/Alamy

What properties make metals useful?

The properties of metals determine their uses. Copper conducts thermal energy, which makes it useful for cookware. Aluminum has low density, so it is used in aircraft bodies. What other properties make metals useful?

1. Read and complete a lab safety form.

2. With your group, observe the **metal objects** in your **container.** For each object, discuss what properties allow the metal to be used in that way.

3. Observe the **photographs of gold and silver jewelry.** What properties make these two metals useful in jewelry?

4. Examine **other objects around the room** that you think are made of metal. Do they share the same properties as the objects in your container? Do they have other properties that make them useful?

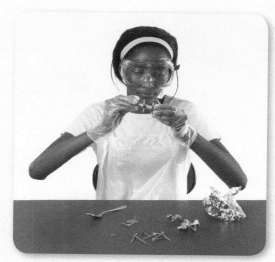

Think About This

1. What properties do all the metals share? What properties are different?

2. 🗝 **Key Concept** In your Science Journal, list at least four properties of metals that determine their uses.

What is a metal?

What do stainless steel knives and forks, copper wire, aluminum foil, and gold jewelry have in common? They are all made from metals.

As you read in Lesson 1, most of the elements on the periodic table are metals. In fact, of all the known elements, more than three-quarters are metals. With the exception of hydrogen, all of the elements in groups 1–12 on the periodic table are metals. In addition, some of the elements in groups 13–15 are metals. To be a metal, an element must have certain properties.

🗝 **Key Concept Check** How does the position of an element on the periodic table allow you to determine if the element is a metal?

Physical Properties of Metals

Recall that physical properties are characteristics used to describe or identify something without changing its makeup. All metals share certain physical properties.

A **metal** *is an element that is generally shiny. It is easily pulled into wires or hammered into thin sheets. A metal is a good conductor of electricity and thermal energy.* Gold exhibits the common properties of metals.

Luster and Conductivity People use gold for jewelry because of its beautiful color and metallic luster. **Luster** *describes the ability of a metal to reflect light.* Gold is also a good conductor of thermal energy and electricity. However, gold is too expensive to use in normal electrical wires or metal cookware. Copper is often used instead.

Hutchings Photography/Digital Light Source

Figure 8 Gold has many uses based on its properties.

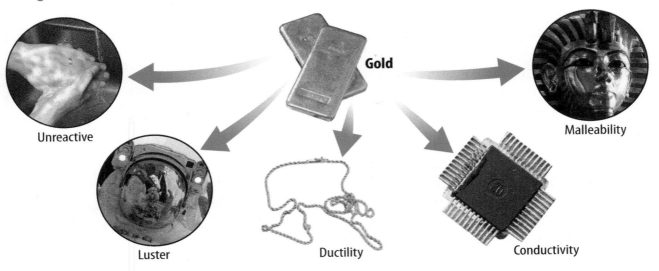

Unreactive

Luster

Ductility

Conductivity

Malleability

✓ **Visual Check** Analyze why the properties shown in each photo are an advantage to using gold.

(tl)McGraw-Hill Education, (tc)Paul Katz/Photodisc/Getty Images, (tr)Hisham Ibrahim/Photographer's Choice RF/Getty Images, (bl)NASA, (bc)Hutchings Photography/Digital Light Source, (br)Charles Stirling/Alamy

WORD ORIGIN · · · · · · · · · · ·

ductility
from Latin *ductilis*, means
"may be led or drawn"

REVIEW VOCABULARY · · · · ·

density
the mass per unit volume of a
substance

Make a two-tab book.
Label it as shown. Use
it to record information
about the properties
of metals.

The Physical Properties of Metals | The Chemical Properties of Metals

Ductility and Malleability Gold is the most ductile metal. **Ductility** (duk TIH luh tee) *is the ability to be pulled into thin wires.* A piece of gold with the mass of a paper clip can be pulled into a wire that is more than 3 km long.

Malleability (ma lee uh BIH luh tee) *is the ability of a substance to be hammered or rolled into sheets.* Gold is so malleable that it can be hammered into thin sheets. A pile of a million thin sheets would be only as high as a coffee mug.

Other Physical Properties of Metals In general the density, strength, boiling point, and melting point of a metal are greater than those of other elements. Except for mercury, all metals are solid at room temperature. Many uses of a metal are determined by the metal's physical properties, as shown in **Figure 8.**

🔑 **Key Concept Check** What are some physical properties of metals?

Chemical Properties of Metals

Recall that a chemical property is the ability or inability of a substance to change into one or more new substances. The chemical properties of metals can differ greatly. However, metals in the same group usually have similar chemical properties. For example, gold and other elements in group 11 do not easily react with other substances.

Group 1: Alkali Metals

The elements in group 1 are called **alkali** (AL kuh li) **metals.** The alkali metals include lithium, sodium, potassium, rubidium, cesium, and francium.

Because they are in the same group, alkali metals have similar chemical properties. Alkali metals react quickly with other elements, such as oxygen. Therefore, in nature, they occur only in compounds. Pure alkali metals must be stored so that they do not come in contact with oxygen and water vapor in the air. Figure 9 shows potassium and sodium reacting with water.

Alkali metals also have similar physical properties. Pure alkali metals have a silvery appearance, as shown in Figure 9. They are soft enough to cut with a knife. The alkali metals also have the lowest densities of all metals. A block of pure sodium metal could float on water because of its very low density.

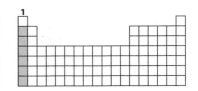

 Animation

Figure 9 Alkali metals react violently with water. Freshly cut surfaces are also shiny.

Potassium

Sodium

Lithium

Group 2: Alkaline Earth Metals

The elements in group 2 on the periodic table are called **alkaline** (AL kuh lun) **earth metals.** These metals are beryllium, magnesium, calcium, strontium, barium, and radium.

Alkaline earth metals also react quickly with other elements. However, they do not react as quickly as the alkali metals do. Like the alkali metals, pure alkaline earth metals do not occur naturally. Instead, they combine with other elements and form compounds. The physical properties of the alkaline earth metals are also similar to those of the alkali metals. Alkaline earth metals are soft and silvery. They also have low density, but they have greater density than alkali metals.

Reading Check Which element reacts faster with oxygen—barium or potassium?

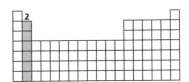

Figure 10 Transition elements are the blocks at the center of the periodic table. Many colorful materials contain small amounts of transition elements.

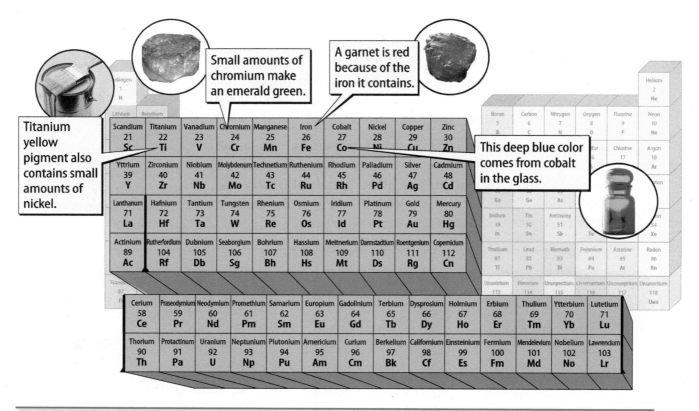

Groups 3–12: Transition Elements

The elements in groups 3-12 are called **transition elements.** The transition elements are in two blocks on the periodic table. The main block is in the center of the periodic table. The other block includes the two rows at the bottom of the periodic table, as shown in Figure 10.

Properties of Transition Elements

All transition elements are metals. They have higher melting points, greater strength, and higher densities than the alkali metals and the alkaline earth metals. Transition elements also react less quickly with oxygen. Some transition elements can exist in nature as free elements. An element is a free element when it occurs in pure form, not in a compound.

Uses of Transition Elements

Transition elements in the main block of the periodic table have many important uses. Because of their high densities, strength, and resistance to corrosion, transition elements such as iron make good building materials. Copper, silver, nickel, and gold are used to make coins. These metals are also used for jewelry, electrical wires, and many industrial applications.

Main-block transition elements can react with other elements and form many compounds. Many of these compounds are colorful. Artists use transition-element compounds in paints and pigments. The color of many gems, such as garnets and emeralds, comes from the presence of small amounts of transition elements, as illustrated in Figure 10.

Lanthanide and Actinide Series

Two rows of transition elements are at the bottom of the periodic table, as shown in Figure 10. These elements were removed from the main part of the table so that periods 6 and 7 were not longer than the other periods. If these elements were included in the main part of the table, the first row, called the lanthanide series, would stretch between lanthanum and halfnium. The second row, called the actinide series, would stretch between actinium and rutherfordium.

Some lanthanide and actinide series elements have valuable properties. For example, lanthanide series elements are used to make strong magnets. Plutonium, one of the actinide series elements, is used as a fuel in some nuclear reactors.

Patterns in Properties of Metals

Recall that the properties of elements follow repeating patterns across the periods of the periodic table. In general, elements increase in metallic properties such as luster, malleability, and electrical conductivity from right to left across a period, as shown in Figure 11. The elements on the far right of a period have no metallic properties at all. Potassium (K), the element on the far left in period 4, has the highest luster, is the most malleable, and conducts electricity better than all the elements in this period.

There are also patterns within groups. Metallic properties tend to increase as you move down a group, also shown in Figure 11. You could predict that the malleability of gold is greater than the malleability of either silver or copper because it is below these two elements in group 11.

✓ **Reading Check** Where would you expect to find elements on the periodic table with few or no metallic properties?

Hutchings Photography/Digital Light Source

MiniLab   20 minutes

How well do materials conduct thermal energy?

How well a material conducts thermal energy can often determine its use.

1. Read and complete a lab safety form.

2. Have your teacher add about 200 mL of very **hot water** to a **250-mL beaker.**

3. Place **rods of metal, plastic, glass, and wood** in the water for 30 seconds.

4. Set four large **ice cubes** on a sheet of **paper towel.** Use **tongs** to quickly remove each rod from the hot water. Place the heated end of the rod on an ice cube.

5. After 30 seconds, remove the rods and examine the ice cubes.

Analyze and Conclude

1. **Conclude** What can you conclude about how well metals conduct thermal energy?

2. 🔑 **Key Concept** Cookware is often made of metal. What property of metals makes them useful for this purpose?

Figure 11 Metallic properties of elements increase as you move to the left and down on the periodic table.

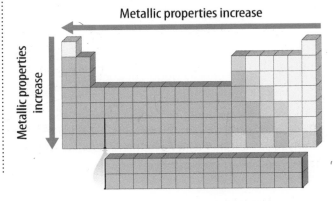

Metallic properties increase

Metallic properties increase

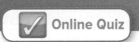
Visual Summary

Properties of metals include conductivity, luster, malleability, and ductility.

Alkali metals and alkaline earth metals react easily with other elements. These metals make up groups 1 and 2 on the periodic table.

Transition elements make up groups 3–12 and the lanthanide and actinide series on the periodic table.

FOLDABLES

Use your lesson Foldable to review the lesson. Save your Foldable for the project at the end of the chapter.

What do you think NOW?

You first read the statements below at the beginning of the chapter.

3. Fewer than half of the elements are metals.

4. Metals are usually good conductors of electricity.

Did you change your mind about whether you agree or disagree with the statements? Rewrite any false statements to make them true.

Use Vocabulary

1 **Use the term** *luster* in a sentence.

2 **Identify** the property that makes copper metal ideal for wiring.

3 Elements that have the lowest densities of all the metals are called _____.

Understand Key Concepts

4 **List** the physical properties that most metals have in common.

5 Which is a chemical property of transition elements?
A. brightly colored
B. great ductility
C. denser than alkali metals
D. reacts little with oxygen

6 **Organize** the following metals from least metallic to most metallic: barium, zinc, iron, and strontium.

Interpret Graphics

7 **Examine** this section of the periodic table. What metal will have properties most similar to those of chromium (Cr)? Why?

Vanadium 23 V	Chromium 24 Cr	Manganese 25 Mn
Niobium 41 Nb	Molybdenum 42 Mo	Technetium 43 Tc

Critical Thinking

8 **Investigate** your classroom and locate five examples of materials made from metal.

9 **Evaluate** the physical properties of potassium, magnesium, and copper. Select the best choice to use for a building project. Explain why this metal is the best building material to use.

Fireworks

Metals add a variety of colors to fireworks.

About 1,000 years ago, the Chinese discovered the chemical formula for gunpowder. Using this formula, they invented the first fireworks. One of the primary ingredients in gunpowder is saltpeter, or potassium nitrate. Find potassium on the periodic table. Notice that potassium is a metal. How does the chemical behavior of a metal contribute to a colorful fireworks show?

Purple: mix of strontium and copper compounds

Blue: copper compounds

Yellow: sodium compounds

Gold: iron burned with carbon

White-hot: barium-oxygen compounds or aluminum or magnesium burn

Metal compounds contribute to the variety of colors you see at a fireworks show. Recall that metals have special chemical and physical properties. Compounds that contain metals also have special properties. For example, each metal turns a characteristic color when burned. Lithium, an alkali metal, forms compounds that burn red. Copper compounds burn blue. Aluminum and magnesium burn white.

Orange: calcium compounds

Green: barium compounds

Red: strontium and lithium compounds

It's Your Turn

FORM AN OPINION Fireworks contain metal compounds. Are they bad for the environment or your health? Research the effects of metals on human health and on the environment. Decide if fireworks are safe to use for holiday celebrations.

Reading Guide

Key Concepts

ESSENTIAL QUESTIONS

- Where are nonmetals and metalloids on the periodic table?
- What are the properties of nonmetals and metalloids?

Vocabulary

nonmetal p. 101

halogen p. 103

noble gas p. 104

metalloid p. 105

semiconductor p. 105

 Multilingual eGlossary

 8.PS.4, SEPS.2, SEPS.8, 6-8.LST.6.2

Nonmetals and Metalloids

nquiry Why don't they melt?

What do you expect to happen to something when a flame is placed against it? As you can see, the nonmetal material this flower sits on protects the flower from the flame. Some materials conduct thermal energy. Other materials, such as this one, do not.

What are some properties of nonmetals?

You now know what the properties of metals are. What properties do nonmetals have?

1. Read and complete a lab safety form.

2. Examine pieces of **copper, carbon, aluminum,** and **sulfur.** Describe the appearance of these elements in your Science Journal.

3. Use a **conductivity tester** to check how well these elements conduct electricity. Record your observations.

4. Wrap each element sample in a **paper towel.** Carefully hit the sample with a **hammer.** Unwrap the towel and observe the sample. Record your observations.

Think About This

1. Locate these elements on the periodic table. From their locations, which elements are metals? Which elements are nonmetals?

2. 🔑 **Key Concept** Using your results, compare the properties of metals and nonmetals.

3. 🔑 **Key Concept** What property of a nonmetal makes it useful to insulate electrical wires?

The Elements of Life

Would it surprise you to learn that more than 96 percent of the mass of your body comes from just four elements? As shown in **Figure 12,** all four of these elements–oxygen, carbon, hydrogen, and nitrogen–are nonmetals. **Nonmetals** *are elements that have no metallic properties.*

Of the remaining elements in your body, the two most common elements also are nonmetals–phosphorus and sulfur. These six elements form the compounds in proteins, fats, nucleic acids, and other large molecules in your body and in all other living things.

✓ **Reading Check** What are the six most common elements in the human body?

Figure 12 Like other living things, this woman's mass comes mostly from nonmetals.

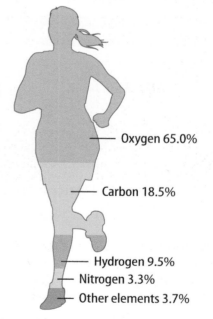

— Oxygen 65.0%

— Carbon 18.5%

— Hydrogen 9.5%
— Nitrogen 3.3%
— Other elements 3.7%

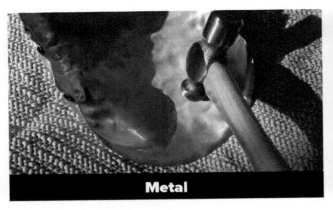
Metal

Nonmetal

▲ Figure 13 Solid metals, such as copper, are malleable. Solid nonmetals, such as sulfur, are brittle.

Figure 14 Nonmetals have properties that are different from those of metals. Phosphorus and carbon are dull, brittle solids that do not conduct thermal energy or electricity. ▼

How are nonmetals different from metals?

Recall that metals have luster. They are ductile, malleable, and good conductors of electricity and thermal energy. All metals except mercury are solids at room temperature.

The properties of nonmetals are different from those of metals. Many nonmetals are gases at room temperature. Those that are solid at room temperature have a dull surface, which means they have no luster. Because nonmetals are poor conductors of electricity and thermal energy, they are good insulators. For example, nose cones on space shuttles are insulated from the intense thermal energy of reentry by a material made from carbon, a nonmetal. **Figure 13** and **Figure 14** show several properties of nonmetals.

 Key Concept Check What properties do nonmetals have?

Properties of Nonmetals 🔑

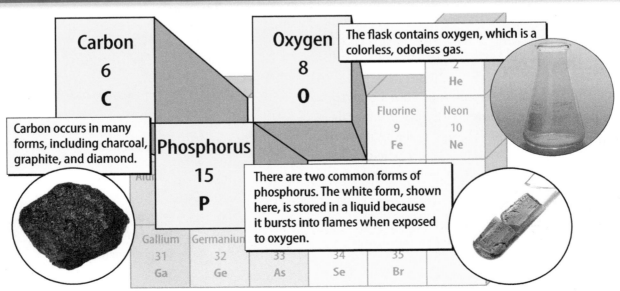

Carbon
6
C

Carbon occurs in many forms, including charcoal, graphite, and diamond.

Phosphorus
15
P

Oxygen
8
O

The flask contains oxygen, which is a colorless, odorless gas.

He

Fluorine
9
Fe

Neon
10
Ne

There are two common forms of phosphorus. The white form, shown here, is stored in a liquid because it bursts into flames when exposed to oxygen.

Gallium
31
Ga

Germanium
32
Ge

33
As

34
Se

35
Br

✔ **Visual Check** Compare the properties of oxygen to those of carbon and phosphorus.

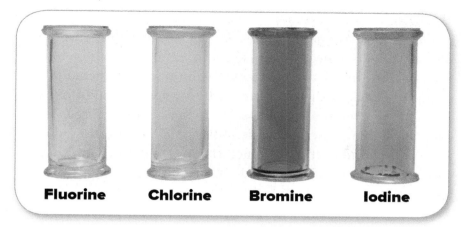

Fluorine   **Chlorine**   **Bromine**   **Iodine**

Figure 15 These glass containers each hold a halogen gas. Although they are different colors in their gaseous state, they react similarly with other elements.

✓ **Visual Check** Compare the colors of these halogens.

Nonmetals in Groups 14–16

Look back at the periodic table in **Figure 4**. Notice that groups 14-16 contain metals, nonmetals, and metalloids. The chemical properties of the elements in each group are similar. However, the physical properties of the elements can be quite different.

Carbon is the only nonmetal in group 14. It is a solid that has different forms. Carbon is in most of the compounds that make up living things. Nitrogen, a gas, and phosphorus, a solid, are the only nonmetals in group 15. These two elements form many different compounds with other elements, such as oxygen. Group 16 contains three nonmetals. Oxygen is a gas that is essential for many organisms. Sulfur and selenium are solids that have the physical properties of other solid nonmetals.

Group 17: The Halogens

An element in group 17 of the periodic table is called a **halogen** (HA luh jun). **Figure 15** shows the halogens fluorine, chlorine, bromine, and iodine. The term *halogen* refers to an element that can react with a metal and form a salt. For example, chlorine gas reacts with solid sodium and forms sodium chloride, or table salt. Calcium chloride is another salt often used on icy roads.

Halogens react readily with other elements and form compounds. They react so readily that halogens only can occur naturally in compounds. They do not exist as free elements. They even form compounds with other nonmetals, such as carbon. In general, the halogens are less reactive as you move down the group.

✓ **Reading Check** Will bromine react with sodium? Explain your answer.

FOLDABLES

Fold a sheet of paper to make a table with three columns and three rows. Label it as shown. Use it to organize information about nonmetals and metalloids.

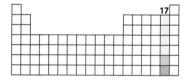

WORD ORIGIN ············

halogen
from Greek *hals*, means "salt"; and *-gen*, means "to produce"

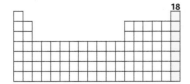

Group 18: The Noble Gases

The elements in group 18 are known as the **noble gases.** The elements helium, neon, argon, krypton, xenon, and radon are the noble gases. Unlike the halogens, the only way elements in this group react with other elements is under special conditions in a laboratory. These elements were not yet discovered when Mendeleev constructed his periodic table because they do not form compounds naturally. Once they were discovered, they fit into a group at the far right side of the table.

Hydrogen

Figure 16 shows the element key for hydrogen. Of all the elements, hydrogen has the smallest atomic mass. It is also the most common element in the universe.

Is hydrogen a metal or a nonmetal? Hydrogen is most often classified as a nonmetal because it has many properties like those of nonmetals. For example, like some nonmetals, hydrogen is a gas at room temperature. However, hydrogen also has some properties similar to those of the group 1 alkali metals. In its liquid form, hydrogen conducts electricity just like a metal does. In some chemical reactions, hydrogen reacts as if it were an alkali metal. However, under conditions on Earth, hydrogen usually behaves like a nonmetal.

 Reading Check Why is hydrogen usually classified as a nonmetal?

ACADEMIC VOCABULARY

construct
(verb) to make by combining and arranging parts

Figure 16 More than 90 percent of all the atoms in the universe are hydrogen atoms. Hydrogen is the main fuel for the nuclear reactions that occur in stars.

Hydrogen is a colorless, odorless gas. It is the most common element in the universe.

Hydrogen
1
H

NASA/ESA/JPL/Arizona State Univ.

Metalloids

Between the metals and the nonmetals on the periodic table are elements known as metalloids. *A **metalloid** (MEH tul oyd) is an element that has physical and chemical properties of both metals and nonmetals.* The elements boron, silicon, germanium, arsenic, antimony, tellurium, polonium, and astatine are metalloids. Silicon is the most abundant metalloid in the universe. Most sand is made of a compound containing silicon. Silicon is also used in many different products, some of which are shown in Figure 17.

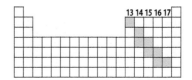

Key Concept Check Where are metalloids on the periodic table?

Semiconductors

Recall that metals are good conductors of thermal energy and electricity. Nonmetals are poor conductors of thermal energy and electricity but are good insulators. A property of metalloids is the ability to act as a semiconductor. *A **semiconductor** conducts electricity at high temperatures, but not at low temperatures.* At high temperatures, metalloids act like metals and conduct electricity. But at lower temperatures, metalloids act like nonmetals and stop electricity from flowing. This property is useful in electronic devices such as computers, televisions, and solar cells.

Applying Practices

What's trending on the periodic table? Go online to identify organizational patterns on the periodic table.

WORD ORIGIN

semiconductor
from Latin *semi-*, means "half"; and *conducere*, means "to bring together"

Figure 17 The properties of silicon make it useful for many different products.

Uses of Silicon

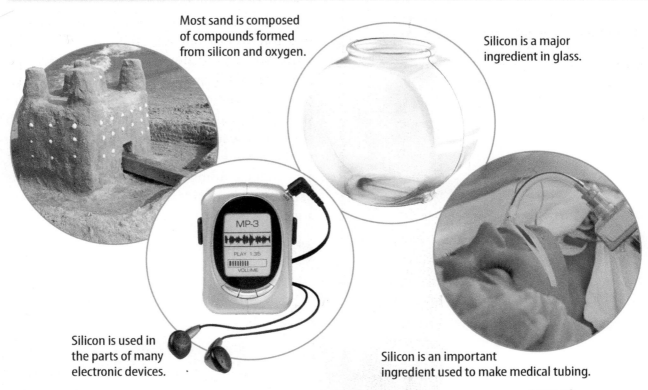

Most sand is composed of compounds formed from silicon and oxygen.

Silicon is a major ingredient in glass.

Silicon is used in the parts of many electronic devices.

Silicon is an important ingredient used to make medical tubing.

(l)Ingemar Aourell/Getty Images, (cl)Don Farrall/Getty Images, (cr)Jacques Cornell/McGraw-Hill Education, (r)Henrik Sorensen/The Image Bank/Getty Images

Figure 18 This microchip conducts electricity at high temperatures using a semiconductor.

 Personal Tutor

 MiniLab   **15 minutes**

Which insulates better?

In this lab, you will compare how well a metal bowl and a nonmetal ball containing a mixture of nonmetals conduct thermal energy.

1. Read and complete a lab safety form.

2. Pour **very warm water** into a **pitcher.**

3. Pour half of the warm water into a **metal bowl.** In your Science Journal, describe how the outside of the bowl feels.

4. Inflate a **beach ball** until it is one-third full. Mold the partially filled beach ball into the shape of a bowl. Pour the remaining warm water into your beach ball bowl. Feel the outside of the bowl. Describe how it feels.

Analyze and Conclude

1. **Explain** the difference in the outside temperatures of the two bowls.

2. **Predict** the results of putting ice in each of the bowls.

3. **Key Concept** Make a statement about how well a nonmetal conducts thermal energy.

Properties and Uses of Metalloids

Pure silicon is used in making semiconductor devices for computers and other electronic products. Germanium is also used as a semiconductor as shown in **Figure 18.** Other metalloids have different uses. Boron is used in water softeners and laundry products. Boron also glows bright green in fireworks. Silicon is one of the most abundant elements on Earth. Sand, clay, and many rocks and minerals are made of silicon compounds.

Metals, Nonmetals, and Metalloids

You have read that all metallic elements have common characteristics, such as malleability, conductivity, and ductility. However, each metal has unique properties that make it different from other metals. The same is true for nonmetals and metalloids. How can knowing the properties of an element help you evaluate its uses?

Look again at the periodic table. An element's position on the periodic table tells you a lot about the element. By knowing that sulfur is a nonmetal, for example, you know that it breaks easily and does not conduct electricity. You would not choose sulfur to make a wire. You would not try to use oxygen as a semiconductor or sodium as a building material. You know that transition elements are strong, malleable, and do not react easily with oxygen or water. Because of these characteristics, these metals make good building materials. Understanding the properties of elements can help you decide which element to use in a given situation.

Reading Check Why would you not use an element on the right side of the periodic table as a building material?

Lesson 3 Review

✓ Online Quiz

Visual Summary

A nonmetal is an element that has no metallic properties. Solid nonmetals are dull, brittle, and do not conduct thermal energy or electricity.

Halogens and noble gases are nonmetals. These elements are found in group 17 and group 18 of the periodic table.

Metalloids have some metallic properties and some nonmetallic properties. The most important use of metalloids is as semiconductors.

FOLDABLES®

Use your lesson Foldable to review the lesson. Save your Foldable for the project at the end of the chapter.

What do you think NOW?

You first read the statements below at the beginning of the chapter.

5. Most of the elements in living things are nonmetals.

6. Even though they look very different, oxygen and sulfur share some similar properties.

Did you change your mind about whether you agree or disagree with the statements? Rewrite any false statements to make them true.

Use Vocabulary

1 **Distinguish** between a nonmetal and a metalloid.

2 An element in group 17 of the periodic table is called a(n) _____.

3 An element in group 18 of the periodic table is called a(n) _____.

Understand Key Concepts

4 The ability of a halogen to react with a metal to form a salt is an example of a _____ property.
   - **A.** chemical
   - **B.** noble gas
   - **C.** periodic
   - **D.** physical

5 **Classify** each of the following elements as a metal, a nonmetal, or a metalloid: boron, carbon, aluminum, and silicon.

6 **Infer** which group you would expect to contain element 120. Use the periodic table to help you answer this question.

Interpret Graphics

7 **Sequence** nonmetals, metals, and metalloids in order from left to right across the periodic table by copying and completing the graphic organizer below.

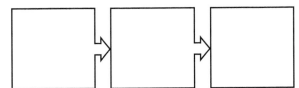

Critical Thinking

8 **Hypothesize** how your classroom would be different if there were no metalloids.

9 **Analyze** why hydrogen is sometimes classified as a metal.

10 **Determine** whether there are more nonmetals in group 14 or in group 16. Explain your answer.

Hutchings Photography/Digital Light Source

Materials

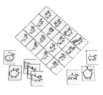

cards

Alien Insect Periodic Table

The periodic table classifies elements according to their properties. In this lab, you will model the procedure used to develop the periodic table. Your model will include developing patterns using pictures of alien insects. You will then use your patterns to predict what missing alien insects look like.

Question

How can I arrange objects into patterns by using their properties?

Procedure

1. Obtain a set of alien insect pictures. Spread them out so you can see all of them. Observe the pictures with a partner. Look for properties that you might use to organize the pictures.

2. Make a list of properties you might use to group the alien insects. These properties are those that a number of insects have in common.

3. Make a list of properties you might use to sequence the insects. These properties change from one insect to the next in some pattern.

4. With your partner, decide what pattern you will use to arrange the alien insects in an organized rectangular block. All the insects in a vertical column, or group, must be the same in some way. They must also share some feature that changes regularly as you move down the group. All the aliens in a horizontal row, or period, must be the same in some way and must also share some feature that changes regularly as you move across the period.

5 Arrange your insects as you planned. Two insects are missing from your set. Leave empty spaces in your rectangular block for these pictures. When you have finished arranging your insects, have the teacher check your pattern.

6 Write a description of the properties you predict each missing alien insect will have. Then draw a picture of each missing insect.

Analyze and Conclude

7 **Explain** Could you have predicted the properties of the missing insects without placing the others in a pattern? Why or why not?

8 **The Big Idea** How is your arrangement similar to the one developed by Mendeleev for elements? How is it different?

9 **Infer** What properties can you use to predict the identity of one missing insect? What do you not know about that insect?

Communicate Your Results

Create a slide show presentation that demonstrates, step by step, how you grouped and sequenced your insects and predicted the properties of the missing insects. Show your presentation to students in another class.

Inquiry Extension

How could you change the insects so that they better represent the properties of elements, such as atomic mass?

Lab Tips

☑ A property is any observable characteristic that you can use to distinguish between objects.

☑ A pattern is a consistent plan or model used as a guide for understanding or predicting something.

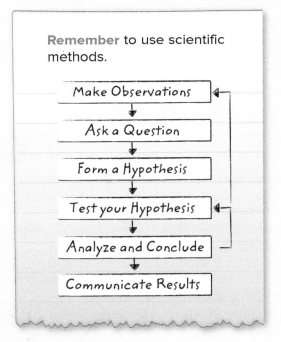

Remember to use scientific methods.

Make Observations

↓

Ask a Question

↓

Form a Hypothesis

↓

Test your Hypothesis

↓

Analyze and Conclude

↓

Communicate Results

 Elements are organized on the periodic table according to increasing atomic number and similar properties.

Key Concepts Summary	Vocabulary

Lesson 1: Using the Periodic Table

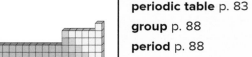

- Elements are organized on the **periodic table** by increasing atomic number and similar properties.
- Elements in the same **group,** or column, of the periodic table have similar properties.
- Elements' properties change across a **period,** which is a row of the periodic table.
- Each element key on the periodic table provides the name, symbol, atomic number, and atomic mass for an element.

periodic table p. 83
group p. 88
period p. 88

Lesson 2: Metals

- **Metals** are located on the left side and middle of the periodic table.
- Metals are elements that have **ductility, malleability, luster,** and conductivity.
- The **alkali metals** are in group 1 of the periodic table, and the **alkaline earth metals** are in group 2.
- **Transition elements** are metals in groups 3–12 of the periodic table, as well as the lanthanide and actinide series.

metal p. 93
luster p. 93
ductility p. 94
malleability p. 94
alkali metal p. 95
alkaline earth metal p. 95
transition element p. 96

Lesson 3: Nonmetals and Metalloids

- **Nonmetals** are on the right side of the periodic table, and **metalloids** are located between metals and nonmetals.
- Nonmetals are elements that have no metallic properties. Solid nonmetals are dull in appearance, brittle, and do not conduct electricity. Metalloids are elements that have properties of both metals and nonmetals.
- Some metalloids are **semiconductors.**
- Elements in group 17 are called **halogens,** and elements in group 18 are **noble gases.**

nonmetal p. 101
halogen p. 103
noble gas p. 104
metalloid p. 105
semiconductor p. 105

(t)David J. Green/Alamy, (b)MarcelC/iStock/360/Getty Images

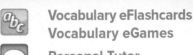
 FOLDABLES® Chapter Project

Assemble your lesson Foldables as shown to make a Chapter Project. Use the project to review what you have learned in this chapter.

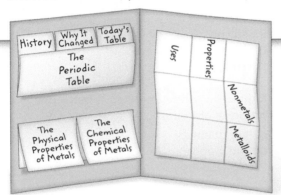

Use Vocabulary

1 The element magnesium (Mg) is in _____ 3 of the periodic table.

2 An element that is shiny, is easily pulled into wires or hammered into thin sheets, and is a good conductor of electricity and heat is a(n) _____.

3 Copper is used to make wire because it has the property of _____.

4 An element that is sometimes a good conductor of electricity and sometimes a good insulator is a(n) _____.

5 An element that is a poor conductor of heat and electricity but is a good insulator is a(n) _____.

Link Vocabulary and Key Concepts

▷ **Interactive Concept Map**

Copy this concept map, and then use vocabulary terms from the previous page to complete the concept map.

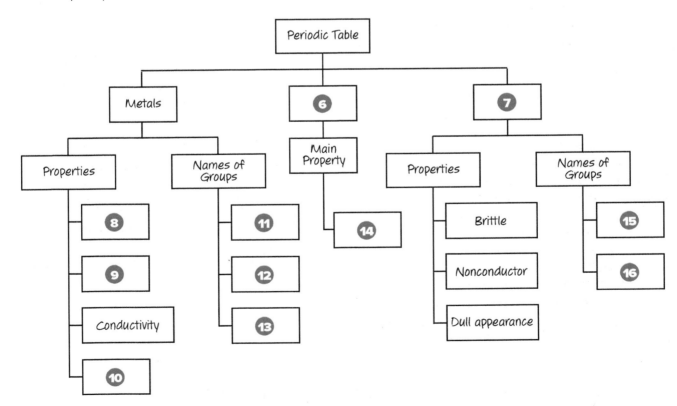

Understand Key Concepts

1 What determines the order of elements on today's periodic table?

A. increasing atomic mass
B. decreasing atomic mass
C. increasing atomic number
D. decreasing atomic number

2 The element key for nitrogen is shown below.

From this key, determine the atomic mass of nitrogen.

A. 7
B. 7.01
C. 14.01
D. 21.01

3 Look at the periodic table in Lesson 1. Which list of elements forms a group on the periodic table?

A. Li, Be, B, C, N, O, F, and Ne
B. He, Ne, Ar, Kr, Xe, and Rn
C. B, Si, As, Te, and At
D. Sc, Ti, V, Cr, Mn, Fe, Co, Cu, Ni, and Zn

4 Which is NOT a property of metals?

A. brittleness
B. conductivity
C. ductility
D. luster

5 What are two properties that make a metal a good choice to use as wire in electronics?

A. conductivity, malleability
B. ductility, conductivity
C. luster, malleability
D. malleability, high density

6 Where are most metals on the periodic table?

A. on the left side only
B. on the right side only
C. in the middle only
D. on the left side and in the middle

7 Look at the periodic table in Lesson 1 and determine which element is a metalloid.

A. carbon
B. silicon
C. oxygen
D. aluminum

8 Iodine is a solid nonmetal. What is one property of iodine?

A. conductivity
B. dull appearance
C. malleability
D. ductility

9 The following table lists some information about certain elements in group 17.

Element Symbol	Atomic Number	Melting Point (°C)	Boiling Point (°C)
F	9	−233	−187
Cl	17	−102	−35
Br	35	−7.3	59
I	53	114	183

Which statement describes what happens to these elements as atomic number increases?

A. Both melting point and boiling point decrease.
B. Melting point increases and boiling point decreases.
C. Melting point decreases and boiling point increases.
D. Both melting point and boiling point increase.

Critical Thinking

10 **Recommend** an element to use to fill bottles that contain ancient paper. The element should be a gas at room temperature, should be denser than helium, and should not easily react with other elements.

11 **Apply** Why is mercury the only metal to have been used in thermometers?

12 **Evaluate** the following types of metals as a choice to make a Sun reflector: alkali metals, alkaline earth metals, or transition metals. The metal cannot react with water or oxygen and must be shiny and strong.

13 The figure below shows a pattern of densities.

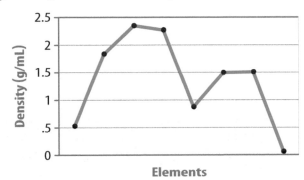

Infer whether you are looking at a graph of elements within a group or across a period. Explain your answer.

14 **Contrast** aluminum and nitrogen. Show why aluminum is a metal and nitrogen is not.

15 **Classify** A student sorted six elements. He placed iron, silver, and sodium in group A. He placed neon, oxygen, and nitrogen in group B. Name one other element that fits in group A and another element that belongs in group B. Explain your answer.

Writing in Science

16 **Write** a plan that shows how a metal, a nonmetal, and a metalloid could be used when constructing a building.

REVIEW THE BIG IDEA

17 Explain how atomic number and properties are used to determine where element 115 is placed on the periodic table.

18 The photo below shows how the properties of materials determine their uses. How can the periodic table be used to help you find elements with properties similar to that of helium?

Math Skills ✓ Math Practice

Use Geometry

19 The table below shows the atomic radii of three elements in group 1 on the periodic table.

Element	Atomic radius
Li	152 pm
Na	186 pm
K	227 pm

a. What is the circumference of each atom?

b. Rubidium (Rb) is the next element in Group 1. What would you predict about the radius and circumference of a rubidium atom?

Standardized Test Practice

Record your answers on the answer sheet provided by your teacher or on a sheet of paper.

Multiple Choice

1 Where are most nonmetals located on the periodic table?

   A in the bottom row

   B on the left side and in the middle

   C on the right side

   D in the top row

Use the figure below to answer question 2.

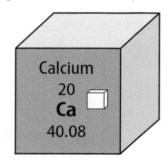

2 What is the atomic mass of calcium?

   A 20

   B 40.08

   C 40.08 ÷ 20

   D 40.08 + 20

3 Which element is most likely to react with potassium?

   A bromine

   B calcium

   C nickel

   D sodium

4 Which group of elements can act as semiconductors?

   A halogens

   B metalloids

   C metals

   D noble gases

Use the table below about group 13 elements to answer question 5.

Element Symbol	Atomic Number	Density (g/cm³)	Atomic Mass
B	5	2.34	10.81
Al	13	2.70	26.98
Ga	31	5.90	69.72
In	49	7.30	114.82

5 How do density and atomic mass change as atomic number increases?

   A Density and atomic mass decrease.

   B Density and atomic mass increase.

   C Density decreases and atomic mass increases.

   D Density increases and atomic mass decreases.

6 Which elements have high densities, strength, and resistance to corrosion?

   A alkali metals

   B alkaline earth metals

   C metalloids

   D transition elements

7 Which is a property of a metal?

   A It is brittle.

   B It is a good insulator.

   C It has a dull appearance.

   D It is malleable.

Use the figure below to answer questions 8 and 9.

17

8   The figure shows a group in the periodic table. What is the name of this group of elements?

   A   halogens

   B   metalloids

   C   metals

   D   noble gases

9   Which is a property of these elements?

   A   They are conductors.

   B   They are semiconductors.

   C   They are nonreactive with other elements.

   D   They react easily with other elements.

10   What is one similarity among elements in a group?

   A   atomic mass

   B   atomic weight

   C   chemical properties

   D   practical uses

Constructed Response

Use the figure below to answer questions 11 and 12.

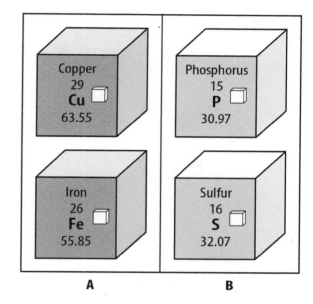

| A | B |

11   Groups A and B each contain two elements. Identify each group as metals, nonmetals, or metalloids. Would silicon belong to one of these groups? Why or why not?

12   Which group in the figure above yields the strongest building elements? Why?

13   How does the periodic table of elements help scientists today?

14   What connection does the human body have with the elements on the periodic table?

NEED EXTRA HELP?													
If You Missed Question...	1	2	3	4	5	6	7	8	9	10	11	12	13	14
Go to Lesson...	1	1	3	3	1	2	2	3	3	1	2, 3	2	1	3

Elements and Chemical Bonds

THE BIG IDEA

How do elements join together to form chemical compounds?

Inquiry · How do they combine?

How many different words could you type using just the letters on a keyboard? The English alphabet has only 26 letters, but a dictionary lists hundreds of thousands of words using these letters! Similarly only about 118 different elements make all kinds of matter.

• How do so few elements form so many different kinds of matter?

• Why do you think different types of matter have different properties?

• How are atoms held together to produce different types of matter?

altrendo images/Getty Images

Get Ready to Read

What do you think?

Before you read, decide if you agree or disagree with each of these statements. As you read this chapter, see if you change your mind about any of the statements.

1 Elements rarely exist in pure form. Instead, combinations of elements make up most of the matter around you.

2 Chemical bonds that form between atoms involve electrons.

3 The atoms in a water molecule are more chemically stable than they would be as individual atoms.

4 Many substances dissolve easily in water because opposite ends of a water molecule have opposite charges.

5 Losing electrons can make some atoms more chemically stable.

6 Metals are good electrical conductors because they tend to hold onto their valence electrons very tightly.

connectED

Your one-stop online resource
connectED.mcgraw-hill.com

 LearnSmart®

 Chapter Resources Files, Reading Essentials, Get Ready to Read, Quick Vocabulary

 Animations, Videos, Interactive Tables

 Self-checks, Quizzes, Tests

 Project-Based Learning Activities

 Lab Manuals, Safety Videos, Virtual Labs & Other Tools

 Vocabulary, Multilingual eGlossary, Vocab eGames, Vocab eFlashcards

 Personal Tutors

Lesson 1

Electrons and Energy Levels

Reading Guide

Key Concepts
ESSENTIAL QUESTIONS

- How is an electron's energy related to its distance from the nucleus?
- Why do atoms gain, lose, or share electrons?

Vocabulary
chemical bond p. 120
valence electron p. 122
electron dot diagram p. 123

 Multilingual eGlossary

 BrainPOP®

 SEPS.2, 6-8.LST.7.1

Inquiry **Are pairs more stable?**

Rowing can be hard work, especially if you are part of a racing team. The job is made easier because the rowers each pull on the water with a pair of oars. How do pairs make the boat more stable?

Douglas Fisher/Alamy

How is the periodic table organized?

How do you begin to put together a puzzle of a thousand pieces? You first sort similar pieces into groups. All edge pieces might go into one pile. All blue pieces might go into another pile. Similarly, scientists placed the elements into groups based on their properties. They created the periodic table, which organizes information about all the elements.

1. Obtain six **index cards** from your teacher. Using one card for each element name, write the names *beryllium, sodium, iron, zinc, aluminum,* and *oxygen* at the top of a card.

2. Open your textbook to the periodic table printed on the inside back cover. Locate the element key for each element written on your cards.

3. For each element, find the following information and write it on the index card: symbol, atomic number, atomic mass, state of matter, and element type.

Think About This

1. What do the elements in the blue blocks have in common? In the green blocks? In the yellow blocks?

2. 🔑 **Key Concept** Each element in a column on the periodic table has similar chemical properties and forms bonds in similar ways. Based on this, for each element you listed on a card, name another element on the periodic table that has similar chemical properties.

The Periodic Table

Imagine trying to find a book in a library if all the books were unorganized. Books are organized in a library to help you easily find the information you need. The periodic table is like a library of information about all chemical elements.

A copy of the periodic table is on the inside back cover of this book. The table has more than 100 blocks—one for each known element. Each block on the periodic table includes basic properties of each element such as the element's state of matter at room temperature and its atomic number. The atomic number is the number of protons in each atom of the element. Each block also lists an element's atomic mass, or the average mass of all the different isotopes of that element.

Periods and Groups

You can learn about some properties of an element from its position on the periodic table. Elements are organized in periods (rows) and groups (columns). The periodic table lists elements in order of atomic number. The atomic number increases from left to right as you move across a period. Elements in each group have similar chemical properties and react with other elements in similar ways. In this lesson, you will read more about how an element's position on the periodic table can be used to predict its properties.

✓ **Reading Check** How is the periodic table organized?

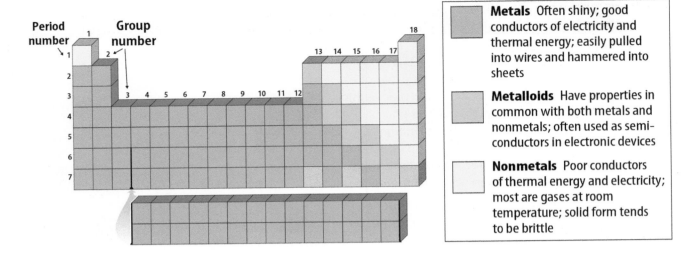

				Metals Often shiny; good conductors of electricity and thermal energy; easily pulled into wires and hammered into sheets
				Metalloids Have properties in common with both metals and nonmetals; often used as semi-conductors in electronic devices
				Nonmetals Poor conductors of thermal energy and electricity; most are gases at room temperature; solid form tends to be brittle

▲ Figure 1 Elements on the periodic table are classified as metals, nonmetals, or metalloids.

 Animation

Figure 2 Protons and neutrons are in an atom's nucleus. Electrons move around the nucleus. ▼

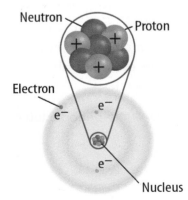

Lithium Atom

Metals, Nonmetals, and Metalloids

The three main regions of elements on the periodic table are shown in **Figure 1.** Except for hydrogen, elements on the left side of the table are metals. Nonmetals are on the right side of the table. Metalloids form the narrow stair-step region between metals and nonmetals.

Reading Check Where are metals, nonmetals, and metalloids on the periodic table?

Atoms Bond

In nature, pure elements are rare. Instead, atoms of different elements chemically combine and form compounds. Compounds make up most of the matter around you, including living and nonliving things. There are only about 118 elements, but these elements combine and form millions of compounds. Chemical bonds hold them together. *A* **chemical bond** *is a force that holds two or more atoms together.*

Electron Number and Arrangement

Recall that atoms contain protons, neutrons, and electrons, as shown in **Figure 2.** Each proton has a positive charge; each neutron has no charge; and each electron has a negative charge. The atomic number of an element is the number of protons in each atom of that element. In a neutral (uncharged) atom, the number of protons equals the number of electrons.

The exact position of electrons in an atom cannot be determined. This is because electrons are in constant motion around the nucleus. However, each electron is usually in a certain area of space around the nucleus. Some are in areas close to the nucleus, and some are in areas farther away.

Electrons and Energy Different electrons in an atom have different amounts of energy. An electron moves around the nucleus at a distance that corresponds to its amount of energy. Areas of space in which electrons move around the nucleus are called energy levels. Electrons closest to the nucleus have the least amount of energy. They are in the lowest energy level. Electrons farthest from the nucleus have the greatest amount of energy. They are in the highest energy level. The energy levels of an atom are shown in Figure 3. Notice that only two electrons can be in the lowest energy level. The second energy level can hold up to eight.

 Key Concept Check How is an electron's energy related to its position in an atom?

Electrons and Bonding Imagine two magnets. The closer they are to each other, the stronger the attraction of their opposite ends. Negatively charged electrons have a similar attraction to the positively charged nucleus of an atom. The electrons in energy levels closest to the nucleus of the same atom have a strong attraction to that nucleus. However, electrons farther from that nucleus are weakly attracted to it. These outermost electrons can easily be attracted to the nucleus of other atoms. This attraction between the positive nucleus of one atom and the negative electrons of another is what causes a chemical bond.

FOLDABLES®
Make two quarter-sheet note cards from a sheet of paper. Use them to organize your notes on valence electrons and electron dot diagrams.

Valence Electrons

Electron Dot Diagrams

Figure 3 Electrons are in certain energy levels within an atom.

Personal Tutor

Electron Energy Levels

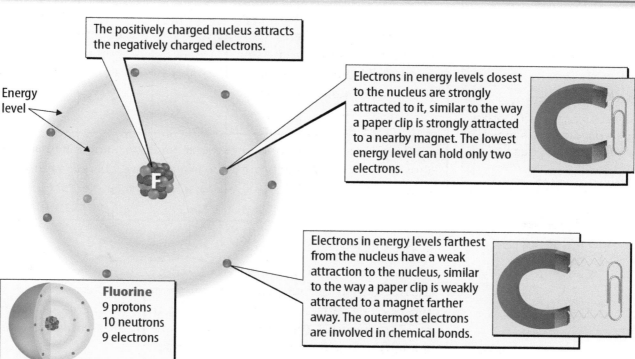

The positively charged nucleus attracts the negatively charged electrons.

Energy level

Electrons in energy levels closest to the nucleus are strongly attracted to it, similar to the way a paper clip is strongly attracted to a nearby magnet. The lowest energy level can hold only two electrons.

Electrons in energy levels farthest from the nucleus have a weak attraction to the nucleus, similar to the way a paper clip is weakly attracted to a magnet farther away. The outermost electrons are involved in chemical bonds.

Fluorine
9 protons
10 neutrons
9 electrons

Valence Electrons

You have read that electrons farthest from their nucleus are easily attracted to the nuclei of nearby atoms. These outermost electrons are the only electrons involved in chemical bonding. Even atoms that have only a few electrons, such as hydrogen or lithium, can form chemical bonds. This is because these electrons are still the outermost electrons and are exposed to the nuclei of other atoms. A **valence electron** *is an outermost electron of an atom that participates in chemical bonding.* Valence electrons have the most energy of all electrons in an atom.

The number of valence electrons in each atom of an element can help determine the type and the number of bonds it can form. How do you know how many valence electrons an atom has? The periodic table can tell you. Except for helium, elements in certain groups have the same number of valence electrons. Figure 4 illustrates how to use the periodic table to determine the number of valence electrons in the atoms of groups 1, 2, and 13–18. Determining the number of valence electrons for elements in groups 3–12 is more complicated. You will learn about these groups in later chemistry courses.

WORD ORIGIN

valence
from Latin *valentia*, means "strength, capacity"

Figure 4 You can use the group numbers at the top of the columns to determine the number of valence electrons in atoms of groups 1, 2, and 13–18.

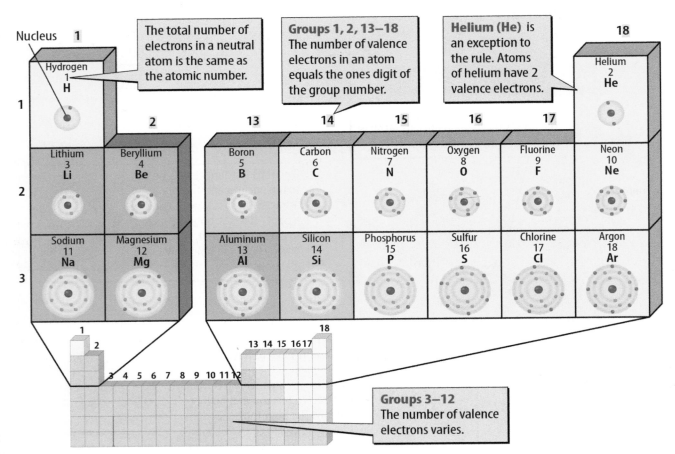

Visual Check How many valence electrons does an atom of phosphorous (P) have?

Figure 5 Electron dot diagrams show the number of valence electrons in an atom.

Steps for writing a dot diagram	Beryllium	Carbon	Nitrogen	Argon
1 Identify the element's group number on the periodic table.	2	14	15	18
2 Identify the number of valence electrons. • This equals the ones digit of the group number.	2	4	5	8
3 Draw the electron dot diagram. • Place one dot at a time on each side of the symbol (top, right, bottom, left). Repeat until all dots are used.	Be·	·Ċ·	·N̈·	:Ar̈:
4 Determine if the atom is chemically stable. • An atom is chemically stable if all dots on the electron dot diagram are paired.	Chemically Unstable	Chemically Unstable	Chemically Unstable	Chemically Stable
5 Determine how many bonds this atom can form. • Count the dots that are unpaired.	2	4	3	0

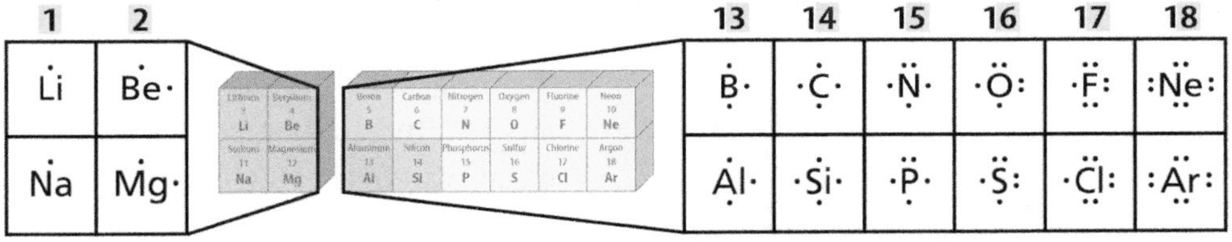

1	2			13	14	15	16	17	18
Li	Be·			Ḃ·	·Ċ·	·N̈·	·Ö:	·F̈:	:N̈e:
Na	Mg·			Äl·	·S̈i·	·P̈·	·S̈:	·C̈l:	:Är:

Electron Dot Diagrams

In 1916 an American Chemist named Gilbert Lewis developed a method to show an element's valence electrons. He developed the **electron dot diagram,** *a model that represents valence electrons in an atom as dots around the element's chemical symbol.*

Electron dot diagrams can help you predict how an atom will bond with other atoms. Dots, representing valence electrons, are placed one-by-one on each side of an element's chemical symbol until all the dots are used. Some dots will be paired up, others will not. The number of unpaired dots is often the number of bonds an atom can form. The steps for writing dot diagrams are shown in **Figure 5**.

Reading Check Why are electron dot diagrams useful?

Recall that each element in a group has the same number of valence electrons. As a result, every element in a group has the same number of dots in its electron dot diagram.

Notice in **Figure 5** that an argon atom, Ar, has eight valence electrons, or four pairs of dots, in the diagram. There are no unpaired dots. Atoms with eight valence electrons do not easily react with other atoms. They are chemically stable. Atoms that have between one and seven valence electrons are reactive, or chemically unstable. These atoms easily bond with other atoms and form chemically stable compounds.

Atoms of hydrogen and helium have only one energy level. These atoms are chemically stable with two valence electrons.

MiniLab

20 minutes

How does an electron's energy relate to its position in an atom?

Electrons in energy levels closest to the nucleus are strongly attracted to it. You can use paper clips and a magnet to model a similar attraction.

1. Read and complete a lab safety form.

2. Pick up a **paper clip** with a **magnet.** Use the first paper clip to pick up another one.

3. Continue picking up paper clips in this way until you have a chain of paper clips and no more will attach.

4. Gently pull off the paper clips one by one.

Analyze and Conclude

1. **Observe** Which paper clip was the easiest to remove? Which was the most difficult?

2. **Use Models** In what way do the magnet and the paper clips act as a model for an atom?

3. **Key Concept** How does an electron's position in an atom affect its ability to take part in chemical bonding?

Noble Gases

The elements in Group 18 are called noble gases. With the exception of helium, noble gases have eight valence electrons and are chemically stable. Chemically stable atoms do not easily react, or form bonds, with other atoms. The electron structures of two noble gases—neon and helium—are shown in **Figure 6.** Notice that all dots are paired in the dot diagrams of these atoms.

Stable and Unstable Atoms

Atoms with unpaired dots in their electron dot diagrams are reactive, or chemically unstable. For example, nitrogen, shown in **Figure 6,** has three unpaired dots in its electron dot diagram, and it is reactive. Nitrogen, like many other atoms, becomes more stable by forming chemical bonds with other atoms.

When an atom forms a bond, it gains, loses, or shares valence electrons with other atoms. By forming bonds, atoms become more chemically stable. Recall that atoms are most stable with eight valence electrons. Therefore, atoms with less than eight valence electrons form chemical bonds and become stable. In Lessons 2 and 3, you will read which atoms gain, lose, or share electrons when forming stable compounds.

Key Concept Check Why do atoms gain, lose, or share electrons?

Figure 6 Atoms gain, lose, or share valence electrons and become chemically stable.

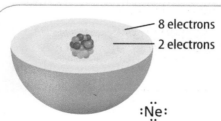

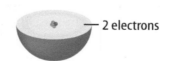

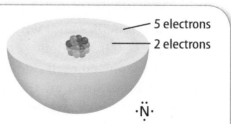

Neon has 10 electrons: 2 inner electrons and 8 valence electrons. A neon atom is chemically stable because it has 8 valence electrons. All dots in the dot diagram are paired.

Helium has 2 electrons. Because an atom's lowest energy level can hold only 2 electrons, the 2 dots in the dot diagram are paired. Helium is chemically stable.

Nitrogen has 7 electrons: 2 inner electrons and 5 valence electrons. Its dot diagram has 1 pair of dots and 3 unpaired dots. Nitrogen atoms become more stable by forming chemical bonds.

Hutchings Photography/Digital Light Source

Lesson 1 Review

Visual Summary

Electrons are less strongly attracted to a nucleus the farther they are from it, similar to the way a magnet attracts a paper clip.

Electrons in atoms are in energy levels around the nucleus. Valence electrons are the outermost electrons.

All noble gases, except He, have four pairs of dots in their electron dot diagrams. Noble gases are chemically stable.

FOLDABLES

Use your lesson Foldable to review the lesson. Save your Foldable for the project at the end of the chapter.

What do you think NOW?

You first read the statements below at the beginning of the chapter.

1. Elements rarely exist in pure form. Instead, combinations of elements make up most of the matter around you.

2. Chemical bonds that form between atoms involve electrons.

Did you change your mind about whether you agree or disagree with the statements? Rewrite any false statements to make them true.

Use Vocabulary

1 **Use the term** *chemical bond* in a complete sentence.

2 **Define** *electron dot diagram* in your own words.

3 The electrons of an atom that participate in chemical bonding are called _____.

Understand Key Concepts

4 **Identify** the number of valence electrons in each atom: calcium, carbon, and sulfur.

5 Which part of the atom is shared, gained, or lost when forming a chemical bond?
  A. electron   **C.** nucleus
  B. neutron   **D.** proton

6 **Draw** electron dot diagrams for oxygen, potassium, iodine, nitrogen, and beryllium.

Interpret Graphics

7 **Determine** the number of valence electrons in each diagram shown below.

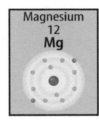
Magnesium
12
Mg

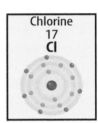
Chlorine
17
Cl

8 **Organize Information** Copy and fill in the graphic organizer below to describe one or more details for each concept: electron energy, valence electrons, stable atoms.

Concept	Description

Critical Thinking

9 **Compare** krypton and bromine in terms of chemical stability.

10 **Decide** An atom of nitrogen has five valence electrons. How could a nitrogen atom become more chemically stable?

New Green Airships

The Difference of One Valence Electron

Faster than ocean liners and safer than airplanes, airships used to be the best way to travel. The largest, the *Hindenburg*, was nearly the size of the *Titanic*. To this day, no larger aircraft has ever flown. So, what happened to the giant airship? The answer lies in a valence electron.

The builders of the *Hindenburg* filled it with a lighter-than-air gas, hydrogen, so that it would float. Their plan was to use helium, a noble gas. However, helium was scarce. They knew hydrogen was explosive, but it was easier to get. For nine years, hydrogen airships floated safely back and forth across the Atlantic. But in 1937, disaster struck. Just before it landed, the *Hindenburg* exploded in flames. The age of the airship was over.

Since the *Hindenburg,* airplanes have become the main type of air transportation. A big airplane uses hundreds of gallons of fuel to take off and fly. As a result, it releases large amounts of pollutants into the atmosphere. Some people are looking for other types of air transportation that will be less harmful to the environment. Airships may be the answer. An airship floats and needs very little fuel to take off and stay airborne. Airships also produce far less pollution than other aircraft.

Today, however, airships use helium not hydrogen. With two valence electrons instead of one, as hydrogen has, helium is unreactive. Thanks to helium's chemical stability, someday you might be a passenger on a new, luxurious, but not explosive, version of the *Hindenburg*.

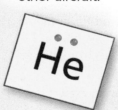

▲ **A new generation of big airships might soon be hauling freight and carrying passengers.**

It's Your Turn

RESEARCH Precious documents deteriorate with age as their surfaces react with air. Parchment turns brown and crumbles. Find out how our founding documents have been saved from this fate by noble gases.

Reading Guide

Key Concepts 🔑

ESSENTIAL QUESTIONS

- How do elements differ from the compounds they form?

- What are some common properties of a covalent compound?

- Why is water a polar compound?

Vocabulary

covalent bond p. 129

molecule p. 130

polar molecule p. 131

chemical formula p. 132

 Multilingual eGlossary

 8.PS.2, SEPS.2

Compounds, Chemical Formulas, and Covalent Bonds

Inquiry How do they combine?

A jigsaw puzzle has pieces that connect in a certain way. The pieces fit together by sharing tabs with other pieces. All of the pieces combine and form a complete puzzle. Like pieces of a puzzle, atoms can join together and form a compound by sharing electrons.

Gazimal/Getty Images

How is a compound different from its elements?

The sugar you use to sweeten foods at home is probably sucrose. Sucrose contains the elements carbon, hydrogen, and oxygen. How does table sugar differ from the elements that it contains?

1 Read and complete a lab safety form.

2 Air is a mixture of several gases, including oxygen and hydrogen. Charcoal is a form of carbon. Write some properties of oxygen, hydrogen, and carbon in your Science Journal.

3 Obtain from your teacher a piece of **charcoal** and a **beaker** with **table sugar** in it.

4 Observe the charcoal. In your Science Journal, describe the way it looks and feels.

5 Observe the table sugar in the beaker. What does it look and feel like? Record your observations.

Think About This

1. Compare and contrast the properties of charcoal, hydrogen, and oxygen.

2. 🔑 **Key Concept** How do you think the physical properties of carbon, hydrogen, and oxygen change when they combined to form sugar?

From Elements to Compounds

Have you ever baked cupcakes? First, combine flour, baking soda, and a pinch of salt. Then, add sugar, eggs, vanilla, milk, and butter. Each ingredient has unique physical and chemical properties. When you mix the ingredients together and bake them, a new product results—cupcakes. The cupcakes have properties that are different from the ingredients.

In some ways, compounds are like cupcakes. Recall that a compound is a substance made up of two or more different elements. Just as cupcakes are different from their ingredients, compounds are different from their elements. An element is made of one type of atom, but compounds are chemical combinations of different types of atoms. Compounds and the elements that make them up often have different properties.

Chemical **bonds** join atoms together. Recall that a chemical bond is a force that holds atoms together in a compound. In this lesson, you will learn that one way that atoms can form bonds is by sharing valence electrons. You will also learn how to write and read a chemical formula.

🔑 **Key Concept Check** How is a compound different from the elements that compose it?

SCIENCE USE V. COMMON USE ⋯

bond

Science Use a force that holds atoms together in a compound

Common Use a close personal relationship between two people

Hutchings Photography/Digital Light Source

Figure 7 A covalent bond forms when two nonmetal atoms share electrons.

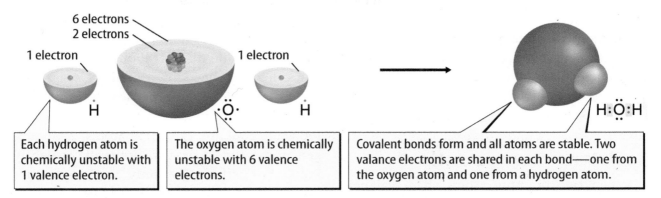

6 electrons
2 electrons
1 electron
1 electron

H   ·Ö·   H

Each hydrogen atom is chemically unstable with 1 valence electron.

The oxygen atom is chemically unstable with 6 valence electrons.

H:Ö:H

Covalent bonds form and all atoms are stable. Two valance electrons are shared in each bond—one from the oxygen atom and one from a hydrogen atom.

Covalent Bonds—Electron Sharing

As you read in Lesson 1, one way that atoms can become more chemically stable is by sharing valence electrons. When unstable, nonmetal atoms bond together, they bond by sharing valence electrons. *A **covalent bond** is a chemical bond formed when two atoms share one or more pairs of valence electrons.* The atoms then form a stable covalent compound.

A Noble Gas Electron Arrangement

Look at the reaction between hydrogen and oxygen in Figure 7. Before the reaction, each hydrogen atom has one valence electron. The oxygen atom has six valence electrons. Recall that most atoms are chemically stable with eight valence electrons—the same electron arrangement as a noble gas. An atom with less than eight valence electrons becomes stable by forming chemical bonds until it has eight valence electrons. Therefore, an oxygen atom forms two bonds to become stable. A hydrogen atom is stable with two valence electrons. It forms one bond to become stable.

Shared Electrons

If the oxygen atom and each hydrogen atom share their unpaired valence electrons, they can form two covalent bonds and become a stable covalent compound. Each covalent bond contains two valence electrons—one from the hydrogen atom and one from the oxygen atom. Since these electrons are shared, they count as valence electrons for both atoms in the bond. Each hydrogen atom now has two valence electrons. The oxygen atom now has eight valence electrons, since it bonds to two hydrogen atoms. All three atoms have the electron arrangement of a noble gas and the compound is stable.

FOLDABLES®

Make three quarter-sheet note cards from a sheet of paper to organize information about single, double, and triple covalent bonds.

Triple Covalent Bonds
Double Covalent Bonds
Single Covalent Bonds

Double and Triple Covalent Bonds

As shown in **Figure 8**, a single covalent bond exists when two atoms share one pair of valence electrons. A double covalent bond exists when two atoms share two pairs of valence electrons. Double bonds are stronger than single bonds. A triple covalent bond exists when two atoms share three pairs of valence electrons. Triple bonds are stronger than double bonds. Multiple bonds are explained in **Figure 8**.

Covalent Compounds

When two or more atoms share valence electrons, they form a stable covalent compound. The covalent compounds carbon dioxide, water, and sugar are very different, but they also share similar properties. Covalent compounds usually have low melting points and low boiling points. They are usually gases or liquids at room temperature, but they can also be solids. Covalent compounds are poor conductors of thermal energy and electricity.

Molecules

The chemically stable unit of a covalent compound is a molecule. *A* **molecule** *is a group of atoms held together by covalent bonding that acts as an independent unit.* Table sugar ($C_{12}H_{22}O_{11}$) is a covalent compound. One grain of sugar is made up of trillions of sugar molecules. Imagine breaking a grain of sugar into the tiniest microscopic particle possible. You would have a molecule of sugar. One sugar molecule contains 12 carbon atoms, 22 hydrogen atoms, and 11 oxygen atoms all covalently bonded together. The only way to further break down the molecule would be to chemically separate the carbon, hydrogen, and oxygen atoms. These atoms alone have very different properties from the compound sugar.

Key Concept Check What are some common properties of covalent compounds?

Multiple Bonds

Figure 8 The more valence electrons that two atoms share, the stronger the covalent bond is between the atoms.

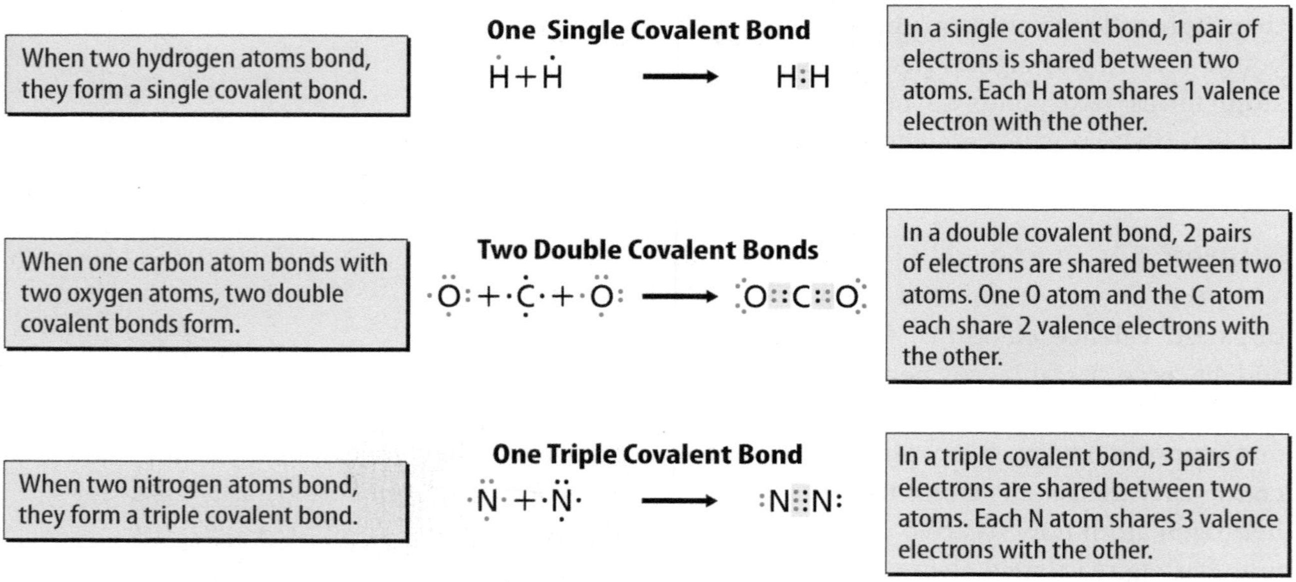

	One Single Covalent Bond	
When two hydrogen atoms bond, they form a single covalent bond.	Ḣ + Ḣ ⟶ H∶H	In a single covalent bond, 1 pair of electrons is shared between two atoms. Each H atom shares 1 valence electron with the other.

	Two Double Covalent Bonds	
When one carbon atom bonds with two oxygen atoms, two double covalent bonds form.	·Ö∶ + ·Ċ· + ·Ö· ⟶ ∶Ö∶∶C∶∶Ö∶	In a double covalent bond, 2 pairs of electrons are shared between two atoms. One O atom and the C atom each share 2 valence electrons with the other.

	One Triple Covalent Bond	
When two nitrogen atoms bond, they form a triple covalent bond.	·N̈· + ·N̈· ⟶ ∶N∶∶∶N∶	In a triple covalent bond, 3 pairs of electrons are shared between two atoms. Each N atom shares 3 valence electrons with the other.

Visual Check Is the bond stronger between atoms in hydrogen gas (H_2) or nitrogen gas (N_2)? Why?

Water and Other Polar Molecules

In a covalent bond, one atom can attract the shared electrons more strongly than the other atom can. Think about the valence electrons shared between oxygen and hydrogen atoms in a water molecule. The oxygen atom attracts the shared electrons more strongly than each hydrogen atom does. As a result, the shared electrons are pulled closer to the oxygen atom, as shown in **Figure 9**. Since electrons have a negative charge, the oxygen atom has a partial negative charge. The hydrogen atoms have a partial positive charge. *A molecule that has a partial positive end and a partial negative end because of unequal sharing of electrons is a* **polar molecule.**

The charges on a polar molecule affect its properties. Sugar, for example, dissolves easily in water because both sugar and water are polar. The negative end of a water molecule pulls on the positive end of a sugar molecule. Also, the positive end of a water molecule pulls on the negative end of a sugar molecule. This causes the sugar molecules to separate from one another and mix with the water molecules.

 Key Concept Check Why is water a polar compound?

Nonpolar Molecules

A hydrogen molecule, H_2, is a nonpolar molecule. Because the two hydrogen atoms are identical, their attraction for the shared electrons is equal. The carbon dioxide molecule, CO_2, in **Figure 9** is also nonpolar. A nonpolar compound will not easily dissolve in a polar compound, but it will dissolve in other nonpolar compounds. Oil is an example of a nonpolar compound. It will not dissolve in water. Have you ever heard someone say "like dissolves like"? This means that polar compounds can dissolve in other polar compounds. Similarly, nonpolar compounds can dissolve in other nonpolar compounds.

WORD ORIGIN

polar
from Latin *polus*, means "pole"

Figure 9 Atoms of a polar molecule share their valence electrons unequally. Atoms of a nonpolar molecule share their valence electrons equally.

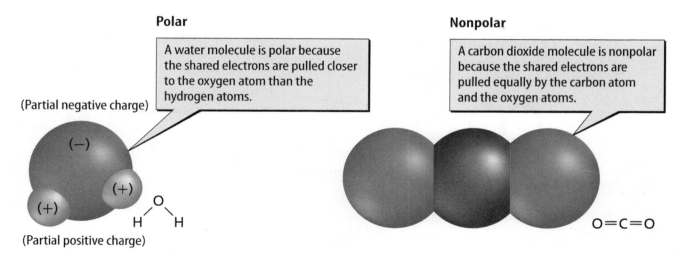

Polar

A water molecule is polar because the shared electrons are pulled closer to the oxygen atom than the hydrogen atoms.

(Partial negative charge)

(−)

(+)

(+)

O

H   H

(Partial positive charge)

Nonpolar

A carbon dioxide molecule is nonpolar because the shared electrons are pulled equally by the carbon atom and the oxygen atoms.

O=C=O

How do compounds form?

Use building blocks to model ways in which elements combine to form compounds.

1. Examine various types of **interlocking plastic blocks.** Notice that the blocks have different numbers of holes and pegs. Attaching one peg to one hole represents a shared pair of electrons.

2. Draw the electron dot diagrams for carbon, nitrogen, oxygen, and hydrogen in your Science Journal. Based on the diagrams, decide which block should represent an atom of each element.

3. Use the blocks to make models of H_2, CO_2, NH_3, H_2O, and CH_4. All pegs on the largest block must fit into a hole, and no blocks can stick out over the edge of a block, either above or below it.

Analyze and Conclude

1. **Explain** how you decided which type of block should be assigned to each type of atom.

2. 🔑 **Key Concept** Name at least one way that your models show the difference between a compound and the elements that combine and form the compound.

Chemical Formulas and Molecular Models

How do you know which elements make up a compound? *A **chemical formula** is a group of chemical symbols and numbers that represent the elements and the number of atoms of each element that make up a compound.* Just as a recipe lists ingredients, a chemical formula lists the elements in a compound. For example, the chemical formula for carbon dioxide shown in **Figure 10** is CO_2. The formula uses chemical symbols that show which elements are in the compound. Notice that CO_2 is made up of carbon (C) and oxygen (O). A subscript, or small number after a chemical symbol, shows the number of atoms of each element in the compound. Carbon dioxide (CO_2) contains two atoms of oxygen bonded to one atom of carbon.

A chemical formula describes the types of atoms in a compound or a molecule, but it does not explain the shape or appearance of the molecule. There are many ways to model a molecule. Each one can show the molecule in a different way. Common types of models for CO_2 are shown in **Figure 10.**

✓ **Reading Check** What information is given in a chemical formula?

Figure 10 Chemical formulas and molecular models provide information about molecules.

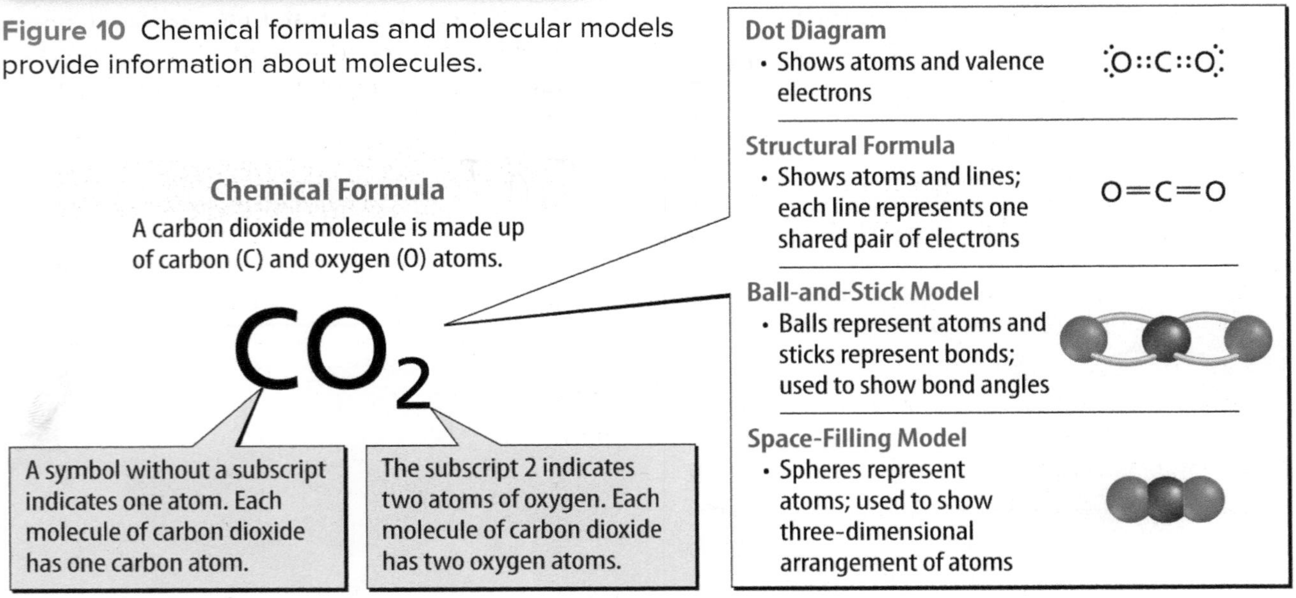

Chemical Formula

A carbon dioxide molecule is made up of carbon (C) and oxygen (O) atoms.

CO₂

A symbol without a subscript indicates one atom. Each molecule of carbon dioxide has one carbon atom.

The subscript 2 indicates two atoms of oxygen. Each molecule of carbon dioxide has two oxygen atoms.

Dot Diagram
- Shows atoms and valence electrons

Structural Formula
- Shows atoms and lines; each line represents one shared pair of electrons

O=C=O

Ball-and-Stick Model
- Balls represent atoms and sticks represent bonds; used to show bond angles

Space-Filling Model
- Spheres represent atoms; used to show three-dimensional arrangement of atoms

Lesson 2 Review

✓ Online Quiz

Visual Summary

A chemical formula is one way to show the elements that make up a compound.

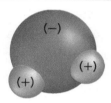

A covalent bond forms when atoms share valence electrons. The smallest particle of a covalent compound is a molecule.

Water is a polar molecule because the oxygen and hydrogen atoms unequally share electrons.

FOLDABLES

Use your lesson Foldable to review the lesson. Save your Foldable for the project at the end of the chapter.

What do you think NOW?

You first read the statements below at the beginning of the chapter.

3. The atoms in a water molecule are more chemically stable than they would be as individual atoms.

4. Many substances dissolve easily in water because opposite ends of a water molecule have opposite charges.

Did you change your mind about whether you agree or disagree with the statements? Rewrite any false statements to make them true.

Use Vocabulary

1 **Define** *covalent bond* in your own words.

2 The group of symbols and numbers that shows the types and numbers of atoms that make up a compound is a _____.

3 **Use the term** *molecule* in a complete sentence.

Understand Key Concepts

4 **Contrast** Name at least one way water (H_2O) is different from the elements that make up water.

5 **Explain** why water is a polar molecule.

6 A sulfur dioxide molecule has one sulfur atom and two oxygen atoms. Which is its correct chemical formula?

  A. SO_2 **C.** S_2O_2
  B. $(SO)_2$ **D.** S_2O

Interpret Graphics

7 **Examine** the electron dot diagram for chlorine below.

In chlorine gas, two chlorine atoms join to form a Cl_2 molecule. How many pairs of valence electrons do the atoms share?

8 **Compare and Contrast** Copy and fill in the graphic organizer below to identify at least one way polar and nonpolar molecules are similar and one way they are different.

Polar and Nonpolar Molecules	
Similarities	
Differences	

Critical Thinking

9 **Develop** an analogy to explain the unequal sharing of valence electrons in a water molecule.

How can you model Substances?

Chemists use models to explain how electrons are arranged in an atom. Electron dot diagrams are models used to show how many valence electrons an atom has. Electron dot diagrams are useful because they can help predict the number and type of bond an atom will form.

Materials

colored
pencils

Learn It

In science, **models** are used to help you visualize objects that are too small, too large, or too complex to understand. A model is a representation of an object, idea, or event.

Try It

1 Use the periodic table to write the electron dot diagrams for hydrogen, oxygen, carbon, and silicon.

2 Using your electron dot diagrams from step 1, write electron dot diagrams for the following substances: H_2O, CO, CO_2, SiO_2, C_2H_2, and CH_4. Use colored pencils to differentiate the electrons for each atom. Remember that all the above atoms, except hydrogen and helium, are chemically stable when they have eight valence electrons. Hydrogen and helium are chemically stable with two valence electrons.

Apply It

3 Based on your model, describe silicon's electron dot diagram and arrangement of valence electrons before and after it forms the compound SiO_2.

4 Distinguish among atoms, elements, molecules, and compounds in your models.

5 🔑 **Key Concept** Which of the covalent compounds you modeled contain double bonds? Which contain triple bonds?

1	2
Hydrogen 1 **H**	
Lithium 3 **Li**	Beryllium 4 **Be**
Sodium 11 **Na**	Magnesium 12 **Mg**
Potassium 19 **K**	Calcium 20 **Ca**
Rubidium 37 **Rb**	Strontium 38 **Sr**
Cesium 55 **Cs**	Barium 56 **Ba**
Francium 87 **Fr**	Radium 88 **Ra**

13	14	15	16	17	18
					Helium 2 **He**
Boron 5 **B**	Carbon 6 **C**	Nitrogen 7 **N**	Oxygen 8 **O**	Fluorine 9 **F**	Neon 10 **Ne**
Aluminum 13 **Al**	Silicon 14 **Si**	Phosphorus 15 **P**	Sulfur 16 **S**	Chlorine 17 **Cl**	Argon 18 **Ar**
Gallium 31 **Ga**	Germanium 32 **Ge**	Arsenic 33 **As**	Selenium 34 **Se**	Bromine 35 **Br**	Krypton 36 **Kr**
Indium 49 **In**	Tin 50 **Sn**	Antimony 51 **Sb**	Tellurium 52 **Te**	Iodine 53 **I**	Xenon 54 **Xe**
Thallium 81 **Tl**	Lead 82 **Pb**	Bismuth 83 **Bi**	Polonium 84 **Po**	Astatine 85 **At**	Radon 86 **Rn**

Lesson 3

Reading Guide

Key Concepts 🔑
ESSENTIAL QUESTIONS

- What is an ionic compound?
- How do metallic bonds differ from covalent and ionic bonds?

Vocabulary

ion p. 136

ionic bond p. 138

metallic bond p. 139

 Multilingual eGlossary

 SEPS.2, SEPS.6, SEPS.8, 6-8.LST.7.1

Ionic and Metallic Bonds

Inquiry What is this?

This scene might look like snow along a shoreline, but it is actually thick deposits of salt on a lake. Over time, tiny amounts of salt dissolved in river water that flowed into this lake and built up as water evaporated. Salt is a compound that forms when elements form bonds by gaining or losing valence electrons, not sharing them.

alexmak72427/Getty Images

How can atoms form compounds by gaining and losing electrons?

Metals often lose electrons when forming stable compounds. Nonmetals often gain electrons.

1 Read and complete a lab safety form.

2 Make two model atoms of sodium, and one model atom each of calcium, chlorine, and sulfur. To do this, write each element's chemical symbol with a **marker** on a **paper plate.** Surround the symbol with small balls of **clay** to represent valence electrons. Use one color of clay for the metals (groups 1 and 2 elements) and another color of clay for nonmetals (groups 16 and 17 elements).

3 To model sodium sulfide (Na_2S), place the two sodium atoms next to the sulfur atom. To form a stable compound, move each sodium atom's valence electron to the sulfur atom.

4 Form as many other compound models as you can by removing valence electrons from the groups 1 and 2 plates and placing them on the groups 16 and 17 plates.

Think About This

1. What other compounds were you able to form?

2. 🔑 **Key Concept** How do you think your models are different from covalent compounds?

FOLDABLES®

Make two quarter-sheet note cards as shown. Use the cards to summarize information about ionic and metallic compounds.

WORD ORIGIN ·············

ion
from Greek *ienai*, means "to go"
··························

Understanding Ions

As you read in Lesson 2, the atoms of two or more nonmetals form compounds by sharing valence electrons. However, when a metal and a nonmetal bond, they do not share electrons. Instead, one or more valence electrons transfers from the metal atom to the nonmetal atom. After electrons transfer, the atoms bond and form a chemically stable compound. Transferring valence electrons results in atoms with the same number of valence electrons as a noble gas.

When an atom loses or gains a valence electron, it becomes an ion. *An **ion** is an atom that is no longer electrically neutral because it has lost or gained valence electrons.* Because electrons have a negative charge, losing or gaining an electron changes the overall charge of an atom. An atom that loses valence electrons becomes an ion with a positive charge. This is because the number of electrons is now less than the number of protons in the atom. An atom that gains valence electrons becomes an ion with a negative charge. This is because the number of electrons is now greater than the number of protons.

✓ **Reading Check** Why do atoms that a gain electrons become an ion with a negative charge?

Hutchings Photography/Digital Light Source

Losing Valence Electrons

Look at the periodic table on the inside back cover of this book. What information about sodium (Na) can you infer from the periodic table? Sodium is a metal. Its atomic number is 11. This means each sodium atom has 11 protons and 11 electrons. Sodium is in group 1 on the periodic table. Therefore, sodium atoms have one valence electron, and they are chemically unstable.

Metal atoms, such as sodium, become more stable when they lose valence electrons and form a chemical bond with a nonmetal. If a sodium atom loses its one valence electron, it would have a total of ten electrons. Which element on the periodic table has atoms with ten electrons? Neon (Ne) atoms have a total of ten electrons. Eight of these are valence electrons. When a sodium atom loses one valence electron, the electrons in the next lower energy level are now the new valence electrons. The sodium ion then has eight valence electrons, the same as the noble gas neon and is chemically stable.

Gaining Valence Electrons

In Lesson 2, you read that nonmetal atoms can share valence electrons with other non-metal atoms. Nonmetal atoms can also gain valence electrons from metal atoms. Either way, they achieve the electron arrangement of a noble gas. Find the nonmetal chlorine (Cl) on the periodic table. Its atomic number is 17. Atoms of chlorine have seven valence electrons. If a chlorine atom gains one valence electron, it will have eight valence electrons. It will also have the same electron arrangement as the noble gas argon (Ar).

When a sodium atom loses a valence electron, it becomes a positively charged ion. This is shown by a plus (+) sign. When a chlorine atom gains a valence electron, it becomes a negatively charged ion. This is shown by a negative (−) sign. **Figure 11** illustrates the process of a sodium atom losing an electron and a chlorine atom gaining an electron.

 Reading Check Are atoms of a group 16 element more likely to gain or lose valence electrons?

Losing and Gaining Electrons

 Animation

Figure 11 Sodium atoms have a tendency to lose a valence electron. Chlorine atoms have a tendency to gain a valence electron.

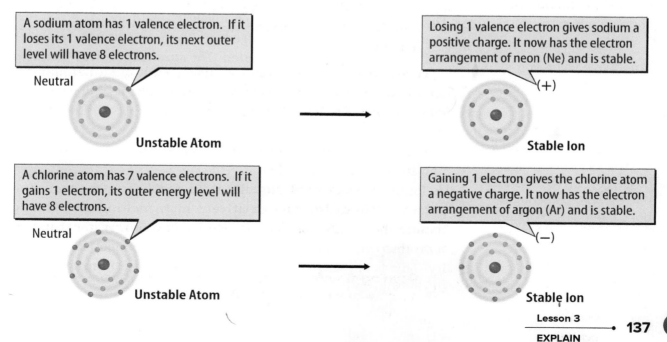

A sodium atom has 1 valence electron. If it loses its 1 valence electron, its next outer level will have 8 electrons.

Neutral

Unstable Atom

Losing 1 valence electron gives sodium a positive charge. It now has the electron arrangement of neon (Ne) and is stable.

(+)

Stable Ion

A chlorine atom has 7 valence electrons. If it gains 1 electron, its outer energy level will have 8 electrons.

Neutral

Unstable Atom

Gaining 1 electron gives the chlorine atom a negative charge. It now has the electron arrangement of argon (Ar) and is stable.

(−)

Stable Ion

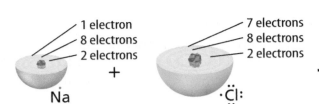

| 1 electron
8 electrons
2 electrons | 7 electrons
8 electrons
2 electrons | 8 electrons
2 electrons | 8 electrons
8 electrons
2 electrons |

Na   +   ·C̈l̈:   →   Na⁺   :C̈l̈:⁻

Sodium and chlorine atoms are stable when they have eight valence electrons. A sodium atoms loses one valence electron and becomes stable. A chlorine atom gains one valence electron and becomes stable.

The positively charged sodium ion and the negatively charged chlorine ion attract each other. Together they form a strong ionic bond.

Figure 12 An ionic bond forms between Na and Cl when an electron transfers from Na to Cl.

 Animation

Math Skills

Use Percentage

An atom's radius is measured in picometers (pm), 1 trillion times smaller than a meter. When an atom becomes an ion, its radius increases or decreases. For example, a Na atom has a radius of **186 pm**. A Na⁺ ion has a radius of **102 pm**. By what percentage does the radius change?

Subtract the atom's radius from the ion's radius.

102 pm − **186 pm** = −84 pm

Divide the difference by the atom's radius.

−84 pm ÷ **186 pm** = −0.45

Multiply the answer by 100 and add a % sign.

−0.45 × 100 = −45%

A negative value is a decrease in size. A positive value is an increase.

Practice

The radius of an oxygen (O) atom is 73 pm. The radius of an oxygen ion (O^{2-}) is 140 pm. By what percentage does the radius change?

 Math Practice

Personal Tutor

Determining an Ion's Charge

Atoms are electrically neutral because they have the same number of protons and electrons. Once an atom gains or loses electrons, it becomes a charged ion. For example, the atomic number for nitrogen (N) is 7. Each N atom has 7 protons and 7 electrons and is electrically neutral. However, an N atom often gains 3 electrons when forming an ion. The N ion then has 10 electrons. To determine the charge, subtract the number of electrons in the ion from the number of protons.

$$7 \text{ protons} - 10 \text{ electrons} = -3 \text{ charge}$$

A nitrogen ion has a −3 charge. This is written as N^{3-}.

Ionic Bonds—Electron Transferring

Recall that metal atoms typically lose valence electrons and nonmetal atoms typically gain valence electrons. When forming a chemical bond, the nonmetal atoms gain the electrons lost by the metal atoms. Take a look at **Figure 12**. In NaCl, or table salt, a sodium atom loses a valence electron. The electron is transferred to a chlorine atom. The sodium atom becomes a positively charged ion. The chlorine atom becomes a negatively charged ion. These ions attract each other and form a stable ionic compound. *The attraction between positively and negatively charged ions in an ionic compound is an* **ionic bond.**

Key Concept Check What holds ionic compounds together?

Ionic Compounds

Ionic compounds are usually solid and brittle at room temperature. They also have relatively high melting and boiling points. Many ionic compounds dissolve in water. Water that contains dissolved ionic compounds is a good conductor of electricity. This is because an electrical charge can pass from ion to ion in the solution.

Comparing Ionic and Covalent Compounds

Recall that in a covalent bond, two or more nonmetal atoms share electrons and form a unit, or molecule. Covalent compounds, such as water, are made up of many molecules. However, when nonmetal ions bond to metal ions in an ionic compound, there are no molecules. Instead, there is a large collection of oppositely charged ions. All of the ions attract each other and are held together by ionic bonds.

Metallic Bonds— Electron Pooling

Recall that metal atoms typically lose valence electrons when forming compounds. What happens when metal atoms bond to other metal atoms? Metal atoms form compounds with one another by combining, or pooling, their valence electrons. A **metallic bond** is *a bond formed when many metal atoms share their pooled valence electrons.*

The pooling of valence electrons in aluminum is shown in **Figure 13**. The aluminum atoms lose their valence electrons and become positive ions, indicated by the plus (+) signs. The negative (−) signs indicate the valence electrons, which move from ion to ion. Valence electrons in metals are not bonded to one atom. Instead, a "sea of electrons" surrounds the positive ions.

 Key Concept Check How do metal atoms bond with one another?

Figure 13 Valence electrons move among all the aluminum (Al) ions.

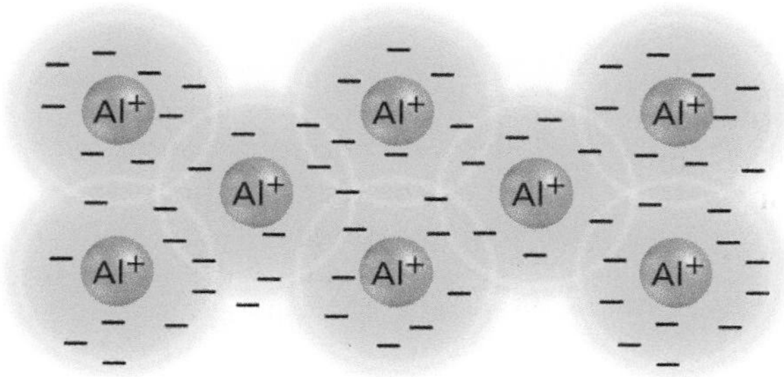

MiniLab   20 minutes

How many ionic compounds can you make?

You have read that in ionic bonding, metal atoms transfer electrons to nonmetal atoms.

1. Copy the table below into your Science Journal.

Group	Elements	Type	Dot Diagram
1	Li, Na, K	Metal	$\dot{X}$
2	Be, Mg, Ca	Metal	
14	C	Nonmetal	
15	N, P	Nonmetal	
16	O, S	Nonmetal	
17	F, Cl	Nonmetal	

2. Fill in the last column with the correct dot diagram for each group. Color the dots of the metal atoms with a **red marker** and the dots of the nonmetal atoms with a **blue marker.**

3. Using the information in your table, create five different ionic bonds. Write (a) the equation for the electron transfer and (b) the formula for each compound. For example:

a. $\dot{Na} + \dot{Na} + \cdot\ddot{O}: \longrightarrow Na^+ + Na^+ + :\ddot{O}:^{2-}$
b. Na_2O

Analyze and Conclude

1. **Explain** What happens to the metal and nonmetal ions after the electrons have been transferred?

2. **Key Concept** Describe the ionic bonds that hold the ions together in your compounds.

ACADEMIC VOCABULARY

conduct
(verb) to serve as a medium through which something can flow

 Interactive Table

Table 1 Bonds can form when atoms share valence electrons, transfer valence electrons, or pool valence electrons.

Properties of Metallic Compounds

Metals are good conductors of thermal energy and electricity. Because the valence electrons can move from ion to ion, they can easily **conduct** an electric charge. When a metal is hammered into a sheet or drawn into a wire, it does not break. The metal ions can slide past one another in the electron sea and move to new positions. Metals are shiny because the valence electrons at the surface of a metal interact with light. **Table 1** compares the covalent, ionic, and metallic bonds that you studied in this chapter.

Reading Check How does valence electron pooling explain why metals can be hammered into a sheet?

Table 1 Covalent, Ionic, and Metallic Bonds

Type of Bond	What is bonding?	Properties of Compounds
Covalent Water	nonmetal atoms; nonmetal atoms	• gas, liquid, or solid • low melting and boiling points • dissolves in water if covalent bonds are polar • do not dissolve in water if covalent bonds are nonpolar • poor conductors of thermal energy and electricity • dull appearance
Ionic Salt Na⁺ Cl⁻	nonmetal ions; metal ions	• solid crystals • high melting and boiling points • dissolves in water • solids are poor conductors of thermal energy and electricity • ionic compounds in water solutions conduct electricity
Metallic Aluminum	metal ions; metal ions	• usually solid at room temperature • high melting and boiling points • do not dissolve in water • good conductors of thermal energy and electricity • shiny surface • can be hammered into sheets and pulled into wires

Visual Summary

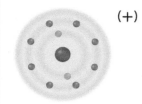 (+)

Metal atoms lose electrons and non-metal atoms gain electrons and form stable compounds. An atom that has gained or lost an electron is an ion.

(+) (−)

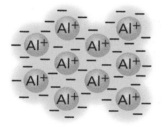

Na⁺ :C̈l:⁻

An ionic bond forms between positively and negatively charged ions.

A metallic bond forms when many metal atoms share their pooled valence electrons.

FOLDABLES®

Use your lesson Foldable to review the lesson. Save your Foldable for the project at the end of the chapter.

What do you think NOW?

You first read the statements below at the beginning of the chapter.

5. Losing electrons can make some atoms more chemically stable.

6. Metals are good electrical conductors because they tend to hold onto their valence electrons very tightly.

Did you change your mind about whether you agree or disagree with the statements? Rewrite any false statements to make them true.

Use Vocabulary

1. **Define** *ionic bond* in your own words.

2. An atom that changes so that it has an electrical charge is a(n) _____.

3. **Use the term** *metallic bond* in a sentence.

Understand Key Concepts

4. **Recall** What holds ionic compounds together?

5. Which element would most likely bond with lithium and form an ionic compound?
   - **A.** beryllium
   - **B.** calcium
   - **C.** fluorine
   - **D.** sodium

6. **Contrast** Why are metals good conductors of electricity while covalent compounds are poor conductors?

Interpret Graphics

7. **Organize** Copy and fill in the graphic organizer below. In each oval, list a common property of an ionic compound.

Ionic Compounds

Critical Thinking

8. **Design** a poster to illustrate how ionic compounds form.

9. **Evaluate** What type of bonding does a material most likely have if it has a high melting point, is solid at room temperature, and easily dissolves in water?

Math Skills    Math Practice

10. The radius of the aluminum (Al) atom is 143 pm. The radius of the aluminum ion (Al^{3+}) is 54 pm. By what percentage did the radius change as the ion formed?

Ions in Solution

You know that ions can combine and form stable ionic compounds. Ions can also separate in a compound and dissolve in solution. For example, pennies become dull over time because the copper ions on the surface of the pennies react with oxygen in the air and form copper(II) oxide. When you place dull pennies in a vinegar-salt solution, the copper ions separate from the oxygen ions. These ions dissolve in the solution.

Question

How do elements join together to make chemical compounds?

Procedure

1. Read and complete a lab safety form.

2. Pour 50 mL of white vinegar into a 250-mL beaker. Using a plastic spoon, add a spoonful of table salt to the vinegar. Stir the mixture with the spoon until the salt dissolves.

3. Add 20 dull pennies to the vinegar-salt solution. Leave the pennies in the solution for 10 minutes. Use a stopwatch or a clock with a second hand to measure the time.

4. After 10 minutes, use the plastic spoon to remove the pennies from the solution. Rinse the pennies in tap water. Place them on paper towels to dry. Record the change to the pennies in your Science Journal.

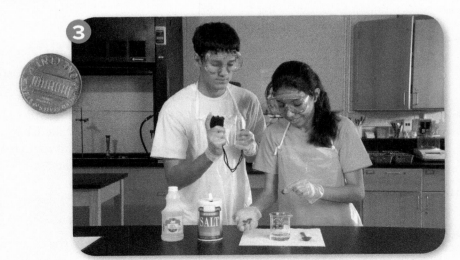

Form a Hypothesis

5 If you place an iron nail in the vinegar-salt solution, predict what changes will occur to the nail.

Test Your Hypothesis

6 Use sandpaper to clean two nails. Place one nail in the vinegar-salt solution, and place the other nail on a clean paper towel. You will compare the dry nail to the one in the solution and observe changes as they occur.

7 Every 5 minutes observe the nail in the solution and record your observations in your Science Journal. Remember to use the dry nail to help detect changes in the wet nail. Use a stopwatch or a clock with a second hand to measure the time. Keep the nail in the solution for 25 minutes.

8 After 25 minutes, use a plastic spoon to remove the nail from the solution. Dispose of all materials as directed by your teacher.

6

Lab Tips

☑ Be sure the pennies are separated when they are in the vinegar-salt solution. You may need to stir them with the plastic spoon.

☑ Use the plastic spoon to bring the nail out of the solution when checking for changes.

Analyze and Conclude

9 **Compare and Contrast** What changes occurred when you placed the dull pennies in the vinegar-salt solution?

10 **Recognize Cause and Effect** What changes occurred to the nail in the leftover solution? Infer why these changes occurred.

11 **The Big Idea** Give two examples of how elements chemically combine and form compounds in this lab.

Communicate Your Results

Create a chart suitable for display summarizing this lab and your results.

The Statue of Liberty is made of copper. Research why the statue is green.

Elements can join together by sharing, transferring, or pooling electrons to make chemical compounds.

Key Concepts Summary 🔑

	Vocabulary
Lesson 1: Electrons and Energy Levels • Electrons with more energy are farther from the atom's nucleus and are in a higher energy level. • Atoms with fewer than eight **valence electrons** gain, lose, or share valence electrons and form stable compounds. Atoms in stable compounds have the same electron arrangement as a noble gas. 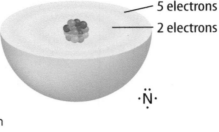	**chemical bond** p. 120 **valence electron** p. 122 **electron dot diagram** p. 123
Lesson 2: Compounds, Chemical Formulas, and Covalent Bonds • A compound and the elements it is made from have different chemical and physical properties. • A **covalent bond** forms when two nonmetal atoms share valence electrons. Common properties of covalent compounds include low melting points and low boiling points. They are usually gas or liquid at room temperature and poor conductors of electricity. • Water is a polar compound because the oxygen atom pulls more strongly on the shared valence electrons than the hydrogen atoms do.	**covalent bond** p. 129 **molecule** p. 130 **polar molecule** p. 131 **chemical formula** p. 132
Lesson 3: Ionic and Metallic Bonds • **Ionic bonds** form when valence electrons move from a metal atom to a nonmetal atom. • An ionic compound is held together by ionic bonds, which are attractions between positively and negatively charged **ions.** • A **metallic bond** forms when valence electrons are pooled among many metal atoms. 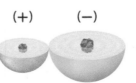	**ion** p. 136 **ionic bond** p. 138 **metallic bond** p. 139

FOLDABLES®

Chapter Project

Assemble your lesson Foldables as shown to make a Chapter Project. Use the project to review what you have learned in this chapter.

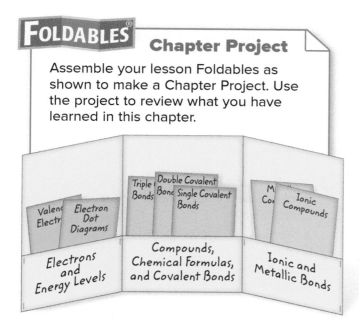

Valence Electrons

Electron Dot Diagrams

Triple Bonds

Double Covalent Bonds

Single Covalent Bonds

Ionic Compounds

Electrons and Energy Levels

Compounds, Chemical Formulas, and Covalent Bonds

Ionic and Metallic Bonds

Use Vocabulary

1. The force that holds atoms together is called a(n) _____.

2. You can predict the number of bonds an atom can form by drawing its _____.

3. The nitrogen and hydrogen atoms that make up ammonia (NH_3) are held together by a(n) _____ because the atoms are both nonmetals.

4. Two hydrogen atoms and one oxygen atom together are a _____ of water.

5. A positively charged sodium ion and a negatively charged chlorine ion are joined by a(n) _____ to form the compound sodium chloride.

Link Vocabulary and Key Concepts

 Interactive Concept Map

Copy this concept map, and then use vocabulary terms from the previous page and other terms from the chapter to complete the concept map.

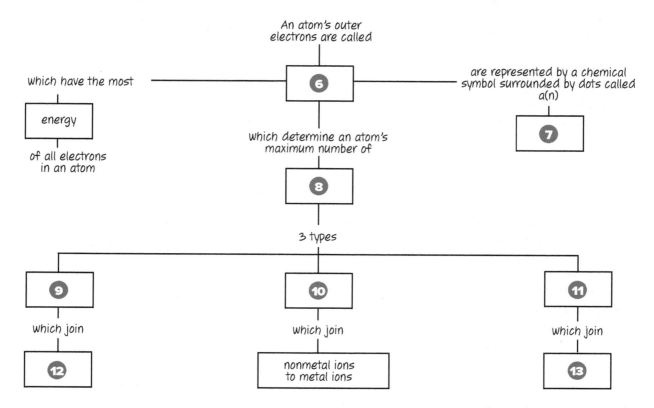

An atom's outer electrons are called

6

which have the most

energy

of all electrons in an atom

are represented by a chemical symbol surrounded by dots called a(n)

7

which determine an atom's maximum number of

8

3 types

9   10   11

which join   which join   which join

12   nonmetal ions to metal ions   13

Understand Key Concepts

1 Atoms lose, gain, or share electrons and become as chemically stable as
 A. an electron.
 B. an ion.
 C. a metal.
 D. a noble gas.

2 Which is the correct electron dot diagram for boron, one of the group 13 elements?

 A. $\overset{\bullet}{\underset{\bullet}{B}}\bullet$

 B. $\bullet\,\overset{\bullet\bullet}{\underset{\bullet\bullet}{B}}\,\bullet$

 C. $\overset{\bullet\bullet}{\underset{\bullet\bullet}{:\!B\!:}}$

 D. $\bullet\,\overset{\bullet\bullet}{\underset{\bullet}{B}}\,\bullet$

3 If an electron transfers from one atom to another atom, what type of bond will most likely form?
 A. covalent
 B. ionic
 C. metallic
 D. polar

4 What change would make an atom represented by this diagram have the same electron arrangement as a noble gas?

 A. gaining two electrons
 B. gaining four electrons
 C. losing two electrons
 D. losing four electrons

5 What would make bromine, a group 17 element, more similar to a noble gas?
 A. gaining one electron
 B. gaining two electrons
 C. losing one electron
 D. losing two electrons

6 Which would most likely be joined by an ionic bond?
 A. a positive metal ion and a positive nonmetal ion
 B. a positive metal ion and a negative nonmetal ion
 C. a negative metal ion and a positive nonmetal ion
 D. a negative metal ion and a negative nonmetal ion

7 Which group of elements on the periodic table forms covalent compounds with other nonmetals?
 A. group 1
 B. group 2
 C. group 17
 D. group 18

8 Which best describes an atom represented by this diagram?

 A. It is likely to bond by gaining six electrons.
 B. It is likely to bond by losing two electrons.
 C. It is not likely to bond because it is already stable.
 D. It is not likely to bond because it has too few electrons.

9 How many dots would a dot diagram for selenium, one of the group 16 elements, have?
 A. 6
 B. 8
 C. 10
 D. 16

Critical Thinking

10 **Classify** Use the periodic table to classify the elements potassium (K), bromine (Br), and argon (Ar) according to how likely their atoms are to do the following.

a. lose electrons to form positive ions
b. gain electrons to form negative ions
c. neither gain nor lose electrons

11 **Describe** the change that is shown in this illustration. How does this change affect the stability of the atom?

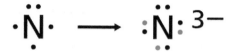

12 **Analyze** One of your classmates draws an electron dot diagram for a helium atom with two dots. He tells you that these dots mean each helium atom has two unpaired electrons and can gain, lose, or share electrons to have four pairs of valence electrons and become stable. What is wrong with your classmate's argument?

13 **Explain** why the hydrogen atoms in a hydrogen gas molecule (H_2) form nonpolar covalent bonds but the oxygen and hydrogen atoms in water molecules (H_2O) form polar covalent bonds.

14 **Contrast** Why is it possible for an oxygen atom to form a double covalent bond, but it is not possible for a chlorine atom to form a double covalent bond?

Writing in Science

15 **Compose** a poem at least ten lines long that explains ionic bonding, covalent bonding, and metallic bonding.

REVIEW THE BIG IDEA

16 Which types of atoms pool their valence electrons to form a "sea of electrons"?

17 Describe a way in which elements joining together to form chemical compounds is similar to the way the letters on a computer keyboard join together to form words.

Math Skills ×÷+−   Math Practice

Element	Atomic Radius	Ionic Radius
Potassium (K)	227 pm	133 pm
Iodine (I)	133 pm	216 pm

18 What is the percent change when an iodine atom (I) becomes an ion (I^-)?

19 What is the percent change when a potassium atom (K) becomes an ion (K^+)?

Standardized Test Practice

Record your answers on the answer sheet provided by your teacher or on a sheet of paper.

Multiple Choice

1 Which information does the chemical formula CO_2 NOT give you?

  A number of valence electrons in each atom

  B ratio of atoms in the compound

  C total number of atoms in one molecule of the compound

  D type of elements in the compound

Use the diagram below to answer question 2.

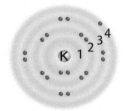

2 The diagram above shows a potassium atom. Which is the second-highest energy level?

  A 1

  B 2

  C 3

  D 4

3 What is shared in a metallic bond?

  A negatively charged ions

  B neutrons

  C pooled valence electrons

  D protons

4 Which is a characteristic of most nonpolar compounds?

  A conduct electricity poorly

  B dissolve easily in water

  C solid crystals

  D shiny surfaces

Use the diagram below to answer question 5.

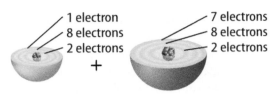

5 The atoms in the diagram above are forming a bond. Which represents that bond?

  A
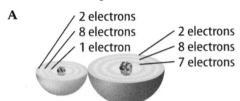

  B
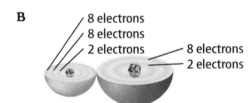

  C

  D
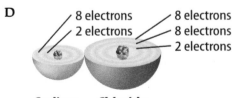

6 Covalent bonds typically form between the atoms of elements that share

  A nuclei.

  B oppositely charged ions.

  C protons.

  D valence electrons.

Use the diagram below to answer question 7.

Water Molecule

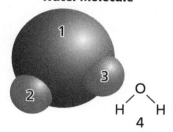

H — O — H
4

7 In the diagram above, which shows an atom with a partial negative charge?

 A 1

 B 2

 C 3

 D 4

8 Which compound is formed by the attraction between negatively and positively charged ions?

 A covalent

 B ionic

 C nonpolar

 D polar

9 The atoms of noble gases do NOT bond easily with other atoms because their valence electrons are

 A absent.

 B moving.

 C neutral.

 D stable.

Constructed Response

Use the table below to answer question 10.

Property	Rust	Iron	Oxygen
Color			Clear
Solid, liquid, or gas			
Strength		Strong	Does NOT apply
Usefulness			

10 Rust is a compound of iron and oxygen. Compare the properties of rust, iron, and oxygen by filling in the missing cells in the table above. What can you conclude about the properties of compounds and their elements?

Use the diagram below to answer questions 11 and 12.

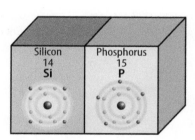

11 In the diagram, how are valence electrons illustrated? How many valence electrons does each element have?

12 Describe a stable electron configuration. For each element above, how many electrons are needed to make a stable electron configuration?

NEED EXTRA HELP?												
If You Missed Question...	1	2	3	4	5	6	7	8	9	10	11	12
Go to Lesson...	2	1	3	3	3	2	2	3	1	2	1	1

Chemical Reactions and Equations

THE BIG IDEA

What happens to atoms and energy during a chemical reaction?

inquiry How does it work?

An air bag deploys in less than the blink of an eye. How does the bag open so fast? At the moment of impact, a sensor triggers a chemical reaction between two chemicals. This reaction quickly produces a large amount of nitrogen gas. This gas inflates the bag with a pop.

- A chemical reaction can produce a gas. How is this different from a gas produced when a liquid boils?

- Where do you think the nitrogen gas that is in an air bag comes from? Do you think any of the chemicals in the air bag contain the element nitrogen?

- What do you think happens to atoms and energy during a chemical reaction?

Get Ready to Read

What do you think?

Before you read, decide if you agree or disagree with each of these statements. As you read this chapter, see if you change your mind about any of the statements.

1 If a substance bubbles, you know a chemical reaction is occurring.

2 During a chemical reaction, some atoms are destroyed and new atoms are made.

3 Reactions always start with two or more substances that react with each other.

4 Water can be broken down into simpler substances.

5 Reactions that release energy require energy to get started.

6 Energy can be created in a chemical reaction.

FO4305

Lesson 1

Understanding Chemical Reactions

Reading Guide

Key Concepts
ESSENTIAL QUESTIONS

* What are some signs that a chemical reaction might have occurred?

* What happens to atoms during a chemical reaction?

* What happens to the total mass in a chemical reaction?

Vocabulary

chemical reaction p. 153

chemical equation p. 156

reactant p. 157

product p. 157

law of conservation of mass p. 158

coefficient p. 160

 Multilingual eGlossary

 8.PS.6, 8.PS.7

 Go to the resource tab in ConnectED to find the PBL *All Things Being Equal.*

Inarwin Dale/Science Source

nquiry Does it run on batteries?

Flashes of light from fireflies dot summer evening skies in many parts of the United States. But, firefly light doesn't come from batteries. Fireflies make light using a process called bioluminescence (bi oh lew muh NE cents). In this process, chemicals in the firefly's body combine in a two-step process and make new chemicals and light.

Where did it come from? 👓 🧤

Does a boiled egg have more mass than a raw egg? What happens when liquids change to a solid?

1 Read and complete a lab safety form.

2 Use a **graduated cylinder** to add 25 mL of **solution A** to a **self-sealing plastic bag.** Place a **stoppered test tube** containing **solution B** into the bag. Be careful not to dislodge the stopper.

3 Seal the bag completely, and wipe off any moisture on the outside with a **paper towel.** Place the bag on the **balance.** Record the total mass in your Science Journal.

4 Without opening the bag, remove the stopper from the test tube and allow the liquids to mix. Observe and record what happens.

5 Place the sealed bag and its contents back on the balance. Read and record the mass.

Think About This

1. What did you observe when the liquids mixed? How would you account for this observation?

2. Did the mass of the bag's contents change? If so, could the change have been due to the precision of the balance, or did the matter in the bag change its mass? Explain.

3. 🔑 **Key Concept** Do you think matter was gained or lost in the bag? How can you tell?

Changes in Matter

When you put liquid water in a freezer, it changes to solid water, or ice. When you pour brownie batter into a pan and bake it, the liquid batter changes to a solid, too. In both cases, a liquid changes to a solid. Are these changes the same?

Physical Changes

Recall that matter can undergo two types of changes—chemical or physical. A physical change does not produce new substances. The substances that exist before and after the change are the same, although they might have different physical properties. This is what happens when liquid water freezes. Its physical properties change from a liquid to a solid, but the water, H_2O, does not change into a different substance. Water molecules are always made up of two hydrogen atoms bonded to one oxygen atom regardless of whether they are solid, liquid, or gas.

Chemical Changes

Recall that during a chemical change, one or more substances change into new substances. The starting substances and the substances produced have different physical and chemical properties. For example, when brownie batter bakes, a chemical change occurs. Many of the substances in the baked brownies are different from the substances in the batter. As a result, baked brownies have physical and chemical properties that are different from those of brownie batter.

A chemical change also is called a chemical reaction. These terms mean the same thing. *A* **chemical reaction** *is a process in which atoms of one or more substances rearrange to form one or more new substances.* In this lesson, you will read what happens to atoms during a reaction and how these changes can be described using equations.

✓ **Reading Check** What types of properties change during a chemical reaction?

Signs of a Chemical Reaction

How can you tell if a chemical reaction has taken place? You have read that the substances before and after a reaction have different properties. You might think that you could look for changes in properties as a sign that a reaction occurred. In fact, changes in the physical properties of color, state of matter, and odor are all signs that a chemical reaction might have occurred. Another sign of a chemical reaction is a change in energy. If substances get warmer or cooler or if they give off light or sound, it is likely that a reaction has occurred. Some signs that a chemical reaction might have occurred are shown in **Figure 1.**

However, these signs are not proof of a chemical change. For example, bubbles appear when water boils. But, bubbles also appear when baking soda and vinegar react and form carbon dioxide gas. How can you be sure that a chemical reaction has taken place? The only way to know is to study the chemical properties of the substances before and after the change. If they have different chemical properties, then the substances have undergone a chemical reaction.

 Key Concept Check What are some signs that a chemical reaction might have occurred?

Figure 1 You can detect a chemical reaction by looking for changes in properties and changes in energy of the substances that reacted.

Change in Properties	
Change in color Bright copper changes to green when the copper reacts with certain gases in the air. 	**Formation of bubbles** Bubbles of carbon dioxide form when baking soda is added to vinegar. 
Change in odor When food burns or rots, a change in odor is a sign of chemical change. 	**Formation of a precipitate** A precipitate is a solid formed when two liquids react. 

Change in Energy	
Warming or cooling Thermal energy is either given off or absorbed during a chemical change. 	**Release of light** A firefly squid gives off light as the result of a chemical change. 

What happens in a chemical reaction?

During a chemical reaction, one or more substances react and form one or more new substances. How are these new substances formed?

Atoms Rearrange and Form New Substances

To understand what happens in a reaction, first review substances. Recall that there are two types of substances—elements and compounds. Substances have a fixed arrangement of atoms. For example, in a single drop of water, there are trillions of oxygen and hydrogen atoms. However, all of these atoms are arranged in the same way—two atoms of hydrogen are bonded to one atom of oxygen. If this arrangement changes, the substance is no longer water. Instead, a different substance forms with different physical and chemical properties. This is what happens during a chemical reaction. Atoms of elements or compounds rearrange and form different elements or compounds.

Bonds Break and Bonds Form

How does the rearrangement of atoms happen? Atoms rearrange when chemical bonds between atoms break. Recall that constantly moving particles make up all substances, including solids. As particles move, they collide with one another. If the particles collide with enough energy, the bonds between atoms can break. The atoms separate, rearrange, and new bonds can form. The reaction that forms hydrogen and oxygen from water is shown in **Figure 2.** Adding electric energy to water molecules can cause this reaction. The added energy causes bonds between the hydrogen atoms and the oxygen atoms to break. After the bonds between the atoms in water molecules break, new bonds can form between pairs of hydrogen atoms and between pairs of oxygen atoms.

 Key Concept Check What happens to atoms during a chemical reaction?

Figure 2 Notice that no new atoms are created in a chemical reaction. The existing atoms rearrange and form new substances.

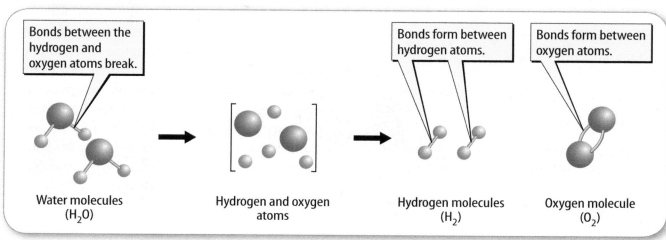

Bonds between the hydrogen and oxygen atoms break.

Bonds form between hydrogen atoms.

Bonds form between oxygen atoms.

Water molecules
(H_2O)

Hydrogen and oxygen atoms

Hydrogen molecules
(H_2)

Oxygen molecule
(O_2)

Table 1 Symbols and Formulas of Some Elements and Compounds

Substance		Formula	# of atoms
Carbon		C	C: 1
Copper		Cu	Cu: 1
Cobalt		Co	Co: 1
Oxygen		O_2	O: 2
Hydrogen		H_2	H: 2
Chlorine		Cl_2	Cl: 2
Carbon dioxide		CO_2	C: 1 O: 2
Carbon monoxide		CO	C: 1 O: 1
Water		H_2O	H: 2 O: 1
Hydrogen peroxide		H_2O_2	H: 2 O: 2
Glucose		$C_6H_{12}O_6$	C: 6 H: 12 O: 6
Sodium chloride		NaCl	Na: 1 Cl: 1
Magnesium hydroxide		$Mg(OH)_2$	Mg: 1 O: 2 H: 2

Table 1 Symbols and subscripts describe the type and number of atoms in an element or a compound.

Visual Check Describe the number of atoms in each element in the following: C, Co, CO, and CO_2.

Interactive Table

Chemical Equations

Suppose your teacher asks you to produce a specific reaction in your science laboratory. How might your teacher describe the reaction to you? He or she might say something such as "react baking soda and vinegar to form sodium acetate, water, and carbon dioxide." It is more likely that your teacher will describe the reaction in the form of a chemical equation. *A* **chemical equation** *is a description of a reaction using element symbols and chemical formulas.* Element symbols represent elements. Chemical formulas represent compounds.

Element Symbols

Recall that symbols of elements are shown in the periodic table. For example, the symbol for carbon is C. The symbol for copper is Cu. Each element can exist as just one atom. However, some elements exist in nature as diatomic molecules–two atoms of the same element bonded together. A formula for one of these diatomic elements includes the element's symbol and the subscript *2*. A subscript describes the number of atoms of an element in a compound. Oxygen (O_2) and hydrogen (H_2) are examples of diatomic molecules. Some element symbols are shown above the blue line in Table 1.

Chemical Formulas

When atoms of two or more different elements bond, they form a compound. Recall that a chemical formula uses elements' symbols and subscripts to describe the number of atoms in a compound. If an element's symbol does not have a subscript, the compound contains only one atom of that element. For example, carbon dioxide (CO_2) is made up of one carbon atom and two oxygen atoms. Remember that two different formulas, no matter how similar, represent different substances. Some chemical formulas are shown below the blue line in Table 1.

Writing Chemical Equations

A chemical equation includes both the substances that react and the substances that are formed in a chemical reaction. *The starting substances in a chemical reaction are* **reactants.** *The substances produced by the chemical reaction are* **products.** Figure 3 shows how a chemical equation is written. Chemical formulas are used to describe the reactants and the products. The reactants are written to the left of an arrow, and the products are written to the right of the arrow. Two or more reactants or products are separated by a plus sign. The general structure for an equation is:

reactant + reactant → product + product

When writing chemical equations, it is important to use correct chemical formulas for the reactants and the products. For example, suppose a certain chemical reaction produces carbon dioxide and water. The product carbon dioxide would be written as CO_2 and not as CO. CO is the formula for carbon monoxide, which is not the same compound as CO_2. Water would be written as H_2O and not as H_2O_2, the formula for hydrogen peroxide.

Figure 3 An equation is read much like a sentence. This equation is read as "carbon plus oxygen produces carbon dioxide."

MiniLab
10 minutes

How does an equation represent a reaction?

Sulfur dioxide (SO_2) and oxygen (O_2) react and form sulfur trioxide (SO_3). How does an equation represent the reaction?

1. Read and complete a lab safety form.

2. Use **yellow modeling clay** to model two atoms of sulfur. Use **red modeling clay** to model six atoms of oxygen.

3. Make two molecules of SO_2 with a sulfur atom in the middle of each molecule. Make one molecule of O_2. Sketch the models in your Science Journal.

4. Rearrange atoms to form two molecules of SO_3. Place a sulfur atom in the middle of each molecule. Sketch the models in your Science Journal.

Analyze and Conclude

1. **Identify** the reactants and the products in this chemical reaction.

2. **Write** a chemical equation for this reaction.

3. **Explain** What do the letters represent in the equation? The numbers?

4. **Key Concept** In terms of chemical bonds, what did you model by pulling molecules apart and building new ones?

Parts of an Equation

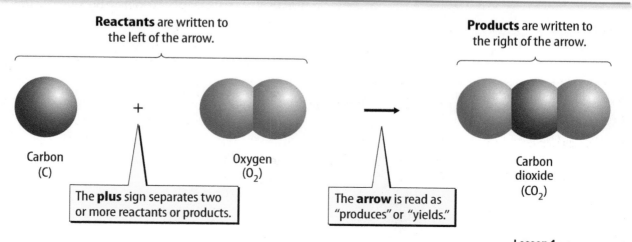

Reactants are written to the left of the arrow.

Products are written to the right of the arrow.

Carbon (C)   +   Oxygen (O_2)   →   Carbon dioxide (CO_2)

The **plus** sign separates two or more reactants or products.

The **arrow** is read as "produces" or "yields."

Hutchings Photography/Digital Light Source

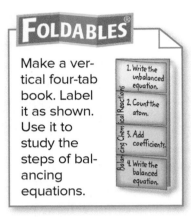

Make a vertical four-tab book. Label it as shown. Use it to study the steps of balancing equations.

Figure 4 As this reaction takes place, the mass on the balance remains the same, showing that mass is conserved.

Conservation of Mass

A French chemist named Antoine Lavoisier (AN twan • luh VWAH see ay) (1743–1794) discovered something interesting about chemical reactions. In a series of experiments, Lavoisier measured the masses of substances before and after a chemical reaction inside a closed container. He found that the total mass of the reactants always equaled the total mass of the products. Lavoisier's results led to the law of conservation of mass. *The **law of conservation of mass** states that the total mass of the reactants before a chemical reaction is the same as the total mass of the products after the chemical reaction.*

Atoms are conserved.

The discovery of atoms provided an explanation for Lavoisier's observations. Mass is conserved in a reaction because atoms are conserved. Recall that during a chemical reaction, bonds break and new bonds form. However, atoms are not destroyed, and no new atoms form. All atoms at the start of a chemical reaction are present at the end of the reaction. Figure 4 shows that mass is conserved in the reaction between baking soda and vinegar.

Key Concept Check What happens to the total mass of the reactants in a chemical reaction?

Conservation of Mass

The baking soda is contained in a balloon. The balloon is attached to a flask that contains vinegar.

When the balloon is tipped up, the baking soda pours into the vinegar. The reaction forms a gas that is collected in the balloon.

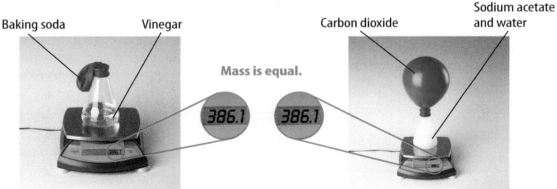

Mass is equal.

386.1   386.1

Baking soda   Vinegar

Carbon dioxide   Sodium acetate and water

baking soda	+	vinegar		sodium acetate	+	water	+	carbon dioxide
$NaHCO_3$		$HC_2H_3O_2$		$NaC_2H_3O_2$		H_2O		CO_2

1 Na:	4 H:		1 Na:	2 H:	1 C:
1 H:	2 C:		2 C:	1 O:	2 O:
1 C:	2 O:		3 H:		
3 O:			2 O:		

Atoms are equal.

Hutchings Photography/Digital Light Source

Is an equation balanced?

How does a chemical equation show that atoms are conserved? An equation is written so that the number of atoms of each element is the same, or balanced, on each side of the arrow. The equation showing the reaction between carbon and oxygen that produces carbon dioxide is shown below. Remember that oxygen is written as O_2 because it is a diatomic molecule. The formula for carbon dioxide is CO_2.

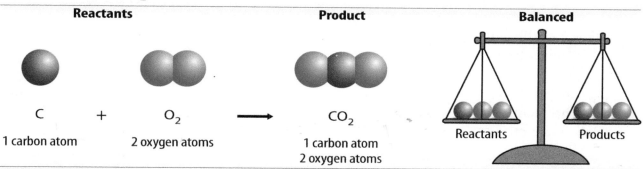

Reactants		**Product**	**Balanced**

C   + O_2 ⟶ CO_2

1 carbon atom   2 oxygen atoms   1 carbon atom / 2 oxygen atoms

Reactants   Products

Is there the same number of carbon atoms on each side of the arrow? Yes, there is one carbon atom on the left and one on the right. Carbon is balanced. Is oxygen balanced? There are two oxygen atoms on each side of the arrow. Oxygen also is balanced. The atoms of all elements are balanced. Therefore, the equation is balanced.

You might think a balanced equation happens automatically when you write the symbols and formulas for reactants and products. However, this usually is not the case. For example, the reaction between hydrogen (H_2) and oxygen (O_2) that forms water (H_2O) is shown below.

Project-Based Learning Activity

All Things Being Equal Go online to develop a model to show how a balanced equation shows that mass is conserved.

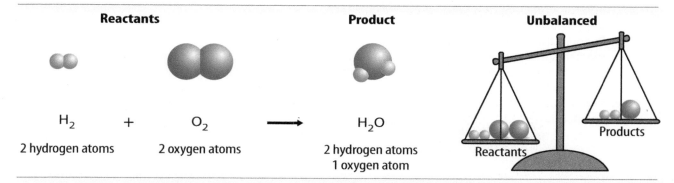

Reactants   **Product**   **Unbalanced**

H_2 + O_2 ⟶ H_2O

2 hydrogen atoms   2 oxygen atoms   2 hydrogen atoms / 1 oxygen atom

Products

Reactants

Count the number of hydrogen atoms on each side of the arrow. There are two hydrogen atoms in the product and two in the reactants. They are balanced. Now count the number of oxygen atoms on each side of the arrow. Did you notice that there are two oxygen atoms in the reactants and only one in the product? Because they are not equal, this equation is not balanced. To accurately represent this reaction, the equation needs to be balanced.

Balancing Chemical Equations

When you balance a chemical equation, you count the atoms in the reactants and the products and then add coefficients to balance the number of atoms. *A **coefficient** is a number placed in front of an element symbol or chemical formula in an equation.* It is the number of units of that substance in the reaction. For example, in the formula $2H_2O$, the 2 in front of H_2O is a coefficient, This means that there are two molecules of water in the reaction. Only coefficients can be changed when balancing an equation. Changing subscripts changes the identities of the substances that are in the reaction.

If one molecule of water contains two hydrogen atoms and one oxygen atom, how many H and O atoms are in two molecules of water ($2H_2O$)? Multiply each by 2.

> 2×2 H atoms $= 4$ H atoms
> 2×1 O atom $= 2$ O atoms

When no coefficient is present, only one unit of that substance takes part in the reaction. Table 2 shows the steps of balancing a chemical equation.

Table 2 Balancing a Chemical Equation 🔑

1 **Write the unbalanced equation.** Make sure that all chemical formulas are correct.	H_2 $+$ O_2 $\rightarrow$ H_2O *reactants* *products*
2 **Count atoms of each element in the reactants and in the products.** **a.** Note which, if any, elements have a balanced number of atoms on each side of the equation. Which atoms are not balanced? **b.** If all of the atoms are balanced, the equation is balanced.	H_2 $+$ O_2 $\rightarrow$ H_2O *reactants* *products* $H = 2$ $H = 2$ $O = 2$ $O = 1$
3 **Add coefficients to balance the atoms.** **a.** Pick an element in the equation that is not balanced, such as oxygen. Write a coefficient in front of a reactant or a product that will balance the atoms of that element. **b.** Recount the atoms of each element in the reactants and the products. Note which atoms are not balanced. Some atoms that were balanced before might no longer be balanced. **c.** Repeat step 3 until the atoms of each element are balanced.	H_2 $+$ O_2 $\rightarrow$ $2H_2O$ *reactants* *products* $H = 2$ $H = 4$ $O = 2$ $O = 2$ $2H_2$ $+$ O_2 $\rightarrow$ $2H_2O$ *reactants* *products* $H = 4$ $H = 4$ $O = 2$ $O = 2$
4 **Write the balanced chemical equation** including the coefficients.	$2H_2$ $+$ O_2 $=$ $2H_2O$

✓ **Visual Check** In row 2 above, which element is not balanced? In the top of row 3, which element is not balanced?

 Personal Tutor

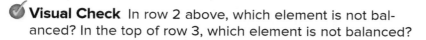

Lesson 1 Review

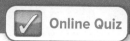

Visual Summary

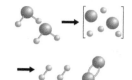

A chemical reaction is a process in which bonds break and atoms rearrange, forming new bonds.

$2H_2 + O_2 \rightarrow 2H_2O$

A chemical equation uses symbols to show reactants and products of a chemical reaction.

The mass and the number of each type of atom do not change during a chemical reaction. This is the law of conservation of mass.

FOLDABLES

Use your lesson Foldable to review the lesson. Save your Foldable for the project at the end of the chapter.

What do you think **NOW?**

You first read the statements below at the beginning of the chapter.

1. If a substance bubbles, you know a chemical reaction is occurring.

2. During a chemical reaction, some atoms are destroyed and new atoms are made.

Did you change your mind about whether you agree or disagree with the statements? Rewrite any false statements to make them true.

Use Vocabulary

1 **Define** *reactants* and *products*.

Understand Key Concepts

2 Which is a sign of a chemical reaction?
  A. chemical properties change
  C. a gas forms
  B. physical properties change
  D. a solid forms

3 **Explain** why subscripts cannot change when balancing a chemical equation.

4 **Infer** Is the reaction below possible? Explain why or why not.

$$H_2O + NaOH \rightarrow NaCl + H_2$$

Interpret Graphics

5 **Describe** the reaction below by listing the bonds that break and the bonds that form.

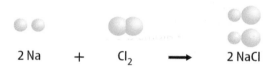

$$2\,Na \quad + \quad Cl_2 \quad \longrightarrow \quad 2\,NaCl$$

6 **Interpret** Copy and complete the table to determine if this equation is balanced:

$$CH_4 + 2O_2 \rightarrow CO_2 + 2H_2O$$

Is this reaction balanced? Explain.

Type of Atom	Number of Atoms in the Balanced Chemical Equation	
	Reactants	Products

Critical Thinking

7 Balance this chemical equation. Hint: Balance Al last and then use a multiple of 2 and 3.

$$Al + HCl \rightarrow AlCl_3 + H_2$$

What can you learn from an experiment?

Materials

test tubes
and rack

ammonium
hydroxide
(NH_4OH)

ALUMINUM FOIL

aluminum foil

sodium
bicarbonate
$(NaHCO_3)$

Also needed:
copper foil,
tongs, salt
water, copper
sulfate solution
$(CuSO_4)$, 25-mL
graduated
cylinder,
Bunsen burner,
plastic spoon,
toothpick, ring
stand and
clamp, splints,
matches,
paper towel

Safety

Observing reactions allows you to compare different types of changes that can occur. You can then design new experiments to learn more about reactions.

Learn It

If you have never tested for a chemical reaction before, it is helpful to **follow a procedure.** A procedure tells you which materials to use and what steps to take.

Try It

1. Read and complete a safety form.

2. Copy the table into your Science Journal. During each procedure, record observations in the table.

3a. Dip a strip of aluminum foil into salt water in a test tube for about 1 min to remove the coating.

3b. Place 5 mL of copper sulfate solution in a test tube. Lift the aluminum foil from the salt water. Drop it into the test tube of copper sulfate so that the bottom part is in the liquid. Look for evidence of a chemical change. Set the test tube in a rack, and do the other procedures.

4. Use tongs to hold a small piece of copper foil in a flame for 3 min. Set the foil on a heat-proof surface, and allow it to cool. Use a toothpick to examine the product.

5. Place a spoonful of sodium bicarbonate in a dry test tube. Clamp the tube to a ring stand at a 45° angle. Point the mouth of the tube away from people. Move a burner flame back and forth under the tube. Observe the reaction. Test for carbon dioxide with a lighted wood splint.

6. Add 1 drop of ammonium hydroxide to a test tube containing 5 mL of copper sulfate solution.

7. Pour the liquid from the test tube in step 3b into a clean test tube. Dump the aluminum onto a paper towel. Record your observations of both the liquid and the solid.

Apply It

8. Using the table, write a balanced equation for each reaction.

9. Why did the color of the copper sulfate disappear in step 3b?

10. 🔑 **Key Concept** What changes in properties and changes in energy indicate that the changes are chemical as well as physical?

Step	Reactants	Products	Observations and Evidence of Chemical Reaction
3 + 7	$Al + CuSO_4$	$Cu + Al_2(SO_4)_3$	
4	$Cu + O_2$	CuO	
5	$NaHCO_3$	$CO_2 + Na_2CO_3 + H_2O$	
6	$NH_4OH + CuSO_4$	$(NH_4)_2SO_4 + Cu(OH)_2$	

Reading Guide

Key Concepts 🔑
ESSENTIAL QUESTIONS

- How can you recognize the type of chemical reaction by the number or type of reactants and products?

- What are the different types of chemical reactions?

Vocabulary

synthesis p. 165

decomposition p. 165

single replacement p. 166

double replacement p. 166

combustion p. 166

 Multilingual eGlossary

 What's Science Got to do With It?

 8.PS.7, SEPS.2, SEPS.8, 6-8.LST.7.1

Types of Chemical Reactions

Inquiry Where did it come from?

When lead nitrate, a clear liquid, combines with potassium iodide, another clear liquid, a yellow solid appears instantly. Where did it come from? Here's a hint—the name of the solid is lead iodide. Did you guess that parts of each reactant combined and formed it? You'll learn about this and other types of reactions in this lesson.

Launch Lab

15 minutes

What combines with what?

The reactants and the products in a chemical reaction can be elements, compounds, or both. In how many ways can these substances combine?

1. Read and complete a lab safety form.

2. Divide a **sheet of paper** into four equal sections labeled *A, B, Y,* and *Z*. Place **red paper clips** in section A, **yellow clips** in section B, **blue clips** in section Y, and **green clips** in section Z.

3. Use another sheet of paper to copy the table shown to the right. Turn the paper so that a long edge is at the top. Print *REACTANTS →PRODUCTS* across the top then complete the table.

4. Using the paper clips, model the equations listed in the table. Hook the clips together to make diatomic elements or compounds. Place each clip model onto your paper over the matching written equation.

	REACTANTS → PRODUCTS	
1	AY →	$A + Y$
2	$B + Z$ →	BZ
3	$2A_2 + Y_2$ →	$2A_2Y$
4	$A + BY$ →	$B + AY$
5	$Z + BY$ →	$Y + BZ$
6	$AY + BZ$ →	$AZ + BY$

5. As you read this lesson, match the types of equations to your paper clip equations.

Think About This

1. Which equation represents hydrogen combining with oxygen and forming water? How do you know?

2. 🔑 **Key Concept** How could you use the number and type of reactants to identify a type of chemical reaction?

Figure 5 When dynamite explodes, it chemically changes into several products and releases energy.

©Adrian Buck/Alamy

Patterns in Reactions

If you have ever used hydrogen peroxide, you might have noticed that it is stored in a dark bottle. This is because light causes hydrogen peroxide to change into other substances. Maybe you have seen a video of an explosion demolishing an old building, like in **Figure 5**. How is the reaction with hydrogen peroxide and light similar to a building demolition? In both, one reactant breaks down into two or more products.

The breakdown of one reactant into two or more products is one of four major types of chemical reactions. Each type of chemical reaction follows a unique pattern in the way atoms in reactants rearrange to form products. In this lesson, you will read how chemical reactions are classified by recognizing patterns in the way the atoms recombine.

Types of Chemical Reactions

There are many different types of reactions. It would be impossible to memorize them all. However, most chemical reactions fit into four major categories. Understanding these categories of reactions can help you predict how compounds will react and what products will form.

Synthesis

A **synthesis** (SIHN thuh sus) *reaction is a type of chemical reaction in which two or more substances combine and form one compound.* In the synthesis reaction shown in **Figure 6**, magnesium (Mg) reacts with oxygen (O_2) in the air and forms magnesium oxide (MgO). You can recognize a synthesis reaction because two or more reactants form only one product.

Decomposition

In a **decomposition** *reaction, one compound breaks down and forms two or more substances.* You can recognize a decomposition reaction because one reactant forms two or more products. For example, hydrogen peroxide (H_2O_2), shown in **Figure 6**, decomposes and forms water (H_2O) and oxygen gas (O_2). Notice that decomposition is the reverse of synthesis.

 Key Concept Check How can you tell the difference between synthesis and decomposition reactions?

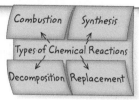

FOLDABLES

Make a horizontal four-door book. Label it as shown. Use it to organize your notes about the different types of chemical reactions.

Combustion | Synthesis
Types of Chemical Reactions
Decomposition | Replacement

WORD ORIGIN

synthesis
from Greek *syn-*, means "together"; and *tithenai,* means "put"

▶ **Animation**

Figure 6 Synthesis and decomposition reactions are opposites of each other.

Synthesis and Decomposition Reactions

Synthesis Reactions

Examples:
$2Na + Cl_2 \rightarrow 2NaCl$
$2H_2 + O_2 \rightarrow 2H_2O$
$H_2O + SO_3 \rightarrow H_2SO_4$

| 2Mg | + | O_2 | → | 2MgO |
| magnesium | | oxygen | | magnesium oxide |

Decomposition Reactions

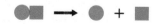

Examples:
$CaCO_3 \rightarrow CaO + CO_2$
$2H_2O \rightarrow 2H_2 + O_2$
$2KClO_3 \rightarrow 2KCl + 3O_2$

| $2H_2O_2$ | → | $2H_2O$ | + | O_2 |
| hydrogen peroxide | | water | | oxygen |

Single Replacement

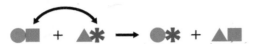

Examples:
Fe + CuSO$_4$ → FeSO$_4$ + Cu
Zn + 2HCl → ZnCl$_2$ + H$_2$

2AgNO$_3$ + Cu → Cu(NO$_3$)$_2$ + 2Ag
silver nitrate   copper   copper nitrate   silver

Double Replacement

Examples:
NaCl + AgNO$_3$ → NaNO$_3$ + AgCl
HCl + FeS → FeCl$_2$ + H$_2$S

Pb(NO$_3$)$_2$ + 2KI → 2KNO$_3$ + PbI$_2$
lead nitrate   potassium iodide   potassium nitrate   lead iodide

▲ **Figure 7** In each of these reactions, an atom or group of atoms replaces another atom or group of atoms.

Combustion Reactions

substance + O$_2$ → substance(s)

C$_3$H$_8$ + 5O$_2$ → 3CO$_2$ + 4H$_2$O
propane   oxygen   carbon   water
                    dioxide

Example:
2C$_4$H$_{10}$ + 13O$_2$ → 8CO$_2$ + 10H$_2$O

▲ **Figure 8** Combustion reactions always contain oxygen (O$_2$) as a reactant and often produce carbon dioxide (CO$_2$) and water (H$_2$O).

Replacement

In a replacement reaction, an atom or group of atoms replaces part of a compound. There are two types of replacement reactions. *In a* **single-replacement** *reaction, one element replaces another element in a compound.* In this type of reaction, an element and a compound react and form a different element and a different compound. *In a* **double-replacement** *reaction, the negative ions in two compounds switch places, forming two new compounds.* In this type of reaction, two compounds react and form two new compounds. **Figure 7** describes these replacement reactions.

Combustion

Combustion *is a chemical reaction in which a substance combines with oxygen and releases energy.* This energy usually is released as thermal energy and light energy. For example, burning is a common combustion reaction. The burning of fossil fuels, such as propane (C$_3$H$_8$) shown in **Figure 8**, produces the energy we use to cook food, power vehicles, and light cities.

 Key Concept Check What are the different types of chemical reactions?

(t)Stephen Frisch/McGraw-Hill Education, (c)sciencephotos/Alamy, (b)Park Dale/Alamy

Lesson 2 Review

✓ Online Quiz
🔬 Virtual Lab

Visual Summary

Chemical reactions are classified according to patterns seen in their reactants and products.

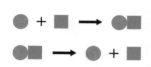

In a synthesis reaction, there are two or more reactants and one product. A decomposition reaction is the opposite of a synthesis reaction.

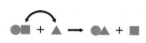

In replacement reactions, an element, or elements, in a compound is replaced with another element or elements.

FOLDABLES

Use your lesson Foldable to review the lesson. Save your Foldable for the project at the end of the chapter.

What do you think NOW?

You first read the statements below at the beginning of the chapter.

3. Reactions always start with two or more substances that react with each other.

4. Water can be broken down into simpler substances.

Did you change your mind about whether you agree or disagree with the statements? Rewrite any false statements to make them true.

Use Vocabulary

1 **Contrast** synthesis and decomposition reactions using a diagram.

2 A reaction in which parts of two substances switch places and make two new substances is a(n) _____.

Understand Key Concepts

3 **Classify** the reaction shown below.

$$2Na + Cl_2 \rightarrow 2NaCl$$

A. combustion

C. single replacement

B. decomposition

D. synthesis

4 Write a balanced equation that produces H_2 and O_2 from H_2O. Classify this reaction.

5 **Classify** In which two groups of reactions can this reaction be classified?

$$2SO_2 + O_2 \rightarrow 2SO_3$$

Interpret Graphics

6 **Complete** this table to identify four types of chemical reactions and the patterns shown by the reactants and the products.

Type of Reaction	Pattern of Reactants and Products
Synthesis	at least two reactants; one product

Critical Thinking

7 **Design** a poster to illustrate single- and double-replacement reactions.

8 **Infer** The combustion of methane (CH_4) produces energy. Where do you think this energy comes from?

Stephen Frisch/McGraw-Hill Education

How does a light stick work?

What makes it glow?

Glowing neon necklaces, bracelets, or sticks—chances are you've worn or used them. Light sticks—also known as glow sticks—come in brilliant colors and provide light without electricity or batteries. Because they are lightweight, portable, and waterproof, they provide an ideal light source for campers, scuba divers, and other activities in which electricity is not readily available. Light sticks also are useful in emergency situations in which an electric current from battery-powered lights could ignite a fire.

Light sticks give off light because of a chemical reaction that happens inside the tube. During the reaction, energy is released as light. This is known as chemiluminescence (ke mee lew muh NE sunts).

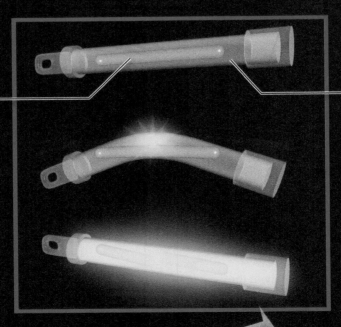

A light stick consists of a plastic tube with a glass tube inside it. Hydrogen peroxide fills the glass tube.

When you bend the outer plastic tube, the inner glass tube breaks, causing the hydrogen peroxide, ester, and dye to mix together.

A solution of phenyl oxalate ester and fluorescent dye surround the glass tube.

When the solutions mix together, they react. Energy produced by the reaction causes the electrons in the dye to produce light.

It's Your Turn

RESEARCH AND REPORT Research bioluminescent organisms, such as fireflies and sea animals. How is the reaction that occurs in these organisms similar to or different from that in a glow stick? Work in small groups, and present your findings to the class.

inak/Stockimo/Alamy

Lesson 3

Energy Changes and Chemical Reactions

Reading Guide

Key Concepts
ESSENTIAL QUESTIONS

* Why do chemical reactions always involve a change in energy?

* What is the difference between an endothermic reaction and an exothermic reaction?

* What factors can affect the rate of a chemical reaction?

Vocabulary

endothermic p. 171

exothermic p. 171

activation energy p. 172

catalyst p. 174

enzyme p. 174

inhibitor p. 174

 Multilingual eGlossary

 8.PS.6, 8.PS.7, SEPS.1, SEPS.2, SEPS.3, SEPS.4, SEPS.6, SEPS.8, 6-8.LST.5.2, 6-8.LST.7.1

PBL Go to the resource tab in ConnectED to find the PBL *Camping Chemistry*.

Inquiry Energy from Bonds?

A deafening roar, a blinding light, and the power to lift 2 million kg—what is the source of all this energy? Chemical bonds in the fuel store all the energy needed to launch a space shuttle. Chemical reactions release the energy in these bonds.

Where's the heat?

Does a chemical change always produce a temperature increase?

1 Read and complete a lab safety form.

2 Copy the table into your Science Journal.

3 Use a **graduated cylinder** to measure 25 mL of **citric acid solution** into a **foam cup**. Record the temperature with a **thermometer**.

4 Use a **plastic spoon** to add a rounded spoonful of **solid sodium bicarbonate** to the cup. Stir.

5 Use a **clock** or **stopwatch** to record the temperature every 15 s until it stops changing. Record your observations during the reaction.

6 Add 25 mL of **sodium bicarbonate solution** to a **second foam cup**. Record the temperature. Add a spoonful of **calcium chloride**. Repeat step 5.

Time	Temperature (°C)	
	Citric Acid Solution	Sodium Bicarbonate Solution
Starting temp.		
15 s		
30 s		
45 s		
1 min		
1 min, 15 s		
1 min, 30 s		
1 min, 45 s		
2 min		
2 min, 15 sec		

Think About This

1. What evidence do you have that the changes in the two cups were chemical reactions?

2. What happened to the temperature in the two cups? How would you explain the changes?

3. **Key Concept** Based on your observations and past experience, would a change in temperature be enough to convince you that a chemical change had taken place? Why or why not? What else could cause a temperature change?

Energy Changes

What is about 1,500 times heavier than a typical car and 300 times faster than a roller coaster? Do you need a hint? The energy it needs to move this fast comes from a chemical reaction that produces water. If you guessed a space shuttle, you are right!

It takes a large amount of energy to launch a space shuttle. The shuttle's main engines burn almost 2 million L of liquid hydrogen and liquid oxygen. This chemical reaction produces water vapor and a large amount of energy. The energy produced heats the water vapor to high temperatures, causing it to expand rapidly. When the water expands, it pushes the shuttle into orbit. Where does all this energy come from?

Chemical Energy in Bonds

Recall that when a chemical reaction occurs, chemical bonds in the reactants break and new chemical bonds form. Chemical bonds contain a form of energy called chemical energy. Breaking a bond absorbs energy from the surroundings. The formation of a chemical bond releases energy to the surroundings. Some chemical reactions release more energy than they absorb. Some chemical reactions absorb more energy than they release. You can feel this energy change as a change in the temperature of the surroundings. Keep in mind that in all chemical reactions, energy is conserved.

Key Concept Check Why do chemical reactions involve a change in energy?

Endothermic Reactions—Energy Absorbed

Have you ever heard someone say that the sidewalk was hot enough to fry an egg? To fry, the egg must absorb energy. *Chemical reactions that absorb thermal energy are* **endothermic** *reactions.* For an endothermic reaction to continue, energy must be constantly added.

$$\text{reactants} + \text{thermal energy} \rightarrow \text{products}$$

In an endothermic reaction, more energy is required to break the bonds of the reactants than is released when the products form. Therefore, the overall reaction absorbs energy. The reaction on the left in **Figure 9** is an endothermic reaction.

Exothermic Reactions—Energy Released

Most chemical reactions release energy as opposed to absorbing it. *An* **exothermic** *reaction is a chemical reaction that releases thermal energy.*

$$\text{reactants} \rightarrow \text{products} + \text{thermal energy}$$

In an exothermic reaction, more energy is released when the products form than is required to break the bonds in the reactants. Therefore, the overall reaction releases energy. The reaction shown on the right in **Figure 9** is exothermic.

Key Concept Check What is the difference between an endothermic reaction and an exothermic reaction?

FOLDABLES

Make a vertical three-tab Venn book. Label it as shown. Use it to compare and contrast energy in chemical reactions.

Exothermic Reaction

Both

Endothermic Reaction

WORD ORIGIN ···········

exothermic
from Greek *exo-*, means "outside"; and *therm,* means "heat"

Figure 9 Whether a reaction is endothermic or exothermic depends on the amount of energy contained in the bonds of the reactants and the products.

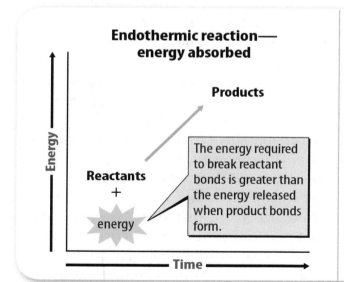
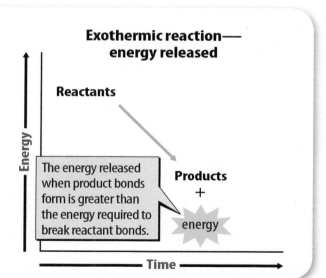

Endothermic reaction— energy absorbed

Energy

Products

Reactants + energy

The energy required to break reactant bonds is greater than the energy released when product bonds form.

Time

Exothermic reaction— energy released

Energy

Reactants

Products + energy

The energy released when product bonds form is greater than the energy required to break reactant bonds.

Time

Visual Check Why does one arrow point upward and the other arrow point downward in these diagrams?

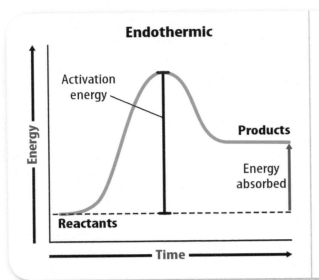
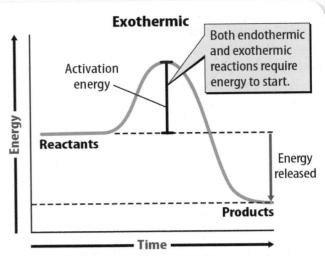

Endothermic

Activation energy

Energy

Products

Energy absorbed

Reactants

Time

Exothermic

Both endothermic and exothermic reactions require energy to start.

Activation energy

Energy

Reactants

Energy released

Products

Time

Figure 10 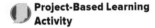 Both endothermic and exothermic reactions require activation energy to start the reaction.

✓ **Visual Check** How can a reaction absorb energy to start but still be exothermic?

● **Project-Based Learning Activity**

Camping Chemistry Go online to design, construct, and test a device that uses chemical changes to release or absorb thermal energy.

Activation Energy

You might have noticed that some chemical reactions do not start by themselves. For example, a newspaper does not burn when it comes into contact with oxygen in air. However, if a flame touches the paper, it starts to burn.

All reactions require energy to start the breaking of bonds. This energy is called activation energy. **Activation energy** *is the minimum amount of energy needed to start a chemical reaction.* Different reactions have different activation energies. Some reactions, such as the rusting of iron, have low activation energy. The energy in the surroundings is enough to start these reactions. If a reaction has high activation energy, more energy is needed to start the reaction. For example, wood requires the thermal energy of a flame to start burning. Once the reaction starts, it releases enough energy to keep the reaction going. **Figure 10** shows the role activation energy plays in endothermic and exothermic reactions.

Reaction Rates

Some chemical reactions, such as the rusting of a bicycle wheel, happen slowly. Other chemical reactions, such as the explosion of fireworks, happen in less than a second. The rate of a reaction is the speed at which it occurs. What controls how fast a chemical reaction occurs? Recall that particles must collide before they can react. Chemical reactions occur faster if particles collide more often or move faster when they collide. There are several factors that affect how often particles collide and how fast particles move.

✓ **Reading Check** How do particle collisions relate to reaction rate?

Surface Area

Surface area is the amount of exposed, outer area of a solid. Increased surface area increases reaction rate because more particles on the surface of a solid come into contact with the particles of another substance. For example, if you place a piece of chalk in vinegar, the chalk reacts slowly with the acid. This is because the acid contacts only the particles on the surface of the chalk. But, if you grind the chalk into powder, more chalk particles contact the acid, and the reaction occurs faster.

Temperature

Imagine a crowded hallway. If everyone in the hallway were running, they would probably collide with each other more often and with more energy than if everyone were walking. This is also true when particles move faster. At higher temperatures, the average speed of particles is greater. This speeds reactions in two ways. First, particles collide more often. Second, collisions with more energy are more likely to break chemical bonds.

Concentration and Pressure

Think of a crowded hallway again. Because the concentration of people is higher in the crowded hallway than in an empty hallway, people probably collide more often. Similarly, increasing the concentration of one or more reactants increases collisions between particles. More collisions result in a faster reaction rate. In gases, an increase in pressure pushes gas particles closer together. When particles are closer together, more collisions occur. Factors that affect reaction rate are shown in **Figure 11**.

Math Skills

Use Geometry

The surface area (SA) of one side of a 1-cm cube is 1 cm × 1 cm, or 1 cm². The cube has 6 equal sides. Its total SA is 6 × 1 cm², or 6 cm². What is the total SA of the two solids made when the cube is cut in half?

1 The new surfaces made each have an area of 1 cm × 1 cm = 1 cm².

2 Multiply the area by the number of new surfaces. 2 ×1 = 2 cm²

3 Add the SA of the original cube to the new SA. 6 cm² + 2 cm² The total SA is 8 cm².

Practice

Calculate the amount of SA gained when a 2-cm cube is cut in half.

✓ Math Practice

💬 Personal Tutor

Figure 11 🔑 Several factors can affect reaction rate.

Slower Reaction Rate

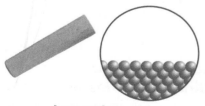

Less surface area

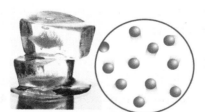

Lower temperature

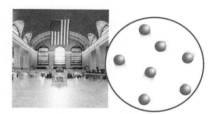

Lower concentration

Faster Reaction Rate

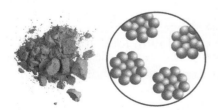

More surface area

Higher temperature

Higher concentration

(tl)Mark Steinmetz, (tc)©Brand X Pictures/PunchStock, (tr)Tetra Images/Getty Images, (bl)McGraw-Hill Education, (bc)©L. Clarke/Corbis, (br)Alexis Grattier/Getty Images

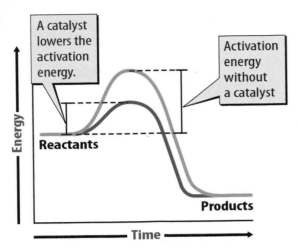

Figure 12 The blue line shows how a catalyst can increase the reaction rate.

Catalysts

A **catalyst** *is a substance that increases reaction rate by lowering the activation energy of a reaction.* One way catalysts speed reactions is by helping reactant particles contact each other more often. Look at **Figure 12.** Notice that the activation energy of the reaction is lower with a catalyst than it is without a catalyst. A catalyst isn't changed in a reaction, and it doesn't change the reactants or products. Also, a catalyst doesn't increase the amount of reactant used or the amount of product that is made. It only makes a given reaction happen faster. Therefore, catalysts are not considered reactants in a reaction.

You might be surprised to know that your body is filled with catalysts called enzymes. *An* **enzyme** *is a catalyst that speeds up chemical reactions in living cells.* For example, the enzyme protease (PROH tee ays) breaks the protein molecules in the food you eat into smaller molecules that can be absorbed by your intestine. Without enzymes, these reactions would occur too slowly for life to exist.

Inhibitors

Recall than an enzyme is a molecule that speeds reactions in organisms. However, some organisms, such as bacteria, are harmful to humans. Some medicines contain molecules that attach to enzymes in bacteria. This keeps the enzymes from working properly. If the enzymes in bacteria can't work, the bacteria die and can no longer infect a human. The active ingredients in these medicines are called inhibitors. *An* **inhibitor** *is a substance that slows, or even stops, a chemical reaction.* Inhibitors can slow or stop the reactions caused by enzymes.

Inhibitors are also important in the food industry. Preservatives in food are substances that inhibit, or slow down, food spoilage.

 Key Concept Check What factors can affect the rate of a chemical reaction?

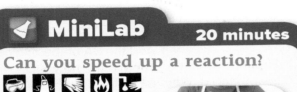

MiniLab
20 minutes

Can you speed up a reaction?

Can you speed up the decomposition of hydrogen peroxide (H_2O_2)? The reaction is $H_2O_2 \rightarrow H_2O$ and O_2.

1 Read and complete a lab safety form.

2 Use **tape** to label three **test tubes** *1*, *2*, and *3*. Place the tubes in a **test-tube rack.**

3 Add 10 mL of **hydrogen peroxide** to each test tube.

4 Observe tube 1 for changes. Add a small piece of **raw potato** to tube 2. Record observations in your Science Journal.

5 Add a pinch of **dry yeast** to tube 3. Shake the tube gently. Record observations.

6 Use **matches** to light a **wood splint,** then blow it out, leaving a glowing tip. One at a time, hold each test tube at a 45° angle and insert the glowing splint into the tube just above the liquid. Record your observations.

Analyze and Conclude

1. **Draw Conclusions** What was the chemical reaction when the potato and yeast were added?

2. 🔑 **Key Concept** Why is the reaction in tube 3 faster than in the other two tubes?

Visual Summary

Endothermic

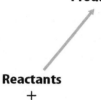

Products

Reactants
+

energy

Chemical reactions that release energy are exothermic, and those that absorb energy are endothermic.

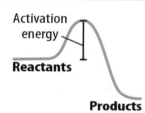

Activation energy

Reactants

Products

Activation energy must be added to a chemical reaction for it to proceed.

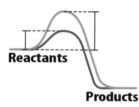

Reactants

Products

Catalysts, including enzymes, speed up chemical reactions. Inhibitors slow them down.

FOLDABLES

Use your lesson Foldable to review the lesson. Save your Foldable for the project at the end of the chapter.

What do you think NOW?

You first read the statements below at the beginning of the chapter.

5. Reactions that release energy require energy to get started.

6. Energy can be created in a chemical reaction.

Did you change your mind about whether you agree or disagree with the statements? Rewrite any false statements to make them true.

Use Vocabulary

1 The smallest amount of energy required by reacting particles for a chemical reaction to begin is the _____.

Understand Key Concepts

2 How does a catalyst increase reaction rate?
   A. by increasing the activation energy
   B. by increasing the amount of reactant
   C. by increasing the contact between particles
   D. by increasing the space between particles

3 **Contrast** endothermic and exothermic reactions in terms of energy.

4 **Explain** When propane burns, heat and light are produced. Where does this energy come from?

Interpret Graphics

5 **List** Copy and complete the graphic organizer to describe four ways to increase the rate of a reaction.

Increase reaction rate

Critical Thinking

6 **Infer** Explain why keeping a battery in a refrigerator can extend its life.

7 **Infer** Explain why a catalyst does not increase the amount of product that can form.

Math Skills   ✓ Math Practice

8 An object measures 4 cm × 4 cm × 4 cm.
   a. What is the surface area of the object?
   b. What is the total surface area if you cut the object into two equal pieces?

Materials

graduated
cylinder

balance

droppers

baking soda

plastic spoon

Also needed:
various brands
of liquid and
solid antacids
(both regular
and maximum
strength),
beakers,
universal
indicator in
dropper bottle,
0.1M HCl
solution,
stirring rods

Safety

Design an Experiment to Test Advertising Claims

Antacids contain compounds that react with excess acid in your stomach and prevent a condition called heartburn. Suppose you work for a laboratory that tests advertising claims about antacids. What kinds of procedures would you follow? How would you decide which antacid is the most effective?

Ask a Question

Ask a question about the claims that you would like to investigate. For example: what does *most effective* mean? What would make an antacid the strongest?

Make Observations

1. Read and complete a lab safety form.

2. Study the selection of antacids available for testing. You will use a 0.1M HCl solution to simulate stomach acid. Use the questions below to discuss with your lab partners which advertising claim you might test and how you might test it.

3. In your Science Journal, write a procedure for each variable that you will test to answer your question. Include the materials and steps you will use to test each variable. Place the steps of each procedure in order. Have your teacher approve your procedures.

4. Make a chart or table to record observations during your experiments.

Questions

Questions
Which advertising claim will I test? What question am I trying to answer?
What will be the independent and the dependent variables for each test? Recall that the independent variable is the variable that is changed. A dependent variable changes when you change the independent variable.
What variables will be held constant in each test?
How many different procedures will I use, and what equipment will I need?
How much of each antacid will I use? How many antacids will I test?
How will I use the indicator?
How many times will I do each test?
How will I record the data and observations?
What will I analyze to form a conclusion?

Form a Hypothesis

5 Write a hypothesis for each variable. Your hypothesis should identify the independent variable and state why you think changing the variable will alter the effectiveness of an antacid tablet.

Test Your Hypothesis

6 On day 2, use the available materials to perform your experiments. Accurately record all observations and data for each test.

7 Add any additional tests you think you need to answer your questions.

8 Examine the data you have collected. If the data are not conclusive, what other tests can you do to provide more information?

9 Write all your observations and measurements in your Science Journal. Use tables to record any quantitative data.

Analyze and Conclude

10 Infer What do you think advertisers mean when they say their product is most effective?

11 Draw Conclusions If you needed an antacid, which one would you use, based on the limited information provided from your experiments? Explain your reasoning.

12 Analyze Would breaking an antacid tablet into small pieces before using it make it more effective? Why or why not?

13 The Big Idea How does understanding chemical reactions enable you to analyze products and their claims?

Communicate Your Results

Combine your data with other teams. Compare the results and conclusions. Discuss the validity of advertising claims for each brand of antacid.

 **Extension**

Research over-the-counter antacids that were once available by prescription only. Do they work in the same way as the antacids you tested? Explain.

6

Lab Tips

☑ Think about how you might measure the amount of acid the tablet neutralizes. Would you add the tablet to the acid or the acid to the tablet? What does the indicator show you?

☑ Try your tests on a small scale before using the full amounts to see how much acid you might need.

☑ Always get your teacher's approval before trying any new test.

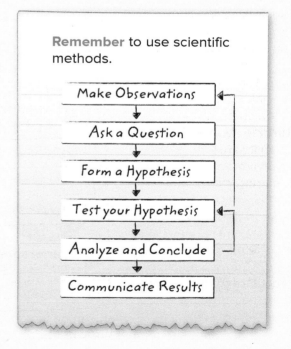

Remember to use scientific methods.

Make Observations
↓
Ask a Question
↓
Form a Hypothesis
↓
Test your Hypothesis
↓
Analyze and Conclude
↓
Communicate Results

THE BIG IDEA Atoms are neither created nor destroyed in chemical reactions. Energy can be released when chemical bonds form or absorbed when chemical bonds are broken.

Key Concepts Summary

Lesson 1: Understanding Chemical Reactions

- There are several signs that a **chemical reaction** might have occurred, including a change in temperature, a release of light, a release of gas, a change in color or odor, and the formation of a solid from two liquids.
- In a chemical reaction, atoms of **reactants** rearrange and form **products.**
- The total mass of all the reactants is equal to the total mass of all the products in a reaction.

Reactants			Products		
1 Na:		Atoms are equal.	1 Na:		
1 H:	4 H:		2 C:	1 C:	
1 C:	2 C:		3 H:	2 H:	
3 O:	2 O:		2 O:	1 O:	2 O:

Lesson 2: Types of Chemical Reactions

- Most chemical reactions fit into one of a few main categories— synthesis, decomposition, combustion, and single- or double-replacement.
- **Synthesis** reactions create one product. **Decomposition** reactions start with one reactant. **Single-** and **double-replacement** reactions involve replacing one element or group of atoms with another element or group of atoms. **Combustion** reactions involve a reaction between one reactant and oxygen, and they release thermal energy.

Lesson 3: Energy Changes and Chemical Reactions

- Chemical reactions always involve breaking bonds, which requires energy, and forming bonds, which releases energy.
- In an **endothermic** reaction, the reactants contain less energy than the products. In an **exothermic** reaction, the reactants contain more energy than the products.
- The rate of a chemical reaction can be increased by increasing the surface area, the temperature, or the concentration of the reactants, or by adding a **catalyst.**

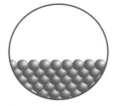 

Less surface area   **More surface area**

Vocabulary

chemical reaction p. 153
chemical equation p. 156
reactant p. 157
product p. 157
law of conservation of mass p. 158
coefficient p. 160

synthesis p. 165
decomposition p. 165
single replacement p. 166
double replacement p. 166
combustion p. 166

endothermic p. 171
exothermic p. 171
activation energy p. 172
catalyst p. 174
enzyme p. 174
inhibitor p. 174

Vocabulary eFlashcards
Vocabulary eGames

Personal Tutor

FOLDABLES® Chapter Project

Assemble your lesson Foldables as shown to make a Chapter Project. Use the project to review what you have learned in this chapter.

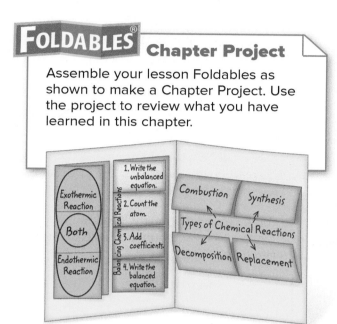

Use Vocabulary

1 When water forms from hydrogen and oxygen, water is the _____.

2 A(n) _____ uses symbols instead of words to describe a chemical reaction.

3 In a(n) _____ reaction, one element replaces another element in a compound.

4 When Na_2CO_3 is heated, it breaks down into CO_2 and Na_2O in a(n) _____ reaction.

5 The chemical reactions that keep your body warm are _____ reactions.

6 Even exothermic reactions require _____ to start.

Link Vocabulary and Key Concepts

 Interactive Concept Map

Copy this concept map, and then use vocabulary terms from the previous page and other terms from the chapter to complete the concept map.

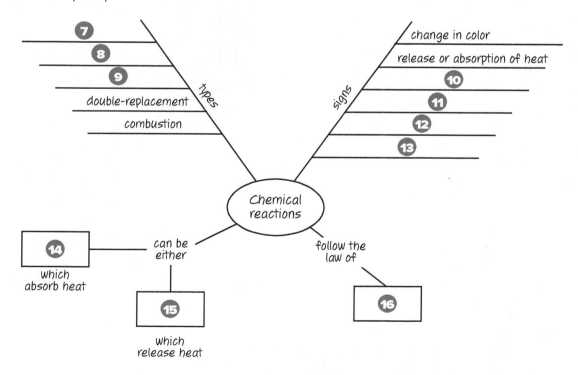

Chapter 5 Review

Understand Key Concepts

1 How many carbon atoms react in this equation?

$$2C_4H_{10} + 13O_2 \rightarrow 8CO_2 + 10H_2O$$

A. 2
B. 4
C. 6
D. 8

2 The chemical equation below is unbalanced.

$$Zn + HCl \rightarrow ZnCl_2 + H_2$$

Which is the correct balanced chemical equation?

A. $Zn + H_2Cl_2 \rightarrow ZnCl_2 + H_2$
B. $Zn + HCl \rightarrow ZnCl + H$
C. $2Zn + 2HCl \rightarrow ZnCl_2 + H_2$
D. $Zn + 2HCl \rightarrow ZnCl_2 + H_2$

3 When iron combines with oxygen gas and forms rust, the total mass of the products

A. depends on the reaction conditions.
B. is less than the mass of the reactants.
C. is the same as the mass of the reactants.
D. is greater than the mass of the reactants.

4 Potassium nitrate forms potassium oxide, nitrogen, and oxygen in certain fireworks.

$$4KNO_3 \rightarrow 2K_2O + 2N_2 + 5O_2$$

This reaction is classified as a

A. combustion reaction.
B. decomposition reaction.
C. single-replacement reaction.
D. synthesis reaction.

5 Which type of reaction is the reverse of a decomposition reaction?

A. combustion
B. synthesis
C. double-replacement
D. single-replacement

6 The compound NO_2 can act as a catalyst in the reaction that converts ozone (O_3) to oxygen (O_2) in the upper atmosphere. Which statement is true?

A. More oxygen is created when NO_2 is present.
B. NO_2 is a reactant in the chemical reaction that converts O_3 to O_2.
C. This reaction is more exothermic in the presence of NO_2 than in its absence.
D. This reaction occurs faster in the presence of NO_2 than in its absence.

7 The graph below is an energy diagram for the reaction between carbon monoxide (CO) and nitrogen dioxide (NO_2).

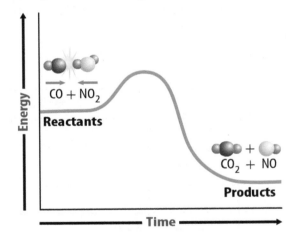

Which is true about this reaction?

A. More energy is required to break reactant bonds than is released when product bonds form.
B. Less energy is required to break reactant bonds than is released when product bonds form.
C. The bonds of the reactants do not require energy to break because the reaction releases energy.
D. The bonds of the reactants require energy to break, and therefore the reaction absorbs energy.

Critical Thinking

8 **Predict** The diagram below shows two reactions—one with a catalyst (blue) and one without a catalyst (orange).

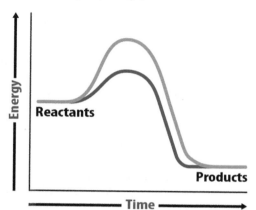

How would the blue line change if an inhibitor were used instead of a catalyst?

9 **Analyze** A student observed a chemical reaction and collected the following data:

Observations before the reaction	A white powder was added to a clear liquid.
Observations during the reaction	The reactants bubbled rapidly in the open beaker.
Mass of reactants	4.2 g
Mass of products	4.0 g

The student concludes that mass was not conserved in the reaction. Explain why this is not a valid conclusion. What might explain the difference in mass?

10 **Explain Observations** How did the discovery of atoms explain the observation that the mass of the products always equals the mass of the reactants in a reaction?

Writing in Science

11 **Write instructions** that explain the steps in balancing a chemical equation. Use the following equation as an example.

$$MnO_2 + HCl \rightarrow MnCl_2 + H_2O + Cl_2$$

REVIEW THE BIG IDEA

12 Explain how atoms and energy are conserved in a chemical reaction.

13 When a car air bag inflates, sodium azide (NaN_3) decomposes and produces nitrogen gas (N_2) and another product. What element does the other product contain? How do you know?

FO4305OZ02

Math Skills ✓ Math Practice

Use Geometry

14 What is the surface area of the cube shown below? What would the total surface area be if you cut the cube into 27 equal cubes?

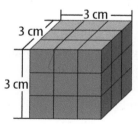

3 cm
3 cm
3 cm

15 Suppose you have ten cubes that measure 2 cm on each side.

a. What is the total surface area of the cubes?

b. What would the surface area be if you glued the cubes together to make one object that is two cubes wide, one cube high, and five cubes long? Hint: draw a picture of the final cube and label the length of each side.

Standardized Test Practice

Record your answers on the answer sheet provided by your teacher or on a sheet of paper.

Multiple Choice

1   How can you verify that a chemical reaction has occurred?

   A   Check the temperature of the starting and ending substances.

   B   Compare the chemical properties of the starting substances and ending substances.

   C   Look for a change in state.

   D   Look for bubbling of the starting substances.

Use the figure below to answer questions 2 and 3.

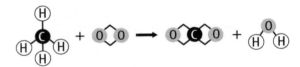

2   The figure above shows models of molecules in a chemical reactions. Which substances are reactants in this reaction?

   A CH_4 and CO_2

   B CH_4 and O_2

   C CO_2 and H_2O

   D O_2 and H_2O

3   Which equation shows that atoms are conserved in the reaction?

   A $CH_4 + O_2 \longrightarrow CO_2 + H_2O$

   B $CH_4 + O_2 \longrightarrow CO_2 + 2H_2O$

   C $CH_4 + 2O_2 \longrightarrow CO_2 + 2H_2O$

   D $2CH_4 + O_2 \longrightarrow 2CO_2 + H_2O$

4   Which occurs before new bonds can form during a chemical reaction?

   A   The atoms in the original substances are destroyed.

   B   The bonds between atoms in the original substances are broken.

   C   The atoms in the original substances are no longer moving.

   D   The bonds between atoms in the original substances get stronger.

Use the figure below to answer question 5.

5   The figure above uses shapes to represent a chemical reaction. What kind of chemical reaction does the figure represent?

   A   decomposition

   B   double replacement

   C   single replacement

   D   synthesis

6   Which type of chemical reaction has only one reactant?

   A   decomposition

   B   double replacement

   C   single replacement

   D   synthesis

7   Which element is always a reactant in a combustion reaction?

   A   carbon

   B   hydrogen

   C   nitrogen

   D   oxygen

Use the figure below to answer question 8.

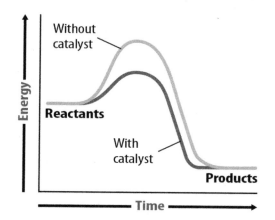

8   The figure above shows changes in energy during a reaction. The lighter line shows the reaction without a catalyst. The darker line shows the reaction with a catalyst. Which is true about these two reactions?

   A The reaction with the catalyst is more exothermic than the reaction without the catalyst.

   B The reaction with the catalyst requires less activation energy than the reaction without the catalyst.

   C The reaction with the catalyst requires more reactants than the reaction without the catalyst.

   D The reaction with the catalyst takes more time than the reaction without the catalyst.

Constructed Response

9   Explain the role of energy in chemical reactions.

10   How does a balanced chemical equation illustrate the law of conservation of mass?

11   Many of the reactions that occur when something decays are decomposition reactions. What clues show that this type of reaction is taking place? What happens during a decomposition reaction?

Use the figure below to answer questions 12 and 13.

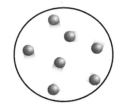 

12   Compare the two gas samples represented in the figure in terms of pressure and concentration.

13   Describe the conditions that would increase the rate of a reaction.

NEED EXTRA HELP?												
If You Missed Question...	1	2	3	4	5	6	7	8	9	10	11	12	13
Go to Lesson...	1	1	1	1	2	2	2	3	3	1	2	3	3

Unit 2
Earth's Systems

1441
Prince Munjong of Korea invents the first rain gauge to gather and measure the amount of liquid precipitation over a period of time.

1450
The first anemometer, a tool to measure wind speed, is developed by Leone Battista Alberti.

1643
Italian physicist Evangelista Torricelli invents the barometer to measure pressure in the air. This tool improves meteorology, which relied on simple sky observations.

1714
German physicist Daniel Fahrenheit develops the mercury thermometer, making it possible to measure temperature.

1752
Swedish astronomer Andres Celsius proposes a centigrade temperature scale where 0° is the freezing point of water and 100° is the boiling point of water.

In fact, hurricanes have winds sustained at around 74 miles per hour!

OOF!

Ha ha, wind too!

PAF!!

I believe it!

Are you getting this?

1800

1806
Francis Beaufort creates a system for naming wind speeds and aptly names it the Beaufort Wind Force Scale. This scale is used mainly to classify sea conditions.

1900

1960
TIROS 1, the world's first weather satellite, is sent into space equipped with a TV camera.

1964
The U.S. National Severe Storms Laboratory begins experimenting with the use of Doppler radar for weather-monitoring purposes.

2000

2006
Meteorologists hold 8,800 jobs in the United States alone. These scientists work in government and private agencies, in research services, on radio and television stations, and in education.

Visit ConnectED for this unit's **STEM** activity.

Models

In 2004 over 200,000 people died as a tsunami swept across the Indian Ocean, shown in **Figure 1.** How can scientists predict future tsunamis to help save lives? Researchers around the world have developed different models to study tsunami waves and their effects. A **model** is a representation of an object, a process, an event, or a system that is similar to the physical object or idea being explained. Scientists use models to study something that is too big or too small, happens too quickly or too slowly, or is too dangerous or too expensive to study directly.

Models of tsunamis help predict how future tsunamis might impact land. Information from these models can help save ecosystems, buildings, and lives.

Types of Models

Mathematical Models and Computer Simulations

A mathematical model represents an event, a process, or a system, using equations. A mathematical model can be one equation, for example: speed $=$ distance/time. Or, they can be several hundred equations, such as those used to calculate tsunami effects.

A computer simulation is a model that combines many mathematical models. Computer simulations allow the user to easily change variables. Simulations often show a change over time or a sequence of events. Computer programs that include animations and graphics are used to visually display mathematical models.

Researchers from Texas A&M University constructed a tsunami simulation using many mathematical models of Seaside, Oregon, as shown in **Figure 2.** Simulations that use equations to model the force of waves hitting buildings are displayed on a computer screen. Researchers change variables, such as the size, the force, or the shape of tsunami waves, to determine how Seaside might be damaged by a tsunami.

▲ Figure 1 A massive wave approaches the shore in the 2004 Indian Ocean tsunami.

Figure 2 This series of images is from an animated simulation model of a tsunami approaching Seaside, Oregon. ▼

©Reuters/Corbis

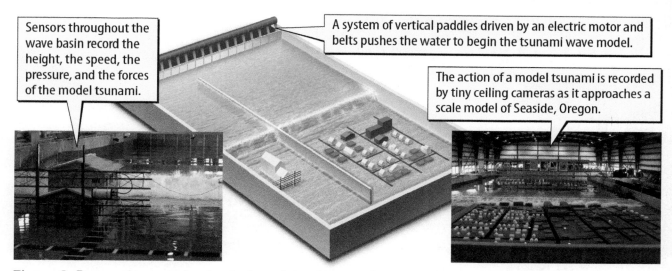

Sensors throughout the wave basin record the height, the speed, the pressure, and the forces of the model tsunami.

A system of vertical paddles driven by an electric motor and belts pushes the water to begin the tsunami wave model.

The action of a model tsunami is recorded by tiny ceiling cameras as it approaches a scale model of Seaside, Oregon.

Figure 3 Researchers study physical models of tsunamis to predict a tsunami's effects.

Physical Models

A physical model is a model that you can see and touch. It shows how parts relate to one another, how something is built, or how complex objects work. Scientists at Oregon State University built physical scale models of Seaside, Oregon, as shown in **Figure 3.** They placed the model at the end of a long wave tank. Sensors in the wave tank and on the model buildings measure and record velocities, forces, and turbulence created by a model tsunami wave. Scientists use these measurements to predict the effects of a tsunami on a coastal town, and to make recommendations for saving lives and preventing damage.

Conceptual Models

Images that represent a process or relationships among ideas are conceptual models. The conceptual model below shows that the United States has a three-part plan for minimizing the effects of tsunamis. Hazard assessment involves identification of areas that are in high risk of tsunamis. Response involves education and public safety. Warning includes a system of sensors that detect the approach of a tsunami.

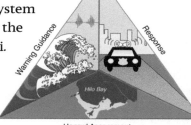

Hazard Assessment

(l)John W. van de Lindt/Colorado State University; (r)Daniel Cox/O.H. Hinsdale Research Laboratory/Oregon State University; (b) Pacific Marine Environmental Laboratory/NOAA

MiniLab

30 minutes

How can you model a tsunami?

What tsunami behaviors can you observe in your own model of a wave tank?

1. Read and complete a lab safety form.
2. Pour **sand** into a **glass pan,** creating a slope from one end of the pan to the other. Fill the pan with water. Place a **cork** in the center of the pan. Draw your setup in your Science Journal.
3. Use a **dowel** to create a wave at the deep end of the pan. Record your observations.
4. Place several **common objects** on end at the shallow end of the pan. Record your observations of the behaviors of the cork and the different objects when you create a wave.

Analyze and Conclude

1. **Describe** What do the different parts of your physical model represent?

2. **Explain** What are some limitations of your physical model?

Weather

THE BIG IDEA How do scientists describe and predict weather?

(Inquiry) Is this a record snowfall?

Buffalo, New York, is famous for its snowstorms, averaging 3 m of snow each year. Other areas of the world might only get a few centimeters of snow a year. In some parts of the world, it never snows.

- Why do some areas get less snow than others?

- How do scientists describe and predict weather?

George Frey/Getty Images

Get Ready to Read

What do you think?

Before you read, decide if you agree or disagree with each of these statements. As you read this chapter, see if you change your mind about any of the statements.

1 Weather is the long-term average of atmospheric patterns of an area.

2 All clouds are at the same altitude within the atmosphere.

3 Precipitation often occurs at the boundaries of large air masses.

4 There are no safety precautions for severe weather, such as tornadoes and hurricanes.

5 Weather variables are measured every day at locations around the world.

6 Modern weather forecasts are done using computers.

Your one-stop online resource
connectED.mcgraw-hill.com

 LearnSmart®

 Chapter Resources Files, Reading Essentials, Get Ready to Read, Quick Vocabulary

 Animations, Videos, Interactive Tables

 Self-checks, Quizzes, Tests

 Project-Based Learning Activities

 Lab Manuals, Safety Videos, Virtual Labs & Other Tools

 Vocabulary, Multilingual eGlossary, Vocab eGames, Vocab eFlashcards

 Personal Tutors

Describing Weather

Reading Guide

Key Concepts 🔑

ESSENTIAL QUESTIONS

- What is weather?
- What variables are used to describe weather?
- How is weather related to the water cycle?

Vocabulary

weather p. 191

air pressure p. 192

humidity p. 192

relative humidity p. 193

dew point p. 193

precipitation p. 195

water cycle p. 195

 Multilingual eGlossary

 **BrainPOP®
Science Video**

 8.ESS.2, SEPS.2, SEPS.5

inquiry Why are clouds different?

If you look closely at the photo, you'll see that there are different types of clouds in the sky. How do clouds form? If all clouds consist of water droplets and ice crystals, why do they look different? Are clouds weather?

Peter de Clercq/Alamy

Can you make clouds in a bag?

When water vapor in the atmosphere cools, it condenses. The resulting water droplets make up clouds.

1. Read and complete a lab safety form.

2. Half-fill a **500-mL beaker** with **ice** and **cold water.**

3. Pour 125 mL of **warm water** into a **resealable plastic bag** and seal the bag.

4. Carefully lower the bag into the ice water. Record your observations in your Science Journal.

Think About This

1. What did you observe when the warm water in the bag was put into the beaker?

2. What explanation can you give for what happened?

3. **Key Concept** What could you see in the natural world that results from the same process?

What is weather?

Everybody talks about the weather. "Nice day, isn't it?" "How was the weather during your vacation?" Talking about weather is so common that we even use weather terms to describe unrelated topics. "That homework assignment was a breeze." Or "I'll take a rain check."

Weather *is the atmospheric conditions, along with short-term changes, of a certain place at a certain time.* If you have ever been caught in a rainstorm on what began as a sunny day, you know the weather can change quickly. Sometimes it changes in just a few hours. But other times your area might have the same sunny weather for several days in a row.

Weather Variables

Perhaps some of the first things that come to mind when you think about weather are temperature and rainfall. As you dress in the morning, you need to know what the temperature will be throughout the day to help you decide what to wear. If it is raining, you might cancel your picnic.

Temperature and rainfall are just two of the variables used to describe weather. Meteorologists, scientists who study and predict weather, use several specific variables that describe a variety of atmospheric conditions. These variables include air temperature, air pressure, wind speed and direction, humidity, cloud coverage, and precipitation.

Key Concept Check What is weather?

REVIEW VOCABULAR

variable
a quantity that ♦
. . .

The measure of the average kinetic energy of molecules in the air is air temperature. When the temperature is high, molecules have a high kinetic energy. Therefore, molecules in warm air move faster than molecules in cold air. Air temperatures vary with time of day, season, location, and altitude.

Air Pressure

The force that a column of air applies on the air or a surface below it is called **air pressure.** Study **Figure 1.** Is air pressure at Earth's surface more or less than air pressure at the top of the atmosphere? Air pressure decreases as altitude increases. Therefore, air pressure is greater at low altitudes than at high altitudes.

You might have heard the term *barometric pressure* during a weather forecast. Barometric pressure refers to air pressure. Air pressure is measured with an instrument called a barometer, shown in **Figure 2.** Air pressure is typically measured in millibars (mb). Knowing the barometric pressure of different areas helps meteorologists predict the weather.

✅ **Reading Check** What instrument measures air pressure?

Wind

As air moves from areas of high pressure to areas of low pressure, it creates wind. Wind direction is the direction from which the wind is blowing. For example, winds that blow from west to east are called westerlies. Meteorologists measure wind speed using an instrument called an anemometer (a nuh MAH muh tur). An anemometer is also shown in **Figure 2.**

Humidity

The amount of water vapor in the air is called **humidity** (hyew MIH duh tee). Humidity can be measured in grams of water per cubic meter of air (g/m^3). When the humidity is high, there is more water vapor in the air. On a day with high humidity, your skin might feel sticky, and sweat might not evaporate from your skin as quickly.

REVIEW VOCABULARY

kinetic energy
energy an object has due to its motion

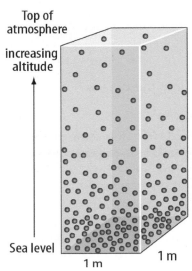

Figure 1 Increasing air pressure comes from having more molecules overhead.

✅ **Visual Check** What happens to air pressure as altitude decreases?

Top of atmosphere
increasing altitude
Sea level
1 m   1 m

Figure 2 Barometers, left, and anemometers, right, are used to measure weather variables.

Relative Humidity

Think about how a sponge can absorb water. At some point, it becomes full and cannot absorb any more water. In the same way, air can only contain a certain amount of water vapor. When air is saturated, it contains as much water vapor as possible. Temperature determines the maximum amount of water vapor air can contain. Warm air can contain more water vapor than cold air. *The amount of water vapor present in the air compared to the maximum amount of water vapor the air could contain at that temperature is called* **relative humidity.**

Relative humidity is measured using an instrument called a psychrometer and is given as a percent. For example, air with a relative humidity of 100 percent cannot contain any more moisture and dew or rain will form. Air that contains only half the water vapor it could hold has a relative humidity of 50 percent.

 Reading Check Compare and contrast humidity and relative humidity.

Dew Point

When a sponge becomes saturated with water, the water starts to drip from the sponge. Similarly, when air becomes saturated with water vapor, the water vapor will condense and form water droplets. When air near the ground becomes saturated, the water vapor in air will condense to a liquid. If the temperature is above 0°C, dew forms. If the temperature is below 0°C, ice crystals, or frost, form. Higher in the atmosphere clouds form. The graph in **Figure 3** shows the total amount of water vapor that air can contain at different temperatures.

When the temperature decreases, the air can hold less moisture. As you just read, the air becomes saturated, condensation occurs, and dew forms. *The temperature at which air is saturated and condensation can occur is called the* **dew point.**

MiniLab   20 minutes

When will dew form?

The relative humidity on a summer day is 80 percent. The temperature is 35°C. Will the dew point be reached if the temperature drops to 25°C later in the evening? Use **Figure 3** below to find the amount of water vapor needed for saturation at each temperature.

1 Calculate the amount of water vapor in air that is 35°C and has 80 percent relative humidity. (Hint: multiply the amount of water vapor air can contain at 35°C by the percent of relative humidity.)

2 At 25°C, air can hold 2.2 g/cm³ of water vapor. If your answer from step 1 is less than 2.2 g/cm³, the dew point is not reached and dew will not form. If the number is greater, dew will form.

Analyze and Conclude

Key Concept After the Sun rises in the morning the air's temperature increases. How does the relative humidity change after sunrise? What does the line represent?

Figure 3 As air temperature increases, the air can contain more water vapor.

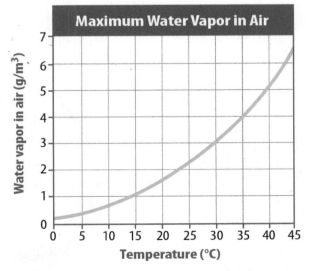

Figure 4 Clouds have different shapes and can be found at different altitudes.

Stratus clouds
- flat, white, and layered
- altitude up to 2,000 m

Cumulus clouds
- fluffy, heaped, or piled up
- 2,000 to 6,000 m altitude

Cirrus clouds
- wispy
- above 6,000 m

Clouds and Fog

When you exhale outside on a cold winter day, you can see the water vapor in your breath condense into a foggy cloud in front of your face. This also happens when warm air containing water vapor cools as it rises in the atmosphere. When the cooling air reaches its dew point, water vapor condenses on small particles in the air and forms droplets. Surrounded by thousands of other droplets, these small droplets block and reflect light. This makes them visible as clouds.

Clouds are water droplets or ice crystals suspended in the atmosphere. Clouds can have different shapes and be present at different altitudes within the atmosphere. Different types of clouds are shown in **Figure 4.** Because we observe that clouds move, we recognize that water and thermal energy are transported from one location to another. Recall that clouds are also important in reflecting some of the Sun's incoming radiation.

A cloud that forms near Earth's surface is called fog. Fog is a suspension of water droplets or ice crystals close to or at Earth's surface. Fog reduces visibility, the distance a person can see into the atmosphere.

Reading Check What is fog?

FOLDABLES

Make a horizontal two-tab book and label the tabs as illustrated. Use it to collect information on clouds and fog. Find similarities and differences.

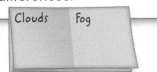

Precipitation

Recall that droplets in clouds form around small solid particles in the atmosphere. These particles might be dust, salt, or smoke. Precipitation occurs when cloud droplets combine and become large enough to fall back to Earth's surface. **Precipitation** *is water, in liquid or solid form, that falls from the atmosphere.* Examples of precipitation–rain, snow, sleet, and hail–are shown in Figure 5.

Rain is precipitation that reaches Earth's surface as droplets of water. Snow is precipitation that reaches Earth's surface as solid, frozen crystals of water. Sleet may originate as snow. The snow melts as it falls through a layer of warm air and refreezes when it passes through a layer of below-freezing air. Other times it is just freezing rain. Hail reaches Earth's surface as large pellets of ice. Hail starts as a small piece of ice that is repeatedly lifted and dropped by an updraft within a cloud. A layer of ice is added with each lifting. When it finally becomes too heavy for the updraft to lift, it falls to Earth.

 Key Concept Check What variables are used to describe weather?

The Water Cycle

Precipitation is an important process in the water cycle. Evaporation and condensation are phase changes that are also important to the water cycle. *The* **water cycle** *is the series of natural processes by which water continually moves among oceans, land, and the atmosphere.* As illustrated in Figure 6, most water vapor enters the atmosphere when water at the ocean's surface is heated and evaporates. Water vapor cools as it rises in the atmosphere and condenses back into a liquid. Eventually, droplets of liquid and solid water form clouds. Clouds produce precipitation, which falls to Earth's surface and later evaporates, continuing the cycle.

 Key Concept Check How is weather related to the water cycle?

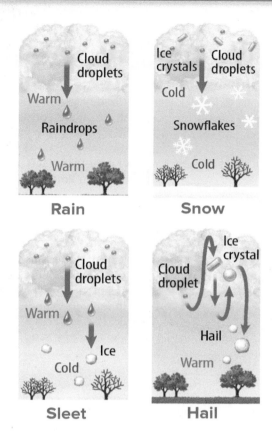

Rain

Snow

Sleet

Hail

▲ **Figure 5** Rain, snow, sleet, and hail are forms of precipitation.

Visual Check What is the difference between snow and sleet?

The Water Cycle  Personal Tutor

Figure 6 The Sun's energy powers the water cycle, which is the continual movement of water between the ocean, the land, and the atmosphere.

Lesson 1 Review

Visual Summary

Weather is the atmospheric conditions, along with short-term changes, of a certain place at a certain time.

Meteorologists use weather variables to describe atmospheric conditions.

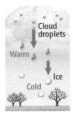

Forms of precipitation include rain, sleet, snow, and hail.

FOLDABLES

Use your lesson Foldable to review the lesson. Save your Foldable for the project at the end of the chapter.

What do you think NOW?

You first read the statements below at the beginning of the chapter.

1. Weather is the long-term average of atmospheric patterns of an area.

2. All clouds are at the same altitude within the atmosphere.

Did you change your mind about whether you agree or disagree with the statements? Rewrite any false statements to make them true.

Use Vocabulary

1. **Define** *humidity* in your own words.

2. **Use the term** *precipitation* in a sentence.

3. _____ is the pressure that a column of air exerts on the surface below it.

Understand Key Concepts

4. Which is NOT a standard weather variable?
   - **A.** air pressure
   - **B.** moon phase
   - **C.** temperature
   - **D.** wind speed

5. **Identify** and describe the different variables used to describe weather.

6. **Relate** humidity to cloud formation.

7. **Describe** how processes in the water cycle are related to weather.

Interpret Graphics

8. **Identify** Which type of precipitation is shown in the diagram below? How does this precipitation form?

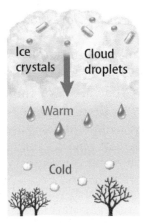

Critical Thinking

9. **Analyze** Why would your ears pop if you climbed a tall mountain?

10. **Differentiate** among cloud formation, fog formation, and dew point.

AMERICAN
MUSEUM OF
NATURAL
HISTORY

Flooding caused widespread devastation in New Orleans, a city that lies below sea level. The storm surge broke through levees that had protected the city.

Is there a link between hurricanes and global warming?

Scientists worry that hurricanes might be getting bigger and happening more often.

On August 29, 2005, Hurricane Katrina roared through New Orleans, Louisiana. The storm destroyed homes and broke through levees, flooding most of the low-lying city. In the wake of the disaster, many wondered whether global warming was responsible. If warm oceans are the fuel for hurricanes, could rising temperatures cause stronger or more frequent hurricanes?

Climate scientists have several ways to investigate this question. They examine past hurricane activity, sea surface temperature, and other climate data. They compare these different types of data and look for patterns. Based on the laws of physics, they put climate and hurricane data into equations. A computer solves these equations and makes computer models. Scientists analyze the models to see whether there is a connection between hurricane activity and different climate variables.

What have scientists learned? So far they have not found a link between warming oceans and the frequency of hurricanes. However, they have found a connection between warming oceans and hurricane strength. Models suggest that rising ocean temperatures might create more destructive hurricanes with stronger winds and more rainfall.

The warm waters of the Gulf of Mexico fueled Hurricane Katrina as it spun toward Louisiana.

But global warming is not the only cause of warming oceans. As the ocean circulates, it goes through cycles of warming and cooling. Data show that the Atlantic Ocean has been in a warming phase for the past few decades.

Whether due to global warming or natural cycles, ocean temperatures are expected to rise even more in coming years. While rising ocean temperatures might not produce more hurricanes, climate research shows they could produce more powerful hurricanes. Perhaps the better question is not what caused Hurricane Katrina, but how we can prepare for equal-strength or more destructive hurricanes in the future.

It's Your Turn

DIAGRAM With a partner, create a storyboard with each frame showing one step in hurricane formation. Label your drawings. Share your storyboard with the class.

Lesson 2

Weather Patterns

Reading Guide

Key Concepts 🔑
ESSENTIAL QUESTIONS

- What are two types of pressure systems?
- What drives weather patterns?
- Why is it useful to understand weather patterns?
- What are some examples of severe weather?

Vocabulary

high-pressure system p. 199

low-pressure system p. 199

air mass p. 200

front p. 202

tornado p. 205

hurricane p. 206

blizzard p. 207

  Multilingual eGlossary

 What's Science Got to do With It?

 SEPS.5

Kyle Niemi/U.S. Coast Guard via Getty Images

Inquiry What caused this flooding?

Surging waves and rain from Hurricane Katrina caused flooding in New Orleans, Louisiana. Why are flooding and other types of severe weather dangerous? How does severe weather form?

Launch Lab

10 minutes

How can temperature affect pressure?

Air molecules that have low energy can be packed closely together. As energy is added to the molecules they begin to move and bump into one another.

1. Read and complete a lab safety form.

2. Close a **resealable plastic bag** except for a small opening. Insert a **straw** through the opening and blow air into the bag until it is as firm as possible. Remove the straw and quickly seal the bag.

3. Submerge the bag in a **container** of **ice water** and hold it there for 2 minutes. Record your observations in your Science Journal.

4. Remove the bag from the ice water and submerge it in **warm water** for 2 minutes. Record your observations.

Think About This

1. What do the results tell you about the movement of air molecules in cold air and in warm air?

2. 🔑 **Key Concept** What property of the air is demonstrated in this activity?

Pressure Systems

Weather is often associated with pressure systems. Recall that air pressure is the weight of the molecules in a large mass of air. When air molecules are cool, they are closer together than when they are warm. Cool air masses have high pressure, or more weight. Warm air masses have low pressure.

A **high-pressure system,** shown in **Figure 7,** *is a large body of circulating air with high pressure at its center and lower pressure outside of the system.* Because air moves from high pressure to low pressure, the air inside the system moves away from the center. Dense air sinks, bringing clear skies and fair weather.

A **low-pressure system,** also shown in **Figure 7,** *is a large body of circulating air with low pressure at its center and higher pressure outside of the system.* This causes air inside the low pressure system to rise. The rising air cools and the water vapor condenses, forming clouds and sometimes precipitation–rain or snow.

🔑 **Key Concept Check** Compare and contrast two types of pressure systems.

Figure 7 Air moving from areas of high pressure to areas of low pressure is called wind.

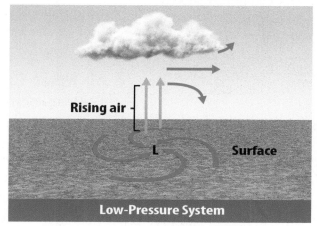

Sinking air

H   Surface

High-Pressure System

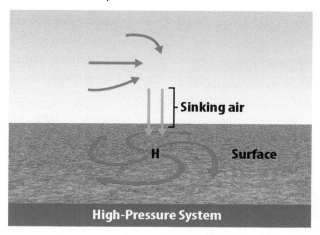

Rising air

L   Surface

Low-Pressure System

Figure 8 Five main air masses impact climate across North America.

✓ **Visual Check** Where does continental polar air come from?

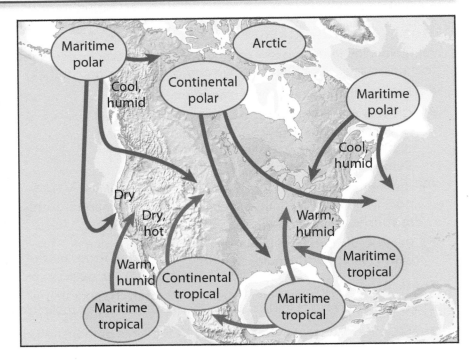

Air Masses

Have you ever noticed that the weather sometimes stays the same for several days in a row? For example, during winter in the northern United States, extremely cold temperatures often last for three or four days in a row. Afterward, several days might follow with warmer temperatures and snow showers.

Air masses are responsible for this pattern. **Air masses** *are large bodies of air that have uniform temperature, humidity, and pressure.* An air mass forms when a large high pressure system lingers over an area for several days. As a high pressure system comes in contact with Earth, the air in the system takes on the temperature and moisture characteristics of the surface below it.

Like high- and low-pressure systems, air masses can extend for a thousand kilometers or more. Sometimes one air mass covers most of the United States. Examples of the main air masses that affect weather in the United States are shown in Figure 8.

Air Mass Classification

Air masses are classified by their temperature and moisture characteristics. Air masses that form over land are referred to as continental air masses. Those that form over water are referred to as maritime masses. Warm air masses that form in the equatorial regions are called tropical. Those that form in cold regions are called polar. Air masses near the poles, over the coldest regions of the globe, are called arctic and antarctic air masses.

FOLDABLES

Fold a sheet of paper into thirds along the long axis. Label the outside *Air Masses*. Make another fold about 2 inches from the long edge of the paper to make a three-column chart. Label as shown.

Arctic Air Masses	Polar Air Masses	Tropical Air Masses

Arctic Air Masses Forming over Siberia and the Arctic are arctic air masses. They contain bitterly cold, dry air. During winter, an arctic air mass can bring temperatures down to -40°C.

Continental Polar Air Masses Because land cannot transfer as much moisture to the air as oceans can, air masses that form over land are drier than air masses that form over oceans. Continental polar air masses are fast-moving and bring cold temperatures in winter and cool weather in summer. Find the continental polar air masses over Canada in **Figure 8.**

Maritime Polar Air Masses Forming over the northern Atlantic and Pacific Oceans, maritime polar air masses are cold and humid. They often bring cloudy, rainy weather.

Continental Tropical Air Masses Because they form in the tropics over dry, desert land, continental tropical air masses are hot and dry. They bring clear skies and high temperatures. Continental tropical air masses usually form during the summer.

Maritime Tropical Air Masses As shown in **Figure 8,** maritime tropical air masses form over the western Atlantic Ocean, the Gulf of Mexico, and the eastern Pacific Ocean. These moist air masses bring hot, humid air to the southeastern United States during summer. In winter, they can bring heavy snowfall.

Air masses can change as they move over the land and ocean. Warm, moist air can move over land and become cool and dry. Cold, dry air can move over water and become moist and warm.

 Key Concept Check What drives weather patterns?

Math Skills

Conversions

To convert Fahrenheit (°F) units to Celsius (°C) units, use this equation:

$$°C = \frac{(°F - 32)}{1.8}$$

Convert **76°F** to °C

1. Always perform the operation in parentheses first.

   (76°F − 32) = 44°F

2. Divide the answer from Step 1 by 1.8.

   $$\frac{44°F}{1.8} = 24°C$$

To convert °C to °F, follow the same steps using the following equation:

°F = (°C × 1.8) + 32

Practice
1. Convert 86°F to °C.
2. Convert 37°C to °F.

 Math Practice

 Personal Tutor

MiniLab
20 minutes

How can you observe air pressure?

Although air seems very light, air molecules do exert pressure. You can observe air pressure in action in this activity.

1. Read and complete a lab safety form.
2. Tightly cap the empty **plastic bottle.**
3. Place the bottle in a **bucket of ice** for 10 minutes. Record your observations in your Science Journal.

Analyze and Conclude

1. **Interpret** how air pressure affected the bottle.

2. **Key Concept** Discuss how changing air pressure in Earth's atmosphere affects other things on Earth, such as weather.

Hutchings Photography/Digital Light Source

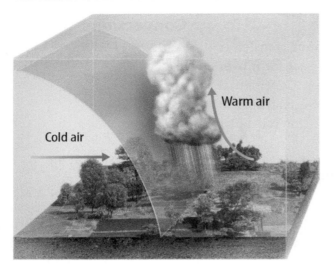
Cold

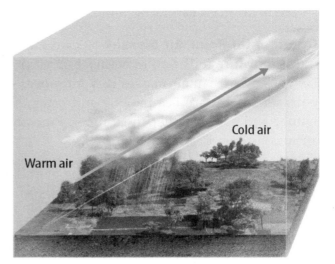
Warm

Figure 9 Certain types of fronts are associated with specific weather.

Visual Check Describe the difference between a cold front and a warm front.

SCIENCE USE V. COMMON USE

front

Science Use a boundary between two air masses

Common Use the foremost part or surface of something

Fronts

In 1918, Norwegian meteorologist Jacob Bjerknes (BYURK nehs) and his coworkers were busy developing a new method for forecasting the weather. Bjerknes noticed that specific types of weather occur at the boundaries between different air masses. Because he was trained in the army, Bjerknes used a military term to describe this boundary—front.

A military front is the boundary between opposing armies in a battle. *A weather* **front**, *however, is a boundary between two air masses.* Drastic weather changes often occur at fronts. As wind carries an air mass away from the area where it formed, the air mass will eventually collide with another air mass. Changes in temperature, humidity, cloud types, wind, and precipitation are common at fronts.

Cold Fronts

When a colder air mass moves toward a warmer air mass, a cold front forms, as shown in **Figure 9.** The cold air, which is denser than the warm air, pushes underneath the warm air mass. The warm air rises and cools. Water vapor in the air condenses and clouds form. Showers and thunderstorms often form along cold fronts. It is common for temperatures to decrease as much as 10°C when a cold front passes through. The wind becomes gusty and changes direction. In many cases, cold fronts give rise to severe storms.

Reading Check What types of weather are associated with cold fronts?

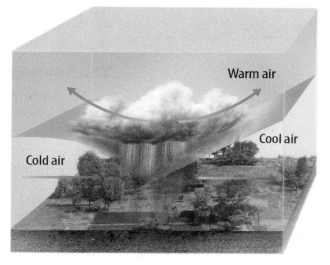

Stationary   **Occluded**

Warm Fronts

As shown in Figure 9, a warm front forms when less dense, warmer air moves toward colder, denser air. The warm air rises as it glides above the cold air mass. When water vapor in the warm air condenses, it creates a wide blanket of clouds. These clouds often bring steady rain or snow for several hours or even days. A warm front not only brings warmer temperatures, but it also causes the wind to shift directions.

Both a cold front and a warm front form at the edge of an approaching air mass. Because air masses are large, the movement of fronts is used to make weather forecasts. When a cold front passes through your area, temperatures will remain low for the next few days. When a warm front arrives, the weather will become warmer and more humid.

Stationary and Occluded Fronts

Sometimes an approaching front will stall for several days with warm air on one side of it and cold air on the other side. When the boundary between two air masses stalls, the front is called a stationary front. Study the stationary front shown in Figure 9. Cloudy skies and light rain are found along stationary fronts.

Cold fronts move faster than warm fronts. When a fast-moving cold front catches up with a slow-moving warm front, an occluded or blocked front forms. Occluded fronts, shown in Figure 9, usually bring precipitation.

 Key Concept Check Why is it useful to understand weather patterns associated with fronts?

Severe Weather

Some weather events can cause major damage, injuries, and death. These events, such as thunderstorms, tornadoes, hurricanes, and blizzards, are called severe weather.

Thunderstorms

Also known as electrical storms because of their lightning, thunderstorms have warm temperatures, moisture, and rising air, which may be supplied by a low-pressure system. When these conditions occur, a cumulus cloud can grow into a 10-km-tall thundercloud, or cumulonimbus cloud, in as little as 30 minutes.

A typical thunderstorm has a three-stage life cycle, shown in Figure 10. The cumulus stage is dominated by cloud formation and updrafts. Updrafts are air currents moving vertically away from the ground. After the cumulus cloud has been created, downdrafts begin to appear. Downdrafts are air currents moving vertically toward the ground. In the mature stage, heavy winds, rain, and lightning dominate the area. Within 30 minutes of reaching the mature stage, the thunderstorm begins to fade, or dissipate. In the dissipation stage, updrafts stop, winds die down, lightning ceases, and precipitation weakens.

Strong updrafts and downdrafts within a thunderstorm cause millions of tiny ice crystals to rise and sink, crashing into each other. This creates positively and negatively charged particles in the cloud. The difference in the charges of particles between the cloud and the charges of particles on the ground eventually creates electricity. This is seen as a bolt of lightning. Lightning can move from cloud to cloud, cloud to ground, or ground to cloud. It can heat the nearby air to more than 27,000°C. Air molecules near the bolt rapidly expand and then contract, creating the sound identified as thunder.

ACADEMIC VOCABULARY

dominate
(verb) to exert the guiding influence on

Figure 10 Thunderstorms have distinct stages characterized by the direction in which air is moving.

Thunderstorms 🔑

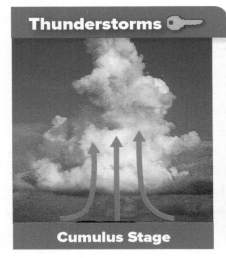

Cumulus Stage

Mature Stage

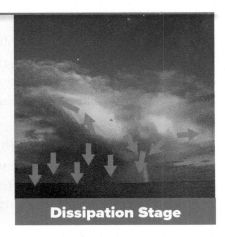

Dissipation Stage

✓ **Visual Check** Describe what happens during each stage of a thunderstorm.

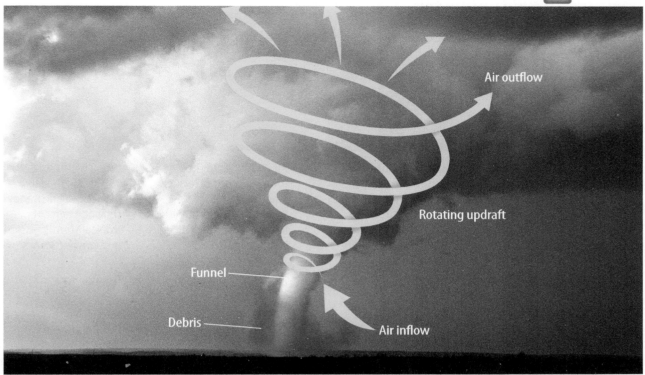

Air outflow

Rotating updraft

Funnel

Debris

Air inflow

Figure 11 A funnel cloud forms when updrafts within a thunderstorm begin rotating.

Tornadoes

Perhaps you have seen photos of the damage from a tornado. *A **tornado** is a violent, whirling column of air in contact with the ground.* Most tornadoes have a diameter of several hundred meters. The largest tornadoes exceed 1,500 m in diameter. The intense, swirling winds within tornadoes can reach speeds of more than 400 km/h. These winds are strong enough to send cars, trees, and even entire houses flying through the air. Tornadoes usually last only a few minutes. More destructive tornadoes, however, can last for several hours.

Formation of Tornadoes When thunderstorm updrafts begin to rotate, as shown in Figure 11, tornadoes can form. Swirling winds spiral downward from the thunderstorm's base, creating a funnel cloud. When the funnel reaches the ground, it becomes a tornado. Although the swirling air is invisible, you can easily see the debris lifted by the tornado.

✔️ **Reading Check** How do tornadoes form?

Tornado Alley More tornadoes occur in the United States than anywhere else on Earth. The central United States, from Nebraska to Texas, experiences the most tornadoes. This area has been nicknamed Tornado Alley. In this area, cold air blowing southward from Canada frequently collides with warm, moist air moving northward from the Gulf of Mexico. These conditions are ideal for severe thunderstorms and tornadoes.

Classifying Tornadoes Dr. Ted Fujita developed a method for classifying tornadoes based on the damage they cause. On the Enhanced Fujita Scale, F0 tornadoes cause light damage, breaking tree branches and damaging billboards. F1 though F4 tornadoes cause moderate to devastating damage, including tearing roofs from homes, derailing trains, and throwing vehicles in the air. F5 tornadoes cause incredible damage, such as demolishing concrete and steel buildings and pulling the bark from trees.

Figure 12 Hurricanes consist of alternating bands of heavy precipitation and sinking air.

Hurricane Formation

Low pressure

1 As warm, moist air rises into the atmosphere, it cools, water vapor condenses, and clouds form. As more air rises, it creates an area of low pressure over the ocean.

2 As air continues to rise, a tropical depression forms. Tropical depressions bring thunderstorms with winds between 37–62 km/h.

3 Air continues to rise, rotating counterclockwise. The storm builds to a tropical storm with winds in excess of 63 km/h. It produces strong thunderstorms.

4 When winds exceed 119 km/h, the storm becomes a hurricane. Only one percent of tropical storms become hurricanes.

Inside a Hurricane

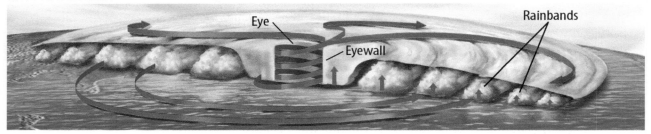

Eye

Eyewall

Rainbands

✓ **Visual Check** How do hurricanes form?

WORD ORIGIN

hurricane
from Spanish *huracan,* means "tempest"

Hurricanes

An intense tropical storm with winds exceeding 119 km/h is a **hurricane.** Hurricanes are the most destructive storms on Earth. Like tornadoes, hurricanes have a circular shape with intense, swirling winds. However, hurricanes do not form over land. Hurricanes typically form in late summer over warm, tropical ocean water. **Figure 12** sequences the steps in hurricane formation. A typical hurricane is 480 km across, more than 150 thousand times larger than a tornado. At the center of a hurricane is the eye, an area of clear skies and light winds.

Damage from hurricanes occurs as a result of strong winds and flooding. While still out at sea, hurricanes create high waves that can flood coastal areas. As a hurricane crosses the coastline, or makes landfall, strong rains intensify and can flood and devastate entire areas. But once a hurricane moves over land or colder water, it loses its energy and dissipates.

In other parts of the world, these intense tropical storms have other names. In Asia, the same type of storm is called a typhoon. In Australia it is called a tropical cyclone.

Winter Storms

Winter weather can be severe and hazardous. Ice storms, as shown in **Figure 13,** can down power lines and tree branches and make driving dangerous. A **blizzard** *is a violent winter storm characterized by freezing temperatures, strong winds, and blowing snow.* During a blizzard, swirling snow reduces visibility, and freezing temperatures can cause frostbite and hypothermia (hi poh THER mee uh).

Freezing Rain

Figure 13 The weight of ice from freezing rain can cause trees, power lines, and other structures to break.

 Key Concept Check What are examples of severe weather?

Severe Weather Safety

The U.S. National Weather Service issues watches and warnings for different types of severe weather. A watch means that severe weather is possible. A warning means that severe weather is already occurring. Paying close attention to severe weather watches and warnings is important and could save your life.

It is also important to know how to protect yourself during dangerous weather. During thunderstorms, you should stay inside if possible, and stay away from metal objects and electrical cords. If you are outside, stay away from water, high places, and isolated trees. Dressing properly is important in all kinds of weather. When windchill temperatures are below −20°C, you should dress in layers, keep your head and fingers covered, and limit your time outdoors.

Not all weather safety pertains to bad weather. The Sun's ultraviolet (UV) radiation can cause health risks, including skin cancer. The U.S. National Weather Service issues a daily UV Index Forecast. Precautions on sunny days include covering up, using sunscreen, and wearing a hat and sunglasses. Surfaces such as snow, water, and beach sand can double the effects of the Sun's UV radiation.

AP Photo/Dick Blume, Syracuse Newspapers

Lesson 2 Review

Visual Summary

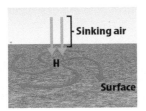

Low-pressure systems, high-pressure systems, and air masses all influence weather.

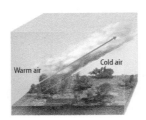

Weather often changes as a front passes through an area.

The National Weather Service issues warnings about severe weather such as thunderstorms, tornadoes, hurricanes, and blizzards.

FOLDABLES

Use your lesson Foldable to review the lesson. Save your Foldable for the project at the end of the chapter.

What do you think NOW?

You first read the statements below at the beginning of the chapter.

3. Precipitation often occurs at the boundaries of large air masses.

4. There are no safety precautions for severe weather, such as tornadoes and hurricanes.

Did you change your mind about whether you agree or disagree with the statements? Rewrite any false statements to make them true.

Use Vocabulary

1 **Distinguish** between an air mass and a front.

2 **Define** *low-pressure system* using your own words.

3 **Use the term** *high-pressure system* in a sentence.

Understand Key Concepts

4 Which air mass is humid and warm?
   A. continental polar
   B. continental tropical
   C. maritime polar
   D. maritime tropical

5 **Give an example** of cold-front weather.

6 **Compare and contrast** hurricanes and tornadoes.

7 **Explain** how thunderstorms form.

Interpret Graphics

8 **Compare and Contrast** Copy and fill in the graphic organizer below to compare and contrast high-pressure and low-pressure systems.

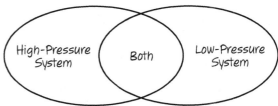

Critical Thinking

9 **Suggest** a reason that low-pressure systems are cloudy and rainy or snowy.

10 **Design** a pamphlet that contains tips on how to stay safe during different types of severe weather.

Math Skills  Math Practice

11 Convert 212°F to °C.

12 Convert 20°C to °F.

©Eric Nguyen/Corbis

Why does the weather change?

One day it is sunny, the next day it is pouring rain. If you look at only one location, the patterns that cause the weather to change are difficult to see. However, when you look on the large scale, the patterns become apparent.

Learn It

Recognizing cause and effect is an important part of science and conducting experiments. Scientists look for cause-and-effect relationships between variables. The maps below show the movement of fronts and pressure systems over a two-day period. What effect will these systems have on the weather as they move across the United States?

Try It

1. Examine the weather maps below. The thin black lines on each map represent areas where the barometric pressure is the same. The pressure is indicated by the number on the line. The center of a low- or high-pressure system is indicated by the word LOW or HIGH. Identify the location of low- and high- pressure systems on each map. Use the key below the maps to the identify the location of warm and cold fronts.

2. Find locations A, B, C, and where you live on the map. For each location, describe how the systems change positions over the two days.

3. What is the cause of and effect on precipitation and temperature at each location?

Apply It

4. The low-pressure system produced several tornadoes. Which location did they occur closest to? Explain.

5. The weather patterns generally move from west to east. Predict the weather on the third day for each location.

6. One day it is clear and sunny, but you notice that the pressure is less than it was the day before. What weather might be coming? Why?

7. 🔑 **Key Concept** How does understanding weather patterns help make predicting the weather more accurate?

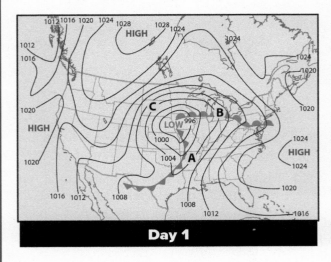

Day 1

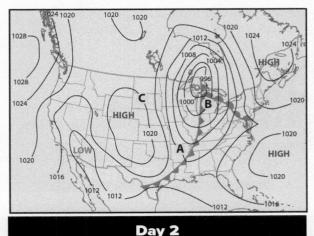

Day 2

Cold front

Warm front

Lesson 3

Reading Guide

Key Concepts

ESSENTIAL QUESTIONS

- What instruments are used to measure weather variables?

- How are computer models used to predict the weather?

Vocabulary

surface report p. 211

upper-air report p. 211

Doppler radar p. 212

isobar p. 213

computer model p. 214

 Multilingual eGlossary

8.ESS.1, SEPS.1, SEPS.2, SEPS.3, SEPS.4, SEPS.5, SEPS.8, 6-8.LST.5.1, 6-8.LST.7.1

Weather Forecasts

Inquiry **What's inside?**

Information about weather variables is collected by the weather radar station shown here. Data, such as the amount of rain falling in a weather system, help meteorologists make accurate predictions about severe weather. What other instruments do meteorologists use to forecast weather? How do they collect and use data?

Signature Exposures Photography by Shannon Bileski/Getty Images

Can you understand the weather report?

Weather reports use numbers and certain vocabulary terms to help you understand the weather conditions in a given area for a given time period. Listen to a weather report for your area. Can you record all the information reported?

1. In your Science Journal, make a list of data you would expect to hear in a weather report.

2. Listen carefully to a **recording of a weather report** and jot down numbers and measurements you hear next to those on your list.

3. Listen a second time and make adjustments to your original notes, such as adding more data, if necessary.

4. Listen a third time, then share the weather forecast as you heard it.

Think About This

1. What measurements were difficult for you to apply to understanding the weather report?

2. Why are so many different types of data needed to give a complete weather report?

3. List the instruments that might be used to collect each kind of data.

4. 🔑 **Key Concept** Where do meteorologists obtain the data they use to make a weather forecast?

Measuring the Weather

Being a meteorologist is like being a doctor. Using specialized instruments and visual observations, the doctor first measures the condition of your body. The doctor later combines these measurements with his or her knowledge of medical science. The result is a forecast of your future health, such as, "You'll feel better in a few days if you rest and drink plenty of fluids."

Similarly, meteorologists, scientists who study weather, use specialized instruments to measure conditions in the atmosphere, as you read in Lesson 1. These instruments include thermometers to measure temperature, barometers to measure air pressure, psychrometers to measure relative humidity, and anemometers to measure wind speed.

Surface and Upper-Air Reports

A **surface report** *describes a set of weather measurements made on Earth's surface.* Weather variables are measured by a weather station—a collection of instruments that report temperature, air pressure, humidity, precipitation, and wind speed and direction. Cloud amounts and visibility are often measured by human observers.

An **upper-air report** *describes wind, temperature, and humidity conditions above Earth's surface.* These atmospheric conditions are measured by a radiosonde (RAY dee oh sahnd), a package of weather instruments carried many kilometers above the ground by a weather balloon. Radiosonde reports are made twice a day simultaneously at hundreds of locations around the world.

Satellite and Radar Images

Images taken from satellites orbiting about 35,000 km above Earth provide information about weather conditions on Earth. A visible light image, such as the one shown in **Figure 14,** shows white clouds over Earth. The infrared image, also shown in **Figure 14,** shows infrared energy in false color, a color that is different from the actual color of the image. The infrared energy comes from Earth and is stored in the atmosphere as thermal energy. Monitoring infrared energy provides information about cloud height and atmospheric temperature.

Figure 14 Meteorologists use visible light and infrared satellite images to identify fronts and air masses.

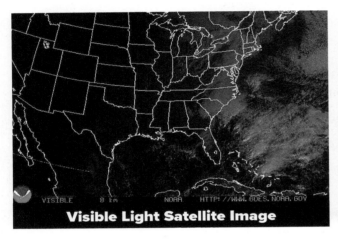

Visible Light Satellite Image

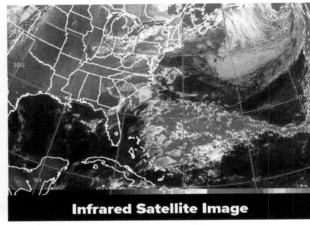

Infrared Satellite Image

Visual Check How is an infrared satellite image different from a visible light satellite image?

Radar measures precipitation when radio waves bounce off raindrops and snowflakes. **Doppler radar** *is a specialized type of radar that can detect precipitation as well as the movement of small particles, which can be used to approximate wind speed.* Because the movement of precipitation is caused by wind, Doppler radar can be used to estimate wind speed. This can be especially important during severe weather, such as tornadoes or thunderstorms.

Key Concept Check Identify the weather variables that radiosondes, infrared satellites, and Doppler radar measure.

Weather Maps

Every day, thousands of surface reports, upper-air reports, and satellite and radar observations are made around the world. Meteorologists have developed tools that help them simplify and understand this enormous amount of weather data.

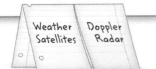
National Oceanic and Atmospheric Administration (NOAA)

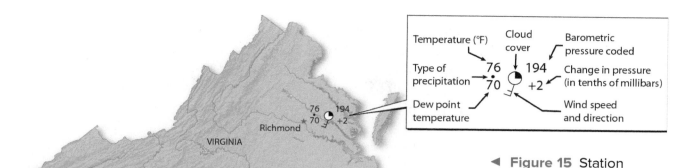

Richmond

VIRGINIA

Temperature (°F)   Cloud cover   Barometric pressure coded

Type of precipitation   76   194   Change in pressure (in tenths of millibars)
                        70   +2

Dew point temperature   Wind speed and direction

◄ **Figure 15** Station models contain information about weather variables.

The Station Model

As shown in **Figure 15,** the station model diagram displays data from many different weather measurements for a particular location. It uses numbers and symbols to display data and observations from surface reports and upper-air reports.

Mapping Temperature and Pressure

In addition to station models, weather maps also have other symbols. For example, **isobars** *are lines that connect all places on a map where pressure has the same value.* Locate an isobar on the map in **Figure 16.** Isobars show the location of high- and low-pressure systems. Isobars also provide information about wind speed. Winds are strong when isobars are close together. Winds are weaker when isobars are farther apart.

In a similar way, isotherms (not shown) are lines that connect places with the same temperature. Isotherms show which areas are warm and which are cold. Fronts are represented as lines with symbols on them, as indicated in **Figure 16.**

WORD ORIGIN · · · · · · · · · · · ·

isobar
from Greek *isos,* means "equal"; and *baros,* means "heavy"

✓ **Reading Check** Compare isobars and isotherms.

Weather Map

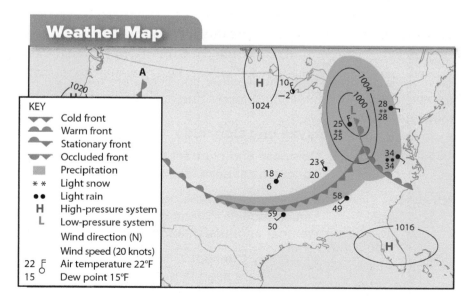

KEY
▼▼▼	Cold front
▲▲▲	Warm front
▲▼	Stationary front
▼▼	Occluded front
▨	Precipitation
✱ ✱	Light snow
••	Light rain
H	High-pressure system
L	Low-pressure system
	Wind direction (N)
	Wind speed (20 knots)
22	Air temperature 22°F
15	Dew point 15°F

▶ Animation

◄ **Figure 16** Weather maps contain symbols that provide information about the weather.

✓ **Visual Check** Which symbols represent high-pressure and low-pressure systems?

Figure 17 Meteorologists analyze data from various sources—such as radar and computer models—in order to prepare weather forecasts.

Predicting the Weather

Modern weather forecasts are made with the help of computer models, such as the ones shown in Figure 17. **Computer models** *are detailed computer programs that solve a set of complex mathematical formulas.* The formulas predict what temperatures and winds might occur, when and where it will rain and snow, and what types of clouds will form.

Government meteorological offices also use computers and the Internet to exchange weather measurements continuously throughout the day. Weather maps are created and forecasts are made using computer models. Then, through television, radio, newspapers, and the Internet, the maps and forecasts are made available to the public.

 Key Concept Check How are computers used to predict the weather?

MiniLab

20 minutes

How is weather represented on a map?

Meteorologists often use station models to record what the weather conditions are for a particular location. A station model is a diagram containing symbols and numbers that displays many different weather measurements.

Use the **station model legend** provided by your teacher to interpret the data in each station model shown here.

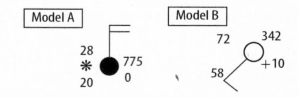

Model A

28
* 775
20
● 0

Model B

72   342
○ +10
58

Analyze and Conclude

1. **Compare and contrast** the weather conditions at each station model.

2. **Explain** why meteorologists might use station models instead of reporting weather information another way.

3. **Key Concept** Discuss what variables are used to describe weather.

Dennis MacDonald/Alamy

Lesson 3 Review

Visual Summary

Weather variables are measured by weather stations, radiosondes, satellites, and Doppler radar.

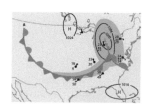

Weather maps contain information in the form of a station model, isobars and isotherms, and symbols for fronts and pressure systems.

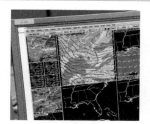

Meteorologists use computer models to help forecast the weather.

FOLDABLES®

Use your lesson Foldable to review the lesson. Save your Foldable for the project at the end of the chapter.

What do you think NOW?

You first read the statements below at the beginning of the chapter.

5. Weather variables are measured every day at locations around the world.

6. Modern weather forecasts are done using computers.

Did you change your mind about whether you agree or disagree with the statements? Rewrite any false statements to make them true.

Use Vocabulary

1 **Define** *computer model* in your own words.

2 A line connecting places with the same pressure is called a(n) _____.

3 **Use the term** *surface report* in a sentence.

Understand Key Concepts 🔑

4 Which diagram shows surface weather measurements?
- **A.** an infrared satellite image
- **B.** an upper air chart
- **C.** a station model
- **D.** a visible light satellite image

5 **List** two ways that upper-air weather conditions are measured.

6 **Describe** how computers are used in weather forecasting.

7 **Distinguish** between isobars and isotherms.

Interpret Graphics

8 **Identify** Copy and fill in the graphic organizer below to identify the components of a surface map.

Symbol	Meaning
H	

Critical Thinking

9 **Suggest** ways to forecast the weather without using computers.

10 **Explain** why isobars and isotherms make it easier to understand a weather map.

Materials

graph paper

local weather maps

outdoor thermometer

barometer

Can you predict the weather?

Weather forecasts are important–not just so you are dressed right when you leave the house, but also to help farmers know when to plant and harvest, to help cities know when to call in the snow plows, and to help officials know when and where to evacuate in advance of severe weather.

Ask a Question

Can you predict the weather?

Make Observations

1 Read and complete a lab safety form.

2 Collect weather data daily for a period of one week. Temperature and pressure should be recorded as a number, but precipitation, wind conditions, and cloud cover can be described in words. Make your observations at the same time each day.

3 Graph temperature in degrees and air pressure in millibars on the same sheet of paper, placing the graphs side by side, as shown on the next page. Beneath the graphs, for each day, add notes that describe precipitation, wind conditions, and cloud cover.

(t to b)Aaron Haupt; (others)Hutchings Photography/Digital Light Source;

3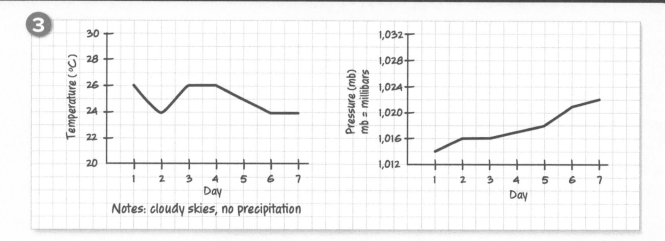

Notes: cloudy skies, no precipitation

Form a Hypothesis

4 Examine your data and the weather maps. Look for factors that appear to be related. For example, your data might suggest that when the pressure decreases, clouds follow.

5 Find three sets of data pairs that seem to be related. Form three hypotheses, one for each set of data pairs.

Test Your Hypothesis

6 Look at your last day of data. Using your hypotheses, predict the weather for the next day.

7 Collect weather data the next day and evaluate your predictions.

8 Repeat steps 6 and 7 for at least two more days.

Analyze and Conclude

9 **Analyze** Compare your hypotheses with the results of your predictions. How successful were you? What additional information might have improved your predictions?

10 **The Big Idea** Scientists have more complex and sophisticated tools to help them predict their weather, but with fairly simple tools, you can make an educated guess. Write a one-paragraph summary of the data you collected and how you interpreted it to predict the weather.

Communicate Your Results

For each hypothesis you generated, make a small poster that states the hypothesis, shows a graph that supports it, and shows the results of your predictions. Write a concluding statement about the reliability of your hypothesis. Share your results with the class.

 **Extension**

Investigate other forms of data you might collect and find out how they would help you to make a forecast. Try them out for a week and see if your ability to make predictions improves.

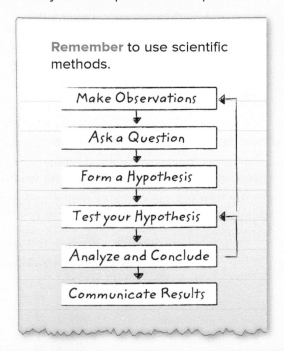

Remember to use scientific methods.

Make Observations → Ask a Question → Form a Hypothesis → Test your Hypothesis → Analyze and Conclude → Communicate Results

Chapter 6 Study Guide

THE BIG IDEA Scientists use weather variables to describe weather and study weather systems. Scientists use computers to predict the weather.

Key Concepts Summary 🔑

Lesson 1: Describing Weather

- **Weather** is the atmospheric conditions, along with short-term changes, of a certain place at a certain time.
- Variables used to describe weather are air temperature, **air pressure,** wind, **humidity,** and **relative humidity.**
- The processes in the water cycle—evaporation, condensation, and **precipitation**—are all involved in the formation of different types of weather.

Lesson 2: Weather Patterns

- **Low-pressure systems** and **high-pressure systems** are two systems that influence weather.
- Weather patterns are driven by the movement of **air masses.**
- Understanding weather patterns helps make weather forecasts more accurate.
- Severe weather includes thunderstorms, **tornadoes, hurricanes,** and **blizzards.**

Lesson 3: Weather Forecasts

- Thermometers, barometers, anemometers, radiosondes, satellites, and **Doppler radar** are used to measure weather variables.
- **Computer models** use complex mathematical formulas to predict temperature, wind, cloud formation, and precipitation.

Vocabulary

weather p. 191
air pressure p. 192
humidity p. 192
relative humidity p. 193
dew point p. 193
precipitation p. 195
water cycle p. 195

high-pressure system p. 199
low-pressure system p. 199
air mass p. 200
front p. 202
tornado p. 205
hurricane p. 206
blizzard p. 207

surface report p. 211
upper-air report p. 211
Doppler radar p. 212
isobar p. 213
computer model p. 214

FOLDABLES® Chapter Project

Assemble your lesson Foldables as shown to make a Chapter Project. Use the project to review what you have learned in this chapter.

Use Vocabulary

1 The pressure that a column of air exerts on the area below it is called _____.

2 The amount of water vapor in the air is called _____.

3 The natural process in which water constantly moves among oceans, land, and the atmosphere is called the _____.

4 A(n) _____ is a boundary between two air masses.

5 At the center of a(n) _____, air rises and forms clouds and precipitation.

6 A continental polar _____ brings cold temperatures during winter.

7 When the same _____ passes through two locations on a weather map, both locations have the same pressure.

8 The humidity in the air compared to the amount air can hold is the _____.

Link Vocabulary and Key Concepts

 Interactive Concept Map

Copy this concept map, and then use vocabulary terms from the previous page to complete the concept map.

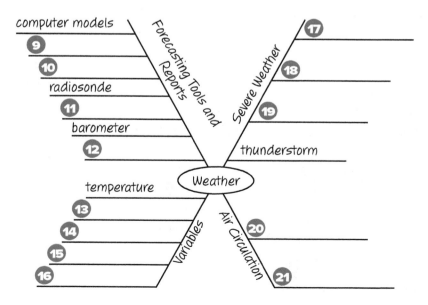

Understand Key Concepts

1 Clouds form when water changes from
- A. gas to liquid.
- B. liquid to gas.
- C. solid to gas.
- D. solid to liquid.

2 Which type of precipitation reaches Earth's surface as large pellets of ice?
- A. hail
- B. rain
- C. sleet
- D. snow

3 Which of these sinking-air situations usually brings fair weather?
- A. air mass
- B. cold front
- C. high-pressure system
- D. low-pressure system

4 Which air mass contains cold, dry air?
- A. continental polar
- B. continental tropical
- C. maritime tropical
- D. maritime polar

5 Study the front below.

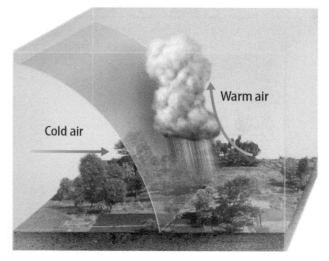

How does this type of front form?
- A. A cold front overtakes a warm front.
- B. Cold air moves toward warmer air.
- C. The boundary between two fronts stalls.
- D. Warm air moves toward colder air.

6 Which is an intense tropical storm with winds exceeding 119 km/h?
- A. blizzard
- B. hurricane
- C. thunderstorm
- D. tornado

7 Which contains measurements of temperature, air pressure, humidity, precipitation, and wind speed and direction?
- A. a radar image
- B. a satellite image
- C. a surface report
- D. a weather station

8 What does Doppler radar measure?
- A. air pressure
- B. air temperature
- C. the rate at which air pressure changes
- D. the speed at which precipitation travels

9 Study the station model below.

What is the temperature according to the station model?
- A. 3°F
- B. 55°F
- C. 81°F
- D. 138°F

10 Which describes cirrus clouds?
- A. flat, white, and layered
- B. fluffy, at middle altitudes
- C. heaped or piled up
- D. wispy, at high altitudes

11 Which instrument measures wind speed?
- A. anemometer
- B. barometer
- C. psychrometer
- D. thermometer

Critical Thinking

12 Predict Suppose you are on a ship near the equator in the Atlantic Ocean. You notice that the barometric pressure is dropping. Predict what type of weather you might experience.

13 Compare a continental polar air mass with a maritime tropical air mass.

14 Assess why clouds usually form in the center of a low-pressure system.

15 Predict how maritime air masses would change if the oceans froze.

16 Compare two types of severe weather.

17 Interpret Graphics Identify the front on the weather map below. Predict the weather for areas along the front.

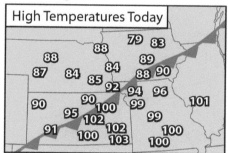

High Temperatures Today

18 Assess the validity of the weather forecast: "Tomorrow's weather will be similar to today's weather."

19 Compare and contrast surface weather reports and upper-air reports. Why is it important for meterologists to monitor weather variables high above Earth's surface?

Writing in Science

20 Write a paragraph about the ways computers have improved weather forecasts. Be sure to include a topic sentence and a concluding sentence.

REVIEW THE B|G IDEA

21 Identify the instruments used to measure weather variables.

22 How do scientists use weather variables to describe and predict weather?

23 Describe the factors that influence weather.

24 Use the factors listed in question 23 to describe how a continental polar air mass can change to a maritime polar air mass.

Math Skills ×÷

 Math Practice

Use Conversions

25 Convert from Fahrenheit to Celsius.
  a. Convert 0°F to °C.
  b. Convert 104°F to °C.

26 Convert from Celsius to Fahrenheit.
  a. Convert 0°C to °F.
  b. Convert −40°C to °F.

27 The Kelvin scale of temperature measurement starts at zero and has the same unit size as Celsius degrees. Zero degrees Celsius is equal to 273 kelvin.

Convert 295 K to Fahrenheit.

Standardized Test Practice

Record your answers on the answer sheet provided by your teacher or on a sheet of paper.

Multiple Choice

1 Which measures the average kinetic energy of air molecules?

  A humidity

  B pressure

  C speed

  D temperature

Use the diagram below to answer question 2.

2 Which weather system does the above diagram illustrate?

  A high pressure

  B hurricane

  C low pressure

  D tornado

3 What causes weather to remain the same several days in a row?

  A air front

  B air mass

  C air pollution

  D air resistance

4 Which lists the stages of a thunderstorm in order?

  A cumulus, dissipation, mature

  B cumulus, mature, dissipation

  C dissipation, cumulus, mature

  D dissipation, mature, cumulus

5 What causes air to reach its dew point?

  A decreasing air currents

  B decreasing humidity

  C dropping air pressure

  D dropping temperatures

6 Which measures air pressure?

  A anemometer

  B barometer

  C psychrometer

  D thermometer

Use the diagram below to answer question 7.

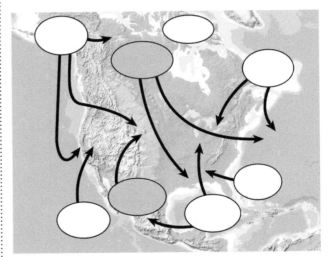

7 Which type of air masses do the shaded ovals in the diagram depict?

  A antarctic

  B arctic

  C continental

  D maritime

8 Which BEST expresses moisture saturation?

  A barometric pressure

  B relative humidity

  C weather front

  D wind direction

Use the diagram below to answer question 9.

Maximum Water Vapor in Air

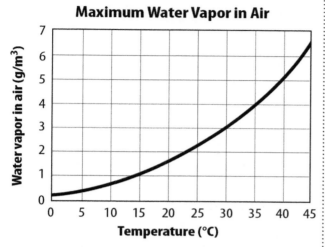

9 What happens to maximum moisture content when air temperatures increase from 15°C to 30°C?

   A increases from 1 to 2 g/m^3

   B increases from 1 to 3 g/m^3

   C increases from 2 to 3 g/m^3

   D increases from 2 to 4 g/m^3

10 When isobars are close together on a weather map,

   A cloud cover is extensive.

   B temperatures are high.

   C warm fronts prevail.

   D winds are strong.

11 Which provides energy for the water cycle?

   A air currents

   B Earth's core

   C ocean currents

   D the Sun

Constructed Response

Use the table below to answer question 12.

Weather Variable	Measurement

12 In the table above, list the variables weather scientists use to describe weather. Then describe the unit of measurement for each variable.

Use the diagram below to answer questions 13 and 14.

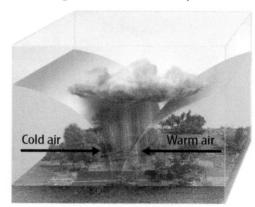

Cold air Warm air

13 What does the diagram above depict?

14 Describe the weather conditions associated with the diagram.

15 How do weather fronts form?

NEED EXTRA HELP?														
If You Missed Question...	1	2	3	4	5	6	7	8	9	10	11	12	13	14	15
Go to Lesson...	1	2	2	2	1	1, 3	2	1	1	3	1	1	2	2	2

Climate

THE BIG IDEA

What is climate and how does it impact life on Earth?

Inquiry **What happened to this tree?**

Climate differs from one area of Earth to another. Some areas have little rain and high temperatures. Other areas have low temperatures and lots of snow. Where this tree grows—on Humphrey Head Point in England—there is constant wind.

- What are the characteristics of different climates?

- What factors affect the climate of a region?

- What is climate and how does it impact life on Earth?

Get Ready to Read

What do you think?

Before you read, decide if you agree or disagree with each of these statements. As you read this chapter, see if you change your mind about any of the statements.

1. Locations at the center of large continents usually have the same climate as locations along the coast.

2. Latitude does not affect climate.

3. Climate on Earth today is the same as it has been in the past.

4. Climate change occurs in short-term cycles.

5. Human activities can impact climate.

6. You can help reduce the amount of greenhouse gases released into the atmosphere.

connectED

Your one-stop online resource
connectED.mcgraw-hill.com

LS   LearnSmart®

   Chapter Resources Files, Reading Essentials, Get Ready to Read, Quick Vocabulary

▶   Animations, Videos, Interactive Tables

✓   Self-checks, Quizzes, Tests

PBL   Project-Based Learning Activities

   Lab Manuals, Safety Videos, Virtual Labs & Other Tools

abc   Vocabulary, Multilingual eGlossary, Vocab eGames, Vocab eFlashcards

💬   Personal Tutors

Lesson 1

Climates of Earth

Reading Guide

Key Concepts
ESSENTIAL QUESTIONS

- What is climate?
- Why is one climate different from another?
- How are climates classified?

Vocabulary

climate p. 227

rain shadow p. 229

specific heat p. 229

microclimate p. 231

 Multilingual eGlossary

 SEPS.2, SEPS.4, SEPS.6, SEPS.8

Inquiry What makes a desert a desert?

How much precipitation do deserts get? Are deserts always hot? What types of plants grow in the desert? Scientists look at the answers to all these questions to determine if an area is a desert.

Launch Lab

How do climates compare?

Climate describes long-term weather patterns for an area. Temperature and precipitation are two factors that help determine climate.

1. Read and complete a lab safety form.
2. Select a location on a **globe.**
3. Research the average monthly temperatures and levels of precipitation for this location.
4. Record your data in a chart like the one shown here in your Science Journal.

Think About This

1. Describe the climate of your selected location in terms of temperature and precipitation.

2. Compare your data to Omsk, Russia. How do the climates differ?

3. 🔑 **Key Concept** Mountains, oceans, and latitude can affect climates. Do any of these factors account for the differences you observed? Explain.

Omsk, Russia 73.5° E, 55° N		
Month	Average Monthly Temperature	Average Monthly Level of Precipitation
January	–14° C	13 mm
February	–12° C	9 mm
March	–5° C	9 mm
April	8° C	18 mm
May	18° C	31 mm
June	24° C	52 mm
July	25° C	61 mm
August	22° C	50 mm
September	17° C	32 mm
October	7° C	26 mm
November	–4° C	19 mm
December	–12° C	15 mm

What is climate?

You probably already know that the term *weather* describes the atmospheric conditions and short term changes of a certain place at a certain time. The weather changes from day to day in many places on Earth. Other places on Earth have more constant weather. For example, temperatures in Antarctica rarely are above 0°C, even in the summer. Areas in Africa's Sahara, shown in the photo on the previous page, have temperatures above 20°C year-round.

Climate *is the long-term average weather conditions that occur in a particular region.* A region's climate depends on average temperature and precipitation, as well as how these variables change throughout the year.

What affects climate?

Several factors determine a region's climate. The latitude of a location affects climate. For example, areas close to the equator have the warmest climates. Large bodies of water, including lakes and oceans, also influence the climate of a region. Along coastlines, weather is more constant throughout the year. Hot summers and cold winters typically happen in the center of continents. The altitude of an area affects climate. Mountainous areas are often rainy or snowy. Buildings and concrete, which retain solar energy, cause temperatures to be higher in urban areas. This creates a special climate in a small area.

🔑 **Key Concept Check** What is climate?

Figure 1 Latitudes near the poles receive less solar energy and have lower average temperatures.

Latitude

Recall that, starting at the equator, latitude increases from 0° to 90° as you move toward the North Pole or the South Pole. The amount of solar energy per unit of Earth's surface area depends on latitude. **Figure 1** shows that locations close to the equator receive more solar energy per unit of surface area annually than locations located farther north or south. This is due mainly to the fact that Earth's curved surface causes the angle of the Sun's rays to spread out over a larger area. Locations near the equator also tend to have warmer climates than locations at higher latitudes. Polar regions are colder because annually they receive less solar energy per unit of surface area. In the middle latitudes, between 30° and 60°, summers are generally hot and winters are usually cold.

Altitude

Climate is also influenced by altitude. Recall that temperature decreases as altitude increases in the troposphere. So, as you climb a tall mountain you might experience the same cold, snowy climate that is near the poles. **Figure 2** shows the difference in average temperatures between two cities in Colorado at different altitudes.

Altitude and Climate 🔑

Figure 2 As altitude increases, temperature decreases.

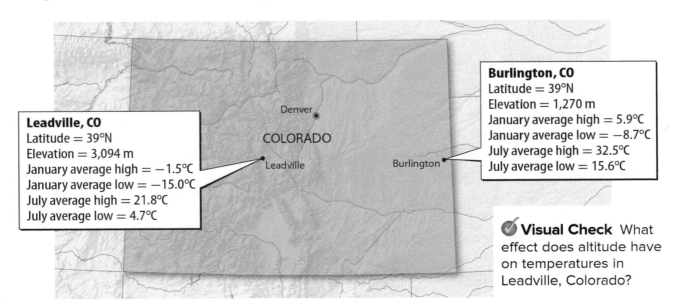

Leadville, CO
Latitude = 39°N
Elevation = 3,094 m
January average high = −1.5°C
January average low = −15.0°C
July average high = 21.8°C
July average low = 4.7°C

Burlington, CO
Latitude = 39°N
Elevation = 1,270 m
January average high = 5.9°C
January average low = −8.7°C
July average high = 32.5°C
July average low = 15.6°C

✅ **Visual Check** What effect does altitude have on temperatures in Leadville, Colorado?

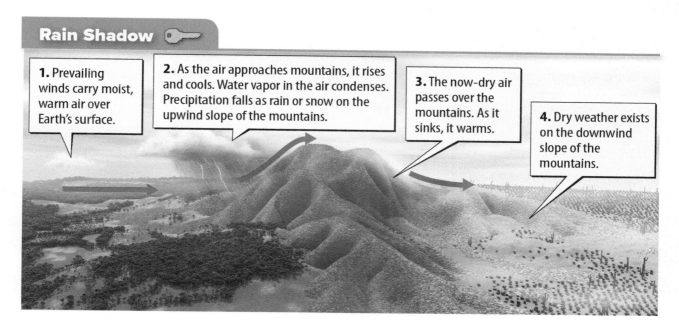

1. Prevailing winds carry moist, warm air over Earth's surface.

2. As the air approaches mountains, it rises and cools. Water vapor in the air condenses. Precipitation falls as rain or snow on the upwind slope of the mountains.

3. The now-dry air passes over the mountains. As it sinks, it warms.

4. Dry weather exists on the downwind slope of the mountains.

Rain Shadows

Mountains influence climate because they are barriers to prevailing winds. This leads to unique precipitation patterns called rain shadows. *An area of low rainfall on the downwind slope of a mountain is called a* **rain shadow,** as shown in Figure 3. Different amounts of precipitation on either side of a mountain range influence the types of vegetation that grow. Abundant amounts of vegetation grow on the side of the mountain exposed to the precipitation. The amount of vegetation on the downwind slope is sparse due to the dry weather.

Large Bodies of Water

On a sunny day at the beach, why does the sand feel warmer than the water? It is because water has a high specific heat. **Specific heat** *is the amount (joules) of thermal energy needed to raise the temperature of 1 kg of a material by 1°C.* The specific heat of water is about six times higher than the specific heat of sand. This means the ocean water would have to absorb six times as much thermal energy to be the same temperature as the sand.

The high specific heat of water causes the climates along coastlines to remain more constant than those in the middle of a continent. For example, the West Coast of the United States has moderate temperatures year-round.

Ocean currents can also modify climate. The Gulf Stream is a warm current flowing northward along the coast of eastern North America. It brings warmer temperatures to portions of the East Coast of the United States and parts of Europe.

✓ **Reading Check** How do large bodies of water influence climate?

Figure 3 Rain shadows form on the downwind slope of a mountain.

🕵 **Visual Check** Why don't rain shadows form on the upwind slope of mountains?

REVIEW VOCABULARY ·······

precipitation

water, in liquid or solid form, that falls from the atmosphere

Figure 4 The map shows a modified version of Köppen's climate classification system.

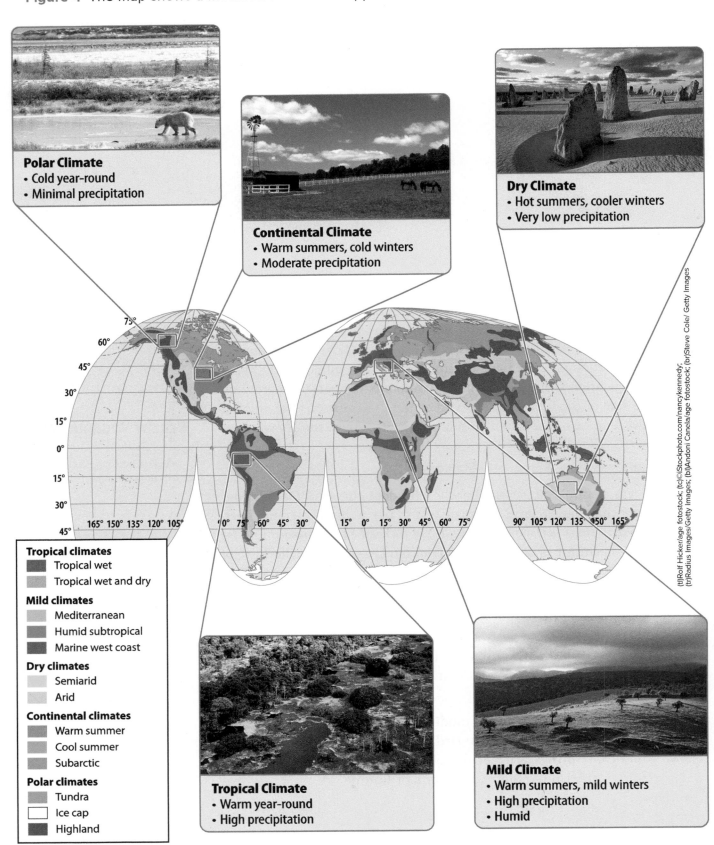

Polar Climate
- Cold year-round
- Minimal precipitation

Continental Climate
- Warm summers, cold winters
- Moderate precipitation

Dry Climate
- Hot summers, cooler winters
- Very low precipitation

Tropical Climate
- Warm year-round
- High precipitation

Mild Climate
- Warm summers, mild winters
- High precipitation
- Humid

Tropical climates
- Tropical wet
- Tropical wet and dry

Mild climates
- Mediterranean
- Humid subtropical
- Marine west coast

Dry climates
- Semiarid
- Arid

Continental climates
- Warm summer
- Cool summer
- Subarctic

Polar climates
- Tundra
- Ice cap
- Highland

(tl)Rolf Hicker/age fotostock; (tc)©iStockphoto.com/nancykennedy; (tr)Radius Images/Getty Images; (bl)Andoni Canela/age fotostock; (br)Steve Cole/ Getty Images

Classifying Climates

What is the climate of any particular region on Earth? This can be a difficult question to answer because many factors affect climate. In 1918 German scientist Wladimir Köppen (vlah DEE mihr • KAWP pehn) developed a system for classifying the world's many climates. Köppen classified a region's climate by studying its temperature, precipitation, and native vegetation. Native vegetation is often limited to particular climate conditions. For example, you would not expect to find a warm-desert cactus growing in the cold, snowy arctic. Köppen identified five climate types. A modified version of Köppen's classification system is shown in Figure 4.

 Key Concept Check How are climates classified?

Microclimates

Roads and buildings in cities have more concrete than surrounding rural areas. The concrete absorbs solar radiation, causing warmer temperatures than in the surrounding countryside. The result is a common microclimate called the urban heat island, as shown in Figure 5. *A* **microclimate** *is a localized climate that is different from the climate of the larger area surrounding it.* Other examples of microclimates include forests, which are often cooler and less windy than the surrounding countryside, and hilltops, which are windier than nearby lower land.

 Key Concept Check Why is one climate different from another?

WORD ORIGIN · · · · · · · · · ·

microclimate
from Greek *mikros*, means "small"; and *klima*, means "region, zone"

Microclimate

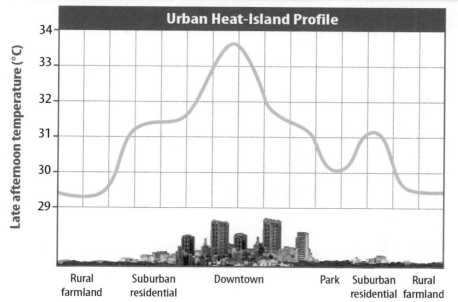

Urban Heat-Island Profile

Late afternoon temperature (°C)

Rural farmland | Suburban residential | Downtown | Park | Suburban residential | Rural farmland

Figure 5 The temperature is often warmer in urban areas when compared to temperatures in the surrounding countryside.

Visual Check What is the temperature difference between downtown and rural farmland?

How Climate Affects Living Organisms

Organisms have adaptations for the climates where they live. For example, polar bears have thick fur and a layer of fat that helps keep them warm in the Arctic. Many animals that live in deserts, such as the camels in **Figure 6,** have adaptations for surviving in hot, dry conditions. Some desert plants have extensive shallow root systems that collect rainwater. Deciduous trees, found in continental climates, lose their leaves during the winter, which reduces water loss when soils are frozen.

Climate also influences humans in many ways. Average temperature and rainfall in a location help determine the type of crops humans grow there. Thousands of orange trees grow in Florida, where the climate is mild. Wisconsin's continental climate is ideal for growing cranberries.

Climate also influences the way humans design buildings. In polar climates, the soil is frozen year-round—a condition called permafrost. Humans build houses and other buildings in these climates on stilts. This is done so that thermal energy from the building does not melt the permafrost.

✓ **Reading Check** How are organisms adapted to different climates?

Figure 6 Camels are adapted to dry climates and can survive up to three weeks without drinking water.

MiniLab
40 minutes

Where are microclimates found?
Microclimates differ from climates in the larger region around them. In this lab, you will identify a microclimate.

1. Read and complete a lab safety form.
2. Select two areas near your school. One area should be in an open location. The other area should be near the school building.
3. Make a data table like the one at the right in your Science Journal.
4. Measure and record data at the first area. Find wind direction using a **wind sock,** temperature using a **thermometer,** and relative humidity using a **psychrometer** and a **relative humidity chart.**
5. Repeat step 4 at the second area.

	Sidewalk	Soccer Fields
Temperature		
Wind direction		
Relative humidity		

Analyze and Conclude

1. **Graph Data** Make a bar graph showing the temperature and relative humidity at both sites.

2. **Use** the data in your table to compare wind direction.

3. **Interpret Data** How did weather conditions at the two sites differ? What might account for these differences?

4. 🔑 **Key Concept** How might you decide which site is a microclimate? Explain.

Visual Summary

Climate is influenced by several factors including latitude, altitude, and an area's location relative to a large body of water or mountains.

Rain shadows occur on the downwind slope of mountains.

Microclimates can occur in urban areas, forests, and hilltops.

FOLDABLES

Use your lesson Foldable to review the lesson. Save your Foldable for the project at the end of the chapter.

What do you think NOW?

You first read the statements below at the beginning of the chapter.

1. Locations at the center of large continents usually have the same climate as locations along the coast.

2. Latitude does not affect climate.

Did you change your mind about whether you agree or disagree with the statements? Rewrite any false statements to make them true.

Use Vocabulary

1 The amount of thermal energy needed to raise the temperature of 1 kg of a material by 1°C is called _____.

2 **Distinguish** between climate and microclimate.

3 **Use the term** *rain shadow* in a sentence.

Understand Key Concepts

4 How are climates classified?
- **A.** by cold- and warm-water ocean currents
- **B.** by latitude and longitude
- **C.** by measurements of temperature and humidity
- **D.** by temperature, precipitation, and vegetation

5 **Describe** the climate of an island in the tropical Pacific Ocean.

6 **Compare** the climates on either side of a large mountain range.

7 **Distinguish** between weather and climate.

Interpret Graphics

8 **Summarize** Copy and fill in the graphic organizer below to summarize information about the different types of climate worldwide.

Climate Type	Description
Tropical	
Dry	
Mild	
Continental	
Polar	

Critical Thinking

9 **Distinguish** between the climates of a coastal location and a location in the center of a large continent.

10 **Infer** how you might snow ski on the island of Hawaii.

Can reflection of the Sun's rays change the climate?

Materials

bowl

polyester film

transparent tape

stopwatch

light source

thermometer

Safety

Albedo is the term used to refer to the percent of solar energy that is reflected back into space. Clouds, for example, reflect about 50 percent of the solar energy they receive, whereas dark surfaces on Earth might reflect as little as 5 percent. Snow has a very high albedo and reflects 75 to 90 percent of the solar energy it receives. The differences in how much solar energy is reflected back into the atmosphere from different regions of Earth can cause differences in climate. Also, changes in albedo can affect the climate of that region.

Learn It

When an observation cannot be made directly, a simulation can be used to draw reasonable conclusions. This strategy is known as **inferring.** Simulating natural occurrences on a small scale can provide indirect observations so realistic outcomes can be inferred.

Try It

1. Read and complete a lab safety form.

2. Make a data table for recording temperatures in your Science Journal.

3. Cover the bottom of a bowl with a sheet of polyester film. Place a thermometer on top of the sheet. Record the temperature in the bottom of the bowl.

4. Put the bowl under the light source and set the timer for 5 minutes. After 5 minutes, record the temperature. Remove the thermometer and allow it to return to its original temperature. Repeat two more times.

5. Repeat the experiment, but this time tape the sheet of polyester film over the top of the bowl and the thermometer.

Apply It

6. **Analyze** the data you collected. What difference did you find when the polyester film covered the bowl?

7. **Conclude** What can you conclude about the Sun's rays reaching the bottom of the bowl when it was covered by the polyester film?

8. **Infer** what happens to the Sun's rays when they reach clouds in the atmosphere. Explain.

9. **Describe** how the high albedo of the ice and snow in the polar regions contribute to the climate there.

10. **Key Concept** If a region of Earth were to be covered most of the time by smog or clouds, would the climate of that region change? Explain your answer.

Climate Cycles

Reading Guide

Key Concepts
ESSENTIAL QUESTIONS

- How has climate varied over time?
- What causes seasons?
- How does the ocean affect climate?

Vocabulary

ice age p. 236

interglacial p. 236

El Niño/Southern Oscillation p. 240

monsoon p. 241

drought p. 241

 Multilingual eGlossary

SEPS.2, SEPS.4, SEPS.5

Inquiry How did this lake form?

A melting glacier formed this lake. How long ago did this happen? What type of climate change occurred to cause a glacier to melt? Will it happen again?

Quasarphoto/Getty Images

How does Earth's tilted axis affect climate?

Earth's axis is tilted at an angle of 23.5°. This tilt influences climate by affecting the amount of sunlight that reaches Earth's surface.

1. Read and complete a lab safety form.

2. Hold a **penlight** about 25 cm above a sheet of paper at a 90° angle. Use a **protractor** to check the angle.

3. Turn off the overhead lights and turn on the penlight. Your partner should trace the circle of light cast by the penlight onto the paper.

4. Repeat steps 2 and 3, but this time hold the penlight at an angle of 23.5° from perpendicular.

Think About This

1. How did the circles of light change during each trial?

2. Which trial represented the tilt of Earth's axis?

3. **Key Concept** How might changes in the tilt of Earth's axis affect climate? Explain.

Figure 7 Scientists study the different layers in an ice core to learn more about climate changes in the past.

Long-Term Cycles

Weather and climate have many cycles. In most areas on Earth, temperatures increase during the day and decrease at night. Each year, the air is warmer during summer and colder during winter. But climate also changes in cycles that take much longer than a lifetime to complete.

Much of our knowledge about past climates comes from natural records of climate. Scientists study ice cores, shown in **Figure 7**, drilled from ice layers in glaciers and ice sheets. Fossilized pollen, ocean sediments, and the growth rings of trees also are used to gain information about climate changes in the past. Scientists use the information to compare present-day climates to those that occurred many thousands of years ago.

✓ **Reading Check** How do scientists find information about past climates on Earth?

Ice Ages and Interglacials

Earth has experienced many major atmospheric and climate changes in its history. **Ice ages** *are cold periods lasting millions of years when glaciers cover much of Earth.* Glaciers and ice sheets advance during cold periods, called glacials, and retreat during **interglacials**–*the warm periods that occur during ice ages.* There have been at least five major ice ages in Earth's history.

(t)Hutchings Photography/Digital Light Source; (b)©Ragnar Th Sigurdsson/ARCTIC IMAGES/Alamy

Major Ice Ages and Warm Periods

The most recent ice age began about 2.6 million years ago. The ice sheets reached maximum size about 22,000 years ago. At that time, about half the northern hemisphere was covered by ice. About 11,700 years ago, Earth entered its current interglacial period, called the Holocene Epoch.

Temperatures on Earth have fluctuated during the Holocene. For example, the period between 950 and 1100 was one of the warmest in Europe. The Little Ice Age, which lasted from 1250 to about 1850, was a period of bitterly cold temperatures.

 Key Concept Check How has climate varied over time?

Causes of Long-Term Climate Cycles

As the amount of solar energy reaching Earth changes, Earth's climate also changes. One factor that affects how much energy Earth receives is the shape of its orbit. The shape of Earth's orbit appears to vary between elliptical and circular over the course of about 100,000 years. As shown in **Figure 8,** when Earth's orbit is more circular, Earth averages a greater distance from the Sun. This results in below-average temperatures on Earth.

Another factor that scientists suspect influences climate change on Earth is changes in the tilt of Earth's axis. The tilt of Earth's axis changes in 41,000-year cycles. Changes in the angle of Earth's tilt affect the range of temperatures throughout the year. For example, a decrease in the angle of Earth's tilt, as shown in **Figure 8,** could result in a decrease in temperature differences between summer and winter. Long-term climate cycles are also influenced by the slow movement of Earth's continents, as well as changes in ocean circulation.

WORD ORIGIN · · · · · · · · · · · ·

interglacial
from Latin *inter-*, means "among, between"; and *glacialis*, means "icy, frozen"

Figure 8 This exaggerated image shows how the shape of Earth's orbit varies between elliptical and circular. The angle of the tilt varies from 22° to 24.5° about every 41,000 years. Earth's current tilt is 23.5°.

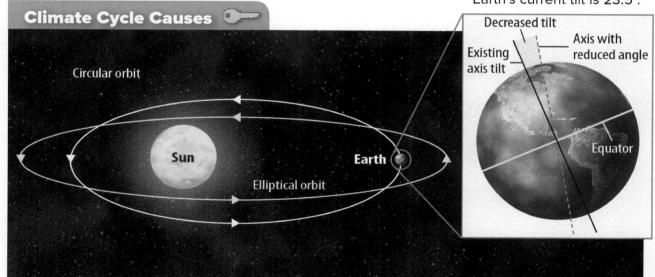

Climate Cycle Causes

Circular orbit

Sun

Earth

Elliptical orbit

Decreased tilt

Existing axis tilt

Axis with reduced angle

Equator

Short-Term Cycles

In addition to its long-term cycles, climate also changes in short-term cycles. Seasonal changes and changes that result from the interaction between the ocean and the atmosphere are some examples of short-term climate change.

Seasons

Changes in the amount of solar energy received at different latitudes during different times of the year give rise to the seasons. Seasonal changes include regular changes in temperature and the number of hours of day and night.

Recall from Lesson 1 that the amount of solar energy per unit of Earth's surface is related to latitude. Another factor that affects the amount of solar energy received by an area is the tilt of Earth's axis. **Figure 9** shows that when the northern hemisphere is tilted toward the Sun, the angle at which the Sun's rays strike Earth's surface is higher. There are more daylight hours than dark hours. During this time, temperatures are warmer, and the northern hemisphere experiences summer. At the same time, the southern hemisphere is tilted away from the Sun and the angle at which the Sun's rays strike Earth's surface is lower. There are fewer hours of daylight, and the southern hemisphere experiences winter.

Figure 9 shows that the opposite occurs when six months later the northern hemisphere is tilted away from the Sun. The angle at which Sun's rays strike Earth's surface is lower, and temperatures are colder. During this time, the northern hemisphere experiences winter. The southern hemisphere is tilted toward the Sun and the angle between the Sun's rays and Earth's surface is higher. The southern hemisphere experiences summer.

Key Concept Check What causes seasons?

Personal Tutor

Figure 9 The solar energy rays reaching a given area of Earth's surface is more intense when tilted toward the Sun.

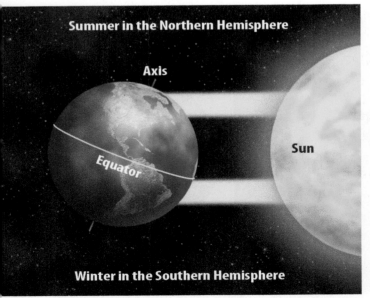

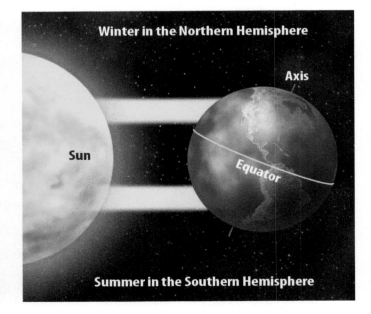

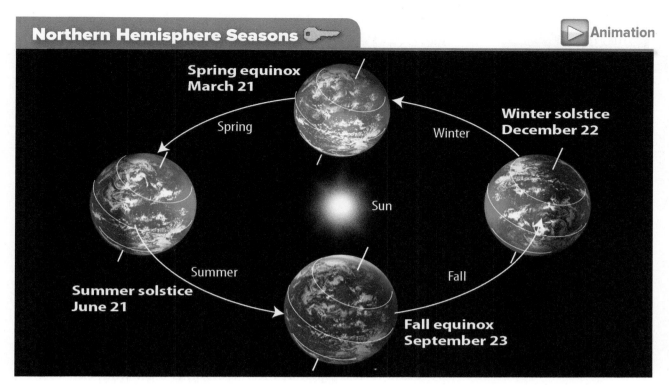

Northern Hemisphere Seasons

▶ Animation

Spring equinox
March 21

Spring

Winter

Winter solstice
December 22

Sun

Summer

Fall

Summer solstice
June 21

Fall equinox
September 23

Figure 10 Seasons change as Earth completes its yearly revolution around the Sun.

Visual Check How does the amount of sunlight striking the North Pole change from summer to winter?

Solstices and Equinoxes

Earth revolves around the Sun once about every 365 days. During Earth's revolution, there are four days that mark the beginning of each of the seasons. These days are a summer solstice, a fall equinox, a winter solstice, and a spring equinox.

As shown in Figure 10, the solstices mark the beginnings of summer and winter. In the northern hemisphere, the summer solstice occurs on June 21 or 22. On this day, the northern hemisphere is tilted toward the Sun. In the southern hemisphere, this day marks the beginning of winter. The winter solstice begins on December 21 or 22 in the northern hemisphere. On this day, the northern hemisphere is tilted away from the Sun. In the southern hemisphere, this day marks the beginning of summer.

Equinoxes, also shown in Figure 10, are days when Earth is positioned so that neither the northern hemisphere nor the southern hemisphere is tilted toward or away from the Sun. The equinoxes are the beginning of spring and fall. On equinox days, the number of daylight hours almost equals the number of nighttime hours everywhere on Earth. In the northern hemisphere, the spring equinox occurs on March 21 or 22. This is the beginning of fall in the southern hemisphere. On September 22 or 23, fall begins in the northern hemisphere and spring begins in the southern hemisphere.

✓ **Reading Check** Compare and contrast solstices and equinoxes.

SCIENCE USE V. COMMON USE

revolution

Science Use the action by a celestial body of going around in an orbit or an elliptical course

Common Use a sudden, radical, or complete change

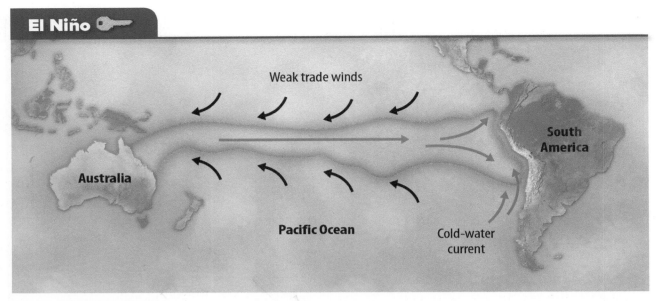

Figure 11 During El Niño, the trade winds weaken and warm water surges toward South America.

✅ **Visual Check** Where is the warm water during normal conditions?

ACADEMIC VOCABULARY

phenomenon
(noun) an observable fact or event

El Niño and the Southern Oscillation

Close to the equator, the trade winds blow from east to west. These steady winds push warm surface water in the Pacific Ocean away from the western coast of South America. This allows cold water to rush upward from below—a process called upwelling. The air above the cold, upwelling water cools and sinks, creating a high-pressure area. On the other side of the Pacific Ocean, air rises over warm, equatorial waters, creating a low-pressure area. This difference in air pressures across the Pacific Ocean helps keep the trade winds blowing.

As Figure 11 shows, sometimes the trade winds weaken, reversing the normal pattern of high and low pressures across the Pacific Ocean. Warm water surges back toward South America, preventing cold water from upwelling. This phenomenon, called El Niño, shows the connection between the atmosphere and the ocean. During El Niño, the normally dry, cool western coast of South America warms and receives lots of precipitation. Climate changes can be seen around the world. Droughts occur in areas that are normally wet. The number of violent storms in California and the southern United States increases.

✅ **Reading Check** How do conditions in the Pacific Ocean differ from normal during El Niño?

*The combined ocean and atmospheric cycle that results in weakened trade winds across the Pacific Ocean is called **El Niño/Southern Oscillation,*** or ENSO. A complete ENSO cycle occurs every 3–8 years. The North Atlantic Oscillation (NAO) is another cycle that can change the climate for decades at a time. The NAO affects the strength of storms throughout North America and Europe by changing the position of the jet stream.

Monsoons

Another climate cycle involving both the atmosphere and the ocean is a monsoon. A **monsoon** *is a wind circulation pattern that changes direction with the seasons.* Temperature differences between the ocean and the land cause winds, as shown in **Figure 12.** During summer, warm air over land rises and creates low pressure. Cooler, heavier air sinks over the water, creating high pressure. The winds blow from the water toward the land, bringing heavy rainfall. During winter, the pattern reverses and winds blow from the land toward the water.

The world's largest monsoon is found in Asia. Cherrapunji, India, is one of the world's wettest locations—receiving an average of 10 m of monsoon rainfall each year. Precipitation is even greater during El Niño events. A smaller monsoon occurs in southern Arizona. As a result, weather is dry during spring and early summer with thunderstorms occurring more often from July to September.

 Key Concept Check How does the ocean affect climate?

Droughts, Heat Waves, and Cold Waves

A **drought** *is a period with below-average precipitation.* A drought can cause crop damage and water shortages.

Droughts are often accompanied by heat waves—periods of unusually high temperatures. Droughts and heat waves occur when large hot-air masses remain in one place for weeks or months. Cold waves are long periods of unusually cold temperatures. These events occur when a large continental polar air mass stays over a region for days or weeks. Severe weather of these kinds can be the result of climatic changes on Earth or just extremes in the average weather of a climate.

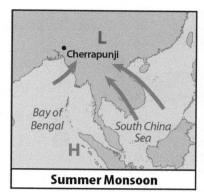
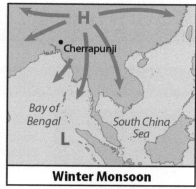

Figure 12 Monsoon winds reverse with the change of seasons.

MiniLab — 20 minutes

How do climates vary?

Unlike El Niño, La Niña is associated with cold ocean temperatures in the Pacific Ocean.

1. As the map shows, average temperatures change during a La Niña winter.
2. The color key shows the range of temperature variation from normal.
3. Find a location on the map. How much did temperatures during La Niña depart from average temperatures?

Temperature Change During La Niña

−0.2   0.2   0.2   0

0.2

0.4

0.4

0.2   0.2

−0.4   −0.4

Temperature change (°C)

0.5
0.3
0.1
−0.1
−0.3
−0.5

Analyze and Conclude

1. **Recognize Cause and Effect** Did La Niña affect the climate in your chosen area?
2. **Key Concept** Describe any patterns you see. How did La Niña affect climate in your chosen area? Use data from the map to support your answer.

Visual Summary

Scientists learn about past climates by studying natural records of climate, such as ice cores, fossilized pollen, and growth rings of trees.

Long-term climate changes, such as ice ages and inter-glacials, can be caused by changes in the shape of Earth's orbit and the tilt of its axis.

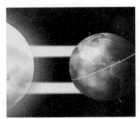

Short-term climate changes include seasons, El Niño/Southern Oscillation, and monsoons.

FOLDABLES

Use your lesson Foldable to review the lesson. Save your Foldable for the project at the end of the chapter.

What do you think NOW?

You first read the statements below at the beginning of the chapter.

3. Climate on Earth today is the same as it has been in the past.

4. Climate change occurs in short-term cycles.

Did you change your mind about whether you agree or disagree with the statements? Rewrite any false statements to make them true.

Use Vocabulary

1 **Distinguish** an ice age from an interglacial.

2 A(n) _____ is a period of unusually high temperatures.

3 **Define** *drought* in your own words.

Understand Key Concepts

4 What happens during El Niño/Southern Oscillation?
   A. An interglacial climate shift occurs.
   B. The Pacific pressure pattern reverses.
   C. The tilt of Earth's axis changes.
   D. The trade winds stop blowing.

5 **Identify** causes of long-term climate change.

6 **Describe** how upwelling can affect climate.

Interpret Graphics

7 **Sequence** Copy and fill in the graphic organizer below to describe the sequence of events during El Niño/Southern Oscillation.

Critical Thinking

8 **Assess** the possibility that Earth will soon enter another ice age.

9 **Evaluate** the relationship between heat waves and drought.

10 **Identify** and explain the climate cycle shown below. Illustrate how conditions change during the summer.

Winter Monsoon

©Ragnar Th Sigurdsson/ARCTIC IMAGES/Alamy

Frozen in Time

Looking for clues to past climates, Lonnie Thompson races against the clock to collect ancient ice from melting glaciers.

Earth's climate is changing. To understand why, scientists investigate how climates have changed throughout Earth's history by looking at ancient ice that contains clues from past climates. Scientists collected these ice samples only from glaciers at the North Pole and the South Pole. Then, in the 1970s, geologist Lonnie Thompson began collecting ice from a new location—the tropics.

Thompson, a geologist from the Ohio State University, and his team scale glaciers atop mountains in tropical regions. On the Quelccaya ice cap in Peru, they collect ice cores—columns of ice layers that built up over hundreds to thousands of years. Each layer is a capsule of a past climate, holding dust, chemicals, and gas that were trapped in the ice and snow during that period.

To collect ice cores, they drill hundreds of feet into the ice. The deeper they drill, the further back in time they go. One core is nearly 12,000 years old!

Collecting ice cores is not easy. The team hauls heavy equipment up rocky slopes in dangerous conditions—icy windstorms, thin air, and avalanche threats. Thompson's greatest challenge is the warming climate. The Quelccaya ice cap is melting. It has shrunk by 30 percent since Thompson's first visit in 1974. It's a race against time to collect ice cores before the ice disappears. When the ice is gone, so are the secrets it holds about climate change.

Thousands of ice core samples are stored in deep freeze at Thompson's lab. One core from Antarctica is over 700,000 years old, which is well before the existence of humans. ▶

◀ **Thompson has led expeditions to 15 countries and Antarctica.**

Secrets in the Ice

In the lab, Thompson and his team analyze the ice cores to determine

- **Age of ice:** Every year, snow accumulations form a new layer. Layers help scientists date the ice and specific climate events.

- **Precipitation:** Each layer's thickness and composition help scientists determine the amount of snowfall that year.

- **Atmosphere:** As snow turns to ice, it traps air bubbles, providing samples of the Earth's atmosphere. Scientists can measure the trace gases from past climates.

- **Climate events:** The concentration of dust particles helps scientists determine periods of increased wind, volcanic activity, dust storms, and fires.

American Museum of Natural History

It's Your Turn

WRITE AN INTRODUCTION Imagine Lonnie Thompson is giving a speech at your school. You have been chosen to introduce him. Write an introduction highlighting his work and achievements.

Recent Climate Change

Lesson 3

Reading Guide

Key Concepts

ESSENTIAL QUESTIONS

- How can human activities affect climate?
- How are predictions for future climate change made?

Vocabulary

global warming p. 246

greenhouse gas p. 246

deforestation p. 247

global climate model p. 249

 Multilingual eGlossary

 BrainPOP®

 8.ESS.1, SEPS.1, SEPS.2, SEPS.3, SEPS.4, SEPS.5, SEPS.6, SEPS.8, 6-8.LST.5.1, 6-8.LST.7.1

PBL Go to the resource tab in ConnectED to find the PBL *Question the Experts.*

Inquiry Will Tuvalu sink or swim?

This small island sits in the middle of the Pacific Ocean. What might happen to this island if the sea level rose? What type of climate change might cause sea level to rise?

Ashley Cooper/Global Warming Images/Alamy

Launch Lab

20 minutes

What changes climates?

Natural events such as volcanic eruptions spew dust and gas into the atmosphere. These events can cause climate change.

1. Read and complete a lab safety form.

2. Place a **thermometer** on a sheet of **paper.**

3. Hold a **flashlight** 10 cm above the paper. Shine the light on the thermometer bulb for 5 minutes. Observe the light intensity. Record the temperature in your Science Journal.

4. Use a **rubber band** to secure 3–4 layers of **cheesecloth or gauze** over the bulb end of the flashlight. Repeat step 3.

Think About This

1. Describe the effect of the cheesecloth on the flashlight in terms of brightness and temperature.

2. **Key Concept** Would a volcanic eruption cause temperatures to increase or decrease? Explain.

Regional and Global Climate Change

Average temperatures on Earth have been increasing for the past 100 years. As the graph in **Figure 13** shows, the warming has not been steady. Globally, average temperatures were fairly steady from 1880 to 1900. From 1900 to 1945, they increased by about 0.5°C. A cooling period followed, ending in 1975. Since then, average temperatures have steadily increased. The greatest warming has been in the northern hemisphere. However, temperatures have been steady in some areas of the southern hemisphere. Parts of Antarctica have cooled.

Reading Check How have temperatures changed over the last 100 years?

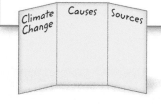

FOLDABLES

Make a tri-fold book from a sheet of paper. Label it as shown. Use it to organize your notes about climate change and the possible causes.

Climate Change	Causes	Sources

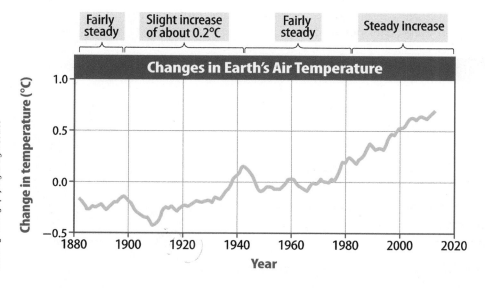

Fairly steady | **Slight increase of about 0.2°C** | **Fairly steady** | **Steady increase**

Changes in Earth's Air Temperature

Change in temperature (°C)

1.0
0.5
0.0
−0.5

1880 1900 1920 1940 1960 1980 2000 2020

Year

Figure 13 Temperature change has not been constant throughout the past 100 years.

Visual Check What 20-year period has seen the most change?

Human Impact on Climate Change

The rise in Earth's average surface temperature during the past 100 years is often referred to as **global warming.** Scientists have been studying this change and the possible causes of it. In 2014, the Intergovernmental Panel on Climate Change (IPCC), an international organization created to study global warming, concluded that most of this temperature increase is due to human activities. These activities include the release of increasing amounts of greenhouse gases into the atmosphere through burning fossil fuels and large-scale cutting and burning of forests. Although many scientists agree with the IPCC, some scientists propose that global warming is due to natural climate cycles.

Greenhouse Gases

Gases in the atmosphere that absorb Earth's outgoing infrared radiation are **greenhouse gases.** Greenhouse gases help keep temperatures on Earth warm enough for living things to survive. Recall that this phenomenon is referred to as the greenhouse effect. Without greenhouse gases, the average temperature on Earth would be much colder, about −18°C. Carbon dioxide (CO_2), methane (CH_4), and water vapor (H_2O) are all greenhouse gases.

Study the graph in **Figure 14.** What has happened to the levels of CO_2 in the atmosphere over the last century? Levels of CO_2 have been increasing. Higher levels of greenhouse gases create a greater greenhouse effect. Most scientists suggest that global warming is due to the greater greenhouse effect. What are some sources of the excess CO_2?

Reading Check How do greenhouse gases affect temperatures on Earth?

WORD ORIGIN

deforestation
from Latin *de-*, means "down from, concerning"; and *forestum silvam*, means "the outside woods"

Project-Based Learning Activity

Question the Experts Go online to research global temperatures over the past century. Compare and contrast data found in scientific theories about climate change.

Climate Change

Figure 14 Over the recent past, globally averaged temperatures and carbon dioxide concentration in the atmosphere have both increased.

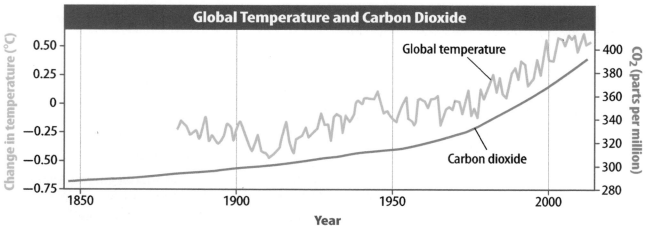

Human-Caused Sources Carbon dioxide enters the atmosphere when fossil fuels, such as coal, oil, and natural gas, burn. Burning fossil fuels releases energy that provides electricity, heats homes and buildings, and powers automobiles.

Deforestation *is the large-scale cutting and/ or burning of forests.* Forest land is often cleared for agricultural and development purposes. Deforestation, shown in **Figure 15**, affects global climate by increasing carbon dioxide in the atmosphere in two ways. Living trees remove carbon dioxide from the air during photosynthesis. Cut trees, however, do not. Sometimes cut trees are burned to clear a field, adding carbon dioxide to the atmosphere as the trees burn. According to the Food and Agriculture Organization of the United Nations, deforestation makes up about 25 percent of the carbon dioxide released from human activities.

Natural Sources Carbon dioxide occurs naturally in the atmosphere. Its sources include volcanic eruptions and forest fires. Cellular respiration in organisms contributes additional CO_2.

Aerosols

The burning of fossil fuels releases more than just greenhouse gases into the atmosphere. Aerosols, tiny liquid or solid particles, are also released. Most aerosols reflect sunlight back into space. This prevents some of the Sun's energy from reaching Earth, potentially cooling the climate over time.

Aerosols also cool the climate in another way. When clouds form in areas with large amounts of aerosols, the cloud droplets are smaller. Clouds with small droplets, as shown in **Figure 16**, reflect more sunlight than clouds with larger droplets. By preventing sunlight from reaching Earth's surface, small-droplet clouds help cool the climate.

Key Concept Check How can human activities affect climate?

▲ **Figure 15** When forests are cut down, trees can no longer use carbon dioxide from the atmosphere. In addition, any wood left rots and releases more carbon dioxide into the atmosphere.

Figure 16 Clouds made up of small droplets reflect more sunlight than clouds made up of larger droplets. ▼

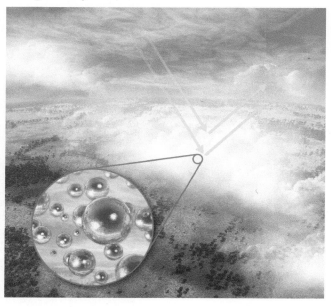

Chris Cheadle/Getty Images

Climate and Society

A changing climate can present serious problems for society. Heat waves and droughts can cause food and water shortages. Excessive rainfall can cause flooding and mudslides. However, climate change can also benefit society. Warmer temperatures can mean longer growing seasons. Farmers can grow crops in areas that were previously too cold. Governments throughout the world are responding to the problems and opportunities created by climate change.

Environmental Impacts of Climate Change

Recall that ENSO cycles can change the amount of precipitation in some areas. Warmer ocean surface temperatures can cause more water to evaporate from the ocean surface. The increased water vapor in the atmosphere can result in heavy rainfall and frequent storms in North and South America. Increased precipitation in these areas can lead to decreased precipitation in other areas, such as parts of southern Africa, the Mediterranean, and southern Asia.

Increasing temperatures can also impact the environment in other ways. Melting glaciers and polar ice sheets can cause the sea level to rise. Ecosystems can be disrupted as coastal areas flood. Coastal flooding is a serious concern for the one billion people living in low-lying areas on Earth.

Extreme weather events are also becoming more common. What effect will heat waves, droughts, and heavy rainfall have on infectious disease, existing plants and animals, and other systems of nature? Will increased CO_2 levels work similarly?

The annual thawing of frozen ground has caused the building shown in **Figure 17** to slowly sink as the ground becomes soft and muddy. Permanently higher temperatures would create similar events worldwide. This and other ecosystem changes can affect migration patterns of insects, birds, fish, and mammals.

Figure 17 Buildings in the Arctic that were built on frozen soil are now being damaged by the constant freezing and thawing of the soil.

©Pete Ryan/National Geographic Image Collection/Alamy

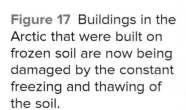

Predicting Climate Change

Weather forecasts help people make daily choices about their clothing and activities. In a similar way, climate forecasts help governments decide how to respond to future climate changes.

A **global climate model,** *or GCM, is a set of complex equations used to predict future climates.* GCMs are similar to models used to forecast the weather. GCMs and weather forecast models are different. GCMs make long-term, global predictions, but weather forecasts are short-term and can be only regional predictions. GCMs combine mathematics and physics to predict temperature, amount of precipitation, wind speeds, and other characteristics of climate. Powerful supercomputers solve mathematical equations and the results are displayed as maps. GCMs include the effects of greenhouse gases and oceans in their calculations. In order to test climate models, past records of climate change can and have been used.

 Reading Check What is a GCM?

One drawback of GCMs is that the forecasts and predictions cannot be immediately compared to real data. A weather forecast model can be analyzed by comparing its predictions with meteorological measurements made the next day. GCMs predict climate conditions for several decades in the future. For this reason, it is difficult to evaluate the accuracy of climate models.

Most GCMs predict further global warming as a result of greenhouse gas emissions. By the year 2100, temperatures are expected to rise by between 1°C and 4°C. The polar regions are expected to warm more than the tropics. Summer Arctic sea ice is expected to completely disappear by the end of the twenty-first century. Global warming and sea-level rise are predicted to continue for several centuries.

 Key Concept Check How are predictions for future climate change made?

 MiniLab **30 minutes**

How much CO_2 do vehicles emit?

Much of the carbon dioxide emitted into the atmosphere by households comes from gasoline-powered vehicles. Different vehicles emit different amounts of CO_2.

1. To calculate the amount of CO_2 given off by a vehicle, you must know how many miles per gallon of gasoline the vehicle gets. This information is shown in the chart below.

2. Assume that each vehicle is driven about 15,000 miles annually. Calculate how many gallons each vehicle uses per year. Record your data in your Science Journal in a chart like the one below.

3. One gallon of gasoline emits about 20 lbs of CO_2. Calculate and record how many pounds of CO_2 are emitted by each vehicle annually.

	Estimated MPG	Gallons of Gas Used Annually	Amount of CO_2 Emitted Annually (lbs)
SUV	15		
Hybrid	45		
Compact car	25		

Analyze and Conclude

1. **Compare and contrast** the amount of CO_2 emitted by each vehicle.

2. 🔑 **Key Concept** Write a letter to a person who is planning to buy a vehicle. Explain which vehicle would have the least impact on global warming and why.

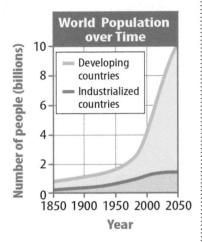

World Population over Time

Number of people (billions)

- Developing countries
- Industrialized countries

Year: 1850 1900 1950 2000 2050

▲ **Figure 18** Earth's population is predicted to increase to more than 9 billion people by 2050.

Human Population

In 2015, more than 7 billion people inhabited Earth. As shown in **Figure 18**, Earth's population is expected to increase to 9 billion by the year 2050. What effects will an increase in population have on Earth's atmosphere?

It is predicted that by the year 2030, two of every three people on Earth will live in urban areas. Many of these areas will be in developing countries in Africa and Asia. Large areas of forests are already being cleared to make room for expanding cities. Significant amounts of greenhouse gases and other air pollutants will be added to the atmosphere.

 Reading Check How could an increase in human population affect climate change?

Ways to Reduce Greenhouse Gases

People have many options for reducing levels of pollution and greenhouse gases. One way is to develop alternative sources of energy that do not release carbon dioxide into the atmosphere, such as solar energy or wind energy. Automobile emissions can be reduced by as much as 35 percent by using hybrid vehicles. Hybrid vehicles use an electric motor part of the time, which reduces fuel use.

Emissions can be further reduced by green building. Green building is the practice of creating energy-efficient buildings, such as the one shown in **Figure 19**. People can also help remove carbon dioxide from the atmosphere by planting trees in deforested areas.

You can also help control greenhouse gases and pollution by conserving fuel and recycling. Turning off lights and electronic equipment when you are not using them reduces the amount of electricity you use. Recycling metal, paper, plastic, and glass reduces the amount of fuel required to manufacture these materials.

Figure 19 Solar heating, natural lighting, and water recycling are some of the technologies used in green buildings. ▶

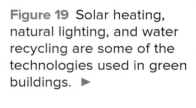

Bruce Harber/age fotostock

Lesson 3 Review

Visual Summary

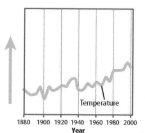

Many scientists suggest that global warming is due to increased levels of greenhouse gases in atmosphere.

Human activities, such as deforestation and burning fossil fuels, can contribute to global warming.

Ways to reduce greenhouse gas emissions include using solar and wind energy, and creating energy-efficient buildings.

FOLDABLES

Use your lesson Foldable to review the lesson. Save your Foldable for the project at the end of the chapter.

What do you think NOW?

You first read the statements below at the beginning of the chapter.

5. Human activities can impact climate.

6. You can help reduce the amount of greenhouse gases released into the atmosphere.

Did you change your mind about whether you agree or disagree with the statements? Rewrite any false statements to make them true.

Use Vocabulary

1 **Define** *global warming* in your own words.

2 A set of complex equations used to predict future climates is called _____.

3 **Use the term** *deforestation* in a sentence.

Understand Key Concepts

4 Which human activity can have a cooling effect on climate?
- **A.** release of aerosols
- **B.** global climate models
- **C.** greenhouse gas emission
- **D.** large area deforestation

5 **Describe** how human activities can impact climate.

6 **Identify** the advantages and disadvantages of global climate models.

7 **Describe** two ways deforestation contributes to the greenhouse effect.

Interpret Graphics

8 **Determine Cause and Effect** Draw a graphic organizer like the one below to identify two ways burning fossil fuels impacts climate.

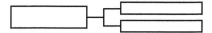

Critical Thinking

9 **Suggest** ways you can reduce greenhouse gas emissions.

10 **Assess** the effects of global warming in the area where you live.

Math Skills Math Practice

11 A 32-inch LCD flat-panel TV uses about 125 watts of electricity. If the screen size is increased to 40 inches, the TV uses 200 watts of electricity. What is the percent reduction of electricity if you use a 32-inch TV instead of a 40-inch TV?

Materials

plastic wrap

2 jars with lids

sand

thermometer

desk lamp

stopwatch

rubber band

Safety

The greenhouse effect is a gas!

Human survival on Earth depends on the greenhouse effect. How can you model the greenhouse effect to help understand how it keeps Earth's temperature in balance?

Ask a Question

How will the temperature in a greenhouse compare to that of an open system when exposed to solar energy?

Make Observations

1. Read and complete a lab safety form.

2. Decide which type of container you think will make a good model of a greenhouse. Make two identical models.

3. Place equal amounts of sand in the bottom of each greenhouse.

4. Place a thermometer in each greenhouse in a position where you can read the temperature. Secure it on the wall of the container so you are not measuring the temperature of the sand.

5. Leave one container open, and close the other container.

6. Place the greenhouses under a light source—the Sun or a lamp. Have the light source the same distance from each greenhouse and at the same angle.

7. Read the starting temperature and then every 5–10 minutes for at least three readings. Record the temperatures in your Science Journal and organize them in a table like the one shown on the next page.

Form a Hypothesis

8. Think about some adjustments you could make to your greenhouses to model other components of the greenhouse effect. For example, translucent tops, or white tops, could represent materials that would reflect more light and thermal energy.

9. Based on your observations, form a hypothesis about what materials would most accurately model the greenhouse effect.

Temperature (°C)			
	Reading 1	Reading 2	Reading 3
Greenhouse 1			
Greenhouse 2			

Test Your Hypothesis

10 Set up both greenhouse models in the same way for the hypothesis you are testing. Determine how many trials are sufficient for a valid conclusion. Graph your data to give a visual for your comparison.

Analyze and Conclude

11 Did thermal energy escape from either model? How does this compare to solar energy that reaches Earth and radiates back into the atmosphere?

12 If the greenhouse gases trap thermal energy and keep Earth's temperature warm enough, what would happen if they were not in the atmosphere?

13 If too much of a greenhouse gas, such as CO_2, entered the atmosphere, would the temperature rise?

14 **The Big Idea** If you could add water vapor or CO_2 to your model greenhouses to create an imbalance of greenhouse gases, would this affect the temperature of either system? Apply this to Earth's greenhouse gases.

Communicate Your Results

Discuss your findings with your group and organize your data. Share your graphs, models, and conclusions with the class. Explain why you chose certain materials and how these related directly to your hypothesis.

 **Extension**

Now that you understand the importance of the function of the greenhouse effect, do further investigating into what happens when the balance of greenhouse gases changes. This could result in global warming, which can have a very negative impact on Earth and the atmosphere. Design an experiment that could show how global warming occurs.

Lab Tips

☑ Focus on one concept in designing your lab so you do not get confused with the complexities of materials and data.

☑ Do not add clouds to your greenhouse as part of your model. Clouds are condensed water; water vapor is a gas.

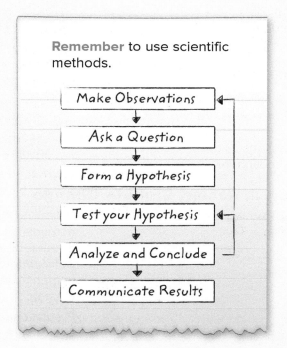

Remember to use scientific methods.

Make Observations

Ask a Question

Form a Hypothesis

Test your Hypothesis

Analyze and Conclude

Communicate Results

 WebQuest

 THE BIG IDEA

Climate is the long-term average weather conditions that occur in an area. Living things have adaptations to the climate in which they live.

Key Concepts Summary

| Vocabulary |

Lesson 1: Climates of Earth

- **Climate** is the long-term average weather conditions that occur in a particular region.
- Climate is affected by factors such as latitude, altitude, **rain shadows** on the downwind slope of mountains, vegetation, and the **specific heat** of water.
- Climate is classified based on precipitation, temperature, and native vegetation.

climate p. 227
rain shadow p. 229
specific heat p. 229
microclimate p. 231

Lesson 2: Climate Cycles

- Over the past 4.6 billion years, climate on Earth has varied between **ice ages** and warm periods. **Interglacials** mark warm periods on Earth during or between ice ages.
- Earth's axis is tilted. This causes seasons as Earth revolves around the Sun.
- The **El Niño/Southern Oscillation** and **monsoons** are two climate patterns that result from interactions between oceans and the atmosphere.

ice age p. 236
interglacial p. 236
El Niño/Southern Oscillation p. 240
monsoon p. 241
drought p. 241

Lesson 3: Recent Climate Change

- Releasing carbon dioxide and aerosols into the atmosphere through burning fossil fuels and **deforestation** are two ways humans can affect climate change.
- Predictions about future climate change are made using computers and **global climate models.**

global warming p. 246
greenhouse gas p. 246
deforestation p. 247
global climate model p. 249

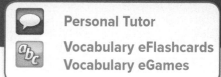

FOLDABLES®

Chapter Project

Assemble your lesson Foldables as shown to make a Chapter Project. Use the project to review what you have learned in this chapter.

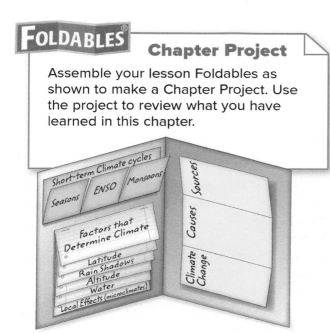

Use Vocabulary

1 A(n) _____ is an area of low rainfall on the downwind slope of a mountain.

2 Forests often have their own _____, with cooler temperatures than the surrounding countryside.

3 The lower _____ of land causes it to warm up faster than water.

4 A wind circulation pattern that changes direction with the seasons is a(n) _____.

5 Upwelling, trade winds, and air pressure patterns across the Pacific Ocean change during a(n) _____.

6 Earth's current _____ is called the Holocene Epoch.

7 A(n) _____ such as carbon dioxide absorbs Earth's infrared radiation and warms the atmosphere.

8 Additional CO_2 is added to the atmosphere when _____ of large land areas occurs.

Link Vocabulary and Key Concepts

Interactive Concept Map

Copy this concept map, and then use vocabulary terms from the previous page and other terms in this chapter to complete the concept map.

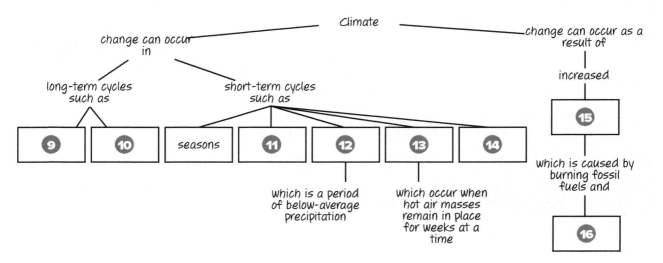

Understand Key Concepts 🔑

1 The specific heat of water is _____ than the specific heat of land.

A. higher
B. lower
C. less efficient
D. more efficient

2 The graph below shows average monthly temperature and precipitation of an area over the course of a year.

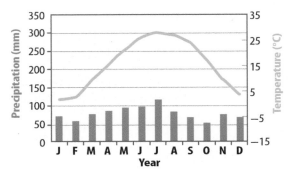

Which is the most likely location of the area?

A. in the middle of a large continent
B. in the middle of the ocean
C. near the North Pole
D. on the coast of a large continent

3 Which are warm periods during or between ice ages?

A. ENSO
B. interglacials
C. monsoons
D. Pacific oscillations

4 Long-term climate cycles are caused by all of the following EXCEPT

A. changes in ocean circulation.
B. Earth's revolution of the Sun.
C. the slow movement of the continents.
D. variations in the shape of Earth's orbit.

5 A rain shadow is created by which factor that affects climate?

A. a large body of water
B. buildings and concrete
C. latitude
D. mountains

6 During which event do trade winds weaken and the usual pattern of pressure across the Pacific Ocean reverses?

A. drought
B. El Niño/Southern Oscillation event
C. North Atlantic Oscillation event
D. volcanic eruption

7 The picture below shows Earth as it revolves around the Sun.

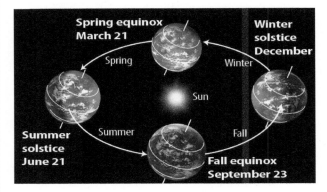

Which season is it in the southern hemisphere in July?

A. fall
B. spring
C. summer
D. winter

8 Which is not a greenhouse gas?

A. carbon dioxide
B. methane
C. oxygen
D. water vapor

9 Which cools the climate by preventing sunlight from reaching Earth's surface?

A. aerosols
B. greenhouse gases
C. lakes
D. water vapor molecules

10 Which action can reduce greenhouse gas emissions?

A. building houses on permafrost
B. burning fossil fuels
C. cutting down forests
D. driving a hybrid vehicle

Critical Thinking

11 **Hypothesize** how the climate of your town would change if North America and Asia moved together and became one enormous continent.

12 **Interpret Graphics** Identify the factor that affects climate, as shown in this graph. How does this factor affect climate?

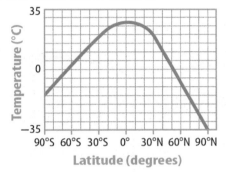

13 **Diagram** Draw a diagram that explains the changes that occur during an El Niño/Southern Oscillation event.

14 **Evaluate** which would cause more problems for your city or town: a drought, a heat wave, or a cold wave. Explain.

15 **Recommend** a life change you could make if the climate in your city were to change.

16 **Formulate** your opinion about the cause of global warming. Use facts to support your opinion.

17 **Predict** the effects of population increase on the climate where you live.

18 **Compare** how moisture affects the climates on either side of a mountain range.

Writing in Science

19 **Write** a short paragraph that describes a microclimate near your school or your home. What is the cause of the microclimate?

REVIEW THE BIG IDEA

20 What is climate? Explain what factors affect climate and give three examples of different types of climate.

21 Explain how life on Earth is affected by climate.

Math Skills ☑ **Math Practice**

Use Percentages

22 Fred switches from a sport-utility vehicle that uses 800 gal of gasoline a year to a compact car that uses 450 gal.

   a. By what percent did Fred reduce the amount of gasoline used?

   b. If each gallon of gasoline released 20 pounds of CO_2, by what percent did Fred reduce the released CO_2?

23 Billions of tons of carbon dioxide are released into the atmosphere by human activities. If humans reduced their CO_2 emissions from 38 billion tons to 30 billion tons, what is the percentage of decrease?

Record your answers on the answer sheet provided by your teacher or on a sheet of paper.

Multiple Choice

1 Which is a drawback of a global climate model?

   A Its accuracy is nearly impossible to evaluate.

   B Its calculations are limited to specific regions.

   C Its predictions are short-term only.

   D Its results are difficult to interpret.

Use the diagram below to answer question 2.

2 What kind of climate would you expect to find at position 4?

   A mild

   B continental

   C tropical

   D dry

3 The difference in air temperature between a city and the surrounding rural area is an example of a(n)

   A inversion.

   B microclimate.

   C seasonal variation.

   D weather system.

4 Which does NOT help explain climate differences?

   A altitude

   B latitude

   C oceans

   D organisms

5 What is the primary cause of seasonal changes on Earth?

   A Earth's distance from the Sun

   B Earth's ocean currents

   C Earth's prevailing winds

   D Earth's tilt on its axis

Use the diagram below to answer question 6.

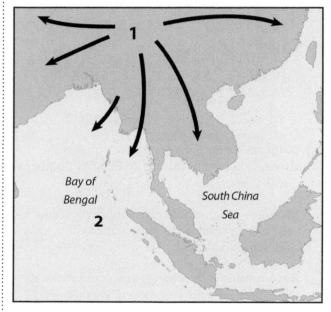

6 In the above diagram of the Asian winter monsoon, what does 1 represent?

   A high pressure

   B increased precipitation

   C low temperatures

   D wind speed

7 Climate is the _____ average weather conditions that occur in a particular region. Which completes the definition of *climate*?

   A global

   B long-term

   C mid-latitude

   D seasonal

Use the diagram below to answer question 8.

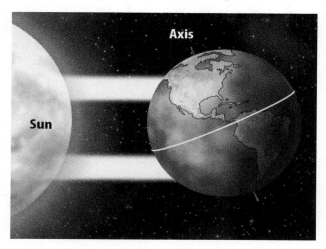

8 In the diagram above, what season is North America experiencing?

   A fall

   B spring

   C summer

   D winter

9 Which climate typically has warm summers, cold winters, and moderate precipitation?

   A continental

   B dry

   C polar

   D tropical

10 Which characterizes interglacials?

   A earthquakes

   B monsoons

   C precipitation

   D warmth

Constructed Response

Use the diagram below to answer question 11.

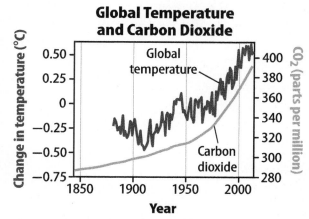

11 Compare the lines in the graph above. What does this graph suggest about the relationship between global temperature and atmospheric carbon dioxide?

Use the table below to answer questions 12 and 13.

Human Sources	Natural Sources

12 List two human and three natural sources of carbon dioxide. How do the listed human activities increase carbon dioxide levels in the atmosphere?

13 Which human activity listed in the table above also produces aerosols? What are two ways aerosols cool Earth?

NEED EXTRA HELP?													
If You Missed Question...	1	2	3	4	5	6	7	8	9	10	11	12	13
Go to Lesson...	3	1	1	1	2	2	1	2	1	2	3	3	3

Chapter 8

8.ESS.2, 8.ESS.3, SEPS.1, SEPS.2, SEPS.4, SEPS.5, SEPS.6, SEPS.8, 6-8.LST.1.1, 6-8.LST.1.2, 6-8.LST.2.2, 6-8.LST.3.2, 6-8.LST.3.3, 6-8.LST.7.1

Earth's Water

THE BIG IDEA

What role does water play on Earth?

Inquiry Why are they there?

Animals that live on the dry grasslands of Africa might travel great distances to find water. All living things need water to survive.

- Why is water so important to the animals?

- How did the water get there?

- What role does water play on Earth?

Gallo Images/Corbis

260

Get Ready to Read

What do you think?

Before you read, decide if you agree or disagree with each of these statements. As you read this chapter, see if you change your mind about any of the statements.

1 A liquid can change to a gas only when the liquid reaches its boiling point.

2 Clouds are made of tiny drops of water.

3 Water molecules can attract other water molecules.

4 Ice has a greater density than water.

5 Factories are responsible for almost all water pollution.

6 Changes in the types of organisms living in water can be a sign of changes in the quality of the water.

Lesson 1

Reading Guide

Key Concepts
ESSENTIAL QUESTIONS

- Why is water important to life?
- How is water distributed on Earth?
- How is water cycled on Earth?

Vocabulary
specific heat p. 265
hydrosphere p. 266
evaporation p. 267
condensation p. 267
water cycle p. 268
transpiration p. 269

 Multilingual eGlossary

 BrainPOP®

 8.ESS.2, SEPS.2, SEPS.8, 6-8.LST.1.1, 6-8.LST.2.2, 6-8.LST.7.1

PBL Go to the resource tab in ConnectED to find the PBL *Campers in the Mist*

The Water Planet

Inquiry A Water Home?

Water is home to these fish. Like all life on Earth, fish need water to survive, but they also depend on water for a habitat. Where does all the water come from?

Pixtal/age fotostock

Which heats faster?

Water and land heat and cool at different rates. This difference in heating and cooling influences climate.

1. Read and complete a lab safety form.

2. Place two **pie pans** on a flat surface. Fill one with **water** and the other with **soil.**

3. Use **thermometers** to measure the temperature of both materials. Record your measurements in your Science Journal.

4. Place a **lamp** over the pans. Turn on the lamp, and measure the temperature of the water and soil every 5 minutes for 15 minutes.

Think About This

1. Compare the rates at which the two materials heated.

2. **Key Concept** Imagine visiting the ocean in summer. Would you expect the climate near the ocean to be warmer or cooler than the climate inland? Why?

Why is water important to life?

You might have read news headlines such as "NASA Finds Evidence of Water on Mars" or "Hidden Ocean Found on Saturn's Moon!" Have you ever wondered why scientists are always looking for water in other areas of our solar system? Water is necessary for life. Scientists look for water in other areas of the solar system as a first step to finding life in these areas.

Water is extremely important on Earth for other reasons. Earth's climate is influenced by ocean currents that move thermal energy, commonly called heat, around Earth. Large bodies of water affect local weather patterns as well. Many organisms, such as the jellyfish in **Figure 1,** have water habitats. People also use water for transporting goods and for recreation.

Biological Functions

Water is necessary for the life processes of all living organisms, from a unicellular bacterium to a blue whale. Did you know that the body of a jellyfish is about 95 percent water? Also, about 60 percent of the mass of the human body is made up of water. Even plant seeds that seem dry have a small amount of water inside them.

Figure 1 Water is the habitat of these jellyfish, but all organisms on Earth depend on water for life.

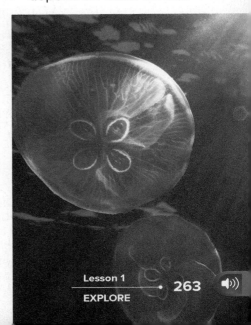

Transport One of the main roles of water in an organism is to transport materials. Water carries nutrients, such as proteins, to cells and even within the cells. It also carries wastes away from cells.

Photosynthesis Water is essential for chemical reactions, such as photosynthesis, to occur within living things. Recall that during photosynthesis, carbon dioxide and water, in the presence of light, react and produce sugar and oxygen. Photosynthesis occurs in plants, algae, and some bacteria. Organisms that undergo photosynthesis are the beginning of almost every food chain.

Body Temperature Regulation Water is an important factor in preventing an organism's body temperature from becoming too high or too low. In humans, as water from the skin, or sweat, changes to a gas, thermal energy transfers to the surrounding air. This helps keep the body cool.

Warming Earth

One reason life can exist on Earth is that Earth's atmosphere traps thermal energy from the Sun. This process is called the greenhouse effect. Some of the Sun's energy that reaches Earth's surface is absorbed and then emitted back toward space. Gases in Earth's atmosphere, such as water vapor (H_2O), methane (CH_4), and carbon dioxide (CO_2), absorb some of this energy and emit it back toward Earth, as shown in **Figure 2**.

Of all the greenhouse gases in the atmosphere, the concentration of water vapor is the highest. Without the greenhouse effect, Earth's average surface temperature would be about $-18°C$. All the water at Earth's surface would be ice and no organisms could survive at that temperature.

 Reading Check Explain how water helps to heat Earth.

The Greenhouse Effect

▶ Animation

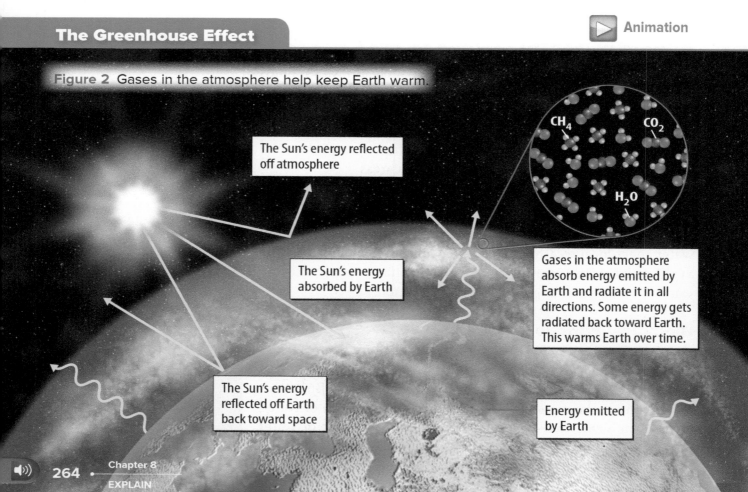

Figure 2 Gases in the atmosphere help keep Earth warm.

The Sun's energy reflected off atmosphere

The Sun's energy absorbed by Earth

The Sun's energy reflected off Earth back toward space

Gases in the atmosphere absorb energy emitted by Earth and radiate it in all directions. Some energy gets radiated back toward Earth. This warms Earth over time.

Energy emitted by Earth

Keeping Earth's Temperature Stable

Think about what happens at the beach on a hot day. If you walk barefoot across the sand, you might burn the bottoms of your feet. But when you reach the water, it is refreshingly cool. Why does the water have a lower temperature than the sand?

Water has a high specific heat. **Specific heat** *is the amount of thermal energy needed to raise the temperature of 1 kg of a material by 1°C.* The specific heat of water is about six times higher than the specific heat of sand. That means the water would have to absorb six times as much thermal energy in order to have the same temperature as the sand.

Water's high specific heat is important to life on Earth for several reasons. Water vapor in the air helps control the rate at which air temperature changes. The temperature of water vapor changes slowly. As a result, the temperature change from one season to the next is gradual. Large bodies of water, such as oceans, also heat and cool slowly. This provides a more stable temperature for aquatic organisms and affects climate in coastal areas. The local weather patterns of inland areas near large lakes are affected as well. Examples of how water is important to life are summarized in Table 1.

 Key Concept Check Why is water important to life?

Math Skills

Use Equations

To calculate the energy needed to change an object's temperature, use the following equation:

Energy = **specific heat × mass × change in temperature** or,

J = **J/kg · °C × kg × °C**

To solve this equation, you need the object's specific heat. For example, how much energy will raise the temperature of **2 kg** of iron from **20°C** to **30°C**? The specific heat of iron is **460 kg · °C**.

J = **460 kg · °C × 2 kg × 10°C**

The amount of energy is 9,200 J.

Practice

If the specific heat of aluminum is 900 J/kg · °C, how much energy is needed to raise the temperature of a 3 kg sample from 35°C to 45°C?

 Math Practice

 Personal Tutor

Table 1 Importance of Water to Life on Earth 🔑 ▶ **Interactive Table**

Importance to Life	Examples	
Biological functions	• transport of nutrients and wastes to and from cells • photosynthesis • body temperature regulation	
Keeps Earth warm	• greenhouse effect • air temperature regulation	
Stabilizes Earth's temperature	• gradual temperature change from one season to the next • high specific heat causes large bodies of water to heat up and cool down slowly • stable temperature for aquatic organisms	

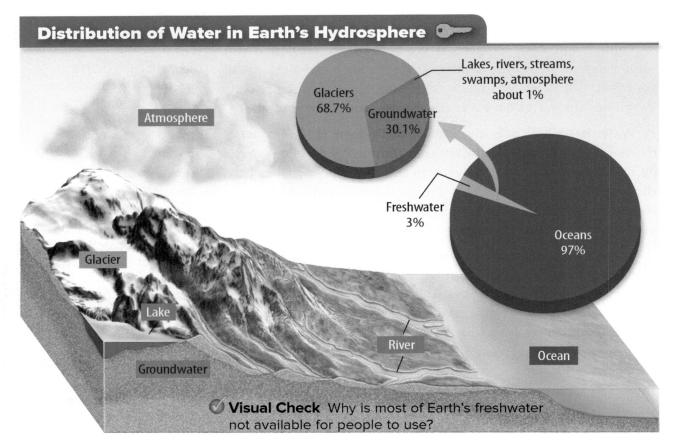

Distribution of Water in Earth's Hydrosphere 🔑

Atmosphere

Glaciers
68.7%

Groundwater
30.1%

Lakes, rivers, streams,
swamps, atmosphere
about 1%

Freshwater
3%

Oceans
97%

Glacier

Lake

Groundwater

River

Ocean

Visual Check Why is most of Earth's freshwater not available for people to use?

Figure 3 About 3 percent of Earth's water is freshwater. Only about 0.001 percent of Earth's water is in the atmosphere.

 **Project-Based Learning Activity**

Campers in the Mist Go online to create a model that describes and explains how water is cycled through Earth's crust, atmosphere, and oceans.

WORD ORIGIN · · · · · · · · ·

hydrosphere
hydro–
from Greek *hydor,* means "water"
–sphere
from Greek *spharia,* means "ball"
· · · · · · · · · · · · · · · · ·

Water on Earth

You have just read several reasons why water is important for life. You also use water every day for bathing, cooking, and drinking. About 70 percent of Earth's surface is covered by water. How is all this water distributed?

Distribution of Water on Earth

Notice in **Figure 3** that most of Earth's water is in oceans. Only about 3 percent is freshwater (not salty). Freshwater is on Earth's surface, in the ground, or in icecaps and glaciers. Only about 1 percent of all water on Earth is in lakes, rivers, swamps, and the atmosphere.

 Key Concept Check How is water on Earth distributed?

Structure of the Hydrosphere

The **hydrosphere** *is all the water on and below Earth's surface and in the atmosphere.* The many parts of the hydrosphere are shown in **Figure 3**. Water is in oceans, lakes, rivers, and streams and underground. Water beneath Earth's surface is called groundwater. Water vapor, or water in the gaseous state, is in the atmosphere. Clouds are a collection of tiny droplets of water or ice crystals. Ice, or water in the solid state, is in glaciers and ice caps. Earth's frozen water is often called the cryosphere.

Water Changes State

The only substance that exists in nature in three states–solid, liquid, and gas–within Earth's temperature range is water. It can easily change state within the hydrosphere. For example, in the spring, snow and ice–both solid water–melt to a liquid. When enough thermal energy is added, the liquid water changes to a gas and enters the atmosphere. When water changes from one state to another, thermal energy is either absorbed or released. Thermal energy always moves from an object with a higher temperature to an object with a lower temperature.

Between Solid and Liquid

When thermal energy is added to ice, the water molecules gain energy. If enough thermal energy is added, the ice eventually reaches its melting point and changes to a liquid. The reverse happens if thermal energy is released from liquid water. The molecules begin to lose energy. If the molecules in water lose enough energy, the liquid reaches its freezing point and ice forms.

Between Liquid and Gas

As thermal energy is added to liquid water, the molecules gain energy and eventually reach the boiling point. At the boiling point, water changes to a gas, or water vapor. It takes less energy for molecules at the surface of water to break free from surrounding molecules, as shown in **Figure 4.** Therefore, water at the surface can change to a gas at temperatures below the boiling point and evaporate. **Evaporation** *is the process of a liquid changing to a gas at the surface of the liquid.* When water vapor molecules lose thermal energy, condensation occurs. **Condensation** *is the process of a gas changing to a liquid.*

Reading Check Why can evaporation of water occur below water's boiling point?

MiniLab
20 minutes

What happens to temperature during a change of state?

1. Read and complete a lab safety form.
2. Fill a **500-mL beaker** with **crushed ice.**
3. Place the beaker on a **hot plate,** near a **ring stand.** Place a **thermometer** in the beaker about 2.5 cm from the bottom. Use a **clamp** on the ring stand to hold the thermometer in place.
4. In your Science Journal, record the temperature of the ice. Turn the hot plate on medium-high.
5. Record the temperature every minute until 3 minutes after the water starts boiling.

Analyze and Conclude

1. **Identify** When did a change of state occur?
2. **Describe** How did the temperature of the water change as its state changed?
3. 🔑 **Key Concept** Why is the range of temperatures between the states of water important to life on Earth?

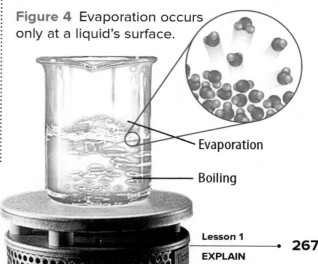

Figure 4 Evaporation occurs only at a liquid's surface.

Evaporation

Boiling

The Water Cycle

The series of natural processes by which water continually moves throughout the hydrosphere is called the **water cycle.** *As water moves through the water cycle, it continually changes state.*

Driving the Water Cycle

Two main factors drive the water cycle—the Sun and gravity. Energy from the Sun causes water on Earth's surface to evaporate. The water later falls back to the ground as precipitation. On Earth's surface, gravity moves water from higher to lower areas. Water eventually returns to oceans and other storage areas in the hydrosphere, and the cycle continues.

✓ **Reading Check** What two main factors drive the water cycle?

Evaporation

Water on Earth's surface evaporates because energy from the Sun breaks the bonds between water molecules. Liquid water changes into water vapor and enters the atmosphere. As shown in **Figure 5,** evaporation occurs throughout the hydrosphere.

Figure 5 Water changes from one state to another as it cycles throughout Earth's hydrosphere.

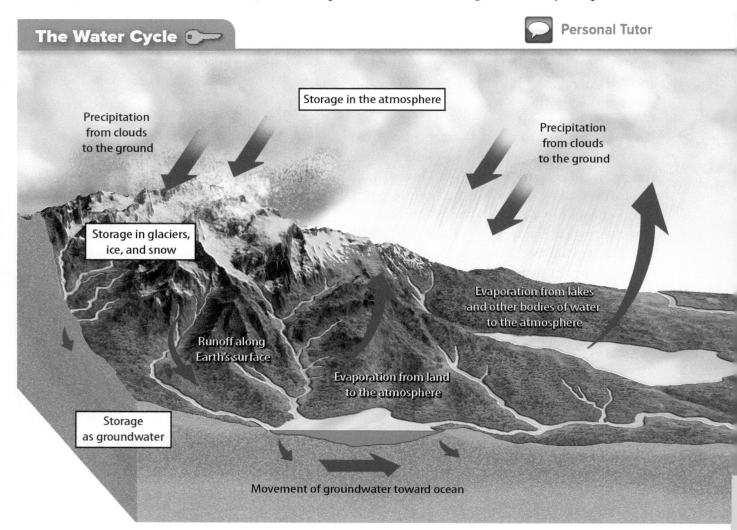

The Water Cycle 🔑

💬 Personal Tutor

Storage in the atmosphere

Precipitation from clouds to the ground

Precipitation from clouds to the ground

Storage in glaciers, ice, and snow

Evaporation from lakes and other bodies of water to the atmosphere

Runoff along Earth's surface

Evaporation from land to the atmosphere

Storage as groundwater

Movement of groundwater toward ocean

Transpiration *The evaporation of water from plants is called* **transpiration.** Water is absorbed by plants mostly from the ground. When a plant has an abundant water supply or air temperatures increase, plants transpire—they release water vapor into the atmosphere. This usually occurs through the leaves.

Condensation and Precipitation

As water vapor from transpiration and evaporation rises in the atmosphere, it cools and condenses into a liquid. Water vapor condenses around particles of dust in the atmosphere and forms droplets. The droplets combine and form clouds. They eventually fall to the ground as rain. If the temperature is low enough, the water droplets will freeze in the atmosphere and reach Earth's surface as other forms of precipitation such as snow, sleet, or hail.

Runoff and Storage

What happens to the precipitation in **Figure 5** once it reaches Earth's surface? Gravity acts on the precipitation. It causes water on Earth's surface to flow downhill. Water from precipitation that flows over Earth's surface is called runoff. Runoff enters streams and rivers and eventually reaches lakes or oceans. Some precipitation soaks into the ground and becomes groundwater.

Although water is constantly moving through the water cycle, most water remains in certain storage areas for relatively long periods of time. A storage area of the water cycle is called a reservoir. Reservoirs can be lakes, oceans, groundwater, glaciers, and ice caps.

 Key Concept Check Explain the steps as water cycles through Earth's hydrosphere.

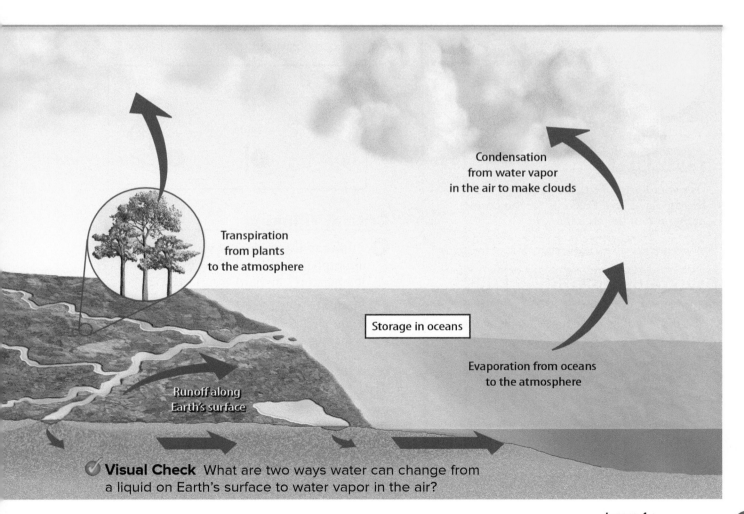

Condensation from water vapor in the air to make clouds

Transpiration from plants to the atmosphere

Storage in oceans

Evaporation from oceans to the atmosphere

Runoff along Earth's surface

Visual Check What are two ways water can change from a liquid on Earth's surface to water vapor in the air?

 **Online Quiz**

Visual Summary

All organisms on Earth depend on water for survival. Water is a habitat for many organisms.

Water's high specific heat causes large bodies of water to take a long time heating up and cooling down.

The water cycle is a natural process in which water constantly moves throughout the hydrosphere.

FOLDABLES

Use your lesson Foldable to review the lesson. Save your Foldable for the project at the end of the chapter.

What do you think NOW?

You first read the statements below at the beginning of the chapter.

1. A liquid can change to a gas only when the liquid reaches its boiling point.

2. Clouds are made of tiny drops of water.

Did you change your mind about whether you agree or disagree with the statements? Rewrite any false statements to make them true.

Use Vocabulary

1 **Distinguish** between evaporation and transpiration.

2 **Use the term** *hydrosphere* in a complete sentence.

3 **Define** *condensation* in your own words.

Understand Key Concepts

4 Where is most of the water on Earth?
   A. glaciers   C. oceans
   B. groundwater   D. rivers

5 **Analyze** What are three reasons water is important to life on Earth?

6 **Explain** how the water cycle is driven by energy from the Sun and the force of gravity.

Interpret Graphics

7 **Identify** the process that occurs at each numbered part of the water cycle below.

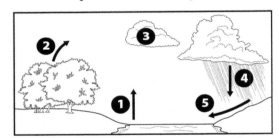

Critical Thinking

8 **Suppose** the amount of water vapor in the atmosphere increased. How would this affect temperatures on Earth's surface? Why?

9 **Evaluate** On a hot day, the water in a swimming pool is much cooler than the cement around the pool. Explain.

Math Skills **Math Practice**

10 About how much energy is needed to increase the temperature of 5 kg of sand from 18°C to 32°C if the specific heat of the sand is 190 J/kg • °C?

Oceans on the Rise—Again

With an eye to the future, a geologist examines past connections between higher sea levels and melting ice sheets.

Way up in the Arctic is the world's largest island—an ice-covered island called Greenland. A vast ice sheet covers much of Greenland. Changes in Earth's climate can have a great effect on this ice sheet. As average global temperatures increase, Greenland's ice sheet is slowly melting along its coastline. If this continues, it could have a big impact on sea levels worldwide.

Greenland's enormous glaciers creep along inch by inch toward the ocean. When they reach the coast, huge chunks of ice break off and crash into the ocean. As the climate warms, the glacier's speed increases, adding more and more ice to polar waters. As more ice enters the ocean, sea levels rise. Scientists estimate that if the Greenland ice sheet melts, sea levels could rise 7 m, or 23 ft. That's enough water to flood coastlines everywhere on Earth, including those with some of the world's largest cities. Imagine New York City under water! Increased flooding also threatens coastal habitats. Animals as well as people would be forced inland. The worst effects would be in a delta—a low-lying area of land where a river flows into a large body of water.

Is this really possible? Scientists, such as Daniel Muhs, know it is possible because it has happened before. Muhs is a geologist with the United States Geological Survey. He investigates rocks for clues about Earth's past. He found a big clue in a limestone wall in the Florida Keys. Today, this wall is several meters above sea level and is filled with fossilized coral. Muhs determined that a coral reef grew there about 125,000 years ago during a warm period when much of the Greenland ice sheet melted. Muhs estimates that sea levels were between 6 m and 8 m higher 125,000 years ago than they are today. This is the same rise in sea levels that other scientists predict would occur if Greenland's ice sheet were to melt again.

▲ **This map shows coastal areas that would be flooded if the sea levels rise 6 m as scientists predict.**

Coral lives and grows under water. Muhs shows where the sea level was in the past at this location in Florida. By measuring the height of the coral fossils, he estimates the ocean was once several meters higher than it is today. ▼

▲ **A chunk of ice from Greenland's Russell Glacier breaks off and splashes into the ocean. The freshwater in the glacier is no longer available as a source of freshwater when it mixes with seawater. If this continues, the overall amount of freshwater on Earth will decrease.**

It's Your Turn

RESEARCH Brainstorm ways that society could respond to rising sea levels. Then, research ways that high sea levels already impact cities and coastlines worldwide. Compare your ideas with real-world solutions and share them with your class.

Lesson 2

Reading Guide

Key Concepts
ESSENTIAL QUESTIONS

- What makes water a unique compound?
- How does water's structure determine its unique properties?
- How does water's density make it important to life on Earth?

Vocabulary
polarity p. 274
cohesion p. 275
adhesion p. 275

 Multilingual eGlossary

SEPS.2, SEPS.4, 6-8.LST.1.1, 6-8.LST.3.3

The Properties of Water

Inquiry Will they freeze?

A thick layer of ice formed over the water where these penguins swim and hunt. Will the rest of the water freeze? How can plants and animals that live in oceans and lakes survive the winter?

Fuse/Getty Images

How many drops can fit on a penny?

The structure of a water molecule gives water many unique properties. In this lab, you will explore one property of water—the strong attraction between individual water molecules.

1. Read and complete a lab safety form.
2. Place two **pennies** on a **paper towel.**
3. Use a **dropper** to place 1 drop of **water** at a time on a penny. After 6 drops, closely observe the water on the penny. Try to add more drops, if possible.
4. Use a clean **dropper** to place drops of **rubbing alcohol** one at a time on a different penny. After 6 drops, closely observe the alcohol on the penny. Try to add more drops.

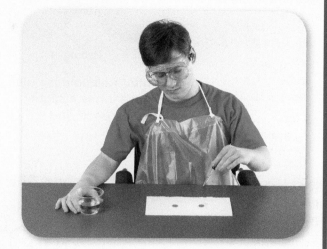

Think About This

1. **Explain** what happened to the water each time you added a drop. What happened when you added the final drop?

2. **Describe** the difference in the shapes of the water and alcohol on the pennies.

3. **Key Concept** Liquids form drops because of the attraction between their particles. Based on this, infer which substance has a stronger attraction between its particles.

Water—A Unique Compound

In Lesson 1 you read that water is the only substance that exists in nature as a solid, a liquid, and a gas. You also read that water has a high specific heat. You might have seen other things that result from water's properties. For example, you have probably noticed that water forms drops if you spill some on a counter, as shown in **Figure 6.** You probably have also seen ice floating in a glass of water or tea. Have you ever dissolved salt in water? Have you ever seen an insect walk on the surface of water?

Water has unusual properties because of its molecules. The properties of water cannot be explained without looking at the way a water molecule is put together. Understanding how water molecules interact with each other and with other materials also helps explain water's unusual properties.

Key Concept Check What makes water a unique compound?

Figure 6 Water forms drops because of strong forces between water molecules.

Figure 7 🔑
The polarity of water molecules is one of the reasons water is so important to life on Earth ▶

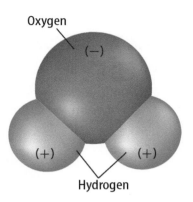

Oxygen
(−)
(+) (+)
Hydrogen

A water molecule is polar because it has a slight charge at each end.

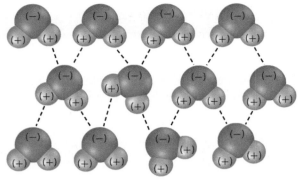

The slightly negative oxygen atom in one water molecule attracts the slightly positive hydrogen atom of another water molecule. This force holds the molecules together.

SCIENCE USE V. COMMON USE····

polar
Science Use having opposite ends, which have opposite charges

Common Use relating to Earth's North Pole or South Pole

▲ **Figure 8** Ionic compounds, such as table salt (NaCl), can easily dissolve in water because water is polar.

A Polar Molecule

A water molecule is made up of one oxygen atom and two hydrogen atoms. Look at **Figure 7.** What do you notice about the charges of the atoms? The oxygen atom has a slightly negative charge. The hydrogen atoms have slightly positive charges. The overall charge of a water molecule is neutral. **Polarity** *is a condition in which opposite ends of a molecule have slightly opposite charges, but the overall charge of the molecule is neutral.* Water is a polar molecule because the oxygen atom and the hydrogen atoms have slightly opposite charges.

Because of their polarity, water molecules can attract other water molecules. In **Figure 7,** a slightly negative oxygen atom of one water molecule attracts a slightly positive hydrogen atom of another water molecule. Several of water's unique properties are due to its polarity. One of these properties is water's ability to dissolve many different substances.

✓ **Reading Check** Describe the polarity of a water molecule.

Water as a Solvent

Water is sometimes called the universal solvent because so many substances can dissolve in it. When table salt, or sodium chloride, is placed in water, it dissolves easily. But how?

Study **Figure 8.** Notice that the positively charged sodium ion (Na^+) of salt is attracted to the negatively charged oxygen atom of the water molecule. The negatively charged chloride ion (Cl^-) of salt is attracted to the positively charged hydrogen atom of the water molecule. These attractions cause the sodium and chloride ions to break apart in water, or dissolve. Many substances that are important to life processes are dissolved in water within cells, blood, and plant tissues.

Cohesion and Adhesion

How can the water strider shown in **Figure 9** walk across the surface of water? You've read that water molecules attract each other because of their polarity. This attraction is called cohesion. **Cohesion** *is the attraction among molecules that are alike.* Some insects can walk on the surface of water because the attractions among water molecules is stronger than the attraction of gravity on the insect. The ability to put more drops of water than alcohol on the penny in the Launch Lab also demonstrates cohesion.

Adhesion *is the attraction among molecules that are not alike.* You might be familiar with one example of adhesion—the formation of a curved surface, called a meniscus, on a liquid in a test tube, as in **Figure 9.** Notice that the water molecules in contact with the sides of the test tube stick to the glass, causing the curved surface across the top of the water.

Water moves from the roots of a plant to its leaves as a result of both cohesion and adhesion. As a water molecule evaporates from the surface of a leaf, it pulls another water molecule up into its place. Water molecules stick to the cells within the plant. This keeps gravity from pulling water back down toward the roots.

 Key Concept Check Name some ways that water's structure determines its unique properties.

WORD ORIGIN

cohesion
from Latin *cohaerere*, means "to stick together"

FOLDABLES®

Fold a sheet of paper into a two-tab concept map. Label it as shown. Use your book to summarize information about water and its properties.

Properties of Water

| Cohesion | Adhesion |

Cohesion and Adhesion

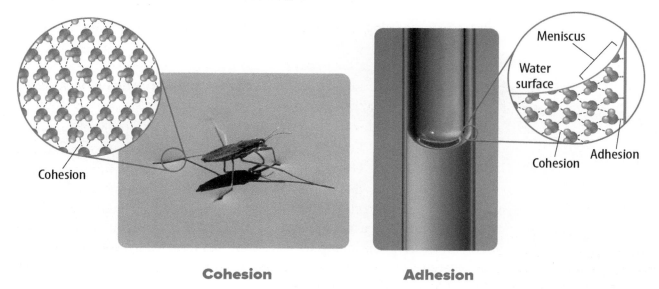

Figure 9 Cohesion is responsible for molecules of water sticking together. Adhesion is responsible for water molecules sticking to other surfaces.

Cohesion

Meniscus

Water surface

Cohesion   Adhesion

Cohesion   **Adhesion**

(l)Matti Suopajarvi/mattisj/Getty Images; (r)©Lester V. Bergman/Corbis

Density

Have you ever wondered why ice cubes float in a glass of water? Water that freezes on a lake also floats. Even huge icebergs like the one in **Figure 10** float in the ocean. Ice floats in liquid water because of an important property–**density.**

The density of a material increases when the particles in the material get closer together. When most liquids freeze, their particles get closer together. The solid that forms is denser than the liquid. For example, recall that lava is molten, or liquid, rock. As lava cools, the particles get closer together. Therefore, the rock that forms from the lava is denser than lava. The rock will sink if placed in the lava.

Water's Unusual Density

If liquids tend to get denser as they freeze, why does ice float in water? Just like any other liquid, as water cools, the molecules lose energy and pack tightly together. However, when water cools to 4°C the molecules begin to move farther apart. Forces among the molecules cause the molecules to spread out and **establish** themselves in a six-sided pattern. When the water molecules freeze, there is space between them. A cube of ice has fewer water molecules than the same volume of water. Therefore, ice is less dense than water, as shown in **Figure 10**.

✓ **Reading Check** Why is it unusual that ice floats?

REVIEW VOCABULARY · · · · · ·

density
mass per unit volume of a material

ACADEMIC VOCABULARY · · ·

establish
(verb) to make; to put in place

💬 Personal Tutor

Figure 10 Water is denser than ice because molecules are packed more closely in water than in ice.

✓ **Visual Check** How does the amount of space between molecules affect the density of the water and ice?

©Ralph A. Clevenger/Corbis

Figure 11 The density of liquid water is greater than that of ice. The density of liquid freshwater is greatest at a temperature of 4°C.

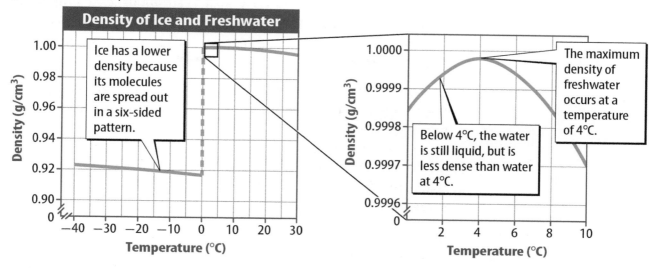

Density and Temperature

To understand more about the unusual density of water, study the two graphs in **Figure 11.** Both graphs illustrate how density changes as the temperature changes. The graph on the left shows the density of both water and ice. The graph on the right is a close-up view of water's density change.

The Density of Ice You can compare the density of ice and water in the graph on the left. The density of ice is much lower than the density of water. Recall that the molecules in ice are more spread out than in water. This explains why ice floats.

The Density of Water Only the density of water is represented in the graph on the right. This graph shows that water is most dense at a temperature of 4°C. Remember that the freezing point of water is 0°C. This means that water between 0°C and 4°C is liquid, but it is less dense than water at 4°C. As you will read on the next page, density of water is important for the survival of life in the water.

 Reading Check How does the density of water at 0°C differ from the density of liquid water at 4°C?

MiniLab
20 minutes

Is every substance less dense in its solid state?
Is olive oil less dense in its solid state?

1. Read and complete a lab safety form.
2. Pour 20 mL of **liquid olive oil** into a 50-mL **graduated cylinder.**
3. Form a hypothesis about whether olive oil is more dense as a solid or as a liquid.
4. Drop a chunk of **solid olive oil** into the liquid olive oil. Record what happens in your Science Journal.

Analyze and Conclude

1. **Analyze** Is liquid olive oil or solid olive oil more dense? How do you know this?

2. 🔑 **Key Concept** How do the densities of solid and liquid olive oil differ from those of solid and liquid water?

Figure 12 🔑 Fish and other organisms in a lake can survive in winter because the water remains below a layer of ice.

① When surface water cools to 4°C and sinks, warmer, less dense water rises. This process continues until all water is 4°C and equally dense.

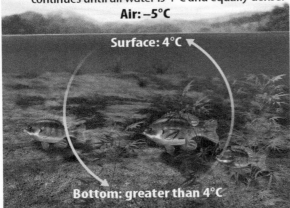

Air: −5°C

Surface: 4°C

Bottom: greater than 4°C

② The air cools the surface water below 4°C. The cooler water remains at the surface because it is less dense than the 4°C water below.

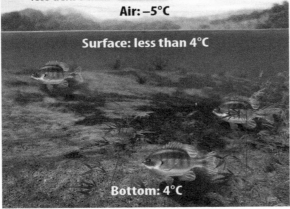

Air: −5°C

Surface: less than 4°C

Bottom: 4°C

③ Ice forms at 0°C and remains at the surface because it is less dense than liquid water. The ice insulates the water below.

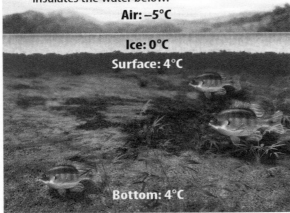

Air: −5°C

Ice: 0°C

Surface: 4°C

Bottom: 4°C

✓ **Visual Check** What is the temperature of the water below the ice?

The Importance of Water's Density

You have just read about two important features of water's density:

- The density of ice is lower than the density of water.
- The density of freshwater is greatest at 4°C.

Imagine a lake in winter, as shown in Figure 12. How is the density of ice and water important to the survival of some organisms on Earth?

① In winter, cold air above a lake cools the surface water. When the surface water cools to 4°C, it reaches its maximum density and is more dense than the water below it. As a result, the surface water sinks while pushing the warmer water to the surface. Once the warmer water reaches the surface, the air cools this water to 4°C. Again, the water becomes more dense and sinks.

② Eventually, all the water in the lake cools to 4°C and is equally dense. However, the air above the water continues to cool the surface water. The temperature of the surface water drops below 4°C, and the density begins to decrease. The colder surface water is less dense than the 4°C water below it and stays on top. All the water below the surface water remains at 4°C and maximum density.

③ When the surface water of the lake cools to 0°C, it changes to ice. The density of the ice decreases further, and it continues to float. Ice on the surface insulates the water below it. Aquatic organisms can survive cold, winter months because beneath the ice, water remains a liquid at 4°C. If water froze from the bottom of a lake to the top, organisms living in the lake would freeze along with the water.

 Key Concept Check How does water's density make it important to life on Earth?

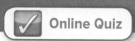

Visual Summary

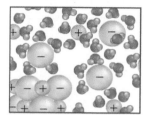

Water can dissolve many substances because a water molecule is polar.

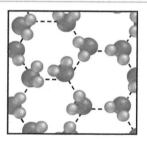

Cohesion is an important property of water molecules. Molecules at the surface of water have enough cohesion that some insects can walk on the surface of water.

Ice is less dense than water because as water freezes the molecules spread out in a six-sided pattern.

FOLDABLES®

Use your lesson Foldable to review the lesson. Save your Foldable for the project at the end of the chapter.

What do you think NOW?

You first read the statements below at the beginning of the chapter.

3. Water molecules can attract other water molecules.

4. Ice has a greater density than water.

Did you change your mind about whether you agree or disagree with the statements? Rewrite any false statements to make them true.

Use Vocabulary

1 A property in which opposite ends of a molecule are slightly charged is _____.

2 **Distinguish** between adhesion and cohesion.

Understand Key Concepts

3 Which has the highest density?
   A. water at 0°C   **C.** water at 6°C
   B. water at 4°C   **D.** water at 8°C

4 **Relate** the structure of water molecules to water's unique properties.

5 **Describe** how water's unusual density is important to organisms in a lake in winter.

Interpret Graphics

6 **Organize Information** Copy and fill in the graphic organizer below to describe examples of adhesion and cohesion.

Adhesion	
Cohesion	

7 **Analyze** Use the graph below to describe how the density of water changes if the water temperature is increased—between 0°C and 4°C; at 4°C; between 4°C and 10°C.

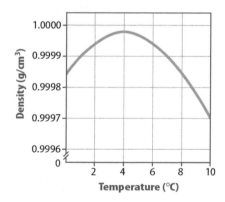

Critical Thinking

8 **Compose** Chris placed two cubes in water. Compose a statement that describes why one cube sank and the other floated. Use the term *density* in your answer.

Why is liquid water denser than ice?

Ice floating on a lake in winter is important to the survival of organisms in the lake. Ice floats because its density is lower than the density of water. What is the cause of this difference in density? What effect does the structure of water have on its density?

Materials

modeling clay (two colors)

24 toothpicks

Safety

Learn It

An important part of science is being able to understand **cause and effect** relationships based on observations. Cause and effect is the concept that an event will produce a certain response. You will use models to observe the cause-and-effect relationship between the structure of water and its density.

Try It

1 Read and complete a lab safety form.

2 Use toothpicks and modeling clay to model 12 water molecules. One color of clay represents oxygen atoms. The other color represents hydrogen atoms.

3 The molecules that make up water move freely and are disorganized. Use six of your models and show the water molecules closely arranged.

4 Recall that water molecules are polar. The oxygen atom of one molecule is attracted to a hydrogen atom of another molecule. However, atoms that are alike push away from each other. As water freezes, these forces cause water molecules to form a six-sided pattern. Use the remaining six models to form one of these six-sided patterns, as shown below.

Apply It

5 **Identify** Which has more empty space between molecules, the model of liquid water or the model of ice? What causes this empty space?

6 🔑 **Key Concept** Based on your observations, what effect does the structure of water molecules have on the density of liquid water and ice?

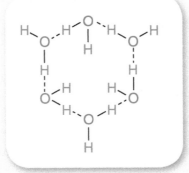

Lesson 3

Reading Guide

Key Concepts
ESSENTIAL QUESTIONS

- Why is water quality important?

- How is water quality tested and monitored?

Vocabulary

water quality p. 282

point-source pollution p. 283

nonpoint-source pollution p. 283

nitrate p. 285

turbidity p. 285

bioindicator p. 286

remote sensing p. 286

 Multilingual eGlossary

8.ESS.3, SEPS.1, SEPS.2, SEPS.4, SEPS.5, SEPS.6, 6-8.LST.1.1, 6-8.LST.1.2, 6-8.LST.2.2, 6-8.LST.3.2, 6-8.LST.3.3

Water Quality

 **Clean Water?**

The water in the pond on this glacier looks clean enough to drink, but is it? Can you always tell just by looking at water whether it is clean? How do human activities affect the quality of water?

Rich Reid/Getty Images

How can you test the cloudiness of water?

All lakes and ponds contain sediment, but too much sediment is one way that water can become cloudy. Cloudy water can sometimes be a problem for organisms that live in the lakes and ponds.

1. Read and complete a lab safety form.

2. Tie a **bolt** onto the end of a **string.** Lower the bolt into a **bucket** of **water.** Record notes in your Science Journal.

3. Add **soil** to the water until the water is cloudy. Use a **long-handled wooden spoon** to stir the sediment.

4. Lower the bolt to the same depth as step 1. Record your observations.

Think About This

1. How did your observation of the bolt change after you added soil to the water?

2. 🔑 **Key Concept** How might scientists use a similar method to study the cloudiness at different depths of a lake or pond?

Human Effect on Water Quality

Suppose you go to the beach, looking forward to swimming and playing in the waves. When you arrive, you find a warning sign like the one in **Figure 13.** What might the sign tell you about the quality of the water and the health of the organisms that live in it?

Water quality *is the chemical, biological, and physical status of a body of water.* It also describes the water's characteristics, such as the amount of oxygen and nutrients in the water, the type and number of organisms living in the water, and the amount of sediment in the water. All of these characteristics are important to the health of aquatic organisms.

Many natural processes, such as seasonal temperature changes and the weathering of rock and soil, affect the quality of water. Human activities can also affect water quality. Pollution from factories and automobiles eventually reaches rivers, lakes, wetlands, and oceans. Deforestation, which removes large numbers of trees, can lead to increased soil erosion. In addition, when it rains, runoff carries soil and other materials into streams and rivers, changing the quality of the water.

✔ **Reading Check** What are some ways human activities affect water quality?

Figure 13 This sign warns about the quality of Earth's water.

Source

◀ **Figure 14** The water pollution shown here is point-source pollution because its source is known.

✔ **Visual Check** Can you identify the origin of pollution in this photo?

Point-Source Pollution

How are sources of pollution classified? The wastewater flowing out of the pipe in **Figure 14** is an example of point-source pollution. **Point-source pollution** *is pollution that can be traced to one location,* such as a drainpipe or a smokestack.

The pollution in **Figure 14** is coming from a factory. Factories are common origins of point-source pollution. Another origin of point-source pollution is sewage treatment plants. In many older sewer systems, water from precipitation is mixed with wastewater before being treated. During heavy rainstorms, the sewage treatment plant cannot process the excess water. As a result, storm water, along with untreated sewage, is released directly into nearby bodies of water.

Nonpoint-Source Pollution

Pollution that cannot be traced to one location is **nonpoint-source pollution.** Runoff from large areas, such as lawns, roads, and urban areas, is considered nonpoint-source pollution. As shown in **Figure 15,** the runoff might flow into rivers or streams. It eventually reaches areas of water storage, such as a wetland, groundwater, or the ocean. The runoff might contain natural and human-made pollutants such as sediment, fertilizers, and oil.

Like point-source pollution, nonpoint-source pollution can lower water quality. It can lead to changes in water, which can harm aquatic organisms. Certain types of fish might not be safe for humans to eat because they have high levels of toxins in their tissues. Nonpoint-source pollution might also affect drinking water.

 Key Concept Check Why is water quality important?

FOLDABLES

Make a half-book from a sheet of paper. Use your book to organize your notes about the effect different types of pollution have on water quality.

Point-Source Pollution

Nonpoint-Source Pollution

Figure 15 Much water pollution is from nonpoint-source pollution. ▼

(t)Photofusion Picture Library/Alamy; (b)Paolo Messina Photography/Moment/Getty Images

Dissolved Oxygen

Figure 16 The aerator in this fish tank releases bubbles that help keep the water moving throughout the tank. This allows oxygen in the air to continually dissolve in the water at its surface.

 MiniLab　　**20 minutes**

How do oxygen levels affect marine life?

The table below contains every other month's average dissolved oxygen levels in the Chesapeake Bay from 1985 through 2002.

On **graph paper,** make a line graph using the data in the table.

Month	Dissolved Oxygen
January	10.0 mg/L
March	10.0 mg/L
May	5.0 mg/L
July	1.5 mg/L
September	3.0 mg/L
November	7.0 mg/L

Analyze and Conclude

1. **Describe** the pattern of dissolved oxygen levels throughout the entire year.

2. 🔑 **Key Concept** Blue crabs need at least 3 mg/L of dissolved oxygen to survive. Infer during which month(s) the levels of dissolved oxygen might affect the population of blue crabs in the Bay.

Testing Water Quality

Scientists examine water quality using a variety of tests. These tests include measuring levels of dissolved gases, temperature, acidity, and cloudiness. Studying the numbers or the health of certain aquatic organisms is another way scientists measure water quality. Using photos taken from the air or space can also help scientists compare the quality of water over time.

Dissolved Oxygen

Why can fish breathe under water but people cannot? Like the air you breathe, water in oceans and lakes contains oxygen. Some of this oxygen is dissolved in the water. Fish, such as the ones in **Figure 16,** use gills to take in this oxygen they need to survive.

The level of dissolved oxygen affects water quality. If the oxygen level in a lake or stream becomes too low, fish might not be able to survive. Different factors can affect oxygen levels. For example, the release of certain chemicals in water can cause an overgrowth of algae. When the algae die, the decay process uses a large amount of oxygen. The oxygen level in the water can drop so low that fish die.

Water Temperature

Many aquatic organisms are also sensitive to changes in water temperature. Coral bleaching is the whitening of coral due to stress in the environment, such as an increase in water temperature or increased exposure to ultraviolet radiation. It is an event that leads to the death of large areas of coral reefs and is often triggered by a temperature increase in water as little as 2°C. As water temperature increases, the amount of oxygen that can dissolve in water decreases. This means that as water temperature increases, there is less oxygen in the water, which can be harmful to aquatic animals.

✓ **Reading Check** How would cooling water affect the level of dissolved oxygen?

©DK Limited/Corbis

Nitrates

Compounds that contain the nitrate ion can be harmful to the environment. *A* **nitrate** *is a nitrogen-based compound often used in fertilizers.* Runoff from fertilizers used in landscaping and farming contribute to high concentrations of nitrate found in water. This can cause an algal bloom, in which the algae population increases at a rapid rate, as shown in Figure 17. Algae growing on the water's surface can block light needed by plants growing at greater depths, causing them to die. The algae can die too. When the algae die, oxygen levels in the water can decrease, producing a very unhealthy ecosystem.

 Reading Check What is an algal bloom?

Acidity

When scientists work in a lab with substances that are strong acids or strong bases, they have to be extremely careful. These substances can be harmful. Strong acids and bases can also be harmful to animals and plants that live in water. Long-term changes in the acidity of water can affect the entire ecosystem. Some fish might not be able to survive. Even if some organisms survive in acidic water, their food sources might not.

Turbidity

A measure of the cloudiness of water, from sediments, microscopic organisms, or pollutants, is **turbidity** (tur BIH duh tee). As the amount of matter floating in water increases, the turbidity increases. Also, the distance light can penetrate into water decreases. Turbidity affects organisms that need light to undergo photosynthesis. High turbidity can also affect filter-feeding organisms. The structures these organisms use to filter food from water can get clogged with sediment. The organisms could die from lack of food. Turbidity is measured using a device called a Secchi disk, shown in Figure 18.

▲ **Figure 17** Nitrates from farm fertilizer flow into this stream, causing an algal bloom.

WORD ORIGIN ··············

turbidity
from Latin *turbidus*, means "disturbance"

Figure 18 A Secchi disk is used to measure turbidity. The farther down in the water the disk is visible, the lower the turbidity of the water. ▼

Measuring Turbidity 🔑

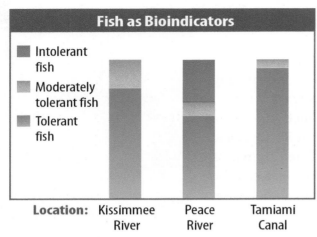

Fish as Bioindicators

- ■ Intolerant fish
- ■ Moderately tolerant fish
- ■ Tolerant fish

Location: Kissimmee River   Peace River   Tamiami Canal

▲ **Figure 19** The presence of intolerant fish indicates that Peace River has good water quality.

✓ **Visual Check** Which area of water most likely has the worst water quality?

Figure 20 These two images were taken on July 28, 2015. The swirls of green are algae blooms in Lake Eerie (top) and Lake St. Clair (bottom). ▼

Bioindicators

An organism that is sensitive to environmental conditions and is one of the first to respond to changes is a **bioindicator.** Bioindicators alert scientists to changes in the level of oxygen, nutrients, or pollutants in the water. For example, the presence of stoneflies, small insects that live on the bottom of streams, usually indicates good water quality. Stoneflies cannot survive when oxygen levels in water are too low.

Larger organisms, such as fish, also can be used as bioindicators. The number of fish species in different locations in Florida are shown in the graph in **Figure 19.** The different species are classified as tolerant, moderately tolerant, and not tolerant of pollution. When species that are not tolerant of pollution are missing from water, this can indicate poor water quality.

Remote Sensing

The collection of data from a distance is called **remote sensing.** Remote sensing data can be collected through photos taken from the air or images taken from satellites. Scientists use remote sensing data to monitor changes in water storage on Earth, such as melting glaciers. Images from satellites can be used to compare water in the same area over time.

Data collected through remote sensing can be used to make inferences about water quality. Notice the swirls of green in the lakes shown in **Figure 20.** The nutrients in farm runoff combined with favorable lake conditions cause an overgrowth of algae around the Great Lakes almost every summer. After the algae dies, bacteria break it down and oxygen levels decrease. This can lead to a decrease in the population levels of fish and other aquatic animals. Algae blooms can also make the water unsafe to drink.

🔑 **Key Concept Check** Name several ways water quality is tested and monitored.

USGS/NASA Landsat

Lesson 3 Review

Visual Summary

Water quality is the chemical, biological, and physical status of a body of water. Sources of pollution are not always obvious.

Various factors can cause a decreased level of dissolved oxygen in water. This can harm aquatic organisms.

High turbidity is another factor that can harm aquatic organisms.

FOLDABLES

Use your lesson Foldable to review the lesson. Save your Foldable for the project at the end of the chapter.

What do you think NOW?

You first read the statements below at the beginning of the chapter.

5. Factories are responsible for almost all water pollution.

6. Changes in the types of organisms living in water can be a sign of changes in the quality of the water.

Did you change your mind about whether you agree or disagree with the statements? Rewrite any false statements to make them true.

Use Vocabulary

1 A measure of the cloudiness of water is called _____.

2 **Use the term** *bioindicator* in a complete sentence.

3 **Define** the terms *point-source pollution* and *nonpoint-source pollution* in your own words.

Understand Key Concepts

4 What is a way that water changes as the temperature of the water increases?
- **A.** Acidity decreases.
- **B.** Acidity increases.
- **C.** Oxygen level decreases.
- **D.** Oxygen level increases.

5 **Explain** how a change in water acidity can affect organisms living in a lake.

6 **Decide** A scientist is monitoring the water quality of two lakes. One lake contains a high level of intolerant fish. The other lake contains a low level of intolerant fish. Which lake most likely has better water quality? Why?

Interpret Graphics

7 **Sequence** Draw a graphic organizer like the one below to sequence how an overgrowth of algae in a lake can kill fish.

Chemicals are released into water.	→	→	→

Critical Thinking

8 **Predict** A river recently experienced an algal bloom. There are no stoneflies in the river. What might a scientist find about the level of nitrates, the level of oxygen, or the turbidity of the water?

9 **Recommend** A scientist in New York wants to study changes in the size of glaciers in Antarctica over the next ten years. What type of remote sensing could she use?

Materials

food coloring

hot plate

250-mL
beakers (3)

ice

stirring rods (2)

droppers (2)

heat-resistant
glove

Safety

Temperature and Water's Density

If water were like most substances, ice would sink in liquid water, and underwater organisms would die as lakes and ponds froze completely in winter. But the properties of water are different from most substances, and these properties are important for life on Earth. In this lab, you will investigate the relationship between water's temperature and its density. If one material floats in another, the material that floats has a lower density.

Question

What effect does temperature have on water's density?

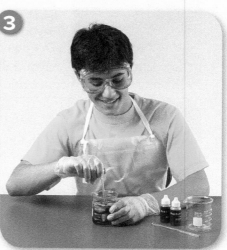

Procedure

1. Read and complete a lab safety form.

2. Copy the data table in your Science Journal.

3. Stir 3 drops of blue food coloring into 150 mL of water in a beaker. Stir in ice until the water is cold.

4. Based on your observations, conclude which has a lower density—the ice or the cold water. Record your observations and conclusion in your data table.

5. Stir 3 drops of red food coloring into 150 mL of water in a beaker. Heat the water on a hot plate until the water is warm but not boiling.

6. Place a small amount of ice in the warm water. Observe whether the ice floats. Conclude whether the ice or warm water has a lower density. Record your observations and conclusion.

What was compared?	Observations	Conclusions
Ice and cold water		
Ice and warm water		
Cold water Room temperature water Warm water		

(t to b, 2-5, 7, r)Hutchings Photography/Digital Light Source; (6)Jacques Cornell/McGraw-Hill Education

Form a Hypothesis

7 Think about what you have observed about the relationship of temperature to the density of water. Form a hypothesis about the differences in density of cold water, room temperature water, and warm water.

Test Your Hypothesis

8 Design an investigation to test your hypothesis about the relationship of density to the temperature of water.

⚠ *Use a heat-resistant glove to handle the heated glass beaker and stirring rod.*

9 Place 150 mL of room-temperature water into a beaker.

10 Carefully add several drops of warm, dyed-red water into the room temperature water. Then add several drops of cold, dyed-blue water into the room-temperature water. Record observations in your data table.

Analyze and Conclude

11 List the following from least dense to most dense: ice, cold water, room-temperature water, warm water.

12 **Conclude** Write a statement that describes how differences in temperature cause differences in the density of water.

13 🔵 **The Big Idea** Explain the effect of temperature and density of water on underwater organisms.

Communicate Your Results

Create a poster that explains how the temperature of water is related to its density. Include colorful drawings to illustrate your observations.

Inquiry Extension

The density of water depends on its temperature. However, in ocean water, differences in the saltiness of water can cause differences in density. Design an experiment that tests this effect.

10

Lab Tips

☑ Use a dropper to place small amounts of one temperature of water into water which has a different temperature.

☑ Be sure the water in a beaker is as still as possible before placing a different temperature of water in it.

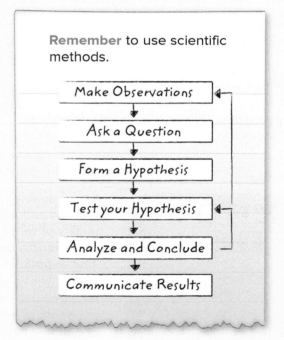

Remember to use scientific methods.

Make Observations
↓
Ask a Question
↓
Form a Hypothesis
↓
Test your Hypothesis
↓
Analyze and Conclude
↓
Communicate Results

Hutchings Photography/Digital Light Source

 THE BIG IDEA Water cycles throughout Earth's hydrosphere and is necessary for the survival of all living things.

Key Concepts Summary	Vocabulary
Lesson 1: The Water Planet  • All organisms on Earth depend on water. Water regulates Earth's temperature. • Water provides a stable temperature for aquatic organisms because of its high **specific heat.** • Water is in the **hydrosphere**—on and below Earth's surface and in the atmosphere. • Water moves through the **water cycle** by **evaporation, transpiration, condensation,** precipitation, and runoff.	**specific heat** p. 265 **hydrosphere** p. 266 **evaporation** p. 267 **condensation** p. 267 **water cycle** p. 268 **transpiration** p. 269
Lesson 2: The Properties of Water • Water is the only substance that exists naturally as a solid, a liquid, and a gas on Earth. • Because of its **polarity,** water dissolves many substances. • Together, **cohesion** and **adhesion** allow water to transport nutrients and wastes within plants. • Since the density of ice is less than that of water, ice floats and insulates the water below. This allows aquatic organisms to survive in the winter.  Air: −5°C Ice: 0°C Surface: 4°C Bottom: 4°C	**polarity** p. 274 **cohesion** p. 275 **adhesion** p. 275
Lesson 3: Water Quality  • **Water quality** affects the health of humans and aquatic organisms. The quality of water can be harmed by **point-source pollution** or by **nonpoint-source pollution.** • The quality of water can be tested by monitoring levels of dissolved oxygen, temperature, **nitrates,** acidity, **turbidity,** and **bioindicators. Remote sensing** is one method of monitoring.	**water quality** p. 282 **point-source pollution** p. 283 **nonpoint-source pollution** p. 283 **nitrate** p. 285 **turbidity** p. 285 **bioindicator** p. 286 **remote sensing** p. 286

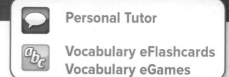

Personal Tutor

Vocabulary eFlashcards
Vocabulary eGames

Chapter Project

Assemble your lesson Foldables as shown to make a Chapter Project. Use the project to review what you have learned in this chapter.

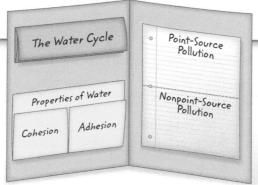

Use Vocabulary

1 Water moves through Earth's _____ by a process called the water cycle.

2 The process of water changing to a gas at its surface is _____.

3 Slightly opposite charges on opposite ends of water molecules cause the _____ of water.

4 The attraction between molecules that are alike is called _____.

5 The chemical, biological, and physical status of a body of water is _____.

6 An organism that is sensitive to environmental conditions and is one of the first to respond to changes is a(n) _____.

Link Vocabulary and Key Concepts

Interactive Concept Map

Copy this concept map, and then use vocabulary terms from the previous page to complete the concept map.

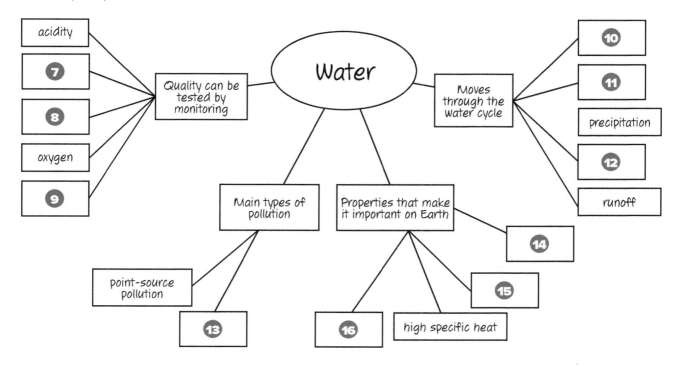

Chapter 8 Review

Understand Key Concepts

1 The atmosphere has the highest concentration of which greenhouse gas?
A. carbon dioxide
B. carbon monoxide
C. methane
D. water vapor

2 Which main factors drive the water cycle?
A. gravity and precipitation
B. gravity and the Sun's energy
C. precipitation and evaporation
D. the Sun's energy and evaporation

3 The diagram below shows the distribution of freshwater on Earth.

Earth's Freshwater

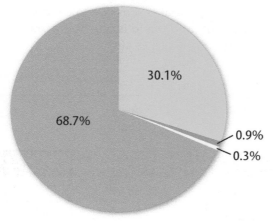

According to the graph and what you have read in this chapter, about how much of Earth's freshwater is in places other than glaciers, icebergs, and groundwater?
A. 0.3%
B. 1.2%
C. 68.7%
D. 98.8%

4 What is the freezing point of water?
A. −2°C
B. 0°C
C. 4°C
D. 10°C

5 Which BEST describes the diagram below?

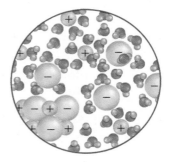

A. Sodium and chloride ions are adhering to each other.
B. Sodium and chloride ions are sinking in water.
C. Sodium chloride is dissolving in water.
D. Sodium chloride is floating in water.

6 Which property of water is most responsible for an insect being able to walk on the surface of a pond?
A. adhesion
B. cohesion
C. density
D. transpiration

7 What causes an algal bloom?
A. a very high acidity level
B. a very low turbidity level
C. too much nitrate in the water
D. too much oxygen in the water

8 Which is nonpoint-source pollution?
A. leakage from a sewage treatment plant
B. an oil spill from a tanker ship
C. runoff from an urban area
D. warm water from a factory drainpipe

9 Which can be used to measure the level of turbidity of water?
A. Erlenmeyer flask
B. microscope
C. Secchi disk
D. remote sensing

Critical Thinking

10 **Explain** how the high specific heat of water is important to living things on Earth.

11 **Imagine** How would life on Earth change if water did not naturally exist in all three states in the range of temperatures on Earth?

12 **Design** a demonstration that compares an effect of water's high specific heat to other substances, such as soil or asphalt.

13 **Cause and Effect** Copy and fill in the graphic organizer below to list a cause and several effects of water's ability to dissolve many substances.

14 **Evaluate** Detergent breaks the bonds between water molecules. This helps remove grease and oil stains from clothes in the washing machine. However, detergent can enter rivers and lakes in wastewater and runoff. How can this affect the organisms that live in these habitats?

15 **Construct** a flow chart that explains how the deforestation of an area can affect the water quality of a nearby river.

16 **Illustrate** why water is a polar molecule.

17 **Give an example** of how scientists use bioindicators to monitor water quality.

Writing in Science

18 **Design** a four-page brochure in which you describe and illustrate different ways that human activities affect water quality. Be sure to include ways that human activities both benefit and harm water quality.

REVIEW **THE BIG IDEA**

19 What role does water play in regulating Earth's temperature?

20 The photo below shows animals that live on the dry grasslands of Africa. Why is water so important to the animals?

Math Skills ✗ ÷ ✓ Math Practice

Use Equations

Substance	Specific Heat (J/kg · °C)
Water (H$_2$O)	4186
Hard plastic	400
Copper (Cu)	90

21 One kilogram of water, plastic, and copper at room temperature receive the same amount of energy from the Sun over a 10 min period. Which material will have the smallest increase in temperature? Explain.

22 How much energy is needed to warm 8.0 kg of copper from 120°C to 145°C?

23 Two kilograms of a substance needs 20,000 J of energy to warm from 200°C to 300°C. What is the specific heat of the substance? Use this form of the equation:

$$\text{Specific heat} = \frac{\text{energy}}{(\text{mass} \times \text{temperature change})}$$

Standardized Test Practice

Record your answers on the answer sheet provided by your teacher or on a sheet of paper.

Multiple Choice

1 Which is point-source pollution?

  A acid rain

  B broken drainpipe

  C field runoff

  D weathering rock

Use the diagram below to answer questions 2 and 3.

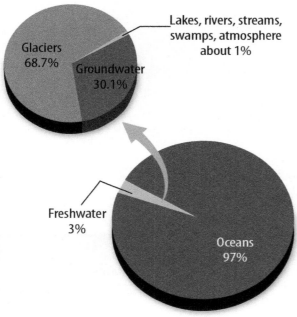

2 According to the graphs, approximately how much of Earth's water resides in glaciers?

  A 2 percent

  B 3 percent

  C 30 percent

  D 68 percent

3 What is the ratio of freshwater to saltwater on Earth?

  A 3:97

  B 3:100

  C 97:3

  D 97:100

4 What property of the molecules in ice makes ice float on water?

  A They are farther apart than water molecules.

  B They are much larger than water molecules.

  C They contain more oxygen atoms than water molecules.

  D They move more quickly than water molecules.

Use the diagram below to answer question 5.

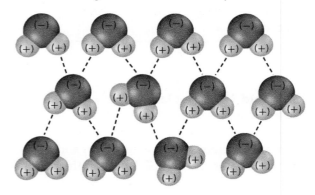

5 What property of water molecules does the diagram illustrate?

  A consistency

  B layering

  C neutrality

  D polarity

6 Which is the physical, chemical, and biological status of a body of water?

  A its density

  B its quality

  C its specific heat

  D its volume

Use the diagram below to answer question 7.

Fish as Bioindicators

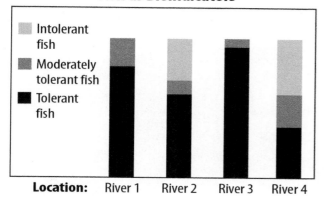

Location: River 1 | River 2 | River 3 | River 4

Legend:
- Intolerant fish
- Moderately tolerant fish
- Tolerant fish

7 In the graph above, which has the best water quality?

A river 1

B river 2

C river 3

D river 4

8 When a lake freezes in winter, what happens beneath the ice layer?

A Organisms freeze at 4°C.

B The water at the bottom turns to ice.

C Warm water sinks to the bottom.

D Water remains liquid at 4°C.

9 Which explains why water in a cylinder forms a meniscus across the top?

A adhesion

B density

C specific heat

D turbidity

Constructed Response

Use the table below to answer question 10.

Stage	Description
Condensation	
Evaporation	
Precipitation	
Runoff	
Storage	

10 In the table above, describe each stage of the water cycle and where it occurs.

Use the table below to answer questions 11 and 12.

Factor	Effect
Acidity	
Dissolved oxygen	
Nitrates	
Temperature	
Turbidity	

11 Explain the effect each factor in the table above has on water quality.

12 How does human activity contribute to the effects these factors have on water quality? Give two examples.

NEED EXTRA HELP?												
If You Missed Question...	1	2	3	4	5	6	7	8	9	10	11	12
Go to Lesson...	3	1	1	2	2	3	3	2	2	1	3	3

Chapter 9

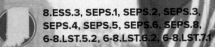

8.ESS.3, SEPS.1, SEPS.2, SEPS.3, SEPS.4, SEPS.5, SEPS.6, SEPS.8, 6-8.LST.5.2, 6-8.LST.6.2, 6-8.LST.7.1

Environmental Impacts

THE BIG IDEA

How do human activities impact the environment?

  How many people are there?

More than 7 billion people live on Earth. Every day, people all over the world travel, eat, use water, and participate in recreational activities.

- What resources do people need and use?

- What might happen if any resources run out?

- How do human activities impact the environment?

Get Ready to Read

What do you think?

Before you read, decide if you agree or disagree with each of these statements. As you read this chapter, see if you change your mind about any of the statements.

1. Earth can support an unlimited number of people.

2. Humans can have both positive and negative impacts on the environment.

3. Deforestation does not affect soil quality.

4. Most trash is recycled.

5. Sources of water pollution are always easy to identify.

6. The proper method of disposal for used motor oil is to pour it down the drain.

7. The greenhouse effect is harmful to life on Earth.

8. Air pollution can affect human health.

People and the Environment

Inquiry What's the impact?

This satellite image shows light coming from Europe and Africa at night. You can see where large cities are located. What do you think the dark areas represent? When you turn on the lights at night, where does the energy to power the lights come from? How might this daily activity impact the environment?

Craig Mayhew and Robert Simmon, NASA GSFC

What happens as populations increase in size?

In the year 200, the human population consisted of about a quarter of a billion people. By the year 2000, it had increased to more than 6 billion, and by 2050, it is projected to be more than 9 billion. However, the amount of space available on Earth will remain the same.

1. Read and complete a lab safety form.

2. Place 10 **dried beans** in a **100-mL beaker.**

3. At the start signal, double the number of beans in the beaker. There should now be 20 beans.

4. In your Science Journal, make a table to record your data. The table should indicate the number of beans added and the total number of beans in the beaker after each addition.

5. Double the number of beans each time the start signal sounds. Continue until the stop signal sounds.

Think About This

1. Can you add any more beans to the beaker? Why or why not?

2. How many times did you have to double the beans to fill the beaker?

3. **Key Concept** How might the growth of a population affect the availability of resources, such as space?

Population and Carrying Capacity

Have you ever seen a sign such as the one shown in **Figure 1?** The sign shows the population of a city. In this case, population means how many people live in the city. Scientists use the term *population,* too, but in a slightly different way. For scientists, a **population** *is all the members of a species living in a given area.* You are part of a population of humans. The other species in your area, such as birds or trees, each make up a separate population.

The Human Population

When the first American towns were settled, most had low populations. Today, some of those towns are large cities, crowded with people. In a similar way, Earth was once home to relatively few humans. Today, about 7.1 billion people live on Earth. The greatest increase in human population occurred during the last few centuries.

Figure 1 This sign shows the population of the city. Scientists use the word *population* to describe all the members of a species in an area.

Figure 2 Human population stayed fairly steady for most of history and then "exploded" in the last few hundred years.

✔️ **Visual Check** How does the rate of human population growth from the years 200 to 1800 compare to the rate of growth from 1800 to 2000?

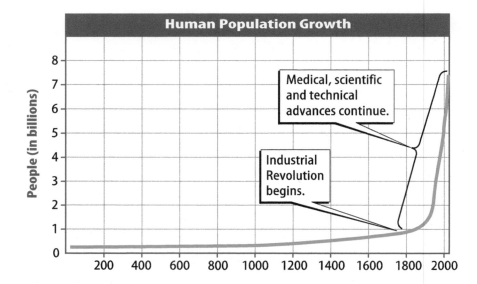

Human Population Growth

People (in billions) — vertical axis: 0, 1, 2, 3, 4, 5, 6, 7, 8

Horizontal axis: 200, 400, 600, 800, 1000, 1200, 1400, 1600, 1800, 2000

Medical, scientific and technical advances continue.

Industrial Revolution begins.

WORD ORIGIN ··········

population
from Latin *populus*, means "people"

FOLDABLES®

Use a sheet of paper to make a small vertical shutterfold. Draw the arrows on each tab and label as illustrated. Use the Foldable to discuss how human population growth is related to resources.

Resources

Human Population

Population Trends

Have you ever heard the phrase *population explosion?* Population explosion describes the sudden rise in human population that has happened in recent history. The graph in **Figure 2** shows how the human population has changed. The population increased at a fairly steady rate for most of human history. In the 1800s, the population began to rise sharply.

What caused this sharp increase? Improved health care, clean water, and other technological advancements mean that more people are living longer and reproducing. In approximately one hour, 15,000 babies are born worldwide.

✔️ **Reading Check** What factors contributed to the increase in human population?

Population Limits

Every human being needs certain things, such as food, clean water, and shelter, to survive. People also need clothes, transportation, and other items. All the items used by people come from resources found on Earth. Does Earth have enough resources to support an unlimited number of humans?

Earth has limited resources. It cannot support a population of any species in a given environment beyond its carrying capacity. **Carrying capacity** *is the largest number of individuals of a given species that Earth's resources can support and maintain for a long period of time.* If the human population continues to grow beyond Earth's carrying capacity, eventually Earth will not have enough resources to support humans.

Key Concept Check What is the relationship between the availability of resources and human population growth?

Impact of Daily Actions

Each of the over 7.1 billion people on Earth uses resources in some way. The use of these resources affects the environment. Consider the impact of one activity—a shower.

Consuming Resources

Like many people, you might take a shower each day. The metal in the water pipes comes from resources mined from the ground. Mining can destroy habitats and pollute soil and water. Your towel might be made of cotton, a resource obtained from plants. Growing plants often involves the use of fertilizers and other chemicals that run off into water and affect its quality.

The water itself also is a resource—one that is scarce in some areas of the world. Most likely, fossil fuels are used to heat the water. Recall that fossil fuels are nonrenewable resources, which means they are used up faster than they can be replaced by natural processes. Burning fossil fuels also releases pollution into the atmosphere.

Now, think about all the activities that you do in one day, such as going to school, eating meals, or playing computer games. All of these activities use resources. Over the course of your lifetime, your potential impact on the environment is great. Multiply this impact by the billions of people on Earth, and you can understand why it is important to use resources wisely.

 Key Concept Check What are three things you did today that impacted the environment?

Positive and Negative Impacts

As shown in Figure 3, not all human activities have a negative impact on the environment. In the following lessons, you will learn how human activities affect soil, water, and air quality. You will also learn things you can do to help reduce the impact of your actions on the environment.

SCIENCE USE v. COMMON USE

resource
Science Use a natural source of supply or support

Common Use a source of information or expertise

Applying Practices

What is the environmental impact of human use of natural resources? Go online to research how use of natural resources and other human activities impact the environment.

Figure 3 Cleaning up streams and picking up litter are ways people can positively impact the environment.

Jeff Greenberg/Alamy

Lesson 1 Review

Visual Summary

Human population has exploded since the 1800s. Every day billions of people use Earth's resources. The human population will eventually reach its carrying capacity.

When humans use resources, they can have both negative and positive impacts on the environment. It is important for humans to use resources wisely.

FOLDABLES

Use your lesson Foldable to review the lesson. Save your Foldable for the project at the end of the chapter.

What do you think NOW?

You first read the statements below at the beginning of the chapter.

1. Earth can support an unlimited number of people.

2. Humans can have both positive and negative impacts on the environment.

Did you change your mind about whether you agree or disagree with the statements? Rewrite any false statements to make them true.

Use Vocabulary

1 **Define** *carrying capacity* in your own words.

2 All the members of a certain species living in a given area is a(n) _____.

Understand Key Concepts

3 Approximately how many people live on Earth?
- **A.** 2.4 billion
- **B.** 7.1 billion
- **C.** 9.2 billion
- **D.** 12.1 billion

4 **Identify** something you could do to reduce your impact on the environment.

5 **Reason** Why do carrying capacities exist for all species on Earth?

Interpret Graphics

6 **Take Notes** Copy the graphic organizer below. List two human activities and the effect of each activity on the environment.

Activity	Effect on the Environment

7 **Summarize** how human population growth has changed over time, using the graph below.

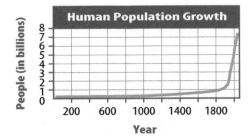

Critical Thinking

8 **Predict** What might happen if a species reaches Earth's carrying capacity?

9 **Reflect** Technological advances allow farmers to grow more crops. Do you think these advances affect the carrying capacity for humans? Explain.

What amount of Earth's resources do you use in a day?

Many of the practices we engage in today became habits long before we realized the negative effects that they have on the environment. By analyzing your daily resource use, you might identify some different practices that can help protect Earth's resources.

Learn It

In science, **data** are **collected** as accurate numbers and descriptions and organized in specific ways. The meaning of your observations can be determined by **analyzing** the data you collected.

Try It

1. With your group, design a data collection form for recording each group member's resource use for one 24-h period.

2. You should include space to collect data on water use, fossil fuel use (which may include electricity use and transportation), how much meat and dairy products you eat, how much trash you discard, and any other resources you might use in a typical 24-h period. Indicate the units in which you will record the data.

3. Share your form with the other groups, and complete a final draft using the best features from each group's design.

4. Distribute copies of the form to each group member. Record each instance and quantity of resource use during a 24-h period.

5. For each resource, calculate how much you would use in 1 year, based on your usage in the 24-h period.

Apply It

6. Consider whether a single 24-h period is representative of each of the 365 days of your year. Explain your answer.

7. How would you modify your data collection design to reflect a more realistic measure of your resource use over a year?

8. 🔑 **Key Concept** Explain how two of the activities that you recorded deplete resources or pollute the soil, the water, or the air. How can you change your activities to reduce your impact or have a positive impact?

Lesson 2

Impacts on the Land

Reading Guide

Key Concepts 🔑
ESSENTIAL QUESTIONS

- What are the consequences of using land as a resource?
- How does proper waste management help prevent pollution?
- What actions help protect the land?

Vocabulary

deforestation p. 305

desertification p. 306

urban sprawl p. 308

reforestation p. 310

reclamation p. 310

🔤 Multilingual eGlossary

▶ Science Video
What's Science Got to do With It?

8.ESS.3, SEPS.1, SEPS.2, SEPS.3, SEPS.4, SEPS.6

Inquiry How do people use land?

Study this photo of an area in England, and list three ways people use land. What other possible land uses are not shown in the photo? What impact do humans have on land resources?

How can items be reused?

As an individual, you can have an effect on the use and the protection of Earth's resources by reducing, reusing, and recycling the materials you use every day.

1. Read and complete a lab safety form.
2. Have one member of your group pull an item from the **item bag.**
3. Discuss the item with your group and take turns describing as many different ways to reuse it as possible.
4. List the different uses in your Science Journal.
5. Repeat steps 2–4.
6. Share your lists with the other groups. What uses did other groups think of that were different from your group's ideas for the same item?

Think About This

1. Describe your group's items and three different ways that you thought to reuse each item.

2. How does reusing these items help to reduce the use of Earth's resources?

3. 🔑 **Key Concept** How do you think the action of reusing items helps to protect the land?

Using Land Resources

What do the metal in staples and the paper in your notebook have in common? Both come from resources found in or on land. People use land for timber production, agriculture, and mining. All of these activities impact the environment.

Forest Resources

Trees are cut down to make wood and paper products, such as your notebook. Trees are also cut for fuel and to clear land for agriculture, grazing, or building houses or highways.

Sometimes forests are cleared, as shown in **Figure 4.** **Deforestation** *is the removal of large areas of forests for human purposes.* Approximately 130,000 km^2 of tropical rain forests are cut down each year, an area equal in size to the state of Louisiana. Tropical rain forests are home to an estimated 50 percent of all the species on Earth. Deforestation destroys habitats, which can lead to species' extinction.

Deforestation also can affect soil quality. Plant roots hold soil in place. Without these natural anchors, soil erodes away. In addition, deforestation affects air quality. Recall that trees remove carbon dioxide from the air when they undergo photosynthesis. When there are fewer trees on Earth, more carbon dioxide remains in the atmosphere. You will learn more about carbon dioxide in Lesson 4.

Figure 4 Deforestation occurs when forests are cleared for agriculture, grazing, or other purposes.

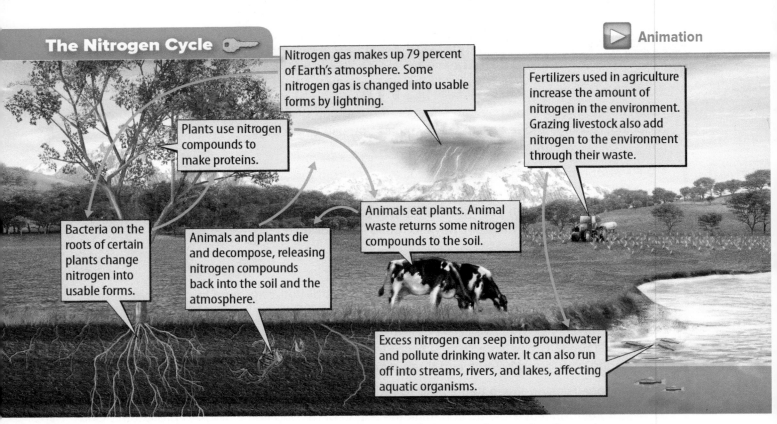

The Nitrogen Cycle ▶ Animation

Nitrogen gas makes up 79 percent of Earth's atmosphere. Some nitrogen gas is changed into usable forms by lightning.

Plants use nitrogen compounds to make proteins.

Fertilizers used in agriculture increase the amount of nitrogen in the environment. Grazing livestock also add nitrogen to the environment through their waste.

Bacteria on the roots of certain plants change nitrogen into usable forms.

Animals and plants die and decompose, releasing nitrogen compounds back into the soil and the atmosphere.

Animals eat plants. Animal waste returns some nitrogen compounds to the soil.

Excess nitrogen can seep into groundwater and pollute drinking water. It can also run off into streams, rivers, and lakes, affecting aquatic organisms.

Figure 5 Agricultural practices can increase the amount of nitrogen that cycles through ecosystems.

✓ Visual Check How does the use of fertilizers affect the environment?

Agriculture and the Nitrogen Cycle

It takes a lot of food to feed 7.1 billion people. To meet the food demands of the world's population, farmers often add fertilizers that contain nitrogen to soil to increase crop yields.

As shown in **Figure 5,** nitrogen is an element that naturally cycles through ecosystems. Living things use nitrogen to make proteins. And when these living things die and decompose or produce waste, they release nitrogen into the soil or the atmosphere.

Although nitrogen gas makes up about 79 percent of Earth's atmosphere, most living things cannot use nitrogen in its gaseous form. Nitrogen must be converted into a usable form. Bacteria that live on the roots of certain plants convert atmospheric nitrogen to a form that is usable by plants. Modern agricultural practices include adding fertilizer that contains a usable form of nitrogen to soil.

Scientists estimate that human activities such as manufacturing and applying fertilizers to crops have doubled the amount of nitrogen cycling through ecosystems. Excess nitrogen can kill plants adapted to low nitrogen levels and affect organisms that depend on those plants for food. Fertilizers can seep into groundwater supplies, polluting drinking water. They can also run off into streams and rivers, affecting aquatic organisms.

Other Effects of Agriculture

Agriculture can impact soil quality in other ways, too. Soil erosion can occur when land is overfarmed or overgrazed. High rates of soil erosion can lead to desertification. **Desertification** *is the development of desertlike conditions due to human activities and/or climate change.* A region of land that undergoes desertification is no longer useful for food production.

✓ Reading Check What causes desertification?

Figure 6 🔑 Some resources must be mined from the ground.

Mining

Many useful rocks and minerals are removed from the ground by mining. For example, copper is removed from the surface by digging a strip mine, such as the one shown in Figure 6. Coal and other in-ground resources also can be removed by digging underground mines.

Mines are essential for obtaining much-needed resources. However, digging mines disturbs habitats and changes the landscape. If proper regulations are not followed, water can be polluted by runoff that contains heavy metals from mines.

🔑 **Key Concept Check** What are some consequences of using land as a resource?

Construction and Development

You have read about important resources that are found on or in land. But did you know that land itself is a resource? People use land for living space. Your home, your school, your favorite stores, and your neighborhood streets are all built on land.

REVIEW VOCABULARY

runoff
the portion of precipitation that moves over land and eventually reaches streams, rivers, lakes, and oceans

---

✦ MiniLab

20 minutes

What happens when you mine? 🥽 🧪 🧹 🚫 🧤

Coal is a fossil fuel that provides energy for many activities. People obtain coal by mining, or digging, into Earth's surface.

1 Read and complete a lab safety form.

2 Research the difference between strip-mining and underground mining.

3 Use **salt dough** and **other materials** to build a model hill that contains coal deposits. Follow the instructions provided on how to build the model.

4 Sketch the profile of the hill. Use a **ruler** to measure the dimensions of the hill.

5 Decide which mining method to use to remove the coal. Mine the coal.

6 Try to restore the hill to its original size, shape, and forest cover.

Analyze and Conclude

1. **Compare** the appearance of your restored hill to the drawing of the original hill.

2. 🔑 **Key Concept** Describe two consequences of the lost forest cover and loose soil on the mined hill.

Figure 7 Urban sprawl can lead to the loss of farmland to make room for housing developments.

Math Skills

Use Percentages

Between 1960 and today, interstate highways increased from a total of 16,000 km to 47,000 km. What percent increase does this represent?

1. Subtract the starting value from the final value.

   47,000 km − 16,000 km = 31,000 km

2. Divide the difference by the starting value.

   $$\frac{31,000 \text{ km}}{16,000 \text{ km}} = 1.94$$

3. Multiply by 100 and add a % sign.

   $1.94 \times 100 = 194\%$

Practice

In 1950, the U.S. population was about 150,000,000. By 2007, it was nearly 300,000,000. What was the percent increase?

 Math Practice

Personal Tutor

Urban Sprawl

In the 1950s, large tracts of rural land in the United States were developed as suburbs, residential areas on the outside edges of a city. When the suburbs became crowded, people moved farther out into the country, as shown in **Figure 7**. More open land was cleared for still more development. *The development of land for houses and other buildings near a city is called* **urban sprawl.** The impacts of urban sprawl include habitat destruction and loss of farmland. Increased runoff also occurs, as large areas are paved for sidewalks and streets. An increase in runoff, especially if it contains sediments or chemical pollutants, can reduce the water quality of streams, rivers, and groundwater.

Roadways

Urban sprawl occurred at the same time as another trend in the United States–increased motor vehicle use. Only a small percentage of Americans owned cars before the 1940s. By 2005, there were 240 million vehicles for 295 million people, greatly increasing the need for roadways. In 1960, the United States had about 16,000 km of interstate highways. Today, the interstate highway system includes 47,000 km of paved roadways. Like urban sprawl, roadways increase runoff and disturb habitats.

Reading Check What two trends triggered the need for more highways?

Recreation

Not all of the land used by people is paved and developed. People also use land for recreation. They hike, bike, ski, and picnic, among other activities. In urban areas, some of these activities take place in public parks. As you will learn later in this lesson, parks and other green spaces help decrease runoff.

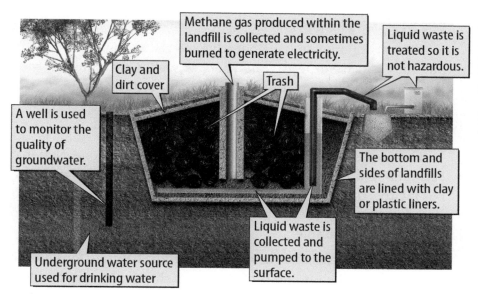

Methane gas produced within the landfill is collected and sometimes burned to generate electricity.

Clay and dirt cover

Trash

Liquid waste is treated so it is not hazardous.

A well is used to monitor the quality of groundwater.

The bottom and sides of landfills are lined with clay or plastic liners.

Liquid waste is collected and pumped to the surface.

Underground water source used for drinking water

Figure 8 About 54 percent of the trash in the United States is disposed of in landfills.

Visual Check How can the methane gas produced within a landfill be used?

Waste Management

On a typical day, each person in the United States generates about 2.1 kg of trash. That adds up to about 230 million metric tons per year! Where does all that trash go?

Landfills

About 31 percent of the trash is recycled and composted. About 14 percent is burned, and the remaining 55 percent is placed in landfills, such as the one shown in **Figure 8**. Landfills are areas where trash is buried. Landfills are another way that people use land.

A landfill is carefully designed to meet government regulations. Trash is covered by soil to keep it from blowing away. Special liners help prevent pollutants from leaking into soil and groundwater supplies.

 Key Concept Check What is done to prevent the trash in landfills from polluting air, soil, and water?

Hazardous Waste

Some trash cannot be placed in landfills because it contains harmful substances that can affect soil, air, and water quality. This trash is called hazardous waste. The substances in hazardous waste also can affect the health of humans and other living things.

Both industries and households generate hazardous waste. For example, hazardous waste from the medical industry includes used needles and bandages. Household hazardous waste includes used motor oil and batteries. The U.S. Environmental Protection Agency (EPA) works with state and local agencies to help people safely dispose of hazardous waste.

FOLDABLES

Use a sheet of notebook paper to make a horizontal two-tab concept map. Label and draw arrows as illustrated. Use the Foldable to identify positive and negative factors that have an impact on land.

Impacts on Land

+   −

ACADEMIC VOCABULARY

dispose
(verb) to throw away

Figure 9 Yellowstone National Park, which was created in 1872, is home to many natural features such as Yellowstone Falls shown here.

WORD ORIGIN · · · · · · · · · · · ·

reclamation
from Latin *reclamare*, means
"to call back"
· ·

Positive Actions

Human actions can have negative effects on the environment, but they can have positive impacts as well. Governments, society, and individuals can work together to reduce the impact of human activities on land resources.

Protecting the Land

The area shown in **Figure 9** is part of Yellowstone National Park, the first national park in the world. The park was an example for the United States and other countries as they began setting aside land for preservation. State and local governments also followed this example.

Protected forests and parks are important habitats for wildlife and are enjoyed by millions of visitors each year. Mining and logging are allowed on some of these lands. However, the removal of resources must meet environmental regulations.

Reforestation and Reclamation

A forest is a complex ecosystem. With careful planning, it can be managed as a renewable resource. For example, trees can be select-cut. That means that only some trees in one area are cut down, rather than the entire forest. In addition, people can practice reforestation. **Reforestation** *involves planting trees to replace trees that have been cut or burned down.* Reforestation, shown in **Figure 10,** can keep a forest healthy or help reestablish a deforested area.

Mined land also can be made environmentally healthy through reclamation. **Reclamation** *is the process of restoring land disturbed by mining.* Mined areas can be reshaped, covered with soil, and then replanted with trees and other vegetation.

 Reading Check How do reforestation and reclamation positively impact land?

Figure 10 Reforestation involves planting trees to replace ones that have been removed.

(t) Karl Weatherly/Getty Images, (b) George Clerk/Getty Images

Green Spaces

In urban areas, much of the land is covered with parking lots, streets, buildings, and sidewalks. Many cities use green spaces to create natural environments in urban settings. Green spaces are areas that are left undeveloped or lightly developed. They include parks within cities and forests around suburbs. Green spaces, such as the park shown in **Figure 11,** provide recreational opportunities for people and shelter for wildlife. Green spaces also reduce runoff and improve air quality as plants remove excess carbon dioxide from the air.

How can you help?

Individuals can have a big impact on land-use issues by practicing the three Rs—reusing, reducing, and recycling. Reusing is using an item for a new purpose. For example, you might have made a bird feeder from a used plastic milk jug. Reducing is using fewer resources. You can turn off the lights when you leave a room to reduce your use of electricity.

Recycling is making a new product from a used product. Plastic containers can be recycled into new plastic products. Recycled aluminum cans are used to make new aluminum cans. Paper, shown in **Figure 11,** also can be recycled.

Figure 11 shows another way people can lessen their environmental impact on the land. The student in the bottom photo is composting food scraps into a material that is added to soil to increase its fertility. Compost is a mixture of decaying organic matter, such as leaves, food scraps, and grass clippings. It is used to improve soil quality by adding nutrients to soil. Composting and reusing, reducing, and recycling all help reduce the amount of trash that ends up in landfills.

 Key Concept Check What can you do to help lessen your impact on the land?

Figure 11 🔑 Green spaces, recycling, and composting are three things that can have positive impacts on land resources.

Parks provide recreational opportunities for people and habitats for wildlife, such as birds.

Using recycled paper to make new paper reduces deforestation as well as water use during paper production.

Composting speeds up the rate of decomposition for vegetable scraps, leaving a rich material that can be used as natural fertilizer.

Lesson 2
EXPLAIN

311

Lesson 2 Review

Visual Summary

Deforestation, agriculture, and mining for useful rocks and minerals all can affect land resources negatively.

People use land for living space, which can lead to urban sprawl, an increase in roadways, and the need for proper waste disposal.

Creating national parks, preserves and local green spaces, reforestation, and practicing the three Rs are all ways people can positively impact land resources.

FOLDABLES

Use your lesson Foldable to review the lesson. Save your Foldable for the project at the end of the chapter.

What do you think NOW?

You first read the statements below at the beginning of the chapter.

3. Deforestation does not affect soil quality.

4. Most trash is recycled.

Did you change your mind about whether you agree or disagree with the statements? Rewrite any false statements to make them true.

Use Vocabulary

1 **Distinguish** between deforestation and reforestation.

2 **Use the term** *urban sprawl* in a sentence.

3 **Define** *desertification.*

Understand Key Concepts

4 Which has a positive impact on land?
   A. composting   C. mining
   B. deforestation   D. urban sprawl

5 **Apply** How can the addition of fertilizers to crops affect the nitrogen cycle?

6 **Analyze** Why must waste disposal be carefully managed?

Interpret Graphics

7 **Organize** Copy and fill in the graphic organizer below. In each oval, list one way that people use land.

Land Use

8 **Describe** the function of the liner in the diagram below.

Liner

Math Skills   Math Practice

9 In 1950, 35.1 million people lived in suburban areas. By 1990, the number had increased to 120 million people. What was the percent increase in suburban population?

Materials

creative
construction
materials

paper towels

scissors

masking tape

Safety

How will you design an environmentally safe landfill?

Your city is planning to build an environmentally safe landfill and is accepting design proposals. Your task is to develop and test a design to submit to city officials.

Learn It

When you **design an experiment,** you consider the variables you want to test and how you will measure the results.

Try It

1. Read and complete a lab safety form.

2. Read the information provided about landfill requirements as set by the Environmental Protection Agency.

3. Plan and diagram your landfill design.

4. Use the materials to build your landfill model. Add waste materials.

5. Pour 350 mL of water on your landfill to simulate rain. Observe the path the water takes.

6. Collect the leachate and compare its volume with that of the other groups. Leachate is the liquid that seeps out of your landfill.

7. Compare your landfill design to that of other groups.

Apply It

8. Explain how you designed your landfill to meet requirements and function efficiently.

9. How did your landfill design compare to those of other groups? How much leachate did your group collect compared to other groups?

10. What changes would you make to the design of your landfill? What changes would you make to your procedure to test the effectiveness of your landfill?

11. **Key Concept** Explain how your landfill helped to prevent the pollution of soil and water.

Reading Guide

Key Concepts
ESSENTIAL QUESTIONS

- How do humans use water as a resource?
- How can pollution affect water quality?
- What actions help prevent water pollution?

Vocabulary
point-source pollution p. 316

nonpoint-source pollution p. 317

 Multilingual eGlossary

8.ESS.3, SEPS.1, SEPS.6, SEPS.8, 6-8.LST.7.1

Impacts on Water

inquiry How Much Water?

About 34 percent of all water used in the United States is used to irrigate crops. Where does all this water come from? What other ways do humans use water? What happens when water is polluted or runs out?

Noah Clayton/Getty Images

Launch Lab

20 minutes

Which water filter is the most effective?

Suppose you have been hired by the Super-Clean Water Treatment Plant to test new water filters. Their old filters do not remove all of the particles from the treated water. Your job is to design an effective water filter.

1. Read and complete a lab safety form.
2. Obtain a **water sample,** a **funnel,** and two **500-mL beakers.**
3. Use **coffee filters, paper towels, cotton,** and **gravel** to make a filter in the funnel. Hold the funnel over the first beaker. Pour half of your water sample into the funnel and collect the water in the beaker. Record your results in your Science Journal.
4. Remove the filter and rinse the funnel. Based on your results, make a second, more efficient filter. Repeat step 3 using the second beaker.
5. Draw a diagram of both filtering methods in your Science Journal.

Think About This

1. Were either of your filters successful in removing the particles from the water? Why or why not?
2. What changes would you make to your filter to make it work more efficiently?
3. **Key Concept** How do water treatment plants make more water available for human use?

Water as a Resource

Most of Earth's surface is covered with water, and living things on Earth are made mostly of water. Neither the largest whale nor the smallest algae can live without this important resource. Like other organisms, humans need water to survive. Humans also use water in ways that other organisms do not. People wash cars, do laundry, and use water for recreation and transportation.

Household activities, however, make up only a small part of human water use. As shown in **Figure 12,** most water in the United States is used by power plants. The water is used to generate electricity and to cool equipment. Like the land uses you learned about earlier, the use of water as a resource also impacts the environment.

Key Concept Check How do humans use water as a resource?

Water Use

Water Use in the United States

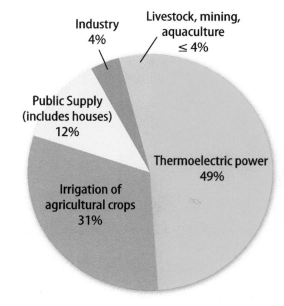

Figure 12 Power plants, industries, farms, and households all use water.

Hutchings Photography/Digital Light Source

Lesson 3
EXPLORE

315

Sources of Water Pollution

Water moves from Earth's surface to the atmosphere and back again in the water cycle. Thermal energy from the Sun causes water at Earth's surface to evaporate into the atmosphere. Water vapor in the air cools as it rises, then condenses and forms clouds. Water returns to Earth's surface as precipitation. Runoff reenters oceans and rivers or it can seep into the ground. Pollution from a variety of sources can impact the quality of water as it moves through the water cycle.

Point-Source Pollution

Point-source pollution *is pollution from a single source that can be identified.* The discharge pipe in **Figure 13** that is releasing industrial waste directly into a river is an example of point-source pollution. Other examples of point-source pollution in **Figure 13** are the oil spilling from the tanker and the runoff from the mining operation.

WORD ORIGIN ....

pollution
from Latin *polluere*, means
"to contaminate"

Sources of Water Pollution 🔑

Personal Tutor

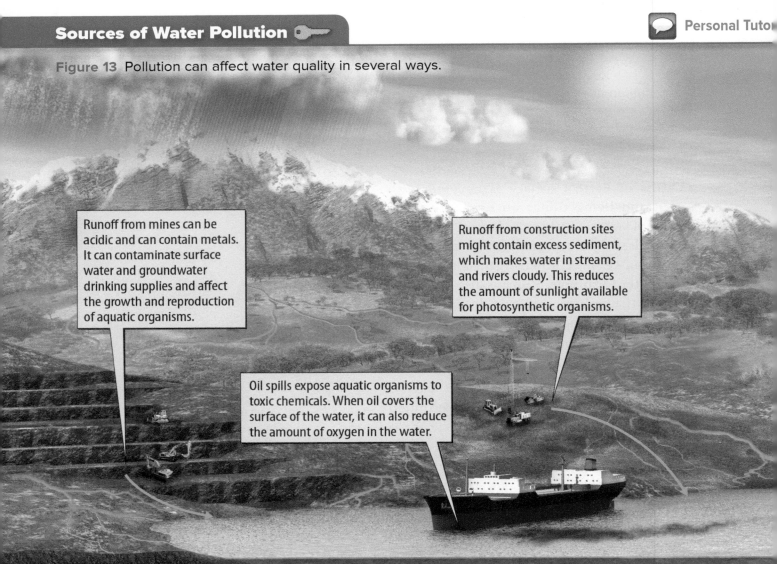

Figure 13 Pollution can affect water quality in several ways.

Runoff from mines can be acidic and can contain metals. It can contaminate surface water and groundwater drinking supplies and affect the growth and reproduction of aquatic organisms.

Runoff from construction sites might contain excess sediment, which makes water in streams and rivers cloudy. This reduces the amount of sunlight available for photosynthetic organisms.

Oil spills expose aquatic organisms to toxic chemicals. When oil covers the surface of the water, it can also reduce the amount of oxygen in the water.

Nonpoint-Source Pollution

Pollution from several widespread sources that cannot be traced back to a single location is called **nonpoint-source pollution.** As precipitation runs over Earth's surface, the water picks up materials and substances from farms and urban developments, such as the ones shown in Figure 13. These different sources might be several kilometers apart. This makes it difficult to trace the pollution in the water back to one specific source. Runoff from farms and urban developments are examples of nonpoint-source pollution. Runoff from construction sites, which can contain excess amounts of sediment, is another example of nonpoint-source pollution.

Most of the water pollution in the United States comes from nonpoint sources. This kind of pollution is harder to pinpoint and therefore harder to control.

 Key Concept Check How can pollution affect water quality?

Point-Source Pollution

Both

Nonpoint-Source Pollution

Visual Check What are the point sources and nonpoint sources of pollution in this illustration?

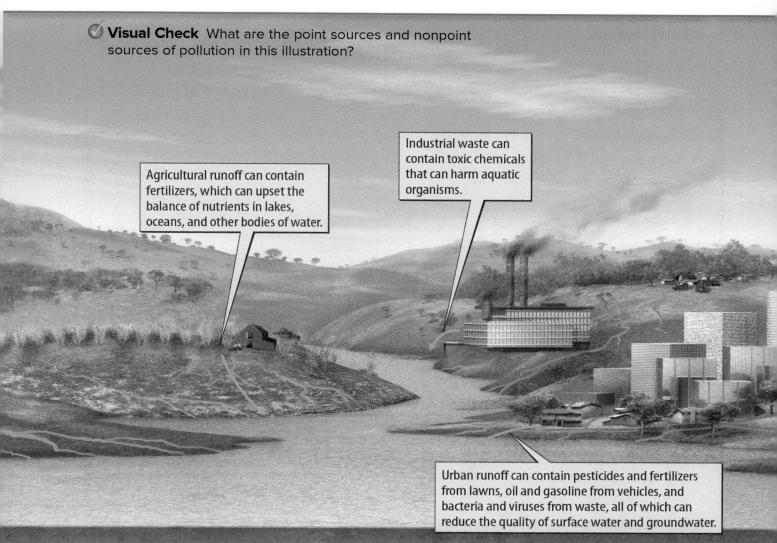

Agricultural runoff can contain fertilizers, which can upset the balance of nutrients in lakes, oceans, and other bodies of water.

Industrial waste can contain toxic chemicals that can harm aquatic organisms.

Urban runoff can contain pesticides and fertilizers from lawns, oil and gasoline from vehicles, and bacteria and viruses from waste, all of which can reduce the quality of surface water and groundwater.

Figure 14 In 1969, burning litter and chemical pollution floating on the Cuyahoga River in northeastern Ohio inspired international efforts to clean up the Great Lakes.

Positive Actions

Once pollution enters water, it is difficult to remove. In fact, it can take decades to clean polluted groundwater! That is why most efforts to reduce water pollution focus on preventing it from entering the environment, rather than cleaning it up.

International Cooperation

In the 1960s, Lake Erie, one of the Great Lakes, was heavily polluted by runoff from fertilized fields and industrial wastes. Rivers that flowed into the lake were polluted, too. Litter soaked with chemicals floated on the surface of one of these rivers—the Cuyahoga River. As shown in **Figure 14,** the litter caught fire. The fire spurred Canada and the United States—the two countries that border the Great Lakes—into action.

The countries formed several agreements to clean up the Great Lakes. The goals of the countries are pollution prevention, as well as cleanup and research. Although, the Great Lakes still face challenges from aquatic species that are not native to the lakes and from the impact of excess sediments, pollution from toxic chemicals has decreased.

Reading Check Why is it important to focus on preventing water pollution before it happens?

MiniLab

20 minutes

What's in well water?

The graph shows the level of nitrates in well water in Spanish Springs Valley, Nevada, over a 10-year period. Nitrate is a form of nitrogen that can contaminate groundwater when it leaches out of septic systems.

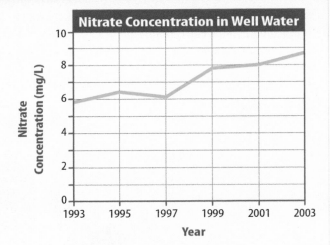

Analyze and Conclude

1. **Describe** what happened to the average level of nitrate in the well water of Spanish Springs Valley between 1993 and 2003.

2. **Analyze** Excess nitrate in drinking water can cause serious illness, especially in infants. The maximum allowable level in public drinking water is 10 mg/L. How close did the highest level of nitrate concentration come to the maximum level allowed?

3. **Key Concept** An article in the newspaper described a Spanish Springs Valley project to connect all houses to the sewer system. Predict how this will affect nitrate levels in the well water.

AP Images

National Initiatives

In addition to working with other governments, the United States has laws to help maintain water quality within its borders. The Clean Water Act, for example, regulates sources of water pollution, including sewage systems. The Safe Drinking Water Act protects supplies of drinking water throughout the country.

How can you help?

Laws are effective ways to reduce water pollution. But simple actions taken by individuals can have positive impacts, too.

Reduce Use of Harmful Chemicals Many household products, such as paints and cleaners, contain harmful chemicals. People can use alternative products that do not contain toxins. For example, baking soda and white vinegar are safe, inexpensive cleaning products. In addition, people can reduce their use of artificial fertilizers on gardens and lawns. As you read earlier, compost can enrich soils without harming water quality.

Dispose of Waste Safely Sometimes using products that contain pollutants is necessary. Vehicles, for example, cannot run without motor oil. This motor oil has to be replaced regularly. People should never pour motor oil or other hazardous substances into drains, onto the ground, or directly into streams or lakes. These substances must be disposed of safely. Your local waste management agency has tips for safe disposal of hazardous waste.

Conserve Water Water pollution can be reduced simply by reducing water use. Easy ways to conserve water include taking shorter showers and turning off the water when you brush your teeth. **Figure 15** shows other ways to reduce water use.

 Key Concept Check How can individuals help prevent water pollution?

Figure 15 People can help reduce water pollution by conserving water.

✔️ **Visual Check** How does sweeping a deck help reduce water pollution?

Keeping water in the refrigerator instead of running water from a faucet until the water is cold helps conserve water.

Sweeping leaves and branches from a deck instead of spraying them off using water from a hose helps conserve water.

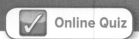
Visual Summary

Water is an important resource; all living things need water to survive. Water is used for agriculture, for electricity production, and in homes and businesses every day.

Runoff from mines

Water pollution can come from many sources, including chemicals from agriculture and industry and oil spills.

International cooperation and national laws help prevent water pollution. Individuals can help conserve water by reducing water use and disposing of wastes properly.

FOLDABLES

Use your lesson Foldable to review the lesson. Save your Foldable for the project at the end of the chapter.

What do you think NOW?

You first read the statements below at the beginning of the chapter.

5. Sources of water pollution are always easy to identify.

6. The proper method of disposal for used motor oil is to pour it down the drain.

Did you change your mind about whether you agree or disagree with the statements? Rewrite any false statements to make them true.

Use Vocabulary

1 **Define** *nonpoint-source pollution* and *point-source pollution* in your own words.

2 **Use the term** *nonpoint-source pollution* in a sentence.

Understand Key Concepts

3 Which uses the most water in the United States?
  A. factories   **C.** households
  B. farms   **D.** power plants

4 **Survey** three classmates to find out how they conserve water at home.

5 **Diagram** Make a diagram showing how runoff from lawns can impact water quality.

Interpret Graphics

6 **Sequence** Draw a graphic organizer such as the one below to illustrate the cleanup of Lake Erie, beginning with the pollution of the lake.

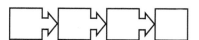

7 **Classify** the pollution source shown below as point-source or nonpoint-source. Explain your reasoning.

Critical Thinking

8 **Visualize** a map of a river that flows through several countries. Explain why international cooperation is needed to reduce water pollution.

9 **Identify** a human activity that impacts water quality negatively. Then describe a positive action that can help reduce the pollution caused by the activity.

Dead Zones

What causes lifeless areas in the ocean?

For thousands of years, people have lived on coasts, making a living by shipping goods or by fishing. Today, fisheries in the Gulf of Mexico provide jobs for thousands of people and food for millions more. Although humans and other organisms depend on the ocean, human activities can harm marine ecosystems. Scientists have been tracking dead zones in the ocean for several decades. They believe that these zones are a result of human activities on land.

A large dead zone in the Gulf of Mexico forms every year when runoff from spring and summer rain in the Midwest drains into the Mississippi River. The runoff contains nitrogen and phosphorous from fertilizer, animal waste, and sewage from farms and cities. This nutrient-rich water flows into the gulf. Algae feed on excess nutrients and multiply rapidly, creating an algal bloom. The results of the algal bloom are shown below.

Some simple changes in human activity can help prevent dead zones. People upstream from the Gulf can decrease the use of fertilizer and apply it at times when it is less likely to be carried away by runoff. Picking up or containing animal waste can help, too. Also, people can modernize and improve septic and sewage systems. How do we know these steps would work? Using them has already restored life to dead zones in the Great Lakes!

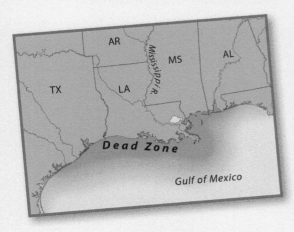

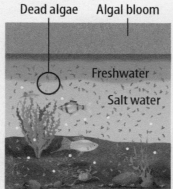

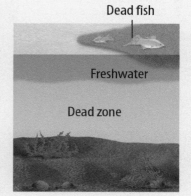

① River water containing nitrogen and phosphorous flows into the Gulf of Mexico.

② After the algal bloom, dead algae sink to the ocean floor.

③ Decomposing algae deplete the water's oxygen, killing other organisms.

It's Your Turn

RESEARCH AND REPORT Earth's oceans contain about 150 dead zones. Choose three. Plot them on a map and write a report about what causes each dead zone.

©Bo Zaunders/Corbis

Impacts on the Atmosphere

Reading Guide

Key Concepts 🔑
ESSENTIAL QUESTIONS

- What are some types of air pollution?
- How are global warming and the carbon cycle related?
- How does air pollution affect human health?
- What actions help prevent air pollution?

Vocabulary

photochemical smog p. 323

acid precipitation p. 324

particulate matter p. 324

global warming p. 325

greenhouse effect p. 326

Air Quality Index p. 327

 Multilingual eGlossary

 BrainPOP®

 8.ESS.3, SEPS.1, SEPS.2, SEPS.6, SEPS.8, 6-8.LST.7.1

quiry Why wear a mask?

In some areas of the world, people wear masks to help protect themselves against high levels of air pollution. Where does this pollution come from? How do you think air pollution affects human health and the environment?

©Fritz Hoffmann/Corbis

Where's the air? 🥽 🦺 ⚡

In 1986, an explosion at a nuclear power plant in Chernobyl, Russia, sent radioactive pollution 6 km into the atmosphere. Within three weeks, the radioactive cloud had reached Italy, Finland, Iceland, and North America.

1. Read and complete a lab safety form.
2. With your group, move to your assigned area of the room.
3. Lay out **sheets of paper** to cover the table.
4. When the **fan** starts blowing, observe whether water droplets appear on the paper. Record your observations in your Science Journal.
5. Lay out another set of paper sheets and record your observations when the fan blows in a different direction.

Think About This

1. Did the water droplets reach your location? Why or why not?

2. How is the movement of air and particles by the fan similar to the movement of the pollution from Chernobyl? How does the movement differ?

3. 🔑 **Key Concept** How do you think the health of a person in Iceland could be affected by the explosion in Chernobyl?

Importance of Clean Air

Your body, and the bodies of other animals, uses oxygen in air to produce some of the energy it needs. Many organisms can survive for only a few minutes without air. But the air you breathe must be clean or it can harm your body.

Types of Air Pollution

Human activities can produce pollution that enters the air and affects air quality. Types of air pollution include smog, acid precipitation, particulate matter, chlorofluorocarbons (CFCs), and carbon monoxide.

Smog

The brownish haze in the sky in **Figure 16** is photochemical smog. **Photochemical smog** *is caused when nitrogen and carbon compounds in the air react in sunlight.* Nitrogen and carbon compounds are released when fossil fuels are burned to provide energy for vehicles and power plants. These compounds react in sunlight and form other substances. One of these substances is ozone. Ozone high in the atmosphere helps protect living things from the Sun's ultraviolet radiation. However, ozone close to Earth's surface is a major component of smog.

Figure 16 🔑 Burning fossil fuels releases compounds that can react in sunlight and form smog.

Acid Precipitation

Another form of pollution that occurs as a result of burning fossil fuels is acid precipitation. **Acid precipitation** *is rain or snow that has a lower pH than that of normal rainwater.* The pH of normal rainwater is about 5.6. Acid precipitation forms when gases containing nitrogen and sulfur react with water, oxygen, and other chemicals in the atmosphere. Acid precipitation falls into lakes and ponds or onto the ground. It makes the water and the soil more acidic. Many living things cannot survive if the pH of water or soil becomes too low. The trees shown in **Figure 17** have been affected by acid precipitation.

Figure 17  Acid precipitation can make the soil acidic and kill trees and other plant life.

💬 Personal Tutor

Particulate Matter

The mix of both solid and liquid particles in the air is called **particulate matter.** Solid particles include smoke, dust, and dirt. These particles enter the air from natural processes, such as volcanic eruptions and forest fires. Human activities, such as burning fossil fuels at power plants and in vehicles, also release particulate matter. Inhaling particulate matter can cause coughing, difficulty breathing, and other respiratory problems.

WORD ORIGIN ·············

particulate
from Latin *particula,* means
"small part"

CFCs

Ozone in the upper atmosphere absorbs harmful ultraviolet (UV) rays from the Sun. Using products that contain CFCs, such as air conditioners and refrigerators made before 1996, affects the ozone layer. CFCs react with sunlight and destroy ozone molecules. As a result, the ozone layer thins and more UV rays reach Earth's surface. Increased skin cancer rates have been linked with an increase in UV rays.

FOLDABLES

Make a two-tab book. Label the tabs as illustrated. Use your Foldable to record factors that increase or decrease air pollution.

Factors That Increase Air Pollution | Factors That Decrease Air Pollution

Carbon Monoxide

Carbon monoxide is a gas released from vehicles and industrial processes. Forest fires also release carbon monoxide into the air. Wood-burning and gas stoves are sources of carbon monoxide indoors. Breathing carbon monoxide reduces the amount of oxygen that reaches the body's tissues and organs.

🔑 **Key Concept Check** What are some types of air pollution?

Piotr Zawisza/Getty Images

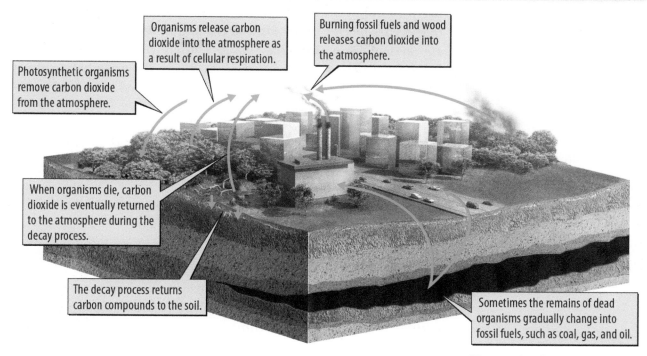

Organisms release carbon dioxide into the atmosphere as a result of cellular respiration.

Burning fossil fuels and wood releases carbon dioxide into the atmosphere.

Photosynthetic organisms remove carbon dioxide from the atmosphere.

When organisms die, carbon dioxide is eventually returned to the atmosphere during the decay process.

The decay process returns carbon compounds to the soil.

Sometimes the remains of dead organisms gradually change into fossil fuels, such as coal, gas, and oil.

Figure 18 Some human activities can increase the amount of carbon dioxide in the atmosphere.

✓ **Visual Check** Which processes add carbon to the atmosphere?

Global Warming and the Carbon Cycle

Air pollution affects natural cycles on Earth. For example, burning fossil fuels for electricity, heating, and transportation releases substances that cause acid precipitation. Burning fossil fuels also releases carbon dioxide into the atmosphere, as shown in **Figure 18.** An increased concentration of carbon dioxide in the atmosphere can lead to **global warming,** *an increase in Earth's average surface temperature.* Earth's temperature has increased about 0.8°C since 1880. Approximately two-thirds of the warming has happened since 1975. Scientists estimate it will rise an additional 1.8 to 4.0°C over the next 100 years. Even a small increase in Earth's average surface temperature can cause widespread problems.

Effects of Global Warming

Warmer temperatures can cause ice to melt, making sea levels rise. Higher sea levels can cause flooding along coastal areas. In addition, warmer ocean waters might lead to an increase in the intensity and frequency of storms.

Global warming also can affect the kinds of living things found in ecosystems. Some hardwood trees, for example, do not thrive in warm environments. These trees will no longer be found in some areas if temperatures continue to rise.

🗝️ **Key Concept Check** How are global warming and the carbon cycle related?

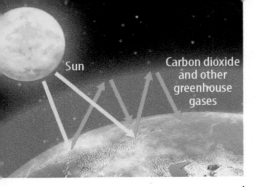

Figure 19 Greenhouse gases absorb and reradiate thermal energy from the Sun and warm Earth's surface.

 Animation

The Greenhouse Effect

Why does too much carbon dioxide in the atmosphere increase Earth's temperature? *The **greenhouse effect** is the natural process that occurs when certain gases in the atmosphere absorb and reradiate thermal energy from the Sun.* As shown in **Figure 19,** this thermal energy warms Earth's surface. Without the greenhouse effect, Earth would be too cold for life as it exists now.

Carbon dioxide is a greenhouse gas. Other greenhouse gases include methane and water vapor. When the amount of greenhouse gases increases, more thermal energy is trapped and Earth's surface temperature rises. Global warming occurs.

Reading Check How are the greenhouse effect and global warming related?

Health Disorders

Air pollution affects the environment and human health as well. Air pollution can cause respiratory problems, including triggering asthma attacks. Asthma is a disorder of the respiratory system in which breathing passageways narrow during an attack, making it hard for a person to breathe. **Figure 20** shows some health disorders caused by pollutants in the air.

Key Concept Check How can air pollution affect human health?

Figure 20 Air pollution can harm the environment and your health.

Health Effects of Air Pollution

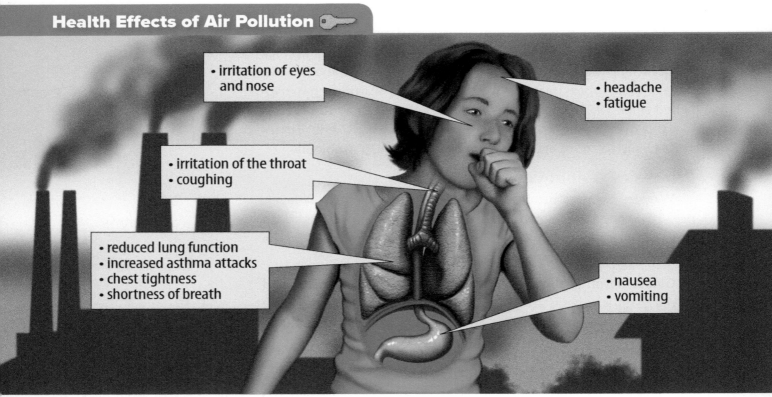

- irritation of eyes and nose
- headache
- fatigue
- irritation of the throat
- coughing
- reduced lung function
- increased asthma attacks
- chest tightness
- shortness of breath
- nausea
- vomiting

Table 1 Air Quality Index

Ozone Concentration (parts per million)	Air Quality Index Values	Air Quality Description	Preventative Actions
0.0 to 0.064	0 to 50	good	No preventative actions needed.
0.065 to 0.084	51 to 100	moderate	Highly sensitive people should limit prolonged outdoor activity.
0.085 to 0.104	101 to 150	unhealthy for sensitive groups	Sensitive people should limit prolonged outdoor activity.
0.105 to 0.124	151 to 200	unhealthy	All groups should limit prolonged outdoor activity.
0.125 to 0.404	201 to 300	very unhealthy	Sensitive people should avoid outdoor activity. All other groups should limit outdoor activity.

 Interactive Table

Measuring Air Quality

Some pollutants, such as smoke from forest fires, are easily seen. Other pollutants, such as carbon monoxide, are invisible. How can people know when levels of air pollution are high?

The EPA works with state and local agencies to measure and report air quality. *The* **Air Quality Index** *(AQI) is a scale that ranks levels of ozone and other air pollutants.* Study the AQI for ozone in **Table 1.** It uses color codes to rank ozone levels on a scale of 0 to 300. Although ozone in the upper atmosphere blocks harmful rays from the Sun, ozone that is close to Earth's surface can cause health problems, including throat irritation, coughing, and chest pain. The EPA cautions that no one should do physical activities outside when AQI values reach 300.

◀ MiniLab

10 minutes

What's in the air?

Suppose your friend suffers from asthma. People with respiratory problems such as asthma are usually more sensitive to air pollution. *Sensitive* is a term used on the AQI. Use the AQI in **Table 1** to answer the questions below.

Analyze and Conclude

1. **Identify** Today's AQI value is 130. What is the concentration of ozone in the air?

2. **Decide** Is today a good day for you and your friend to go to the park to play basketball for a few hours? Why or why not?

3. 🔑 **Key Concept** Predict how you and your friend might be affected by the air if you played basketball today.

Hybrid car

Solar car

Figure 21 🔑 Energy-efficient and renewable-energy vehicles help reduce air pollution.

✓ **Visual Check** How does driving a solar car help reduce air pollution?

Positive Actions

Countries around the world are working together to reduce air pollution. For example, 197 countries, including the United States, have signed the Montreal Protocol to phase out the use of CFCs. Levels of CFCs have since decreased. The Kyoto Protocol aims to reduce emissions of greenhouse gases. Currently, 192 countries have accepted the agreement.

National Initiatives

In the United States, the Clean Air Act sets limits on the amount of certain pollutants that can be released into the air. Since the law was passed in 1970, amounts of carbon monoxide, ozone near Earth's surface, and acid precipitation-producing substances have decreased by more than 50 percent. Toxins from industrial factories have gone down by 90 percent.

Cleaner Energy

Using renewable energy resources such as solar power, wind power, and geothermal energy to heat homes helps reduce air pollution. Recall that renewable resources are resources that can be replaced by natural processes in a relatively short amount of time. People also can invest in more energy-efficient appliances and vehicles. The hybrid car shown in **Figure 21** uses both a battery and fossil fuels for power. It is more energy efficient and emits less pollution than vehicles that are powered by fossil fuels alone. The solar car shown in **Figure 21** uses only the Sun's energy for power.

How can you help?

Reducing energy use means that fewer pollutants are released into the air. You can turn the thermostat down in the winter and up in the summer to save energy. You can walk to the store or use public transportation. Each small step you take to conserve energy helps improve air, water, and soil quality.

🔑 **Key Concept Check** How can people help prevent air pollution?

(l)Toru Hanai/Reuters/Corbis, (r)AP Images

Lesson 4 Review

Visual Summary

Burning fossil fuels releases nitrogen and carbon compounds and particulate matter into the air.

Air pollution can affect human health, causing eye, nose, and throat irritation, increased asthma, and headaches.

Certain laws and international agreements require people to reduce air pollution. Individuals can reduce air pollution by using alternative forms of energy to heat homes and power vehicles.

FOLDABLES

Use your lesson Foldable to review the lesson. Save your Foldable for the project at the end of the chapter.

What do you think NOW?

You first read the statements below at the beginning of the chapter.

7. The greenhouse effect is harmful to life on Earth.

8. Air pollution can affect human health.

Did you change your mind about whether you agree or disagree with the statements? Rewrite any false statements to make them true.

Use Vocabulary

1 **Use the term** *air quality index* in a sentence.

2 The natural heating of Earth's surface that occurs when certain gases absorb and reradiate thermal energy from the Sun is _____.

3 **Define** *global warming* in your own words.

Understand Key Concepts

4 Which is NOT a possible heath effect of exposure to air pollution?
- **A.** chest tightness
- **B.** eye irritation
- **C.** increased lung function
- **D.** shortness of breath

5 **Relate** What happens in the carbon cycle when fossil fuels are burned for energy?

6 **Compare** the goals of the Montreal Protocol and the Kyoto Protocol.

Interpret Graphics

7 **Sequence** Copy and fill in the graphic organizer below to identify types of air pollution.

8 **Describe** air quality when the ozone concentration is 0.112 ppm using the table below.

Ozone Concentration (ppm)	Air Quality Index Values	Air Quality Description
0.105 to 0.124	151 to 200	unhealthy
0.125 to 0.404	201 to 300	very unhealthy

Critical Thinking

9 **Predict** Some carbon is stored in frozen soils in the Arctic. What might happen to Earth's climate if these soils thawed?

Materials

office supplies

magazines

computer with Internet access

Safety

Design a Green City

City planners have asked the architectural firms in town to design an eco-friendly city that will be based on an environmentally responsible use of land, water, and energy. The city should include homes, businesses, schools, green spaces, industry, waste management, and transportation options.

Question

What are the most environmentally friendly materials and practices to use when designing a green city?

Procedure

1. Make a list of the things you will include in your city.

2. Research environmentally responsible structures and practices for the elements of your city. Your research may include using the library or talking with owners, employees, or patrons of businesses to identify existing environmental problems. Use the questions below to help guide your research.

   - What materials can you use for building the structures?

   - What building practices and designs can you use to minimize environmental impact?

   - How will you address energy use by homeowners, businesses, and industry?

   - How will you address water use for homes, businesses, and industry?

   - How will you address energy use and pollution issues related to public transportation?

   - What is the most environmentally friendly system of waste management?

3. Analyze the information you gathered in step 2. Discuss how you will use what you have learned as you design your city.

4. Design your city. Use the colored pencils and markers to draw a map of the city, including all of the elements of the city. Add captions, other graphics, and/or a key to explain any elements or actions and their intended results.

5. Copy and complete the *Required Elements and Actions* chart on the following page. For each element in your city, explain the environmental issue associated with the element and what action you took in your city to address the issue. Does your design include an action for each element?

McGraw-Hill Education

Required Elements and Actions		
Element	Environmental Issue	Action Taken
Waste management	All waste goes into landfills.	designed a curbside recycling program

6 If needed, modify your design to include any other actions you need to take.

Analyze and Conclude

7 Describe one identified environmental issue, the action taken, and the intended outcome in your design plans.

8 Compare your design to the designs of other groups. What did they do differently?

9 **The Big Idea** Predict whether there will be any changes in the quality of your city's water resources after years of use of your design. Explain your answer.

Communicate Your Results

Suppose your classmates are members of the city planning board. Present your design to the board. Explain the structures and practices that are intended to make the city environmentally responsible.

Inquiry Extension

Make a 3-D model of your city. Try to use recycled or environmentally friendly materials to represent the structures in your city.

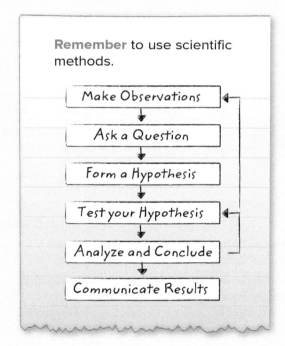

Remember to use scientific methods.

Make Observations

↓

Ask a Question

↓

Form a Hypothesis

↓

Test your Hypothesis

↓

Analyze and Conclude

↓

Communicate Results

 THE BIG IDEA Human activities can impact the environment negatively, including deforestation, water pollution, and global warming, and positively, such as through reforestation, reclamation, and water conservation.

Key Concepts Summary	Vocabulary
Lesson 1: People and the Environment • Earth has limited resources and cannot support unlimited human **population** growth. • Daily actions can deplete resources and pollute soil, water, and air. 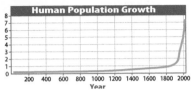	**population** p. 299 **carrying capacity** p. 300
Lesson 2: Impacts on the Land • **Deforestation, desertification,** habitat destruction, and increased rates of extinction are associated with using land as a resource. • Landfills are constructed to prevent contamination of soil and water by pollutants from waste. Hazardous waste must be disposed of in a safe manner. • Positive impacts on land include preservation, **reforestation,** and **reclamation.** 	**deforestation** p. 305 **desertification** p. 306 **urban sprawl** p. 308 **reforestation** p. 310 **reclamation** p. 310
Lesson 3: Impacts on Water 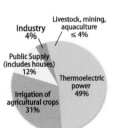• Humans use water in electricity production, industry, and agriculture, as well as for recreation and transportation. • **Point-source pollution** and **nonpoint-source pollution** can reduce water quality. • International agreements and national laws help prevent water pollution. Other positive actions include disposing of waste safely and conserving water.	**point-source pollution** p. 316 **nonpoint-source pollution** p. 317
Lesson 4: Impacts on the Atmosphere • **Photochemical smog,** CFCs, and **acid precipitation** are types of air pollution. • Human activities can add carbon dioxide to the atmosphere. Increased levels of carbon dioxide in the atmosphere can lead to **global warming.** • Air pollutants such as ozone can irritate the respiratory system, reduce lung function, and cause asthma attacks. • International agreements, laws, and individual actions such as conserving energy help decrease air pollution. 	**photochemical smog** p. 323 **acid precipitation** p. 324 **particulate matter** p. 324 **global warming** p. 325 **greenhouse effect** p. 326 **Air Quality Index** p. 327

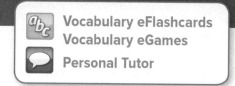

FOLDABLES®

Chapter Project

Assemble your lesson Foldables as shown to make a Chapter Project. Use the project to review what you have learned in this chapter.

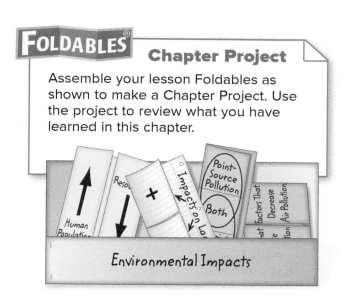

Environmental Impacts

Use Vocabulary

1. Use the term *carrying capacity* in a sentence.

2. Distinguish between desertification and deforestation.

3. Planting trees to replace logged trees is called _____.

4. Distinguish between point-source and nonpoint-source pollution.

5. Define the greenhouse effect in your own words.

6. Solid and liquid particles in the air are called _____.

Link Vocabulary and Key Concepts

▶ **Interactive Concept Map**

Copy this concept map, and then use vocabulary terms from the previous page to complete the concept map.

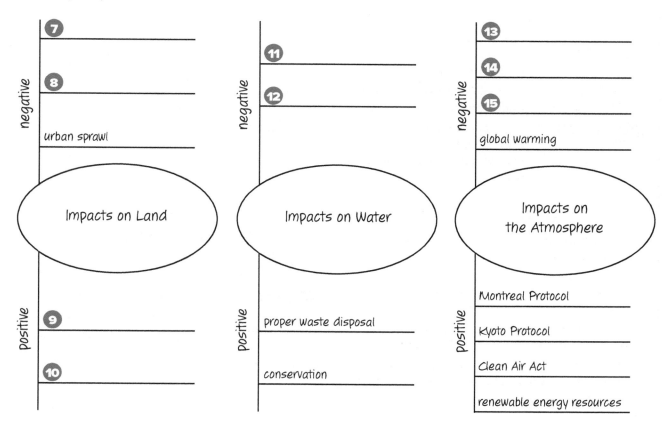

negative
7. _____
8. _____
urban sprawl

Impacts on Land

positive
9. _____
10. _____

negative
11. _____
12. _____

Impacts on Water

positive
proper waste disposal

conservation

negative
13. _____
14. _____
15. _____
global warming

Impacts on the Atmosphere

positive
Montreal Protocol

Kyoto Protocol

Clean Air Act

renewable energy resources

Understand Key Concepts

1 Which is a population?
A. all the animals in a zoo
B. all the living things in a forest
C. all the people in a park
D. all the plants in a meadow

2 Which caused the greatest increase of the growth of the human population?
A. higher death rates
B. increased marriage rates
C. medical advances
D. widespread disease

3 What percentage of species on Earth live in tropical rain forests?
A. 10 percent
B. 25 percent
C. 50 percent
D. 75 percent

4 What process is illustrated in the diagram below?

Newly planted trees

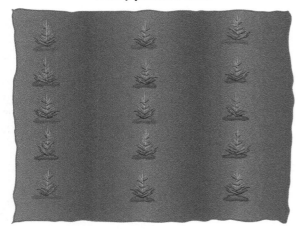

A. desertification
B. recycling
C. reforestation
D. waste management

5 Which could harm human health?
A. compost
B. hazardous waste
C. nitrogen
D. reclamation

6 Which source of pollution would be hardest to trace and control?
A. runoff from a city
B. runoff from a mine
C. an oil leak from an ocean tanker
D. water from a factory discharge pipe

7 According to the diagram below, which is the correct ranking of water use in the United States, in order from most to least?

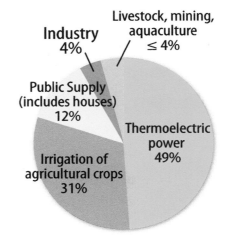

A. industrial, public supply, irrigation, power plants
B. irrigation, industrial, public supply, power plants
C. power plants, irrigation, public supply, industrial
D. public supply, power plants, industrial, irrigation

8 What is the main purpose of the Safe Drinking Water Act?
A. to ban point-source pollution
B. to clean up the Great Lakes
C. to protect drinking-water supplies
D. to regulate landfills

9 Why has the use of CFCs been phased out?
A. They cause acid rain.
B. They produce smog.
C. They destroy ozone molecules.
D. They impact the nitrogen cycle.

Critical Thinking

10 Decide Rates of human population growth are higher in developing countries than in developed countries. Yet, people in developed countries use more resources than those in developing countries. Should international efforts focus on reducing population growth or reducing resource use? Explain.

11 Relate How does the carrying capacity for a species help regulate its population growth?

12 Assess your personal impact on the environment today. Include both positive and negative impacts on soil, water, and air.

13 Infer How does deforestation affect levels of carbon in the atmosphere?

14 Role-Play Suppose you are a soil expert advising a farmer on the use of fertilizers. What would you tell the farmer about the environmental impact of the fertilizers?

15 Create Use the data below to create a circle graph showing waste disposal methods in the United States.

Waste Disposal Methods—United States	
Method	**Percent of Waste Disposed**
Landfill	55%
Recycling/composting	31%
Incineration	14%

Writing in Science

16 Compose a letter to a younger student to help him or her understand air pollution. The letter should identify the different kinds of pollution and explain their causes.

REVIEW THE BIG IDEA

17 How do human activities impact the environment? Give one example each of how human activities impact land, water, and air resources.

18 What positive actions can people take to reduce or reverse negative impacts on the environment?

Math Skills ✓ Math Practice

Use Percentages

19 Between 1960 and 1990, the number of people per square mile in the United States grew from 50.7 people to 70.3 people. What was the percent change?

20 Between 1950 and 1998, the rural population in the United States decreased from 66.2 million to 53.8 million people. What was the percent change in rural population?

21 During the twentieth century, the population of the western states increased from 4.3 million people to 61.2 million people. What was the percent change during the century?

Standardized Test Practice

Record your answers on the answer sheet provided by your teacher or on a sheet of paper.

Multiple Choice

1 Which action can help restore land that has been disturbed by mining?

   A deforestation

   B desertification

   C preservation

   D reclamation

2 Which is a consequence of deforestation?

   A Animal habitats are destroyed.

   B Carbon in the atmosphere is reduced.

   C Soil erosion is prevented.

   D The rate of extinction is slowed.

Use the graph below to answer question 3.

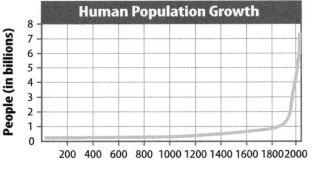

3 During which time span did the human population increase most?

   A 1400–1600

   B 1600–1800

   C 1800–1900

   D 1900–2000

4 Which accounts for the least water use in the United States?

   A electricity-generating power plants

   B irrigation of agricultural crops

   C mines, livestock, and aquaculture

   D public supply, including houses

5 Which is a point source of water pollution?

   A discharge pipes

   B runoff from farms

   C runoff from construction sites

   D runoff from urban areas

6 Which air pollutant contains ozone?

   A acid precipitation

   B carbon monoxide

   C CFCs

   D smog

Use the figure below to answer question 7.

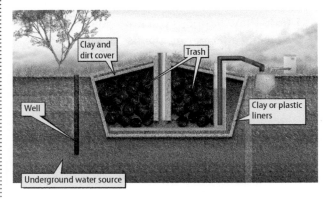

7 What is the function of the well in the figure above?

   A to generate electricity

   B to monitor quality of groundwater

   C to prevent pollution of nearby land

   D to treat hazardous water

8 Which action helps prevent water pollution?

   A pouring motor oil on the ground

   B putting hazardous wastes in the trash

   C using fertilizers when gardening

   D using vinegar when cleaning

9 What effect does ozone near Earth's surface have on the human body?

   A It increases lung function.

   B It increases throat irritation.

   C It reduces breathing problems.

   D It reduces skin cancer.

Use the figure below to answer question 10.

10 Which term describes what is shown in the figure above?

   A acid precipitation

   B global warming

   C greenhouse effect

   D urban sprawl

11 Which results in habitat destruction?

   A reclamation

   B reforestation

   C urban sprawl

   D water conservation

Constructed Response

Use the figure below to answer questions 12 and 13.

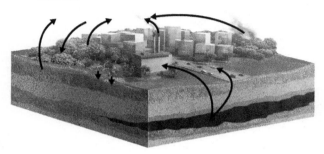

12 Which events shown in the figure remove carbon dioxide from the atmosphere?

13 Relate the carbon cycle shown in the figure to global warming and the greenhouse effect.

14 List two actions that help prevent air pollution. Then explain the pros and the cons of taking each action.

15 Explain how taking a hot shower can impact the environment.

16 Create an advertisement for a solar car. Include information about the environmental impacts of the car in your ad.

NEED EXTRA HELP?																
If You Missed Question...	1	2	3	4	5	6	7	8	9	10	11	12	13	14	15	16
Go to Lesson...	2	2	1	3	3	4	2	3	4	2	2	4	4	4	1	4

Unit 3

EXPLORING LIFE

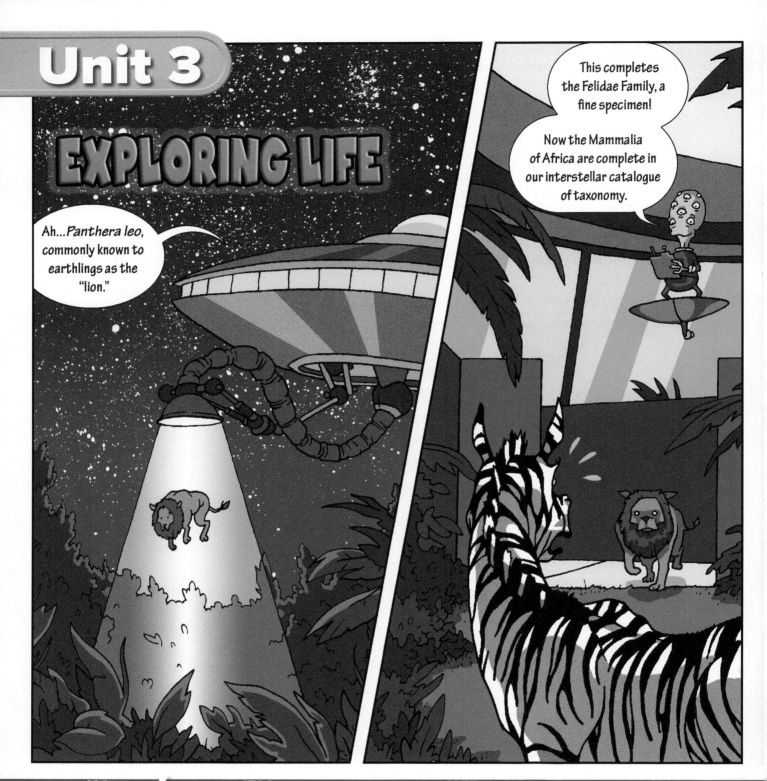

350–341 B.C.
Greek philosopher Aristotle classifies organisms by grouping 500 species of animals into eight classes.

1735
Carl Linnaeus classifies nature within a hierarchy and divides life into three kingdoms: mineral, vegetable, and animal. He uses five ranks: class, order, genus, species and variety. Linnaeus's classification is the basis of modern biological classification.

1859
Charles Darwin publishes *On the Origin of Species,* in which he explains his theory of natural selection.

1866
German biologist Ernst Haeckel coins the term *ecology.*

1969
American ecologist
Robert Whittaker is the
first to propose a five-
kingdom taxonomic
classification of the
world's biota. The five
kingdoms are Animalia,
Plantae, Fungi, Protista
and Monera.

1973
Konrad Lorenz,
Niko Tinbergen,
and Karl von Frisch
are jointly awarded
the Nobel Prize for
their studies in
animal behavior.

1990
Carl Woese
introduces the three-
domain system that
groups cellular life-
forms into Archaea,
Bacteria, and
Eukaryote domains.

Visit ConnectED
for this unit's
STEM activity.

History

Nearly 50,000 years ago, a group of hunter-gatherers might have roamed through the forest searching for food among the lush plants. The plants and animals that lived in that environment provided the nutritional needs of these people. Humans adapted to the nutrients that the wild foods contained.

Many of the foods you eat today are very different from those eaten by hunter-gatherers. Table 1 shows how some of these changes occurred.

Table 1 How Science Has Changed Foods

	What?	Advantages	Disadvantages
	Gathering Wild Foods— Foods found in nature were the diet of humans until farming began around 12,000 years ago.	Wild foods provided all the nutrients needed by the human body.	Finding wild foods is not reliable. People moved from place to place in search of food. Sometimes they didn't find food, so they went hungry or starved.
	Farming—People grew seeds from the plants they ate. Tribes settled on land near where they grew crops. If soil conditions were not ideal, farmers learned to add water or animal manure to improve plant growth.	Farming allowed more food to be grown in less space. Over time, people learned to breed plants for larger size or greater disease resistance.	Sometimes, farming changed the nutrient content of foods. People began to suffer from nutrient deficiencies and were prone to disease.
	Hybridizing Plants— Gregor Mendel fertilized one plant with the genetic material from another, producing a hybrid. A hybrid is the offspring of two genetically different organisms.	Hybridization produced new plant foods that combined the best qualities of two plants. The variety of plants available for food increased.	Hybrid crops are prone to disease because of their genetic similarity. Seeds from hybrids do not always grow into plants that produce food of the same quality as the hybrid.
	Genetically Modified (GM) Foods—Scientists remove or replace genes to improve a plant. For example, removing the gene that controls flowering in spinach results in more leaves.	GM plants can increase crop yields, nutrient content, insect resistance, and shelf-life of foods. The lettuce shown here has been modified to produce insulin.	Inserted genes might spread to other plants, producing "superweeds." Allergies to GM foods might increase. The long-term effect on humans is unknown.

A Matter of Taste

In early history, food was eaten raw, just as it was found in nature. Cooking food probably occurred by accident. Someone might have accidentally dropped a root into a fire. When people ate the burnt root, it might have tasted better or been easier to chew. This possibly led to cooking more foods. Over many generations, and with the influence of different cultures and their various ways to prepare food, the taste buds of people changed. People no longer enjoy as many raw foods.

Today, the taste buds of some people tempt them to eat high-calorie, low-nutrition processed foods, as shown in **Figure 1**. These foods contain large amounts of calories, salt, and fat.

In some parts of the world, people buy and prepare fresh fruits and vegetables every day, as shown in Figure 2. In general, these people have lower rates of obesity and fewer diseases that are common in people who eat more processed foods.

One scientist noted that people with a diet very different from our prehistoric ancestors are more susceptible to heart disease, cancer, diabetes, and other "diseases of civilization." Time to take another bite of your fruits and veggies!

Figure 1 Processing foods increases convenience but removes nutrients and adds calories that could lead to obesity.

Figure 2 People in China shop in markets where farmers sell fresh produce that comes directly from the farms.

MiniLab
30 minutes

What food would you design?

Suppose you could breed any two fruits or vegetables. What hybrid would you produce?

1. With a partner, discuss qualities of fruits and vegetables that you like and don't like. Then decide on a combination that would have the best qualities of two fruits and/or vegetables.

2. Draw and describe your new food in your Science Journal.

3. Develop a 20-second infomercial advertising the benefits of your new food, and present it to your class.

Analyze and Conclude

1. **Explain** What qualities of the original foods does your hybrid combine?

2. **Predict** Why would people buy your hybrid?

3. **Explain** What are some advantages and disadvantages of your hybrid?

Chapter 10

8.LS.2, 8.LS.7, SEPS.6, 6-8.LST.7.1

Life's Classification and Structure

THE BIG IDEA

How is the classification of living things related to the structure of their cells?

Inquiry Why All the Hooks?

This color-enhanced scanning electron micrograph shows the hooked fruit of the goosegrass plant. The hooks attach to the fur of passing animals. This enables the plant's seeds, which are in the fruit, to spread.

- What characteristics would you use to classify this plant?

- How is the classification of living things related to the structure of their cells?

Andrew Syred/Science Source

Get Ready to Read

What do you think?

Before you read, decide if you agree or disagree with each of these statements. As you read this chapter, see if you change your mind about any of the statements.

1 All living things are made of cells.

2 A group of organs that work together and perform a function is called a tissue.

3 Living things are classified based on similar characteristics.

4 *Cell wall* is a term used to describe the cell membrane.

5 Prokaryotic cells contain a nucleus.

6 Plants use chloroplasts to process energy.

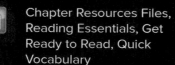

connectED

Your one-stop online resource
connectED.mcgraw-hill.com

LS	LearnSmart®	**PBL**	Project-Based Learning Activities
📄	Chapter Resources Files, Reading Essentials, Get Ready to Read, Quick Vocabulary	🖌	Lab Manuals, Safety Videos, Virtual Labs & Other Tools
▶	Animations, Videos, Interactive Tables	**abc**	Vocabulary, Multilingual eGlossary, Vocab eGames, Vocab eFlashcards
✓	Self-checks, Quizzes, Tests	💬	Personal Tutors

Classifying Living Things

Reading Guide

Key Concepts 🔑

ESSENTIAL QUESTIONS

- What are living things?
- What do living things need?
- How are living things classified?

Vocabulary

autotroph p. 348

heterotroph p. 348

habitat p. 349

binomial nomenclature p. 350

taxon p. 351

 Multilingual eGlossary

 8.LS.2, 8.LS.7, 6-8.LST.7.1

Inquiry Living or Not?

This tide pool contains sea anemones, barnacles, and sea stars that are living and rocks that are not living. How can you tell whether something is alive? Do all living things move? All living things have certain characteristics that you will read about in this lesson.

James Zipp/Science Source

How can you tell whether it is alive?

Living things share several basic characteristics. Think about what you have in common with other living things such as a bug or a tree. Do other things have some of those same characteristics?

1. Read and complete a lab safety form.
2. Observe a **lit candle** for 1–2 min. Pay attention to both the candle and the flame.
3. Write what you observe in your Science Journal.
4. Write what you think you would observe if you were to observe the candle for several hours.

Think About This

1. What characteristics does the flame have that would lead some people to think the flame is alive?

2. What qualities did you think of earlier (that you share with other living things) that the candle does not possess?

3. 🔑 **Key Concept** What characteristics do you think something must have to be considered alive?

What are living things?

It might be easy to tell whether a bird, a tree, or a person is alive. But for some organisms, it is harder to tell whether they are living things. Look at the moldy bread shown in **Figure 1**. Is the bread a living thing? What about the green mold and white mold on the bread? All living things have six characteristics in common:

- Living things are made of cells.
- Living things are organized.
- Living things grow and develop.
- Living things respond to their environment.
- Living things reproduce.
- Living things use energy.

The bread shown in **Figure 1** is not living, but the molds growing on the bread are living things. Mold is a type of fungus. If you looked at the mold using a microscope, you would see that it is made of cells. Mold cells respond to their environment by growing and reproducing. The molds obtain energy, which they need to grow, from the bread.

🔑 **Key Concept Check** What are living things?

Figure 1 🔑 Mold is a living thing.

Living things are organized.

Marching bands are made up of rows of people playing different instruments. Some rows are made up of people playing flutes, and other rows are filled with drummers. Although marching bands are organized into different rows, all band members work together to play a song. Like marching bands, living things also are organized. Some living things are more complex than others, but all organisms are made of cells. In all cells, macromolecules are organized into different structures that help cells function. You might recall that there are four macromolecules in cells—nucleic acids, lipids, proteins, and carbohydrates. Nucleic acids, such as DNA, store information. Lipids are the main component of cell membranes and provide structure. Some proteins are enzymes, and others provide structure. Carbohydrates are used for energy.

 Reading Check Name the four macromolecules in cells.

Unicellular Organisms Some living things are unicellular, which means they are made up of only one cell. In fact, most living things on Earth are unicellular organisms. Unicellular organisms are the oldest forms of life. There are many groups of unicellular organisms, each with unique characteristics. Bacteria, amoebas (uh MEE buhz), and paramecia (per uh MEE see ah) are examples of unicellular organisms. Unicellular organisms have everything needed to obtain and use energy, reproduce, and grow inside one cell. Some unicellular organisms are tiny and cannot be seen without a microscope. Other unicellular organisms, such as the plasmodial (plaz MOH dee ul) slime mold shown in **Figure 2**, can be large.

REVIEW VOCABULARY

macromolecule
substance in a cell that forms by joining many small molecules together

ACADEMIC VOCABULARY

unique
(*adjective*) without an equal, distinctive

Laurie Knight/Getty Images

Figure 2 A plasmodial slime mold is a huge cell formed by many cells that join together and form one cell.

Multicellular Organisms Soccer teams are made up of many types of players, including goalkeepers, forwards, and fullbacks. Each team member has a specific job, but they all work together when playing a game. Many living things are made of more than one cell and are called multicellular organisms. Like the different types of players on a soccer team, multicellular organisms have different types of cells that carry out specialized functions. The ladybug shown in **Figure 3** has cells that form wings and other cells that form eyes.

Multicellular organisms have different levels of organization. Groups of cells that work together and perform a specific function are called tissues. Tissues that work together and carry out a specific function are called organs. Organs that work together and perform a specific function are called organ systems. Organ systems work together and perform all the functions an organism needs to survive.

Living things grow, develop, and reproduce.

During their lifetimes, living things grow, or increase in size. For a unicellular organism, the size of its cell increases. For a multicellular organism, the number of its cells increases. Living things also develop, or change, during their lifetimes. For some organisms, it is easy to see the changes that happen as they grow and develop. As shown in **Figure 4,** ladybug larva grow into pupae (PYEW pee; singular, pupa), an intermediate stage, before developing into adults.

Once an organism is an adult, it can reproduce either asexually or sexually and form new organisms. Unicellular organisms, such as bacteria, reproduce asexually when one cell divides and forms two new organisms. Some multicellular organisms also can reproduce asexually; one parent organism produces offspring when body cells replicate and divide. Sexual reproduction occurs when the reproductive cells of one or two parent organisms join and form a new organism. Multicellular organisms such as humans and other mammals reproduce sexually. Some organisms such as yeast can reproduce both asexually and sexually.

▲ Figure 3 🔑
Multicellular organisms, such as this ladybug, contain groups of cells that carry out special functions.

✅ **Visual Check** What structures can you identify in the ladybug?

Larva   Pupa

◄ Figure 4 🔑
A ladybug grows and develops from a larva to a pupa.

✅ **Visual Check** What differences do you see between the two stages?

Andre Skonieczny/Flonline/Getty Images

▲ **Figure 5** 🔑 Algae are autotrophic because they use sunlight to produce energy.

Living things use energy.

All living things need energy to survive. Some organisms are able to convert light energy to chemical energy that is used for many cellular processes. *Organisms that convert energy from light or inorganic substances to usable energy are called* **autotrophs** (AW tuh trohfs).

Many autotrophs use energy from light and convert carbon dioxide and water into carbohydrates, or sugars. Autotrophs use the carbohydrates for energy. Plants and the algae shown growing on the pond in **Figure 5** are autotrophs.

Other autotrophs, called chemoautotrophs (kee moh AW tuh trohfs), grow on energy released by chemical reactions of inorganic substances such as sulfur and ammonia. Many chemoautotrophs are bacteria that live in extreme environments such as deep in the ocean or in hot sulfur springs.

✓ **Reading Check** How do some autotrophs use energy from sunlight?

Heterotrophs (HE tuh roh trohfs) *are organisms that obtain energy from other organisms.* Heterotrophs eat autotrophs or other heterotrophs to obtain energy. Animals and fungi are examples of heterotrophs.

Living things respond to stimuli.

All living things sense their environments. If an organism detects a change in its external environment, it will respond to that change. A change in an organism's environment is called a stimulus (STIHM yuh lus; plural, stimuli). Responding to a stimulus might help an organism protect itself. For example, the octopus in **Figure 6** responds to predators by releasing ink, a black liquid. In many organisms, nerve cells detect the environment, process the information, and coordinate a response.

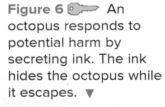

Figure 6 🔑 An octopus responds to potential harm by secreting ink. The ink hides the octopus while it escapes. ▼

What do living things need?

You just read that all living things need energy in order to survive. Some organisms obtain energy from food. What else do living things need to survive? Living things also need water and a place to live. Organisms live in environments specific to their needs where they are protected, can obtain food and water, and can get shelter.

A Place to Live

Living things are everywhere. Organisms live in the soil, in lakes, and in caves. Some living things live on or in other organisms. For example, bacteria live in your intestines and on other body surfaces. *A specific environment where an organism lives is its* **habitat.** Most organisms can survive in only a few habitats. The land iguana shown in **Figure 7** lives in warm, tropical environments and would not survive in cold places such as the Arctic.

Food and Water

Living things also need food and water. Food is used for energy. Water is essential for survival. You will read about how water is in all cells and helps them function in Lesson 2. The type of food that an organism eats depends on the habitat in which it lives. Marine iguanas live near the ocean and eat algae. Land iguanas, such as the one in **Figure 7,** live in hot, dry areas and eat cactus fruits and leaves. The food is processed to obtain energy. Plants and some bacteria use energy from sunlight and produce chemical energy for use in cells.

 Key Concept Check What do living things need?

FOLDABLES®

Make a vertical three-column chart book. Label it as shown. Use it to organize your notes about living things, their needs, and classification criteria.

Definition of a Living Thing	Survival Requirements	Classification Criteria

Figure 7 This Galápagos land iguana is eating the fruit of a prickly pear cactus.

Needs of Living Things 🔑

Carolyn Jenkins/Alamy

Math Skills

Use Ratios

A ratio expresses the relationship between two or more things. Ratios can be written

3 to 5, 3:5, or $\frac{3}{5}$.

Reduce ratios to their simplest form. For example, of about 3 million species in the animal kingdom, about 50,000 are mammals. What is the ratio of mammals to animals?

Write the ratio as a fraction.

$$\frac{50,000}{3,000,000}$$

Reduce the fraction to the simplest form.

$$\frac{50,000}{3,000,000} = \frac{5}{300} = \frac{1}{60}$$

(or 1:60 or 1 to 60)

Practice

Of the 5,000 species of mammals, 250 species are carnivores. What is the ratio of carnivores to mammals? Write the ratio in all three ways.

 Math Practice

 Personal Tutor

How are living things classified?

You might have a notebook with different sections. Each section might contain notes from a different class. This organizes information and makes it easy to find notes on different subjects. Scientists use a classification system to group organisms with similar traits. Classifying living things makes it easier to organize organisms and to recall how they are similar and how they differ.

Naming Living Things

Scientists name living things using a system called binomial nomenclature (bi NOH mee ul • NOH mun klay chur). **Binomial nomenclature** *is a naming system that gives each living thing a two-word scientific name.*

More than 300 years ago a scientist named Carolus Linnaeus created the binomial nomenclature system. All scientific names are in Latin. *Homo sapiens* is the scientific name for humans. As shown in **Table 1,** the scientific name for an Eastern chipmunk is *Tamias striatus.*

Table 1 Classification of the Eastern Chipmunk

Taxonomic Group	Number of Species	Examples
Domain Eukarya	about 4–10 million	
Kingdom Animalia	about 2 million	
Phylum Chordata	about 50,000	
Class Mammalia	about 5,000	
Order Rodentia	about 2,300	
Family Sciuridae	299	
Genus *Tamias*	25	
Species *Tamias striatus*	1	

Frank Cezus/Getty Images

Classification Systems

Linnaeus also classified organisms based on their behavior and appearance. Today, the branch of science that classifies living things is called taxonomy. *A group of organisms is called a* **taxon** (plural, taxa). There are many taxa, as shown in Table 1. Organisms are classified into taxonomic levels according to shared characteristics. An organism's scientific name correlates to these shared characteristics.

Taxonomy

Using taxonomy, scientists divide all living things on Earth into three groups called domains. Domains are divided into kingdoms, and then phyla (FI luh; singular, phylum), classes, orders, families, genera (singular, genus), and species. A species is made of all organisms that can mate with one another and produce offspring that can reproduce. The first word in an organism's scientific name is the organism's genus (JEE nus), and the second word might describe a distinguishing characteristic of the organism. Dogs belong to the genus *Canis*. The *Canis* genus includes organisms with shared characteristics, such as wolves and jackals.

Recall that Linnaeus used similar physical traits to group organisms. Today, scientists also look for other similarities, such as how an organism reproduces, how it processes energy, and the types of genes it has.

Dichotomous Keys

A dichotomous (di KAH tah mus) key is a tool used to identify an organism based on its characteristics. Dichotomous keys contain descriptions of traits that are compared when classifying an organism. Dichotomous keys are organized in steps. Each step might ask a yes or a no question and have two answer choices. Which question is answered next depends on the answer to the previous question. Based on the features, a choice is made that best describes the organism.

Key Concept Check How are living things classified?

MiniLab   20 minutes

Whose shoe is it?

A dichotomous key is a tool to help identify an unknown object or organism.

1. Read and complete a lab safety form.
2. Have each person in your group place one of his or her **shoes** in a pile.
3. Observe the shoes, looking for similarities and differences among them.
4. In your Science Journal, write a question that can be used to separate the shoes into two groups.
5. Divide the shoes into the two groups.
6. Continue asking questions for each subgroup until all of the shoes are identified.
7. Number the questions from the top of the key down, and create your key this way:

   1. Question 1?
   Yes . . . . go to question _____
   No . . . . go to question _____

Analyze and Conclude

1. **Classify** What characteristics probably should not be used when creating a dichotomous key?

2. **Key Concept** Describe how a doctor and a pest exterminator could use a dichotomous key.

 Applying Practices

How can living things be classified?
Go online to explore classification of organisms.

 WebQuest

Classifying and Comparing Worms
Go online to learn more about classification of worms.

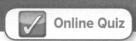

Visual Summary

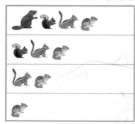

All living things grow, develop, and reproduce.

All living things are organized, respond to their environment, and use energy.

Scientists use a classification system to group organisms with similar traits and genetic makeup.

FOLDABLES®

Use your lesson Foldable to review the lesson. Save your Foldable for the project at the end of the chapter.

What do you think NOW?

You first read the statements below at the beginning of the chapter.

1. All living things are made of cells.

2. A group of organs that work together and perform a function is called a tissue.

3. Living things are classified based on similar characteristics.

Did you change your mind about whether you agree or disagree with the statements? Rewrite any false statements to make them true.

Use Vocabulary

1 **Use the term** *taxon* in a sentence.

2 **Distinguish** between the terms *autotroph* and *heterotroph*.

3 Linnaeus created a two-word naming system for organisms called _____ .

Understand Key Concepts

4 An environment where specific organisms live is called a(n)
  A. autotroph.   C. heterotrophy.
  B. habitat.   D. taxon.

5 **Explain** how binomial nomenclature helps scientists classify organisms.

6 **Relate** the number of cells an organism has to the way it reproduces.

Interpret Graphics

7 **Summarize** Copy and fill in the graphic organizer below to summarize the characteristics of living things.

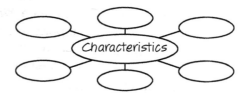

Critical Thinking

8 **Differentiate** between living and nonliving things in the picture at right.

Math Skills   ✓ Math Practice

9 There are 3 million species in the animal kingdom. Of those, about 270 species are carnivores. What is the ratio of carnivores to animals? Write the ratio all three ways.

On a Quest
for Leeches

How do you catch a leech? Let it bite you!

Mark Siddall travels the world searching for creatures that make most people cringe—leeches. He collects leeches to understand how they are related and how they evolved. This is a huge job since there are more than 600 known species of leeches!

Siddall is a scientist at the American Museum of Natural History. He travels to remote places, such as the jungles of Rwanda and the swamps of Argentina, to collect leeches. Once he's there, he lets the leeches find him. Barefoot, he treks through damp forests or wades in streams. Leeches attach to his skin, draw blood until they're full, and then fall off. That's when Mark adds them to the museum's collection.

Siddall identifies the leeches by their body parts. Some have jaws and teeth. Others have thin tubes for sucking in liquid. They use these parts to draw blood or fluids from animals, such as frogs, humans, snails, and other worms. Some even swallow their prey whole!

Through his research, Siddall is helping build a family tree for leeches to learn how they evolved. For example, leeches today live on land, in freshwater, and in the ocean. Siddall's research shows that leeches first appeared in freshwater and then moved onto land and into the ocean. Many species of leeches are being threatened by habitat destruction. Siddall hopes his research will help protect leeches and their habitats.

▲ Mark Siddall uses himself as bait to catch leeches. When a leech is done feeding, it falls off into a collection bag.

In just 30 minutes, a leech can swallow more than five times its weight in blood. It might not need to feed again for a few months.

It's Your Turn

DIAGRAM Leeches are classified according to how they feed. Choose a jawed leech (*Hirudinidae*), a jawless leech (*Erpobdellidae*), or a leech that uses a proboscis (*Glossiphoniidae*). Research how it feeds. Draw a diagram and present your findings.

Lesson 2

Cells

Reading Guide

Key Concepts 🔑
ESSENTIAL QUESTIONS

- What is a cell made of?
- How do the parts of a cell enable it to survive?

Vocabulary
prokaryotic cell p. 356

eukaryotic cell p. 356

cytoplasm p. 358

mitochondrion p. 359

 Multilingual eGlossary

 BrainPOP®

 8.LS.2, 8.LS.7, SEPS.6, 6-8.LST.7.1

Inquiry Weird Web?

This isn't a spider's strange web. These are nerve cells shown in a color-enhanced electron micrograph. The larger green parts are the cell bodies. The threadlike parts carry electrical signals from one nerve cell to another. How do these parts help the cells?

SPL/Science Source

Are all cells alive?

There are many bacteria that live on and in people. These unicellular organisms have all the characteristics of life and are alive. Are human cells, which the bacteria live on and in, also alive?

① In your Science Journal, draw a circle that takes up half of the page. The circle represents a human cell.

② Draw and label the following things in your cell:

A power plant to represent the need for and use of energy; label it *energy production.*

A garbage truck to represent waste removal; label it *waste removal.*

A city hall with a mayor to represent the organization and processes of the cell; label it *organization.*

A road system to represent the transportation that occurs in the cell; label it *transportation.*

A cement truck to represent the construction of new structures in the cell; label it *growth.*

A fire truck to represent a cell's ability to respond to changes in its surroundings; label it *response to environment.*

A copy machine in city hall to represent the cell's ability to follow instructions and make more cells; label it *reproduction.*

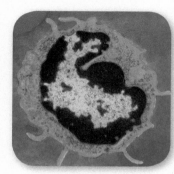

Think About This

1. Does the human cell you drew have all the characteristics of life? Explain your answer.

2. 🔑 **Key Concept** Do you think each of the trillions of cells that are part of you are either alive or once-living? Why?

What are cells?

What is one thing all living things have in common? All living things have cells, the basic unit of an organism. As you read in Lesson 1, most organisms have only one cell. Other organisms have many cells. Humans have about 100 trillion cells! Most cells are so small that they cannot be seen without a microscope. Microscopes, such as the one shown in **Figure 8,** are used to view details of small objects or to view things that are too small to be seen by the unaided eye.

Scientists first used microscopes to look at cells over 300 years ago. Cells come in different shapes and sizes. Nerve cells are long and slender. Many female reproductive cells, or eggs, are large and round.

✓ **Reading Check** Why is a microscope needed to view most cells?

LM Magnification: 21×

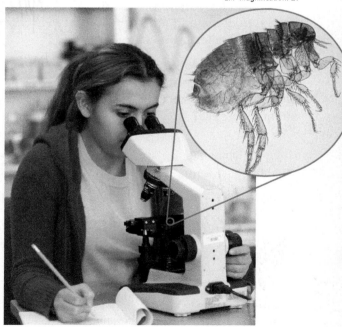

Figure 8 Microscopes increase the size of an image so that a small thing, such as the flea shown here, can be observed.

What are cells made of?

Recall that all cells are made of four macromolecules–nucleic acids, lipids, proteins, and carbohydrates. Cells also have many other characteristics. For example, all cells are surrounded by an outer structure called a cell membrane. The cell membrane keeps substances such as macromolecules inside the cell. It also helps protect cells by keeping harmful substances from entering. About 70 percent of the inside of a cell is water. Many of the substances inside cells are dissolved in water so they can move easily about the cell.

 Key Concept Check What is a cell made of?

Types of Cells

There are two main types of cells, as shown in Figure 9. **Prokaryotic** (pro kayr ee AH tihk) **cells** *do not have a nucleus or other membrane-bound organelles.* Organelles are structures in cells that carry out specific functions. The few organelles in prokaryotic cells are not surrounded by membranes. Organisms with prokaryotic cells are called prokaryotes. Most prokaryotes are unicellular organisms, such as bacteria.

Eukaryotic (yew ker ee AH tihk) **cells** *have a nucleus and other membrane-bound organelles.* Most multicellular organisms and some unicellular organisms are eukaryotes. The eukaryotic cell shown in Figure 9 contains many structures that are not in a prokaryotic cell. In eukaryotes, membranes surround most of the organelles, including the nucleus.

▶ **Animation**

Figure 9 🔑 Prokaryotic cells do not have a nucleus. Eukaryotic cells have a nucleus and many other organelles.

✓ **Visual Check** What structures are in both prokaryotic cells and eukaryotic cells?

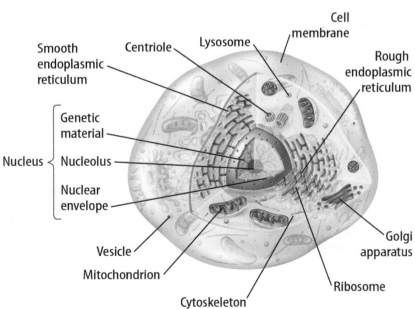

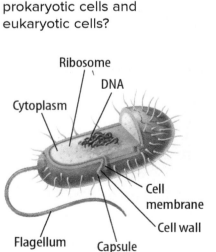

Prokaryotic Cell

Eukaryotic Cell

The Outside of a Cell

As you have just read, the cell membrane surrounds a cell. Much like a fence surrounds a school, the cell membrane helps keep the substances inside a cell separate from the substances outside a cell. Some cells also are surrounded by a more rigid layer called a cell wall.

Cell Membrane

The cell membrane is made of lipids and proteins. Recall that lipids and proteins are macromolecules that help cells function. Lipids in the cell membrane protect the inside of a cell from the external environment. Proteins in the cell membrane transport substances between a cell's environment and the inside of the cell. Proteins in the cell membrane also communicate with other cells and organisms and sense changes in the cell's environment.

 Reading Check Summarize the major components of cell membranes.

Cell Wall

In addition to a cell membrane, some cells also have a cell wall, as shown in **Figure 10.** The cell wall is a strong, rigid layer outside the cell membrane. Cells in plants, fungi, and many types of bacteria have cell walls. Cell walls provide structure and help protect the cell from the outside environment. Most cell walls are made from different types of carbohydrates.

 Animation

Figure 10 🔑 This plant cell has a cell membrane and a cell wall.

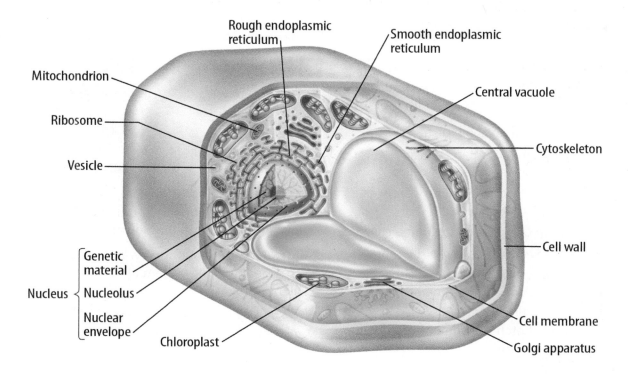

Rough endoplasmic reticulum

Smooth endoplasmic reticulum

Mitochondrion

Central vacuole

Ribosome

Cytoskeleton

Vesicle

Cell wall

Genetic material

Nucleus — Nucleolus

Nuclear envelope

Cell membrane

Chloroplast

Golgi apparatus

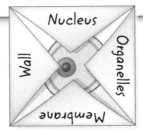
The Inside of a Cell

Recall that the inside of a cell is mainly water. Many substances used for communication, energy, and growth dissolve in water. This makes it easier for the substances to move around inside a cell. Water also gives cells their shapes and helps keep the structures inside a cell organized. The organelles inside a cell perform specific functions. They control cell activities, provide energy, transport materials, and store materials.

Cytoplasm

The liquid part of a cell inside the cell membrane is called the **cytoplasm.** It contains water, macromolecules, and other substances. The organelles in eukaryotic cells are located in the cytoplasm. Proteins in the cytoplasm provide structure and help organelles and other substances move around.

Controlling Cell Activities

The information that controls all of a cell's activities is stored in its genetic material, called DNA. DNA is a type of macromolecule called a nucleic acid. The information in DNA is transferred to another nucleic acid called RNA. RNA gives cells instructions about which proteins need to be made. In prokaryotic cells, DNA is in the cytoplasm. In eukaryotic cells, DNA is stored in an organelle called the nucleus. A membrane, called the nuclear membrane, surrounds the nucleus. Tiny holes in the nuclear membrane let certain substances move between the nucleus and the cytoplasm.

MiniLab

20–30 minutes

What can you see in a cell?

When people developed microscopes, they were able to see things that they could not see with their eyes alone.

1. Read and complete a lab safety form.
2. Carefully remove a thin layer of membrane from a piece of **onion.**
3. Place the membrane on the center of a dry **microscope slide.**
4. Add a drop of **iodine** on top of the sample.
5. Place a **cover slip** on top of the sample.
6. Use a **microscope** to focus on the slide using low power. Sketch what you see in your Science Journal.
7. View and sketch the sample on medium and high powers.

Analyze and Conclude

1. **Observe** What structures did you see at low, medium, and high powers?

2. **Infer** How might your view of the cells change if you view them at an even higher power?

3. **Key Concept** How does a microscope help you learn more about the onion plant?

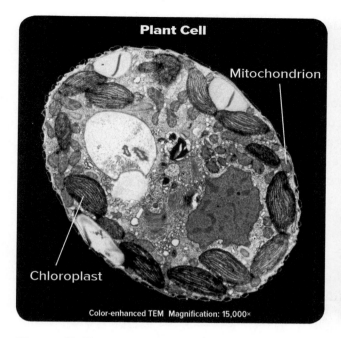

Plant Cell

Chloroplast

Mitochondrion

Color-enhanced TEM Magnification: 15,000×

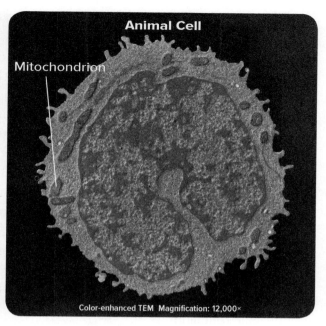

Animal Cell

Mitochondrion

Color-enhanced TEM Magnification: 12,000×

Figure 11 Plant cells have mitochondria and chloroplasts. Animal cells only contain mitochondria.

Visual Check Where are the mitochondria located in a cell?

Energy for the Cell

You read in Lesson 1 that all living things use energy. Proteins in the cytoplasm process energy in prokaryotes. Eukaryotes have special organelles, the chloroplasts and mitochondria (mi tuh KAHN dree uh; singular, mitochondrion) shown in **Figure 11,** that process energy.

Mitochondria Most eukaryotes contain hundreds of mitochondria. **Mitochondria** *are organelles that break down food and release energy.* This energy is stored in molecules called ATP–adenosine triphosphate (uh DEN uh seen • tri FAHS fayt). ATP provides a cell with energy to perform many functions, such as making proteins, storing information, and communicating with other cells.

Reading Check What energy molecule is made in a mitochondrion?

Chloroplasts Energy also can be processed in organelles called chloroplasts, shown in **Figure 11.** Plants and many other autotrophs have chloroplasts and mitochondria. Chloroplasts capture light energy and convert it into chemical energy in a process called photosynthesis. Chloroplasts contain many structures that capture light energy. Like the reactions that occur in mitochondria, ATP molecules are produced during photosynthesis. However, photosynthesis also produces carbohydrates such as glucose that also are used to store energy.

WORD ORIGIN

mitochondrion
from Greek *mitos,* means
"thread"; and *khondrion,* means
"little granule"

(l) Biophoto Associates/Science Source, (r) Eye of Science/Science Source

Protein Production

You just read that cells use protein for many functions. These proteins are made on the surface of ribosomes that are in the cytoplasm of both prokaryotic and eukaryotic cells. In eukaryotic cells, some ribosomes are attached to an organelle called the endoplasmic reticulum (en duh PLAZ mihk • rih TIHK yuh lum), as shown in **Figure 12**. It is made of folded membranes. The proteins can be processed and can move inside the cell through the endoplasmic reticulum.

Color-enhanced TEM Magnification: Unavailable

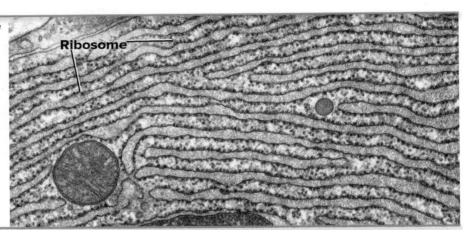

Figure 12 Ribosomes are attached to the rough endoplasmic reticulum. ▶

Cell Storage

What happens to the molecules that are made in a cell? An organelle called the Golgi (GAWL jee) apparatus packages proteins into tiny organelles called vesicles. Vesicles transport proteins around a cell. Other molecules are stored in organelles called vacuoles. A vacuole is usually the largest organelle in a plant cell, as shown in **Figure 13**. In plant cells, vacuoles store water and provide support. In contrast to all plant cells, only some animal and bacterial cells contain vacuoles. The vacuoles in animal and bacterial cells are smaller than the ones in plant cells.

 Key Concept Check How do the parts of a cell enable it to survive?

Color-enhanced TEM Magnification: 2,000×

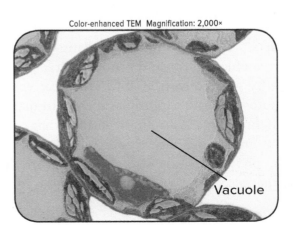

Figure 13 Vacuoles are used by plant cells for storage and to provide structure. ▶

Lesson 2 Review

Visual Summary

Prokaryotic cells are surrounded by a cell membrane but have no internal organelles with membranes.

Eukaryotic cells contain a nucleus and many other organelles.

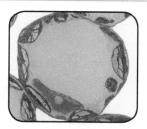

Plant cells have cell walls, chloroplasts, and a large vacuole.

FOLDABLES

Use your lesson Foldable to review the lesson. Save your Foldable for the project at the end of the chapter.

What do you think NOW?

You first read the statements below at the beginning of the chapter.

4. *Cell wall* is a term used to describe the cell membrane.

5. Prokaryotic cells contain a nucleus.

6. Plants use chloroplasts to process energy.

Did you change your mind about whether you agree or disagree with the statements? Rewrite any false statements to make them true.

Use Vocabulary

1 **Distinguish** between prokaryotic cells and eukaryotic cells.

2 Water, proteins, and other substances are found in the _____ of a cell.

3 **Define** *mitochondrion* in your own words.

Understand Key Concepts

4 Which organelles store water, carbohydrates, and wastes in plants?
  A. chloroplasts   **C.** nuclei
  B. mitochondria   **D.** vacuoles

5 **Compare** how energy is processed in animal and plant cells.

6 **Distinguish** between a cell membrane and a cell wall.

Interpret Graphics

7 **Summarize** Use the table below to identify organelles and their functions.

Organelle	Function
Nucleus	
	energy processing
Vacuole	

8 **Compare and contrast** the structures of the two cells shown below.

Critical Thinking

9 **Assess** the role of water in cell function.

10 **Relate** the cell wall to protection in bacteria.

Materials

compound
microscope

dissecting
microscope

magnifying
lens

ruler

Also needed:
specimens

Safety

How can living things be classified?

Thousands of new organisms are discovered each year. Today, an organism's DNA can be used to determine how closely a newly discovered organism is related to living things that are already known. A long time ago, taxonomists had to rely on what they could observe with their senses to determine the relationships between organisms. They looked at characteristics such as an organism's parts, behaviors, or the environments in which they lived to help them determine relationships among organisms. The father of taxonomy, Carolus Linnaeus, developed a system in the 1700s by which he classified over 9,000 organisms, primarily based on their external features.

Question

What characteristics can be used to distinguish among different types of organisms?

Procedure

1. Read and complete a lab safety form.

2. Use your background knowledge of the specimens provided and the available tools to identify distinguishing characteristics of the specimens. Be sure to observe each of the specimens thoroughly and completely.

3. In your Science Journal, record as much information as possible about each of the organisms. This information can include your observations and any knowledge you have of the organism.

(l, l to b, 2–4) Hutchings Photography/Digital Light Source, (tr) Image Source/Getty Images, (cr) IT Stock/age fotostock, (b) Getty Images

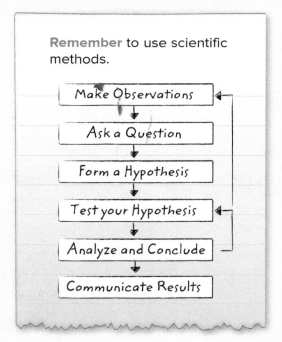

4 Using the information you have recorded, create a dichotomous key that can be used to identify all of the specimens.

5 Trade your key with another student.

6 Verify that the key you received works by trying to identify all ten of the organisms, one at a time.

7 If your key did not work, repeat steps 2–5. If your key did work, move on to the **Analyze and Conclude** section.

Analyze and Conclude

8 **Compare and Contrast** How are the questions in the key you made similar to and different from the questions in the key that you checked?

9 **Classify** How would an elephant, bread mold, and a rose be identified if the key you created was used to identify them? Are these identifications accurate? Why did this happen?

10 **The Big Idea** How would the questions in your key be different if all ten organisms were more closely related, such as ten different plants?

Communicate Your Results

Share your key and questions with a small group of students. After everyone shares, make a group key that combines the most objective questions that were asked among the various keys.

Inquiry Extension

Research the scientific names of the specimens that you observed, and find the meanings of the species name of each organism. Research the characteristics by which bacteria are classified. Design a key to be used by younger students to help identify different polygons (triangles, pentagons, octagons, and so on) using correct mathematical terms.

Lab Tips

☑ Recall from earlier in the chapter the types of characteristics that are good to use in creating a dichotomous key.

Remember to use scientific methods.

Make Observations

↓

Ask a Question

↓

Form a Hypothesis

↓

Test your Hypothesis

↓

Analyze and Conclude

↓

Communicate Results

 THE BIG IDEA

Organisms are classified based on similar characteristics, including cell structure and function.

Key Concepts Summary

Lesson 1: Classifying Living Things

- Living things are organized, process energy, grow, reproduce, respond to stimuli, and contain cells.
- Living things need food, water, and a **habitat.**
- Organisms are classified based on similar characteristics.

Vocabulary

autotroph p. 348

heterotroph p. 348

habitat p. 349

binomial nomenclature p. 350

taxon p. 351

Lesson 2: Cells

- Cells are made of water and macromolecules.
- Different parts of a cell enable it to perform special functions.

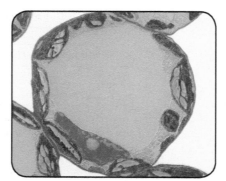

prokaryotic cell p. 356

eukaryotic cell p. 356

cytoplasm p. 358

mitochondrion p. 359

(t) Jeff Rotman/Science Source, (b) Dr. Jeremy Burgess/Science Source

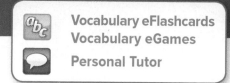
FOLDABLES®

Chapter Project

Assemble your lesson Foldables as shown to make a Chapter Project. Use the project to review what you have learned in this chapter.

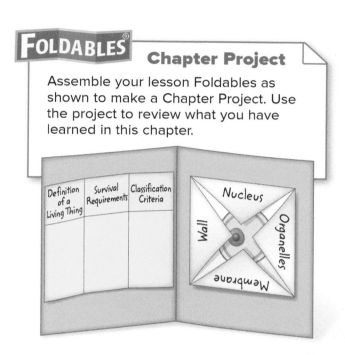

Use Vocabulary

1 The Latin term *Homo sapiens* is an example of _____.

2 Organisms that obtain energy by eating other organisms are called _____.

3 Use the term *habitat* in a sentence.

4 Define the term *cytoplasm* in your own words.

5 Animal cells obtain energy by breaking down food in _____.

6 Use the term *prokaryotic cell* in a sentence.

Link Vocabulary and Key Concepts

 Interactive Concept Map

Copy this concept map, and then use vocabulary terms from the previous page to complete the concept map.

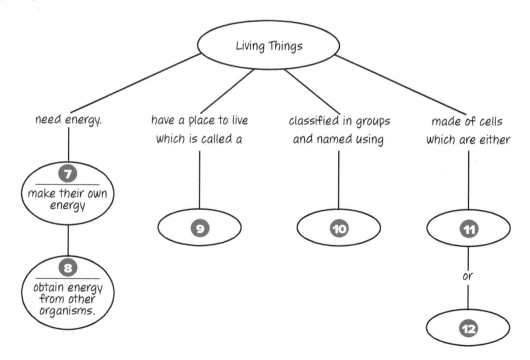

Understand Key Concepts

1 What is a rigid structure that provides support and protection to plants and some types of bacteria?

A. chloroplast
B. nucleus
C. cell membrane
D. cell wall

2 What type of reproduction occurs when a cell divides to form two new cells?

A. autotrophic
B. heterotrophic
C. asexual reproduction
D. sexual reproduction

3 Which is the binomial nomenclature for humans?

A. *Canis lupos*
B. *Felis catus*
C. *Homo sapiens*
D. *Tamias striatus*

4 What is a group of organisms called?

A. taxon
B. tissue
C. dichotomous key
D. organ system

5 Which organelle is the arrow pointing to in the picture below?

A. chloroplast
B. cytoplasm
C. mitochondrion
D. vacuole

6 Which is NOT a characteristic of all living things?

A. grow
B. reproduce
C. have organelles
D. use energy

7 Which organelle is the arrow pointing to in the picture below?

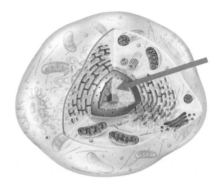

A. chloroplast
B. cytoplasm
C. mitochondrion
D. nucleus

8 What is the name used to describe the specific place where an organism lives?

A. autotroph
B. habitat
C. heterotroph
D. taxon

9 What is the smallest unit of all living things?

A. cell
B. organ
C. organelle
D. tissue

10 What are cells mostly made of?

A. DNA
B. lipids
C. proteins
D. water

Critical Thinking

11 **Summarize** the characteristics of all living things.

12 **Explain** how living things grow and develop. Use the growth and development of a ladybug as an example.

13 **Explain** how shared characteristics are related to taxonomy and scientific names.

14 **Explain** why different organisms live in different habitats.

15 **Assess** the role of organelles in the functions of eukaryotic cells.

16 **Relate** the structure in the plant cell shown at the pointer in the picture below to how it obtains energy.

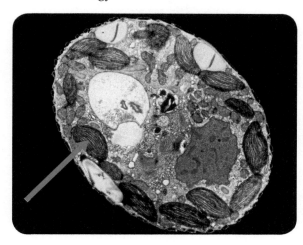

17 **Summarize** the role of nucleic acids in controlling cell functions.

18 **Discuss** how heterotrophs process energy.

Writing in Science

19 **Write** a five-sentence paragraph that describes the characteristics that all living things share.

REVIEW THE BIG IDEA

20 **Assess** how the classification of prokaryotes and eukaryotes relates to the structure of their cells.

21 How is the classification of living things related to the structure of their cells? Use the plant in the photo below as an example.

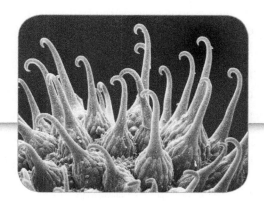

Math Skills ✓ Math Practice

Use Ratios

22 There are about 300,000 species of plants. Of those, 12,000 are mosses. What is the ratio of mosses to plants? Express the answer all three ways.

23 Out of 300,000 plant species, 260,000 are flowering plants. What is the ratio of flowering plants to all plant species? Express the ratio in all three ways.

24 Out of 12,000 species of mosses, only about 400 are club mosses. What is the ratio of club mosses to all mosses? Express the ratio in all three ways.

Standardized Test Practice

Record your answers on the answer sheet provided by your teacher or on a sheet of paper.

Multiple Choice

1 Which would a chemoautotroph use to produce energy?

A sulfur

B sunlight

C carbon dioxide

D other organisms

2 Which taxon is used as the first word in an organism's scientific name?

A class

B genus

C kingdom

D order

Use the diagram below to answer question 3.

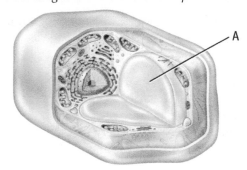

3 The diagram shows the parts of a plant cell. What is the name and function of structure A?

A chloroplast, making carbohydrates

B chloroplast, producing energy

C vacuole, storing water

D vacuole, transporting proteins

4 Which molecule stores energy for cells?

A ATP

B DNA

C proteins

D ribosomes

5 What do scientists call the largest taxonomic level of organization for organisms?

A domains

B genera

C kingdoms

D phyla

Use the image below to answer question 6.

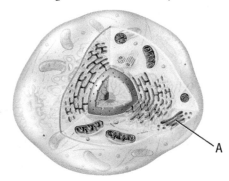

6 In the diagram, the organelle labeled A packages proteins into vesicles. What is this organelle called?

A central vacuole

B endoplasmic reticulum

C Golgi apparatus

D nuclear envelope

7 Which cell structures break down food and release energy?

A chloroplasts

B mitochrondria

C ribosomes

D vacuoles

8 Carl Linnaeus grouped organisms into categories based on which characteristic?

  A energy production

  B gene type

  C physical traits

  D reproduction habits

9 Which term defines a group of cells that work together and perform a function?

  A organ

  B taxon

  C tissue

  D phylum

Use the diagram to answer question 10.

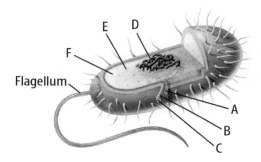

10 In the cell shown, what is the letter for the structure that provides much of the cell's support and helps protect it from the outside environment?

  A A

  B B

  C C

  D D

Constructed Response

Use the figure to answer questions 11 and 12.

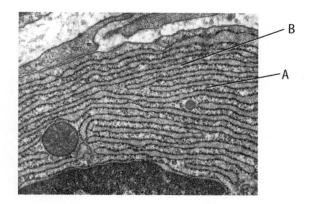

11 Identify the structure labeled *A* in the diagram. What is its function?

12 How are the organelles labeled *A* and *B* related? Are they found in prokaryotic cells, eukaryotic cells, or both?

13 Explain the relationship between cells, tissues, organs, and organ systems in a multicellular organism.

14 Cell membranes are made up mainly of proteins and carbohydrates. How do these molecules function in the cell membrane?

NEED EXTRA HELP?														
If You Missed Question...	1	2	3	4	5	6	7	8	9	10	11	12	13	14
Go to Lesson...	1	1	2	2	1	2	2	1	1	2	2	2	1	2

MedImage/Science Source

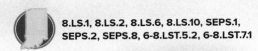
Reproduction of Organisms

THE BIG IDEA

Why do living things reproduce?

Inquiry **Time to bond?**

Have you ever seen a family of animals, such as the one of penguins shown here? Notice the baby penguin beside its parents. Like all living things, penguins reproduce.

• Do you think all living things have two parents?

• What might happen if the penguins did not reproduce?

• Why do living things reproduce?

Bill Coster/Getty Images

Get Ready to Read

What do you think?

Before you read, decide if you agree or disagree with each of these statements. As you read this chapter, see if you change your mind about any of the statements.

1. Humans produce two types of cells: body cells and sex cells.

2. Environmental factors can cause variation among individuals.

3. Two parents always produce the best offspring.

4. Cloning produces identical individuals from one cell.

5. All organisms have two parents.

6. Asexual reproduction occurs only in microorganisms.

Your one-stop online resource
connectED.mcgraw-hill.com

 LearnSmart®

 Chapter Resources Files, Reading Essentials, Get Ready to Read, Quick Vocabulary

 Animations, Videos, Interactive Tables

 Self-checks, Quizzes, Tests

 Project-Based Learning Activities

 Lab Manuals, Safety Videos, Virtual Labs & Other Tools

 Vocabulary, Multilingual eGlossary, Vocab eGames, Vocab eFlashcards

 Personal Tutors

Sexual Reproduction and Meiosis

Reading Guide

Key Concepts 🔑

ESSENTIAL QUESTIONS

- What is sexual reproduction, and why is it beneficial?
- What is the order of the phases of meiosis, and what happens during each phase?
- Why is meiosis important?

Vocabulary

sexual reproduction p. 373

egg p. 373

sperm p. 373

fertilization p. 373

zygote p. 373

diploid p. 374

homologous chromosomes p. 374

haploid p. 375

meiosis p. 375

 Multilingual eGlossary

 BrainPOP®

 8.LS.1, 8.LS.2, 8.LS.6, 6-8.LST.7.1

Inquiry Modern Art?

This photo looks like a piece of modern art. It is actually an image of plant cells. The cells are dividing by a process that occurs during the production of sex cells.

Science Pictures Ltd./Science Source

Why do offspring look different?

Unless you're an identical twin, you probably don't look exactly like any siblings you might have. You might have differences in physical characteristics such as eye color, hair color, ear shape, or height. Why are there differences in the offspring from the same parents?

1 Read and complete a lab safety form.

2 Open the **paper bag** labeled *Male Parent,* and, without looking, remove three **beads.** Record the bead colors in your Science Journal, and replace the beads.

3 Open the **paper bag** labeled *Female Parent,* and remove three **beads.** Record the bead colors, and replace the beads.

4 Repeat steps 2 and 3 for each member of the group.

5 After each member has recorded his or her bead colors, study the results. Each combination of male and female beads represents an offspring.

Think About This

1. Compare your group's offspring to another group's offspring. What similarities or differences do you observe?

2. What caused any differences you observed? Explain.

3. 🔑 **Key Concept** Why might this type of reproduction be beneficial to an organism?

What is sexual reproduction?

Have you ever seen a litter of kittens? One kitten might have orange fur like its mother. A second kitten might have gray fur like its father. Still another kitten might look like a combination of both parents. How is this possible?

The kittens look different because of sexual reproduction. **Sexual reproduction** *is a type of reproduction in which the genetic materials from two different cells combine, producing an offspring.* The cells that combine are called sex cells. Sex cells form in reproductive organs. *The female sex cell, an* **egg,** *forms in an ovary. The male sex cell, a* **sperm,** *forms in a testis. During a process called* **fertilization** (fur tuh luh ZAY shun), *an egg cell and a sperm cell join together.* This produces a new cell. *The new cell that forms from fertilization is called a* **zygote.** As shown in **Figure 1,** the zygote develops into a new organism.

Personal Tutor

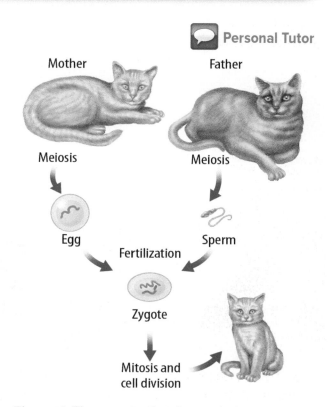

Figure 1 The zygote that forms during fertilization can become a multicellular organism.

Hutchings Photography/Digital Light Source

Diploid Cells

Following fertilization, a zygote goes through mitosis and cell division. These processes produce nearly all the cells in a multicellular organism. Organisms that reproduce sexually form two kinds of cells—body cells and sex cells. In body cells of most organisms, similar chromosomes occur in pairs. **Diploid** *cells are cells that have pairs of chromosomes.*

Chromosomes

Pairs of chromosomes that have genes for the same traits arranged in the same order are called **homologous** (huh MAH luh gus) **chromosomes.** Because one chromosome is inherited from each parent, the chromosomes are not identical. For example, the kittens mentioned earlier in this lesson inherited a gene for orange fur color from their mother. They also inherited a gene for gray fur color from their father. So, some kittens might be orange, and some might be gray. Both genes for fur color are at the same place on homologous chromosomes, but they code for different colors.

Different organisms have different numbers of chromosomes. Recall that diploid cells have pairs of chromosomes. Notice in Table 1 that human diploid cells have 23 pairs of chromosomes for a total of 46 chromosomes. A fruit fly diploid cell has 4 pairs of chromosomes, and a rice diploid cell has 12 pairs of chromosomes.

Table 1 An organism's chromosomes can be matched as pairs of chromosomes that have genes for the same traits.

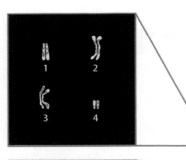

 Interactive Table

Table 1 Chromosomes of Selected Organisms		
Organism	Number of Chromosomes	Number of Homologous Pairs
Fruit fly	8	4
Rice	24	12
Yeast	32	16
Cat	38	19
Human	46	23
Dog	78	39
Fern	1,260	630

Having the correct number of chromosomes is very important. If a zygote has too many or too few chromosomes, it will not develop properly. For example, a genetic condition called Down syndrome occurs when a person has an extra copy of chromosome 21. A person with Down syndrome can have short stature, heart defects, or mental disabilities.

Haploid Cells

Organisms that reproduce sexually also form egg and sperm cells, or sex cells. Sex cells have only one chromosome from each pair of chromosomes. **Haploid** *cells are cells that have only one chromosome from each pair.* Organisms produce sex cells using a special type of cell division called meiosis. *In* **meiosis,** *one diploid cell divides and makes four haploid sex cells.* Meiosis occurs only during the formation of sex cells.

 Reading Check How do diploid cells differ from haploid cells?

The Phases of Meiosis

Next, you will read about the phases of meiosis. Many of the phases might seem familiar to you because they also occur during mitosis. Recall that mitosis and cytokinesis involve one division of the nucleus and the cytoplasm. Meiosis involves two divisions of the nucleus and the cytoplasm. These divisions are called meiosis I and meiosis II. They result in four haploid cells—cells with half the number of chromosomes as the original cell. As you read about meiosis, think about how it produces sex cells with a reduced number of chromosomes.

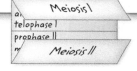

Make a shutter-fold book and label it as shown. Use it to describe and illustrate the phases of meiosis.

MiniLab
20 minutes

How does one cell produce four cells?

When a diploid cell goes through meiosis, it produces four haploid cells. How does this happen?

1 Read and complete a lab safety form.

2 Make a copy of the diagram by tracing circles around a **jar lid** on your **paper.** Label as shown.

3 Use **chenille craft wires** to make red and blue duplicated chromosomes 2.5 cm long and green and yellow duplicated chromosomes 1.5 cm long. Recall that a duplicated chromosome has two sister chromatids connected at the centromere.

4 Place the chromosomes in the diploid cell.

5 Move one long chromosome and one short chromosome into each of the middle cells.

6 Separate the two strands of the chromosomes, and place one strand into each of the haploid cells.

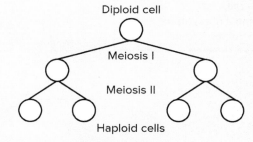

Analyze and Conclude

1. **Describe** What happened to the chromosomes during meiosis I? During meiosis II?

2. **Think Critically** Why are two haploid cells (sperm and egg) needed to form a zygote?

3. **Key Concept** How does one cell form four cells during meiosis?

Phases of Meiosis I

A reproductive cell goes through interphase before beginning meiosis I, which is shown in **Figure 2**. During interphase, the reproductive cell grows and copies, or duplicates, its chromosomes. Each duplicated chromosome consists of two sister chromatids joined together by a centromere.

1 Prophase I In the first phase of meiosis I, duplicated chromosomes condense and thicken. Homologous chromosomes come together and form pairs. The membrane surrounding the nucleus breaks apart, and the nucleolus disappears.

2 Metaphase I Homologous chromosome pairs line up along the middle of the cell. A spindle fiber attaches to each chromosome.

3 Anaphase I Chromosome pairs separate and are pulled toward the opposite ends of the cell. Notice that the sister chromatids stay together.

4 Telophase I A nuclear membrane forms around each group of duplicated chromosomes. The cytoplasm divides through cytokinesis and two daughter cells form. Sister chromatids remain together.

Meiosis 🔑   ▶ **Animation**

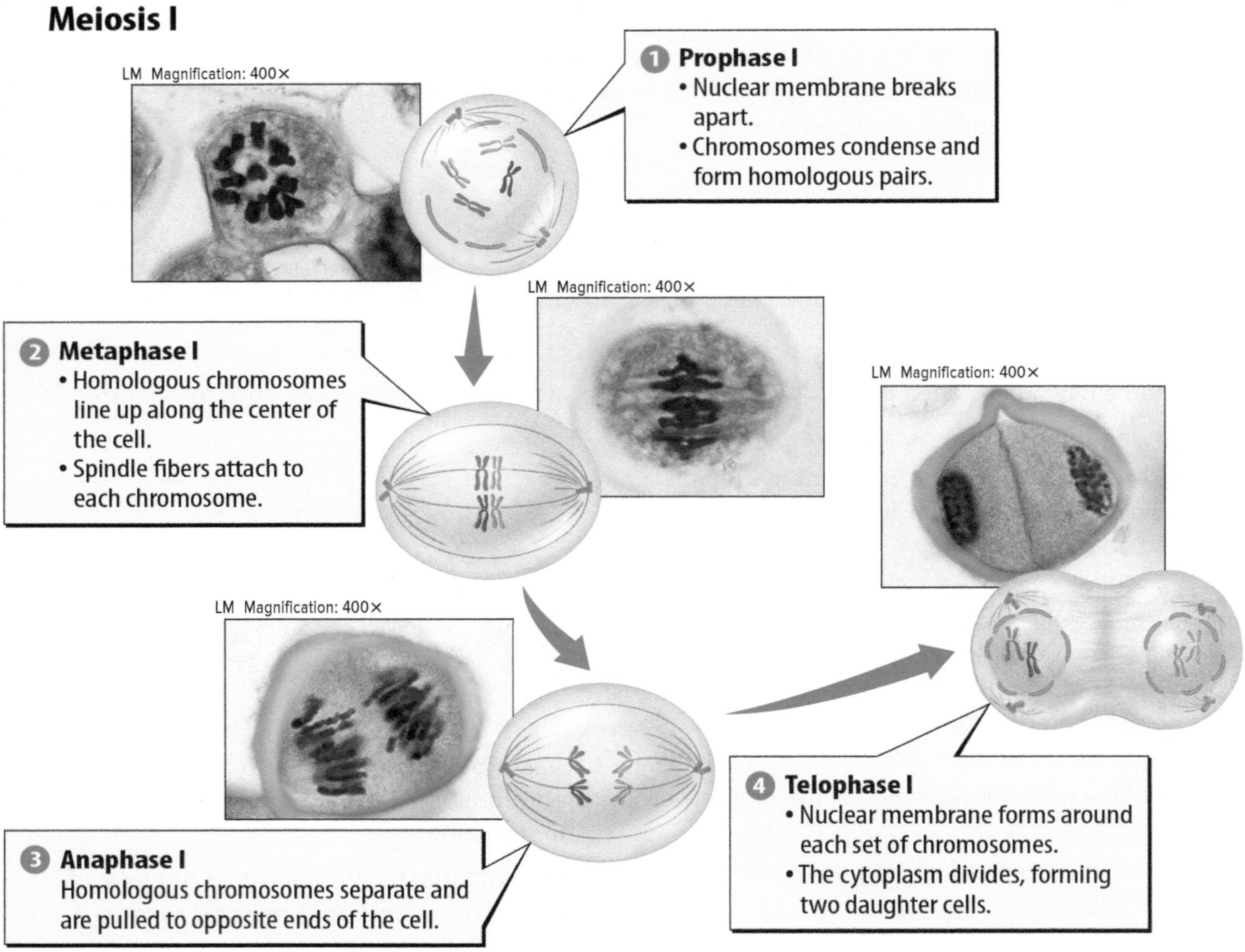

Meiosis I

LM Magnification: 400×

1 Prophase I
• Nuclear membrane breaks apart.
• Chromosomes condense and form homologous pairs.

LM Magnification: 400×

2 Metaphase I
• Homologous chromosomes line up along the center of the cell.
• Spindle fibers attach to each chromosome.

LM Magnification: 400×

LM Magnification: 400×

3 Anaphase I
Homologous chromosomes separate and are pulled to opposite ends of the cell.

4 Telophase I
• Nuclear membrane forms around each set of chromosomes.
• The cytoplasm divides, forming two daughter cells.

Ed Reschke/Getty Images

Figure 2 Unlike mitosis, meiosis involves two divisions of the nucleus and the cytoplasm.

Phases of Meiosis II

After meiosis I, the two cells formed during this stage go through a second division of the nucleus and the cytoplasm. This process, shown in **Figure 2**, is called meiosis II.

5 Prophase II Chromosomes are not copied again before prophase II. They remain as condensed, thickened sister chromatids. The nuclear membrane breaks apart, and the nucleolus disappears in each cell.

6 Metaphase II The pairs of sister chromatids line up along the middle of the cell in single file.

7 Anaphase II The sister chromatids of each duplicated chromosome are pulled away from each other and move toward opposite ends of the cells.

8 Telophase II During the final phase of meiosis–telophase II–a nuclear membrane forms around each set of chromatids, which are again called chromosomes. The cytoplasm divides through cytokinesis, and four haploid cells form.

🔑 **Key Concept Check** List the phases of meiosis in order.

Meiosis II

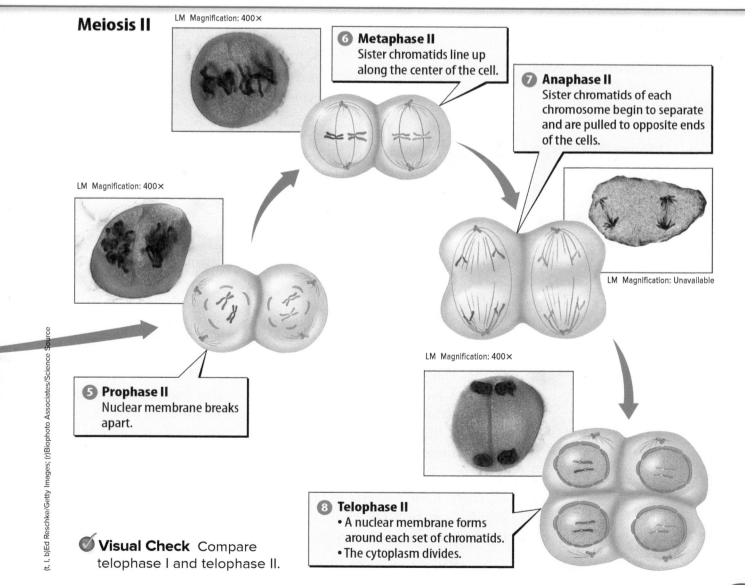

LM Magnification: 400×

6 Metaphase II
Sister chromatids line up along the center of the cell.

7 Anaphase II
Sister chromatids of each chromosome begin to separate and are pulled to opposite ends of the cells.

LM Magnification: Unavailable

LM Magnification: 400×

5 Prophase II
Nuclear membrane breaks apart.

LM Magnification: 400×

8 Telophase II
• A nuclear membrane forms around each set of chromatids.
• The cytoplasm divides.

✓ **Visual Check** Compare telophase I and telophase II.

Why is meiosis important?

Meiosis forms sex cells with the correct haploid number of chromosomes. This maintains the correct diploid number of chromosomes in organisms when sex cells join. Meiosis also creates genetic variation by producing haploid cells.

Maintaining Diploid Cells

Recall that diploid cells have pairs of chromosomes. Meiosis helps to maintain diploid cells in offspring by making haploid sex cells. When haploid sex cells join together during fertilization, they make a diploid zygote, or fertilized egg. The zygote then divides by mitosis and cell division and creates a diploid organism. **Figure 3** illustrates how the diploid number is maintained in ducks.

Figure 3 Meiosis ensures that the chromosome number of a species stays the same from generation to generation.

 Animation

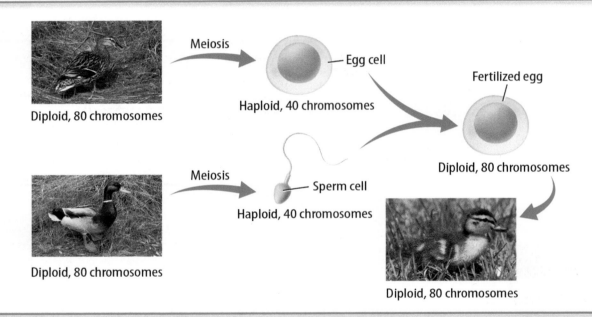

Diploid, 80 chromosomes

Meiosis

Egg cell
Haploid, 40 chromosomes

Fertilized egg

Diploid, 80 chromosomes

Diploid, 80 chromosomes

Meiosis

Sperm cell
Haploid, 40 chromosomes

Diploid, 80 chromosomes

Creating Haploid Cells

The result of meiosis is haploid sex cells. This helps maintain the correct number of chromosomes in each generation of offspring. The formation of haploid cells also is important because it allows for genetic variation. How does this happen? Sex cells can have different sets of chromosomes, depending on how chromosomes line up during metaphase I. Because a cell only gets one chromosome from each pair of homologous chromosomes, the resulting sex cells can be different.

The genetic makeup of offspring is a combination of chromosomes from two sex cells. Variation in the sex cells results in more genetic variation in the next generation.

 Key Concept Check Why is meiosis important?

(t, l)Nature's Images/Science Source, (r)Jeremy West/Getty Images

How do mitosis and meiosis differ?

Sometimes, it's hard to remember the differences between mitosis and meiosis. Use **Table 2** to review these processes.

During mitosis and cell division, a body cell and its nucleus divide once and produce two identical cells. These processes are important for growth and repair or replacement of damaged tissue. Some organisms reproduce by these processes. The two daughter cells produced by mitosis and cell division have the same genetic information.

During meiosis, a reproductive cell and its nucleus divide twice and produce four cells—two pairs of identical haploid cells. Each cell has half the number of chromosomes as the original cell. Meiosis happens in the reproductive organs of multicellular organisms. Meiosis forms sex cells used for sexual reproduction.

 Reading Check How many cells are produced during mitosis? During meiosis?

 Interactive Table

Table 2 Comparison of Types of Cell Division

Characteristic	Meiosis	Mitosis and Cell Division
Number of chromosomes in parent cell	diploid	diploid
Type of parent cell	reproductive	body
Number of divisions of nucleus	2	1
Number of daughter cells produced	4	2
Chromosome number in daughter cells	haploid	diploid
Function	forms sperm and egg cells	growth, cell repair, some types of reproduction

Math Skills

Math Practice   Personal Tutor

Use Proportions

An equation that shows that two ratios are equivalent is a proportion. The ratios $\frac{1}{2}$ and $\frac{3}{6}$ are equivalent, so they can be written as $\frac{1}{2} = \frac{3}{6}$.

You can use proportions to figure out how many daughter cells will be produced during mitosis. If you know that one cell produces two daughter cells at the end of mitosis, you can use proportions to calculate how many daughter cells will be produced by eight cells undergoing mitosis.

Set up an equation of the two ratios. $\frac{1}{2} = \frac{8}{y}$

Cross-multiply. $1 \times y = 8 \times 2$

$1y = 16$

Divide each side by 1. $y = 16$

Practice

You know that one cell produces four daughter cells at the end of meiosis. How many daughter cells would be produced if eight sex cells undergo meiosis?

Advantages of Sexual Reproduction

REVIEW VOCABULARY

DNA

the genetic information in a cell

Did you ever wonder why a brother and a sister might not look alike? The answer is sexual reproduction. The main advantage of sexual reproduction is that offspring inherit half their DNA from each parent. Offspring are not likely to inherit the same DNA from the same parents. Different DNA means that each offspring has a different set of traits. This results in genetic variation among the offspring.

 Key Concept Check Why is sexual reproduction beneficial?

Genetic Variation

As you just read, genetic variation exists among humans. You can look at your friends to see genetic variation. Genetic variation occurs in all organisms that reproduce sexually. Consider the plants shown in **Figure 4.** The plants are members of the same species, but they have different traits, such as the ability to resist disease.

Due to genetic variation, individuals within a population have slight differences. These differences might be an advantage if the environment changes. Some individuals might have traits that enable them to survive unusually harsh conditions such as a drought or severe cold. Other individuals might have traits that make them resistant to disease.

Genetic Variation 🔑

Disease-resistant cassava leaves

Cassava leaves with cassava mosaic disease

Figure 4 These plants belong to the same species. However, one is more disease-resistant than the other.

✓ **Visual Check** How does cassava mosaic disease affect cassava leaves?

Selective Breeding

Did you know that broccoli, kohlrabi, kale, and cabbage all descended from one type of mustard plant? It's true. More than 2,000 years ago farmers noticed that some mustard plants had different traits, such as larger leaves or bigger flower buds. The farmers started to choose which traits they wanted by selecting certain plants to reproduce and grow. For example, some farmers chose only the plants with the biggest flowers and stems and planted their seeds. Over time, the offspring of these plants became what we know today as broccoli, shown in **Figure 5.** This process is called selective breeding. Selective breeding has been used to develop many types of plants and animals with desirable traits. It is another example of the benefits of sexual reproduction.

Figure 5 The wild mustard is the common ancestor to all these plants.

Selective Breeding 🔑

Broccoli

Bok choy

Wild mustard

Cabbage

Kohlrabi

Disadvantages of Sexual Reproduction

Although sexual reproduction produces more genetic variation, it does have some disadvantages. Sexual reproduction takes time and energy. Organisms have to grow and develop until they are mature enough to produce sex cells. Then the organisms have to form sex cells—either eggs or sperm. Before they can reproduce, organisms usually have to find mates. Searching for a mate can take a long time and requires energy. The search for a mate might also expose individuals to predators, diseases, or harsh environmental conditions. In addition, sexual reproduction is limited by certain factors. For example, fertilization cannot take place during pregnancy, which can last as long as two years in some mammals.

 Reading Check What are the disadvantages of sexual reproduction?

(tl)Copyright © Foodcollection; (tr)©Craig Lovell/Corbis; (c)Piotr & Irena Kolasa/Alamy; (bl)image100/SuperStock; (br)Ji?í Chudoba/Getty Images

Lesson 1 Review

Visual Summary

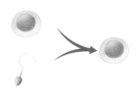
Fertilization occurs when an egg cell and a sperm cell join together.

Organisms produce sex cells through meiosis.

Sexual reproduction results in genetic variation among individuals.

FOLDABLES

Use your lesson Foldable to review the lesson. Save your Foldable for the project at the end of the chapter.

What do you think NOW?

You first read the statements below at the beginning of the chapter.

1. Humans produce two types of cells: body cells and sex cells.

2. Environmental factors can cause variation among individuals.

3. Two parents always produce the best offspring.

Did you change your mind about whether you agree or disagree with the statements? Rewrite any false statements to make them true.

Use Vocabulary

1 **Use the terms** *egg, sperm,* and *zygote* in a sentence.

2 **Distinguish** between haploid and diploid.

3 **Define** *homologous chromosomes* in your own words.

Understand Key Concepts

4 **Define** sexual reproduction.

5 **Draw and label** the phases of meiosis.

6 Homologous chromosomes separate during which phase of meiosis?

   A. anaphase I   **C.** metaphase I

   B. anaphase II   **D.** metaphase II

Interpret Graphics

7 **Organize** Copy and fill in the graphic organizer below to sequence the phases of meiosis I and meiosis II.

Meiosis I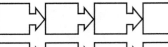

Meiosis II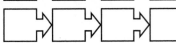

Critical Thinking

8 **Analyze** Why is the result of the stage of meiosis shown below an advantage for organisms that reproduce sexually?

Math Skills ✓ Math Practice

9 If 15 cells undergo meiosis, how many daughter cells would be produced?

10 If each daughter cell from question 9 undergoes meiosis, how many total daughter cells will there be?

The Spider
Mating Dance

Meet Norman Platnick, a scientist studying spiders.

Norman Platnick is fascinated by all spider species—from the dwarf tarantula-like spiders of Panama to the blind spiders of New Zealand. These are just two of the over 1,400 species he's discovered worldwide.

How does Platnick identify new species? One way is the pedipalps. Every spider has two pedipalps, but they vary in shape and size among the over 40,000 species. Pedipalps look like legs but function more like antennae and mouthparts. Male spiders use their pedipalps to aid in reproduction.

Getting Ready When a male spider is ready to mate, he places a drop of sperm onto a sheet of silk he constructs. Then he dips his pedipalps into the drop to draw up the sperm.

Finding a Mate The male finds a female of the same species by touch or by sensing certain chemicals she releases.

Courting and Mating Males of some species court a female with a special dance. For other species, a male might present a female with a gift, such as a fly wrapped in silk. During mating, the male uses his pedipalps to transfer sperm to the female.

What happens to the male after mating? That depends on the species. Some are eaten by the female, while others move on to find new mates.

▲ Spiders reproduce sexually, so each offspring has a unique combination of genes from its parents. Over many generations, this genetic variation has led to the incredible diversity of spiders in the world today.

◄ Norman Platnick is an arachnologist (uh rak NAH luh just) at the American Museum of Natural History. Arachnologists are scientists who study spiders.

It's Your Turn

RESEARCH Spiders undergo sexual reproduction. Research another species of insect, bird, or fish that undergoes sexual reproduction. Find out about any courting or mating behavior related to reproduction in the species you select to research. Share your findings with the class.

Lesson 2

Asexual Reproduction

Reading Guide

Key Concepts 🔑

ESSENTIAL QUESTIONS

* What is asexual reproduction, and why is it beneficial?

* How do the types of asexual reproduction differ?

Vocabulary

asexual reproduction p. 385

fission p. 386

budding p. 387

regeneration p. 388

vegetative reproduction p. 389

cloning p. 390

 Multilingual eGlossary

 8.LS.1, 8.LS.2, 8.LS.10, SEPS.1, SEPS.2, SEPS.8, 6-8.LST.5.2, 6-8.LST.7.1

PBL Go to the resource tab in ConnectED to find the PBLs *It's in the Cards* and *Foods of the Future.*

ʔnquiry) Plants on Plants?

Look closely at the edges of this plant's leaves. Tiny plants are growing there. This type of plant can reproduce without meiosis and fertilization.

©Steven P. Lynch

How do yeast reproduce?

Some organisms can produce offspring without meiosis or fertilization. You can observe this process when you add sugar and warm water to dried yeast.

1. Read and complete a lab safety form.
2. Pour 125 mL of water into a **beaker.** The water should be at a temperature of 34°C.
3. Add 5 g of **sugar** and 5 g of **yeast** to the water. Stir slightly. Record your observations after 5 minutes in your Science Journal.
4. Using a **dropper,** put a drop of the yeast solution on a **microscope slide.** Place a **coverslip** over the drop.
5. View the yeast solution under a **microscope.** Draw what you see in your Science Journal.

Think About This

1. What evidence did you observe that yeast reproduce?

2. 🔑 **Key Concept** How do you think this process differs from sexual reproduction?

What is asexual reproduction?

Lunch is over and you are in a rush to get to class. You wrap up your half-eaten sandwich and toss it into your locker. A week goes by before you spot the sandwich in the corner of your locker. The surface of the bread is now covered with fuzzy mold— not very appetizing. How did that happen?

The mold on the sandwich is a type of fungus (FUN gus). A fungus releases enzymes that break down organic matter, such as food. It has structures that penetrate and anchor to food, much like roots anchor plants to soil. A fungus can multiply quickly in part because generally a fungus can reproduce either sexually or asexually. Recall that sexual reproduction involves two parent organisms and the processes of meiosis and fertilization. Offspring inherit half their DNA from each parent, resulting in genetic variation among the offspring.

In **asexual reproduction,** *one parent organism produces offspring without meiosis and fertilization.* Because the offspring inherit all their DNA from one parent, they are genetically identical to each other and to their parent.

🔑 **Key Concept Check** Describe asexual reproduction in your own words.

FOLDABLES

Fold a sheet of paper into a six-celled chart. Label the front "Asexual Reproduction," and label the chart inside as shown. Use it to compare types of asexual reproduction.

Fission	Mitotic cell division	Budding
Animal regeneration	Vegetative reproduction	Cloning

WORD ORIGIN ·············

fission
from Latin *fissionem,* means "a breaking up, cleaving"

Types of Asexual Reproduction

There are many different types of organisms that reproduce by asexual reproduction. In addition to fungi, bacteria, protists, plants, and animals can reproduce asexually. In this lesson, you will learn how organisms reproduce asexually.

Fission

Recall that prokaryotes have a simpler cell structure than eukaryotes. A prokaryote's DNA is not contained in a nucleus. For this reason, mitosis does not occur and cell division in a prokaryote is a simpler process than in a eukaryote. *Cell division in prokaryotes that forms two genetically identical cells is known as* **fission.**

Fission begins when a prokaryote's DNA molecule is copied. Each copy attaches to the cell membrane. Then the cell begins to grow longer, pulling the two copies of DNA apart. At the same time, the cell membrane begins to pinch inward along the middle of the cell. Finally the cell splits and forms two new identical offspring. The original cell no longer exists.

As shown in **Figure 6,** *E. coli,* a common bacterium, divides through fission. Some bacteria can divide every 20 minutes. At that rate, 512 bacteria can be produced from one original bacterium in about three hours.

Reading Check What advantage might asexual reproduction by fission have over sexual reproduction?

Fission

Figure 6 Bacteria can divide very rapidly through fission.

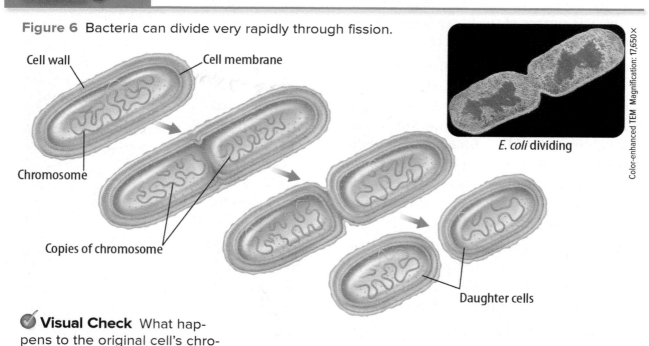

Cell wall

Cell membrane

Chromosome

Copies of chromosome

Daughter cells

E. coli dividing

Color-enhanced TEM Magnification: 17,650×

Visual Check What happens to the original cell's chromosome during fission?

CNRI/Science Source

Mitotic Cell Division

Many unicellular eukaryotes reproduce by mitotic cell division. In this type of asexual reproduction, an organism forms two offspring through mitosis and cell division. In **Figure 7,** an amoeba's nucleus has divided by mitosis. Next, the cytoplasm and its contents divide through cytokinesis and two new amoebas form.

Budding

In **budding,** *a new organism grows by mitosis and cell division on the body of its parent.* The bud, or offspring, is genetically identical to its parent. When the bud becomes large enough, it can break from the parent and live on its own. In some cases, an offspring remains attached to its parent and starts to form a colony. **Figure 8** shows a hydra in the process of budding. The hydra is an example of a multicellular organism that can reproduce asexually. Unicellular eukaryotes, such as yeast, can also reproduce through budding, as you saw in the Launch Lab.

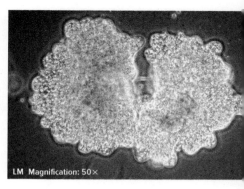

LM Magnification: 50×

▲ **Figure 7** During mitotic cell division, an amoeba divides its chromosomes and cell contents evenly between the daughter cells.

Budding 🔑

Figure 8 The hydra bud has the same genetic makeup as its parent.

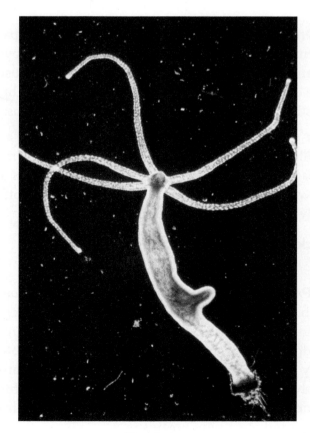

Bud forms.

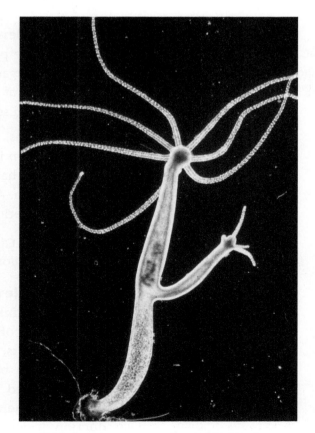

Bud develops a mouth and tentacles.

Biophoto Associates/Science Source

Figure 9 A planarian can reproduce through regeneration.

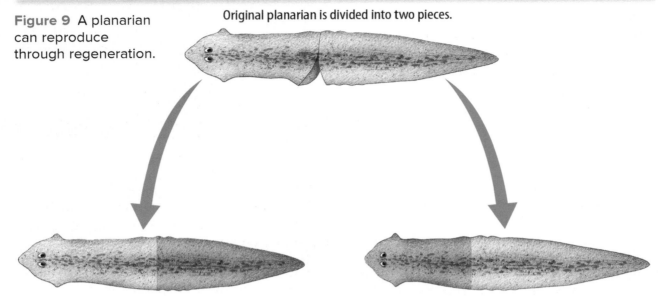

Original planarian is divided into two pieces.

The head end regenerates a new tail.

The tail end regenerates a new head.

Animal Regeneration

Another type of asexual reproduction, **regeneration,** *occurs when an offspring grows from a piece of its parent.* The ability to regenerate a new organism varies greatly among animals.

ACADEMIC VOCABULARY

potential
(noun) possibility

Producing New Organisms Some sea stars have five arms. If separated from the parent sea star, each arm has the potential to grow into a new organism. To regenerate a new sea star, the arm must contain a part of the central disk of the parent. If conditions are right, one five-armed sea star can produce as many as five new organisms.

Sea urchins, sea cucumbers, sponges, and planarians, such as the one shown in **Figure 9,** can also reproduce through regeneration. Notice that each piece of the original planarian becomes a new organism. As with all types of asexual reproduction, the offspring is genetically identical to the parent.

 Reading Check What is true of all cases of asexual reproduction?

Producing New Parts When you hear the term *regeneration,* you might think about a salamander regrowing a lost tail or leg. Regeneration of damaged or lost body parts is common in many animals. Newts, tadpoles, crabs, hydra, and zebra fish are all able to regenerate body parts. Even humans are able to regenerate some damaged body parts, such as the skin and the liver. This type of regeneration, however, is not considered asexual reproduction. It does not produce a new organism.

Vegetative Reproduction

Plants can also reproduce asexually in a process similar to regeneration. **Vegetative reproduction** *is a form of asexual reproduction in which offspring grow from a part of a parent plant.* For example, the strawberry plants shown in Figure 10 send out long horizontal stems called stolons. Wherever a stolon touches the ground, it can produce roots. Once the stolons have grown roots, a new plant can grow–even if the stolons have broken off the parent plant. Each new plant grown from a stolon is genetically identical to the parent plant.

Vegetative reproduction usually involves structures such as the roots, the stems, and the leaves of plants. In addition to strawberries, many other plants can reproduce by this method, including raspberries, potatoes, and geraniums.

Figure 10 The smaller plants were grown from stolons produced by the parent plant.

Visual Check Which plants in the figure are the parent plants?

🔧 MiniLab
15 minutes

What parts of plants can grow?

You probably know that plants can grow from seeds. But you might be surprised to learn that other parts of plants can grow and produce a new plant.

1. Carefully examine the photos of vegetative reproduction.

2. Create a data chart in your Science Journal to record your observations. Identify which part of the plant (leaf, stem, etc.) would be used to grow a new plant.

Analyze and Conclude

1. **Explain** How is the vegetative reproduction you observed a kind of asexual reproduction?

2. **Infer** how farmers or gardeners might use vegetative reproduction.

3. 🔑 **Key Concept** Describe a method you might use to produce a new plant using vegetative reproduction.

SCIENCE USE V. COMMON USE ···

culture
Science Use the process of growing living tissue in a laboratory

Common Use the social customs of a group of people

Figure 11 New carrot plants can be produced from cells of a carrot root using tissue culture techniques.

Cloning

Fission, budding, and regeneration are all types of asexual reproduction that can produce genetically identical offspring in nature. In the past, the term *cloning* described any process that produced genetically identical offspring. Today, however, the word usually refers to a technique developed by scientists and performed in laboratories. **Cloning** *is a type of asexual reproduction performed in a laboratory that produces identical individuals from a cell or from a cluster of cells taken from a multicellular organism.* Cloning is one of a variety of methods humans can use to genetically alter organisms or control the genetic makeup of offspring.

Plant Cloning Some plants can be cloned using a method called tissue culture, as shown in **Figure 11.** Tissue culture enables plant growers and scientists to make many copies of a plant with desirable traits, such as sweet fruit. Also, a greater number of plants can be produced more quickly than by vegetative reproduction.

Tissue culture also enables plant growers to reproduce plants that might have become infected with a disease. To clone such a plant, a scientist can use cells from a part of a plant where they are rapidly undergoing mitosis and cell division. This part of a plant is called a meristem. Cells in meristems are disease-free. Therefore, if a plant becomes infected with a disease, it can be cloned using meristem cells.

Plant Cloning 🔑

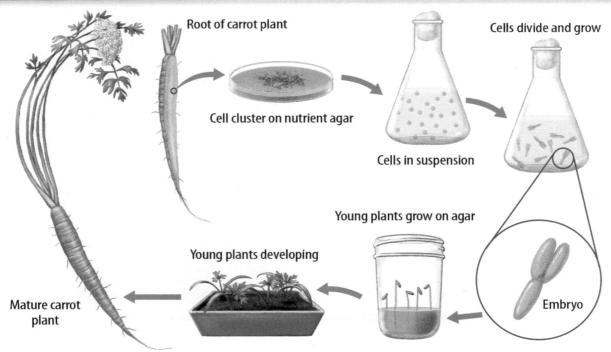

Root of carrot plant

Cell cluster on nutrient agar

Cells in suspension

Cells divide and grow

Young plants grow on agar

Young plants developing

Embryo

Mature carrot plant

Animal Cloning In addition to cloning plants, scientists have been able to clone many animals. Because all of a clone's chromosomes come from one parent (the donor of the nucleus), the clone is a genetic copy of its parent. The first mammal cloned was a sheep named Dolly. **Figure 12** illustrates how this was done.

Scientists are currently working to save some endangered species from extinction by cloning. Although cloning is an exciting advancement in science, some people are concerned about the high cost and the ethics of this technique. Ethical issues include the possibility of human cloning. You might be asked to consider issues like this during your lifetime.

Key Concept Check Compare and contrast the different types of asexual reproduction.

 WebQuest

Genetic Technologies Go online to investigate ways that humans alter organisms genetically and to gather evidence to support a claim about these technologies.

Figure 12 Scientists used two different sheep to produce the cloned sheep known as Dolly.

Animal Cloning

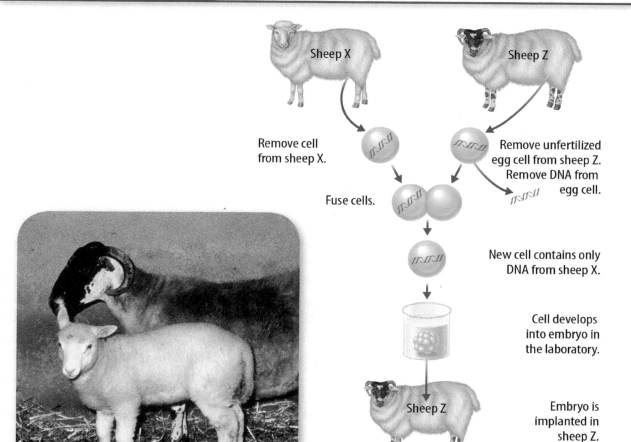

Remove cell from sheep X.

Remove unfertilized egg cell from sheep Z. Remove DNA from egg cell.

Fuse cells.

New cell contains only DNA from sheep X.

Cell develops into embryo in the laboratory.

Embryo is implanted in sheep Z.

Clone of sheep X

Dolly   Sheep Z

 Phototake/AP Images

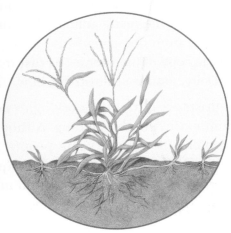

Figure 13 Crabgrass can spread quickly because it reproduces asexually.

Advantages of Asexual Reproduction

What are the advantages to organisms of reproducing asexually? Asexual reproduction enables organisms to reproduce without a mate. Recall that searching for a mate takes time and energy. Asexual reproduction also enables some organisms to rapidly produce a large number of offspring. For example, the crabgrass shown in **Figure 13** reproduces asexually by underground stems called stolons. This enables one plant to spread and colonize an area in a short period of time.

 Key Concept Check How is asexual reproduction beneficial?

Disadvantages of Asexual Reproduction

Although asexual reproduction usually enables organisms to reproduce quickly, it does have some disadvantages. Asexual reproduction produces offspring that are genetically identical to their parent. This results in little genetic variation within a population. Why is genetic variation important? Recall from Lesson 1 that genetic variation can give organisms a better chance of surviving if the environment changes. Think of the crabgrass. Imagine that all the crabgrass plants in a lawn are genetically identical to their parent plant. If a certain weed killer can kill the parent plant, then it can kill all the crabgrass plants in the lawn. This might be good for your lawn, but it is a disadvantage for the crabgrass.

Another disadvantage of asexual reproduction involves genetic changes, called mutations, that can occur. If an organism has a harmful mutation in its cells, the mutation will be passed to asexually reproduced offspring. This could affect the offspring's ability to survive.

Nigel Cattlin/Science Source

Lesson 2 Review

Visual Summary

In asexual reproduction, offspring are produced without meiosis and fertilization.

Cloning is one type of asexual reproduction.

Asexual reproduction enables organisms to reproduce quickly.

FOLDABLES®

Use your lesson Foldable to review the lesson. Save your Foldable for the project at the end of the chapter.

What do you think NOW?

You first read the statements below at the beginning of the chapter.

4. Cloning produces identical individuals from one cell.

5. All organisms have two parents.

6. Asexual reproduction occurs only in microorganisms.

Did you change your mind about whether you agree or disagree with the statements? Rewrite any false statements to make them true.

Use Vocabulary

1 In _____ _____, only one parent organism produces offspring.

2 **Define** the term *cloning* in your own words.

3 **Use the term** *regeneration* in a sentence.

Understand Key Concepts

4 **State** two reasons why asexual reproduction is beneficial.

5 Which is an example of asexual reproduction by regeneration?
- **A.** cloning sheep
- **B.** lizard regrowing a tail
- **C.** sea star arm producing a new organism
- **D.** strawberry plant producing stolons

6 **Construct** a chart that includes an example of each type of asexual reproduction.

Interpret Graphics

7 **Examine** the diagram below and write a short paragraph describing the process of tissue culture.

8 **Organize** Copy and fill in the graphic organizer below to list the different types of asexual reproduction that occur in multicellular organisms.

Asexual reproduction

Critical Thinking

9 **Justify** the use of cloning to save endangered animals.

Materials

pool noodles

Safety

Mitosis and Meiosis

During cellular reproduction, many changes occur in the nucleus of cells involving the chromosomes. You could think about these changes as a set of choreographed moves like you would see in a dance. In this lab you will demonstrate how genetic information is transmitted from parent to off-spring through chromosomes via the process of meiosis and mitosis.

Ask a Question

How do chromosomes change and move during mitosis and meiosis?

Make Observations

1 Read and complete a lab safety form.

2 Form a cell nucleus with four chromosomes represented by students holding four different colors of pool noodles. Other students play the part of the nuclear membrane and form a circle around the chromosomes.

3 The chromosomes duplicate during interphase. Each chromosome is copied, creating a chromosome with two sister chromatids.

4 Perform mitosis.

   a. During prophase, the nuclear membrane breaks apart, and the nucleolus disappears.

   b. In metaphase, duplicated chromosomes align in the middle of the cell.

   c. The sister chromatids separate in anaphase.

   d. In telophase, the nuclear membrane reforms around two daughter cells.

5 Repeat steps 2 and 3. Perform meiosis.

   a. In prophase I, the nuclear membrane breaks apart, the nucleolus disappears, and homologous chromosomes pair up.

   b. In metaphase I, homologous chromosomes line up along the center of the cell.

   c. During anaphase I, the pairs of homologous chromosomes separate.

   d. In telophase I, the nuclear membrane reforms.

   e. Each daughter cell now performs meiosis II independently. In prophase II, the nuclear membrane breaks down, and the nucleolus disappears.

   f. During metaphase II, duplicated chromosomes align in the middle of the cell.

Hutchings Photography/Digital Light Source

g. Sister chromatids separate in anaphase II.

h. In telophase II, the nuclear membrane reforms.

Form a Hypothesis

6 Use your observations to form a hypothesis about the results of an error in meiosis. For example, you might explain the results of an error during anaphase I.

Test your Hypothesis

7 Perform meiosis, incorporating the error you chose in step 6.

8 Compare the outcome to your hypothesis. Does your data support your hypothesis? If not, revise your hypothesis and repeat steps 6–8.

Analyze and Conclude

9 **Compare and Contrast** How are mitosis and meiosis I similar? How are they different?

10 **The Big Idea** What is the difference between the chromosomes in cells at the beginning and the end of mitosis? At the beginning and end of meiosis?

11 **Critique** How did performing cellular replications using pool noodles help you understand mitosis and meiosis?

Communicate Your Results

Create a chart of the changes and movements of chromosomes in each of the steps in meiosis and mitosis. Include colored drawings of chromosomes and remember to draw the cell membranes.

Inquiry Extension

Investigate some abnormalities that occur when mistakes are made during mitosis or meiosis. Draw a chart of the steps of reproduction showing how the mistake is made. Write a short description of the problems that result from the mistake.

5

Lab Tips

☑ Figure out where the boundaries of your cell are before you start.

☑ Review the phases of mitosis and meiosis before beginning to act out how the chromosomes move during each process.

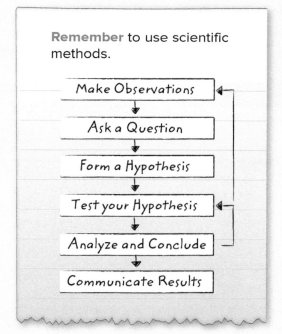

Remember to use scientific methods.

Make Observations

Ask a Question

Form a Hypothesis

Test your Hypothesis

Analyze and Conclude

Communicate Results

Hutchings Photography/Digital Light Source

THE BIG IDEA

Reproduction ensures the survival of species.

Key Concepts Summary 🔑

Lesson 1: Sexual Reproduction and Meiosis

- **Sexual reproduction** is the production of an offspring from the joining of a **sperm** and an **egg.**

- Division of the nucleus and cytokinesis happens twice in **meiosis.** Meiosis I separates homologous chromosomes. Meiosis II separates sister chromatids.

- Meiosis maintains the chromosome number of a species from one generation to the next.

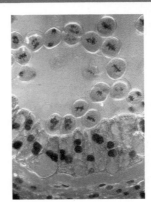

Lesson 2: Asexual Reproduction

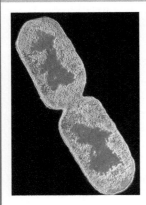

- **Asexual reproduction** is the production of offspring by one parent, which results in offspring that are genetically identical to the parent.

- Types of asexual reproduction include **fission,** mitotic cell division, **budding, regeneration, vegetative reproduction,** and **cloning.**

- Asexual reproduction can produce a large number of offspring in a short amount of time.

Vocabulary

sexual reproduction p. 373

egg p. 373

sperm p. 373

fertilization p. 373

zygote p. 373

diploid p. 374

homologous chromosomes p. 374

haploid p. 375

meiosis p. 375

asexual reproduction p. 385

fission p. 386

budding p. 387

regeneration p. 388

vegetative reproduction p. 389

cloning p. 390

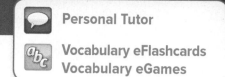

Chapter Project

Assemble your lesson Foldables as shown to make a Chapter Project. Use the project to review what you have learned in this chapter.

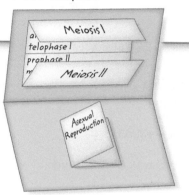

Use Vocabulary

1 Define meiosis in your own words.

2 Distinguish between an egg and a zygote.

3 Use the vocabulary words *haploid* and *diploid* in a sentence.

4 Cell division in prokaryotes is called _____.

5 Define the term *vegetative reproduction* in your own words.

6 Distinguish between regeneration and budding.

7 A type of reproduction in which the genetic materials from two different cells combine, producing an offspring, is called _____ _____.

Link Vocabulary and Key Concepts

▶ **Interactive Concept Map**

Copy this concept map, and then use vocabulary terms from the previous page to complete the concept map.

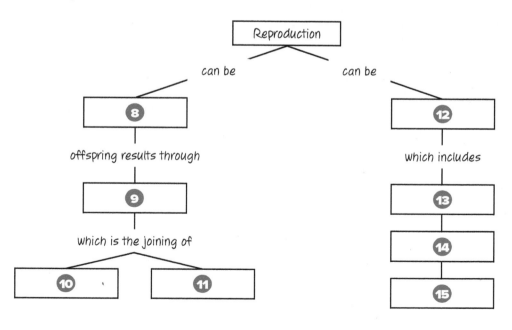

Chapter 11 Review

Understand Key Concepts

1. Which is an advantage of sexual reproduction?
   A. Offspring are identical to the parents.
   B. Offspring with genetic variation are produced.
   C. Organisms don't have to search for a mate.
   D. Reproduction is rapid.

2. Which describes cells that have only one copy of each chromosome?
   A. diploid
   B. haploid
   C. homologous
   D. zygote

Use the figure below to answer questions 3 and 4.

3. Which phase of meiosis I is shown in the diagram?
   A. anaphase I
   B. metaphase I
   C. prophase I
   D. telophase I

4. Which phase of meiosis I comes after the phase in the diagram?
   A. anaphase I
   B. metaphase I
   C. prophase I
   D. telophase I

5. Tissue culture is an example of which type of reproduction?
   A. budding
   B. cloning
   C. fission
   D. regeneration

6. Which type of asexual reproduction is shown in the figure below?

   A. budding
   B. cloning
   C. fission
   D. regeneration

7. A bacterium can reproduce by which method?
   A. budding
   B. cloning
   C. fission
   D. regeneration

8. Which statement best describes why genetic variation is beneficial to populations of organisms?
   A. Individuals look different from one another.
   B. Only one parent is needed to produce offspring.
   C. Populations of the organism increase more rapidly.
   D. Species can better survive environmental changes.

9. In which phase of meiosis II do sister chromatids line up along the center of the cell?
   A. anaphase II
   B. metaphase II
   C. prophase II
   D. telophase II

Critical Thinking

10 **Contrast** haploid cells and diploid cells.

11 **Model** Make a model of homologous chromosomes using materials of your choice.

12 **Form a hypothesis** about the effect of a mistake in separating homologous chromosomes during meiosis.

13 **Analyze** Crabgrass reproduces asexually by vegetative reproduction. Use the figure below to explain why this form of reproduction is an advantage for the crabgrass.

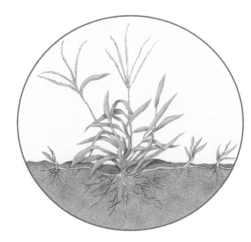

14 **Research** and identify three organisms that undergo asexual reproduction.

15 **Create** a table showing the advantages and disadvantages of asexual reproduction.

16 **Compare and contrast** the transmission of genetic information in sexual reproduction and asexual reproduction.

Writing in Science

17 **Create** a plot for a short story that describes an environmental change and the importance of genetic variation in helping a species survive that change. Include characters, a setting, a climax, and an ending for your plot.

REVIEW THE BIG IDEA

18 Think of all the advantages of sexual and asexual reproduction. Use these ideas to summarize why organisms reproduce.

19 The baby penguin below has a mother and a father. Do all living things have two parents? Explain.

Math Skills ✓ Math Practice

Use Proportions

20 During mitosis, the original cell produces two daughter cells. How many daughter cells will be produced if 250 mouse cells undergo mitosis?

21 During meiosis, the original reproductive cell produces four daughter cells. How many daughter cells will be produced if 250 mouse reproductive cells undergo meiosis?

22 Two reproductive cells undergo meiosis. Each daughter cell also undergoes meiosis. How many cells are produced when the daughter cells divide?

Bill Coster/Getty Images

Record your answers on the answer sheet provided by your teacher or on a sheet of paper.

Multiple Choice

1 How do sea stars reproduce?

  A cloning

  B fission

  C animal regeneration

  D vegetative reproduction

Use the diagram below to answer questions 2 and 3.

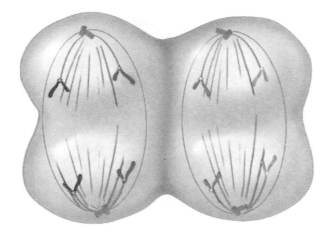

2 What stage of meiosis does the drawing illustrate?

  A anaphase I

  B anaphase II

  C prophase I

  D prophase II

3 Which stage takes place *before* the one in the diagram above?

  A metaphase I

  B metaphase II

  C telophase I

  D telophase II

4 What type of asexual reproduction includes stolons?

  A budding

  B cloning

  C animal regeneration

  D vegetative reproduction

Use the table below to answer question 5.

Comparison of Types of Cell Division		
Characteristic	**Meiosis**	**Mitosis**
Number of divisions of nucleus	2	A
Number of daughter cells produced	B	2

5 Which numbers should be inserted for A and B in the chart?

  A A=1 and B=2

  B A=1 and B=4

  C A=2 and B=2

  D A=2 and B=4

6 Which results in genetic variation?

  A cloning

  B fission

  C sexual reproduction

  D vegetative reproduction

7 Which is NOT true of homologous chromosomes?

  A The are identical.

  B They are in pairs.

  C They have genes for the same traits.

  D They have genes that are in the same order.

Use the figure below to answer question 8.

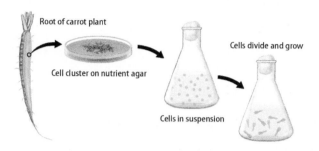

Root of carrot plant

Cell cluster on nutrient agar

Cells in suspension

Cells divide and grow

8 The figure illustrates the first four steps of which reproductive process?

A animal cloning

B regeneration

C tissue culture

D vegetative reproduction

9 If 12 reproductive cells undergo meiosis, how many daughter cells will result?

A 12

B 24

C 48

D 60

10 Which is NOT true of asexual reproduction?

A Many offspring can be produced rapidly.

B Offspring are different from the parents.

C Offspring have no genetic variation.

D Organisms can reproduce without a mate.

Constructed Response

Use the figure below to answer questions 11 and 12.

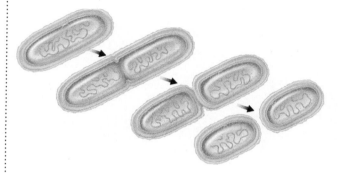

11 Identify the type of asexual reproduction shown in the figure above. How does it differ from sexual reproduction?

12 Compare and contrast budding with the type of asexual reproduction shown in the figure above.

13 What are some differences between the results of selectively breeding plants and cloning them?

14 Use the example of the wild mustard plant to describe the benefits of selective breeding.

15 What are the advantages and disadvantages of cloning animals?

NEED EXTRA HELP?															
If You Missed Question...	1	2	3	4	5	6	7	8	9	10	11	12	13	14	15
Go to Lesson...	2	1	1	2	1	1	1	2	1	2	1, 2	2	1, 2	1	2

Genetics

THE BIG IDEA
How are traits passed from parents to offspring?

inquiry How did this happen?

The color of this calf is caused by a genetic trait called albinism.
Albinism is the absence of body pigment. Notice that the calf's
mother has brown fur.

• Why do you think the calf looks so different from its mother?

• What do you think determines the color of the offspring?

• How do you think traits are passed from generation to generation?

Keith Szafranski/iStock/360/Getty Images

Get Ready to Read

What do you think?

Before you read, decide if you agree or disagree with each of these statements. As you read this chapter, see if you change your mind about any of the statements.

1 Like mixing paints, parents' traits always blend in their offspring.

2 If you look more like your mother than you look like your father, then you received more traits from your mother.

3 All inherited traits follow Mendel's patterns of inheritance.

4 Scientists have tools to predict the form of a trait an offspring might inherit.

5 New DNA is copied from existing DNA.

6 A change in the sequence of an organism's DNA always changes the organism's traits.

Mc Graw Hill Education connectED

Your one-stop online resource
connectED.mcgraw-hill.com

 LearnSmart®

 Project-Based Learning Activities

 Chapter Resources Files, Reading Essentials, Get Ready to Read, Quick Vocabulary

 Lab Manuals, Safety Videos, Virtual Labs & Other Tools

 Animations, Videos, Interactive Tables

 Vocabulary, Multilingual eGlossary, Vocab eGames, Vocab eFlashcards

 Self-checks, Quizzes, Tests

 Personal Tutors

Lesson 1

Reading Guide

Key Concepts
ESSENTIAL QUESTIONS

- Why did Mendel perform cross-pollination experiments?

- What did Mendel conclude about inherited traits?

- How do dominant and recessive factors interact?

Vocabulary

heredity p. 405

genetics p. 405

dominant trait p. 411

recessive trait p. 411

 Multilingual eGlossary

 BrainPOP®

SEPS.3

Mendel and His Peas

 **Inquiry** **Same Species?**

Have you ever seen a black ladybug? It is less common than the orange variety you might know, but both are the same species of beetle. So why do they look different? Believe it or not, a study of pea plants helped scientists explain these differences.

What makes you unique?

Traits such as eye color have many different types, but some traits have only two types. By a show of hands, determine how many students in your class have each type of trait below.

Student Traits		
Trait	Type 1	Type 2
Earlobes	Unattached	Attached
Thumbs	Curved	Straight
Interlacing fingers	Left thumb over right thumb	Right thumb over left thumb

Think About This

1. Why might some students have types of traits that others do not have?

2. If a person has dimples, do you think his or her offspring will have dimples? Explain.

3. 🔑 **Key Concept** What do you think determines the types of traits you inherit?

Early Ideas About Heredity

Have you ever mixed two paint colors to make a new color? Long ago, people thought an organism's characteristics, or traits, mixed like colors of paint because offspring resembled both parents. This is known as blending inheritance.

Today, scientists know that **heredity** (huh REH duh tee)—*the passing of traits from parents to offspring*—is more complex. For example, you might have blue eyes but both of your parents have brown eyes. How does this happen? More than 150 years ago, Gregor Mendel, an Austrian monk, performed experiments that helped answer these questions and disprove the idea of blending inheritance. Because of his research, Mendel is known as the father of **genetics** (juh NEH tihks)—*the study of how traits are passed from parents to offspring.*

WORD ORIGIN ··········

genetics
from Greek *genesis,* means "origin"

Mendel's Experimental Methods

During the 1850s, Mendel studied genetics by doing controlled breeding experiments with pea plants. Pea plants were ideal for genetic studies because

- they reproduce quickly. This enabled Mendel to grow many plants and collect a lot of data.

- they have easily observed traits, such as flower color and pea shape. This enabled Mendel to observe whether or not a trait was passed from one generation to the next.

- Mendel could control which pairs of plants reproduced. This enabled him to determine which traits came from which plant pairs.

Pollination in Pea Plants

To observe how a trait was inherited, Mendel controlled which plants pollinated other plants. Pollination occurs when pollen lands on the pistil of a flower. Sperm cells from the pollen then can fertilize egg cells in the pistil. Pollination in pea plants can occur in two ways. Self-pollination occurs when pollen from one plant lands on the pistil of a flower on the same plant, as shown in **Figure 1**. Cross-pollination occurs when pollen from one plant reaches the pistil of a flower on a different plant. Cross-pollination occurs naturally when wind, water, or animals such as bees carry pollen from one flower to another. Mendel allowed one group of flowers to self-pollinate. With another group, he cross-pollinated the plants himself.

Self-Pollination

Figure 1 Self-pollination occurs when pollen from a stamen lands on a pistil of the same flower or on another flower on the same plant.

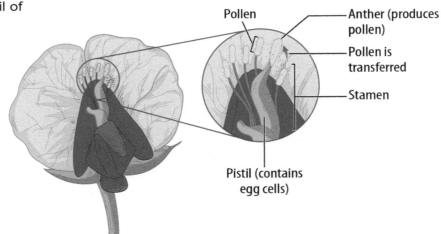

Pollen

Anther (produces pollen)

Pollen is transferred

Stamen

Pistil (contains egg cells)

True-Breeding Plants

Mendel began his experiments with plants that were true-breeding for the trait he would test. When a true-breeding plant self-pollinates, it always produces offspring with traits that match the parent. For example, when a true-breeding pea plant with wrinkled seeds self-pollinates, it produces only plants with wrinkled seeds. In fact, plants with wrinkled seeds appear generation after generation.

Mendel's Cross-Pollination

By cross-pollinating plants himself, Mendel was able to select which plants pollinated other plants. **Figure 2** shows an example of a manual cross between a plant with white flowers and one with purple flowers.

Figure 2 Mendel removed the stamens of one flower and pollinated that flower with pollen from a flower of a different plant. In this way, he controlled pollination.

Cross-Pollination 🔑

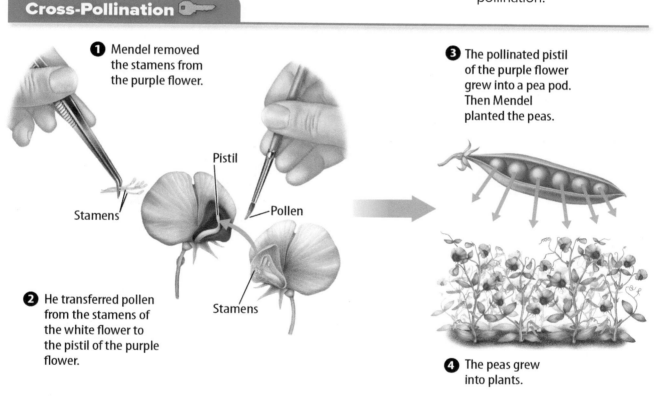

❶ Mendel removed the stamens from the purple flower.

Pistil

Stamens

Pollen

Stamens

❷ He transferred pollen from the stamens of the white flower to the pistil of the purple flower.

❸ The pollinated pistil of the purple flower grew into a pea pod. Then Mendel planted the peas.

❹ The peas grew into plants.

Mendel cross-pollinated hundreds of plants for each set of traits, such as flower color–purple or white; seed color–green or yellow; and seed shape–round or wrinkled. With each cross-pollination, Mendel recorded the traits that appeared in the offspring. By testing such a large number of plants, Mendel was able to predict which crosses would produce which traits.

 Key Concept Check Why did Mendel perform cross-pollination experiments?

Mendel's Results

Once Mendel had enough true-breeding plants for a trait that he wanted to test, he cross-pollinated selected plants. His results are shown in **Figure 3.**

First-Generation Crosses

A cross between true-breeding plants with purple flowers produced plants with only purple flowers. A cross between true-breeding plants with white flowers produced plants with only white flowers. But something unexpected happened when Mendel crossed true-breeding plants with purple flowers and true-breeding plants with white flowers—all the offspring had purple flowers.

New Questions Raised

The results of the crosses between true-breeding plants with purple flowers and true-breeding plants with white flowers led to more questions for Mendel. Why did all the offspring always have purple flowers? Why were there no white flowers? Why didn't the cross produce offspring with pink flowers—a combination of the white and purple flower colors? Mendel carried out more experiments with pea plants to answer these questions.

 Reading Check Predict the offspring of a cross between two true-breeding pea plants with smooth seeds.

First-Generation Crosses

Figure 3 Mendel crossed three combinations of true-breeding plants and recorded the flower colors of the offspring.

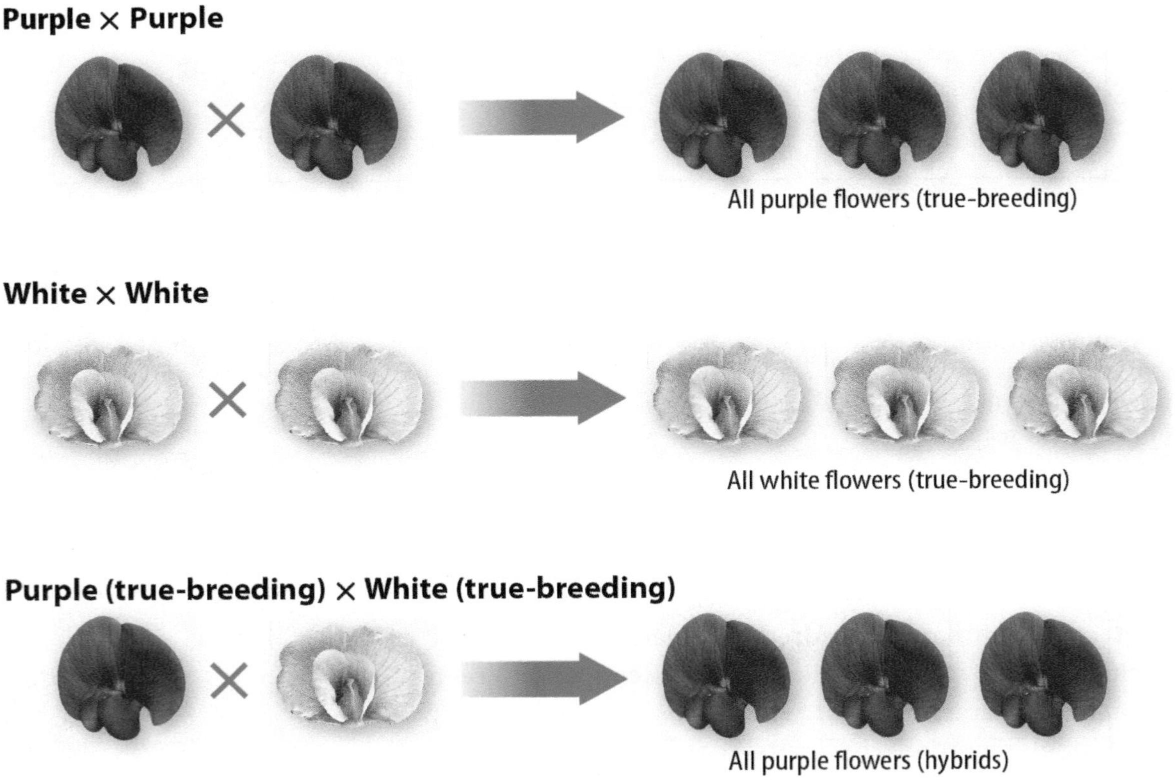

Purple × Purple

All purple flowers (true-breeding)

White × White

All white flowers (true-breeding)

Purple (true-breeding) × White (true-breeding)

All purple flowers (hybrids)

Visual Check Suppose you cross hundreds of true-breeding plants with purple flowers with hundreds of true-breeding plants with white flowers. Based on the results of this cross in the figure above, would any offspring produce white flowers? Explain.

Second-Generation (Hybrid) Crosses

The first-generation purple-flowering plants are called **hybrid** plants. This means they came from true-breeding parent plants with different forms of the same trait. Mendel wondered what would happen if he cross-pollinated two purple-flowering hybrid plants.

As shown in **Figure 4,** some of the offspring had white flowers, even though both parents had purple flowers. The results were similar each time Mendel cross-pollinated two hybrid plants. The trait that had disappeared in the first generation always reappeared in the second generation.

The same result happened when Mendel cross-pollinated pea plants for other traits. For example, he found that cross-pollinating a true-breeding yellow-seeded pea plant with a true-breeding green-seeded pea plant always produced yellow-seeded hybrids. A second-generation cross of two yellow-seeded hybrids always yielded plants with yellow seeds and plants with green seeds.

 Reading Check What is a hybrid plant?

Second-Generation (Hybrid) Crosses

Purple (hybrid) × Purple (hybrid)

Purple and white offspring

Purple (hybrid) × Purple (hybrid)

Purple and white offspring

Figure 4 Mendel cross-pollinated first-generation hybrid offspring to produce second-generation offspring. In each case, the trait that had disappeared from the first generation reappeared in the second generation.

(purple flower)©Shape'n'colour/Alamy; (white flower)Gerhard Egger/Photographer's Choice RF/Getty Images

Table 1 When Mendel crossed two hybrids for a given trait, the trait that had disappeared then reappeared in a ratio of about 3:1.

Table 1 Results of Hybrid Crosses

Characteristic	Trait and Number of Offspring		Trait and Number of Offspring		Ratio
Flower color	Purple 705		White 224		3.15:1
Flower position	Axial (Side of stem) 651		Terminal (End of stem) 207		3.14:1
Seed color	Yellow 6,022		Green 2,001		3.01:1
Seed shape	Round 5,474		Wrinkled 1,850		2.96:1
Pod shape	Inflated (Smooth) 882		Constricted (Bumpy) 299		2.95:1
Pod color	Green 428		Yellow 152		2.82:1
Stem length	Long 787		Short 277		2.84:1

Math Skills

Use Ratios

A ratio is a comparison of two numbers or quantities by division. For example, the ratio comparing 6,022 yellow seeds to 2,001 green seeds can be written as follows:

6,022 to 2,001 or

6,022 : 2,001 or

$\frac{6,022}{2,001}$

To simplify the ratio, divide the first number by the second number.

$\frac{6,022}{2,001} = \frac{3}{1}$ or 3:1

Practice

There are 14 girls and 7 boys in a science class. Simplify the ratio.

 Math Practice

 Personal Tutor

More Hybrid Crosses

Mendel counted and recorded the traits of offspring from many experiments in which he cross-pollinated hybrid plants. Data from these experiments are shown in **Table 1.** He analyzed these data and noticed patterns. For example, from the data of crosses between hybrid plants with purple flowers, he found that the ratio of purple flowers to white flowers was about 3:1. This means purple-flowering pea plants grew from this cross three times more often than white-flowering pea plants grew from the cross. He calculated similar ratios for all seven traits he tested.

Mendel's Conclusions

After analyzing the results of his experiments, Mendel concluded that two genetic factors control each inherited trait. He also proposed that when organisms reproduce, each reproductive cell–sperm or egg–contributes one factor for each trait.

 Key Concept Check What did Mendel conclude about inherited traits?

Dominant and Recessive Traits

Recall that when Mendel cross-pollinated a true-breeding plant with purple flowers and a true-breeding plant with white flowers, the hybrid offspring had only purple flowers. Mendel hypothesized that the hybrid offspring had one genetic factor for purple flowers and one genetic factor for white flowers. But why were there no white flowers?

Mendel also hypothesized that the purple factor is the only factor seen or expressed because it blocks the white factor. *A genetic factor that blocks another genetic factor is called a* **dominant** (DAH muh nunt) **trait.** A dominant trait, such as purple pea flowers, is observed when offspring have either one or two dominant factors. *A genetic factor that is blocked by the presence of a dominant factor is called a* **recessive** (rih SE sihv) **trait.** A recessive trait, such as white pea flowers, is observed only when two recessive genetic factors are present in offspring.

From Parents to Second Generation

For the second generation, Mendel cross-pollinated two hybrids with purple flowers. About 75 percent of the second-generation plants had purple flowers. These plants had at least one dominant factor. Twenty-five percent of the second-generation plants had white flowers. These plants had the same two recessive factors.

 Key Concept Check How do dominant and recessive factors interact?

FOLDABLES

Make a vertical two-tab book and label it as shown. Use it to organize your notes on dominant and recessive factors.

Traits

| Dominant factors | Recessive factors |

MiniLab 20 minutes

Which is the dominant trait?

Imagine you are Gregor Mendel's lab assistant studying pea plant heredity. Mendel has crossed true-breeding plants with axial flowers and true-breeding plants with terminal flowers. Use the data below to determine which trait is dominant.

Pea Flower Location Results		
Generation	Axial (Number of Offspring)	Terminal (Number of Offspring)
First	794	0
Second	651	207

Analyze and Conclude

1. **Determine** which trait is dominant and which trait is recessive. Support your answer with data.

2. **Key Concept** Analyze the first-generation data. What evidence do you have that one trait is dominant over the other?

Lesson 1 Review

Visual Summary

Genetics is the study of how traits are passed from parents to offspring.

Mendel studied genetics by doing cross-breeding experiments with pea plants.

Purple 705

White 224

Mendel's experiments with pea plants showed that some traits are dominant and others are recessive.

FOLDABLES

Use your lesson Foldable to review the lesson. Save your Foldable for the project at the end of the chapter.

What do you think NOW?

You first read the statements below at the beginning of the chapter.

1. Like mixing paints, parents' traits always blend in their offspring.

2. If you look more like your mother than you look like your father, then you received more traits from your mother.

Did you change your mind about whether you agree or disagree with the statements? Rewrite any false statements to make them true.

Use Vocabulary

1 **Distinguish** between heredity and genetics.

2 **Define** the terms *dominant* and *recessive*.

3 **Use the term** *recessive* in a complete sentence.

Understand Key Concepts

4 A recessive trait is observed when an organism has _____ recessive genetic factor(s).

A. 0   C. 2
B. 1   D. 3

5 **Summarize** Mendel's conclusions about how traits pass from parents to offspring.

6 **Describe** how Mendel cross-pollinated pea plants.

Interpret Graphics

7 **Suppose** the two true-breeding plants shown below were crossed.

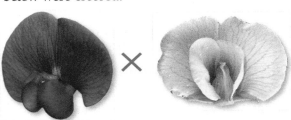

What color would the flowers of the offspring be? Explain.

Critical Thinking

8 **Design an experiment** to test for true-breeding plants.

9 **Examine** how Mendel's conclusions disprove blending inheritance.

Math Skills   Math Practice

10 A cross between two pink camellia plants produced the following offspring: 7 plants with red flowers, 7 with white flowers, and 14 with pink flowers. What is the ratio of red to white to pink?

Pioneering
the Science of Genetics

One man's curiosity leads to a branch of science.

Gregor Mendel—monk, scientist, gardener, and beekeeper—was a keen observer of the world around him. Curious about how traits pass from one generation to the next, he grew and tested almost 30,000 pea plants. Today, Mendel is called the father of genetics. After Mendel published his findings, however, his "laws of heredity" were overlooked for several decades.

In 1900, three European scientists, working independently of one another, rediscovered Mendel's work and replicated his results. Then, other biologists quickly began to recognize the importance of Mendel's work.

Gregor Mendel ▶

1902: American physician Walter Sutton demonstrates that Mendel's laws of inheritance can be applied to chromosomes. He concludes that chromosomes contain a cell's hereditary material on genes.

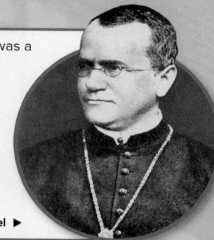

1906: William Bateson, a United Kingdom scientist, coins the term *genetics*. He uses it to describe the study of inheritance and the science of biological inheritance.

1952: American geneticists Martha Chase and Alfred Hershey prove that DNA transmits inherited traits from one generation to the next.

1953: Francis Crick and James Watson determine the structure of the DNA molecule. Their work begins the field of molecular biology and leads to important scientific and medical research in genetics.

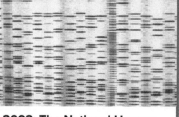

2003: The National Human Genome Research Institute (NHGRI) completes mapping and sequencing human DNA. Researchers and scientists are now trying to discover the genetic basis for human health and disease.

It's Your Turn

RESEARCH What are some genetic diseases? Report on how genome-based research might help cure these diseases in the future.

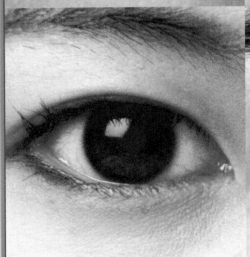

Understanding Inheritance

Reading Guide

Key Concepts 🔑

ESSENTIAL QUESTIONS

- What determines the expression of traits?

- How can inheritance be modeled?

- How do some patterns of inheritance differ from Mendel's model?

Vocabulary

gene p. 416

allele p. 416

phenotype p. 416

genotype p. 416

homozygous p. 417

heterozygous p. 417

Punnett square p. 418

incomplete dominance p. 420

codominance p. 420

polygenic inheritance p. 421

 Multilingual eGlossary

 BrainPOP®

 8.LS.3, 8.LS.4, 8.LS.6, SEPS.2

Inquiry Make the Connection

Physical traits, such as those shown in these eyes, can vary widely from person to person. Take a closer look at the eyes on this page. What traits can you identify among them? How do they differ?

(t to t b)Monica Lau/Getty Images; (2, 7)Ryan McVay/Getty Images; (3)©Bananastock/Punchstock; (4, 12)©Jack Hollingsworth/Corbis; (5, 9)Nick Koudis/Getty Images; (6)Anthony Saint James/Getty Images; (8)Jean Mahaux/Brand X Pictures/PictureQuest; (10)©MCD/Getty Images; (11)©Stan Fellerman/Corbis

Launch Lab

15 minutes

What is the span of your hand?

Mendel discovered some traits have a simple pattern of inheritance—dominant or recessive. However, some traits, such as eye color, have more variation. Is human hand span a Mendelian trait?

1. Read and complete a lab safety form.

2. Use a **metric ruler** to measure the distance (in cm) between the tips of your thumb and little finger with your hand stretched out.

3. As a class, record everyone's name and hand span in a data table.

Think About This

1. What range of hand span measurements did you observe?

2. 🔑 **Key Concept** Do you think hand span is a simple Mendelian trait like pea plant flower color?

What controls traits?

Mendel concluded that two factors—one from each parent—control each trait. Mendel hypothesized that one factor came from the egg cell and one factor came from the sperm cell. What are these factors? How are they passed from parents to offspring?

Chromosomes

When other scientists studied the parts of a cell and combined Mendel's work with their work, these factors were more clearly understood. Scientists discovered that inside each cell is a nucleus that contains threadlike structures called chromosomes. Over time, scientists learned that chromosomes contain genetic information that controls traits. We now know that Mendel's "factors" are part of chromosomes and that each cell in offspring contains chromosomes from both parents. As shown in **Figure 5,** these chromosomes exist as pairs—one chromosome from each parent.

Figure 5 Humans have 23 pairs of chromosomes. Each pair has one chromosome from the father and one chromosome from the mother.

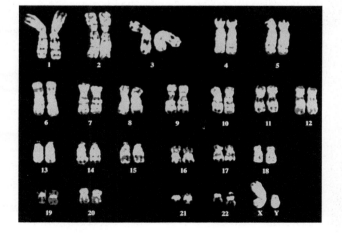

(t)Hutchings Photography/Digital Light Source; (b)Biophoto Associates/Science Source

Genes and Alleles

Scientists have discovered that each chromosome can have information about hundreds or even thousands of traits. *A **gene** (JEEN) is a section on a chromosome that has genetic information for one trait.* For example, a gene of a pea plant might have information about flower color. Recall that an offspring inherits two genes (factors) for each trait—one from each parent. The genes can be the same or different, such as purple or white for pea flower color. *The different forms of a gene are called **alleles** (uh LEELs).* Pea plants can have two purple alleles, two white alleles, or one of each allele. In **Figure 6,** the chromosome pair has information about three traits—flower position, pod shape, and stem length.

 Reading Check How many alleles controlled flower color in Mendel's experiments?

Genotype and Phenotype

Look again at the photo at the beginning of this lesson. What human trait can you observe? You might observe that eye color can be shades of blue or brown. *Geneticists call how a trait appears, or is expressed, the trait's **phenotype** (FEE nuh tipe).* What other phenotypes can you observe in the photo?

Mendel concluded that two alleles control the expression or phenotype of each trait. *The two alleles that control the phenotype of a trait are called the trait's **genotype** (JEE nuh tipe).* Although you cannot see an organism's genotype, you can make inferences about a genotype based on its phenotype. For example, you have already learned that a pea plant with white flowers has two recessive alleles for that trait. These two alleles are its genotype. The white flower is its phenotype.

WORD ORIGIN

phenotype
from Greek *phainein,* means "to show"

Figure 6 The alleles for flower position are the same on both chromosomes. However, the chromosome pair has different alleles for pod shape and stem length.

 **Animation**

Chromosome Pair

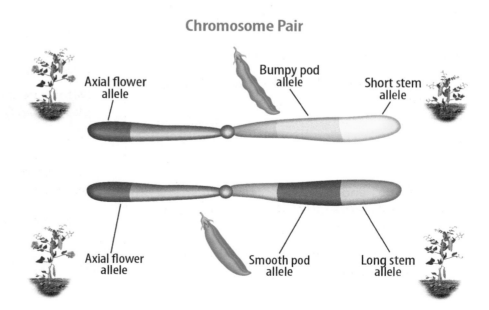

Axial flower allele

Bumpy pod allele

Short stem allele

Axial flower allele

Smooth pod allele

Long stem allele

Symbols for Genotypes Scientists use symbols to represent the alleles in a genotype. In genetics, uppercase letters represent dominant alleles and lowercase letters represent recessive alleles. Table 2 shows the possible genotypes for both round and wrinkled seed phenotypes. Notice that the dominant allele, if present, is written first.

Table 2 Phenotype and Genotype	
Phenotypes (observed traits)	Genotypes (alleles of a gene)
Round	Homozygous dominant *(RR)*
	Heterozygous *(Rr)*
Wrinkled	Homozygous recessive *(rr)*

A round seed can have two genotypes—*RR* and *Rr*. Both genotypes have a round phenotype. Why does *Rr* result in round seeds? This is because the round allele *(R)* is dominant to the wrinkled allele *(r)*.

A wrinkled seed has the recessive genotype, *rr*. The wrinkled-seed phenotype is possible only when the same two recessive alleles *(rr)* are present in the genotype.

Homozygous and Heterozygous *When the two alleles of a gene are the same, its genotype is* **homozygous** (hoh muh ZI gus). *Both RR and rr are homozygous genotypes, as shown in Table 2.*

If the two alleles of a gene are different, its genotype is **heterozygous** (he tuh roh ZI gus). *Rr is a heterozygous genotype.*

Key Concept Check How do alleles determine the expression of traits?

MiniLab 20 minutes

Can you infer genotype?
If you know that dragon traits are either dominant or recessive, can you use phenotypes of traits to infer genotypes?

1 Select one **trait card** from each of three **dragon trait bags.** Record the data in your Science Journal.

2 Draw a picture of your dragon based on your data. Label each trait *homozygous* or *heterozygous.*

3 Copy the table below in your Science Journal. For each of the three traits, place one check mark in the appropriate box.

Dragon Traits		
Phenotype	Homozygous	Heterozygous
Green body		
Red body		
Four legs		
Two legs		
Long wings		
Short wings		

4 Combine your data with your classmates' data.

Analyze and Conclude

1. **Describe** any patterns you find in the data table.

2. **Determine** which trait is dominant and which is recessive. Support your reasoning.

3. **Determine** the genotype(s) for each phenotype. Support your reasoning.

4. **Key Concept** Decide whether you could have correctly determined your dragon's genotype without data from other dragons. Support your reasoning.

Punnett Square

Personal Tutor

Figure 7 A Punnett square can be used to predict the possible genotypes of the offspring. Offspring from a cross between two heterozygous parents can have one of three genotypes.

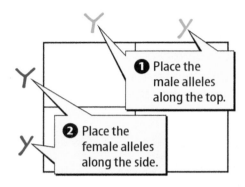

❶ Place the male alleles along the top.

❷ Place the female alleles along the side.

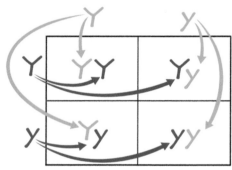

❸ Copy female alleles across each row. Copy male alleles down each column. Always list the dominant trait first.

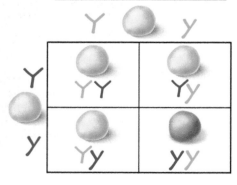

✓ **Visual Check** What phenotypes are possible for pea offspring of this cross?

Modeling Inheritance

Have you ever flipped a coin and guessed heads or tails? Because a coin has two sides, there are only two possible outcomes– heads or tails. You have a 50 percent chance of getting heads and a 50 percent chance of getting tails. The chance of getting an outcome can be represented by a ratio. The ratio of heads to tails is 50:50 or 1:1.

 Reading Check What does a ratio of 2:1 mean?

Plant breeders and animal breeders use a method for predicting how often traits will appear in offspring that does not require performing the crosses thousands of times. Two models–a Punnett square and a pedigree–can be used to predict and identify traits among genetically related individuals.

Punnett Squares

If the genotypes of the parents are known, then the different genotypes and phenotypes of the offspring can be predicted. *A* **Punnett square** *is a model used to predict possible genotypes and phenotypes of offspring.* Follow the steps in **Figure 7** to learn how to make a Punnett square.

Analyzing a Punnett Square

Figure 7 shows an example of a cross between two pea plants that are heterozygous for pea seed color–*Yy* and *Yy*. Yellow is the dominant allele–*Y*. Green is the recessive allele–*y*. The offspring can have one of three genotypes–*YY*, *Yy*, or *yy*. The ratio of genotypes is written as 1:2:1.

Because *YY* and *Yy* represent the same phenotype–yellow–the offspring can have one of only two phenotypes–yellow or green. The ratio of phenotypes is written 3:1. Therefore, about 75 percent of the offspring of the cross between two heterozygous pea plants will produce yellow seeds. About 25 percent of the plants will produce green seeds.

Using Ratios to Predict

Given a 3:1 ratio, you can expect that an offspring from heterozygous parents has a 3:1 chance of having yellow seeds. But you cannot expect that a group of four seeds will have three yellow seeds and one green seed. This is because one offspring does not affect the phenotype of another offspring. In a similar way, the outcome of one coin toss does not affect the outcome of other coin tosses.

However, if you counted large numbers of offspring from a particular cross, the overall ratio would be close to the ratio predicted by a Punnett square. Mendel did not use Punnett squares. However, by studying nearly 30,000 pea plants, his ratios nearly matched those that would have been predicted by a Punnett square for each cross.

Pedigrees

Another model that can show inherited traits is a pedigree. A pedigree shows phenotypes of genetically related family members. It can also help determine genotypes. In the pedigree in Figure 8, three offspring have a trait–attached earlobes–that the parents do not have. If these offspring received one allele for this trait from each parent, but neither parent displays the trait, the offspring must have received two recessive alleles.

 Key Concept Check How can inheritance be modeled?

Pedigree 🔑

Figure 8 In this pedigree, the parents and two offspring have unattached ear lobes—the dominant phenotype. Three offspring have attached ear lobes—the recessive phenotype.

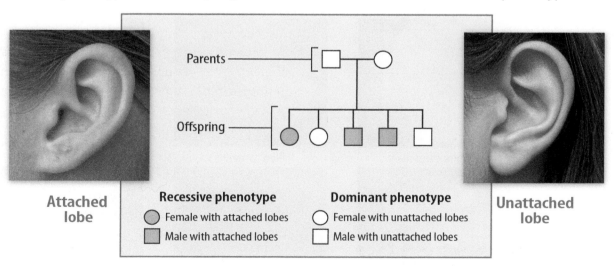

Attached lobe

Recessive phenotype
- 🔴 Female with attached lobes
- 🟥 Male with attached lobes

Dominant phenotype
- ⚪ Female with unattached lobes
- ⬜ Male with unattached lobes

Unattached lobe

✔️ **Visual Check** If the genotype of the offspring with attached lobes is *uu*, what is the genotype of the parents? How can you tell?

Complex Patterns of Inheritance

By chance, Mendel studied traits only influenced by one gene with two alleles. However, we know now that some inherited traits have complex patterns of inheritance.

Types of Dominance

Recall that for pea plants, the presence of one dominant allele produces a dominant phenotype. However, not all allele pairs have a dominant-recessive interaction.

Incomplete Dominance Sometimes traits appear to be combinations of alleles. *Alleles show **incomplete dominance** when the offspring's phenotype is a combination of the parents' phenotypes.* For example, a pink camellia, as shown in **Figure 9,** results from incomplete dominance. A cross between a camellia plant with white flowers and a camellia plant with red flowers produces only camellia plants with pink flowers.

Codominance The coat color of some cows is an example of another type of interaction between two alleles. *When both alleles can be observed in a phenotype, this type of interaction is called* **codominance.** If a cow inherits the allele for white coat color from one parent and the allele for red coat color from the other parent, the cow will have both red and white hairs.

(t)©Peter Smithers/Corbis; (tc)©Bill Ross/Corbis; (tr)Geoff Bryant/Science Source; (bl)J. Schwanke/Alamy; (bc, br)©Yann Arthus-Bertrand/Corbis

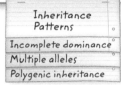

FOLDABLES®

Use two sheets of paper to make a layered book. Label it as shown. Use it to organize your notes on inheritance patterns.

Inheritance Patterns
Incomplete dominance
Multiple alleles
Polygenic inheritance

Types of Dominance

Figure 9 In incomplete dominance, neither parent's phenotype is visible in the offspring's phenotype. In codominance, both parents' phenotypes are visible separately in the offspring's phenotype.

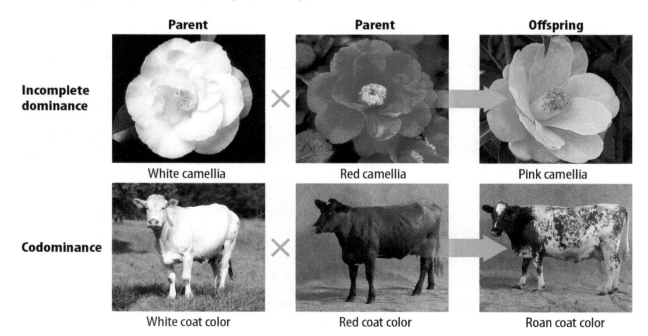

	Parent	Parent	Offspring
Incomplete dominance	White camellia	Red camellia	Pink camellia
Codominance	White coat color	Red coat color	Roan coat color

Table 3 Human ABO Blood Types

Phenotype	Possible Genotypes
Type A	I^AI^A or I^Ai
Type B	I^BI^B or I^Bi
Type O	ii
Type AB	I^AI^B

Multiple Alleles

Unlike the genes in Mendel's pea plants, some genes have more than two alleles, or multiple alleles. Human ABO blood type is an example of a trait that is determined by multiple alleles. There are three different alleles for the ABO blood type– I^A, I^B, and i. The way the alleles combine results in one of four blood types–A, B, AB, or O. The I^A and I^B alleles are codominant to each other, but they both are dominant to the i allele. Even though there are multiple alleles, a person can inherit only two of these alleles–one from each parent, as shown in Table 3.

Polygenic Inheritance

Mendel concluded that each trait was determined by only one gene. However, we now know that a trait can be affected by more than one gene. **Polygenic inheritance** *occurs when multiple genes determine the phenotype of a trait.* Because several genes determine a trait, many alleles affect the phenotype even though each gene has only two alleles. Therefore, polygenic inheritance has many possible phenotypes.

Look again at the photo at the beginning of this lesson. Eye color in humans is an example of polygenic inheritance. There are also many phenotypes for height in humans, as shown in Figure 10. Other human characteristics determined by polygenic inheritance are weight and skin color.

 Key Concept Check How does polygenic inheritance differ from Mendel's model?

ACADEMIC VOCABULARY

ACADEMIC VOCABULARY

conclude
(verb) to reach a logically necessary end by reasoning

Figure 10 The eighth graders in this class have different heights.

 Animation

Genes and the Environment

You read earlier in this lesson that an organism's genotype determines its phenotype. Scientists have learned that genes are not the only factors that can affect phenotypes. An organism's environment can also affect its phenotype. For example, the flower color of one type of hydrangea is determined by the soil in which the hydrangea plant grows. Figure 11 shows that acidic soil produces blue flowers and basic, or alkaline, soil produces pink flowers. Other examples of environmental effects on phenotype are also shown in Figure 11.

For humans, healthful choices can also affect phenotype. Many genes affect a person's chances of having heart disease. However, what a person eats and the amount of exercise he or she gets can influence whether heart disease will develop.

 Reading Check What environmental factors affect phenotype?

Figure 11 Environmental factors, such as temperature and sunlight, can affect phenotype.

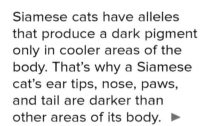

◄ These hydrangea plants are genetically identical. The plant grown in acidic soil produced blue flowers. The plant grown in alkaline soil produced pink flowers.

Siamese cats have alleles that produce a dark pigment only in cooler areas of the body. That's why a Siamese cat's ear tips, nose, paws, and tail are darker than other areas of its body. ►

◄ The wing patterns of the map butterfly, *Araschnia levana*, depend on what time of year the adult develops. Adults that developed in the spring have more orange in their wings than those that developed in the summer.

Lesson 2 Review

Visual Summary

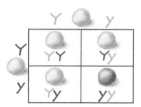

The genes for traits are located on chromosomes.

Geneticists use Punnett squares to predict the possible genotypes and phenotypes of offspring.

In polygenic inheritance, traits are determined by more than one gene and have many possible phenotypes.

FOLDABLES

Use your lesson Foldable to review the lesson. Save your Foldable for the project at the end of the chapter.

What do you think NOW?

You first read the statements below at the beginning of the chapter.

3. All inherited traits follow Mendel's patterns of inheritance.

4. Scientists have tools to predict the form of a trait an offspring might inherit.

Did you change your mind about whether you agree or disagree with the statements? Rewrite any false statements to make them true.

Use Vocabulary

1 **Use** the terms *phenotype* and *genotype* in a complete sentence.

2 **Contrast** homozygous and heterozygous.

3 **Define** *incomplete dominance* in your own words.

Understand Key Concepts

4 How many alleles control a Mendelian trait, such as pea seed color?
A. one   C. three
B. two   D. four

5 **Explain** where the alleles for a given trait are inherited from.

6 **Describe** how the genotypes *RR* and *Rr* result in the same phenotype.

7 **Summarize** how polygenic inheritance differs from Mendelian inheritance.

Interpret Graphics

8 **Analyze** this pedigree. If ■ represents a male with the homozygous recessive genotype (*aa*), what is the mother's genotype?

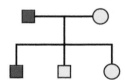

Critical Thinking

9 **Predict** the possible blood genotypes of a child, using the table below, if one parent is type O and the other parent is type A.

Phenotype	Genotype
Blood Type O	ii
Blood Type A	$I^A I^A$ or $I^A i$

How can you use Punnett squares to model inheritance?

Geneticists use models to explain how traits are inherited from one generation to the next. A simple model of Mendelian inheritance is a Punnett square. A Punnett square is a model of reproduction between two parents and the possible genotypes and phenotypes of the resulting offspring. It also models the probability that each genotype will occur.

Learn It

In science, a **model** is a representation of how something in the natural world works. A model is used to explain or predict a natural process. Maps, diagrams, three-dimensional representations, and mathematical formulas can all be used to help model nature.

Try It

1 Copy the Punnett square on this page in your Science Journal. Use it to complete a cross between a fruit fly with straight wings *(cc)* and a fruit fly with curly wings *(CC)*.

2 According to your Punnett square, which genotypes are possible in the offspring?

3 Using the information in your Punnett square, calculate the ratio of the dominant phenotype to the recessive phenotype in the offspring.

Apply It

4 Based on the information in your Punnett square, how many offspring will have curly wings? Straight wings?

5 If you switch the locations of the parent genotypes around the Punnett square, does it affect the potential genotypes of their offspring? Explain.

6 🔑 **Key Concept** Design and complete a Punnett square to model a cross between two fruit flies that are heterozygous for the curly wings *(Cc)*. What are the phenotypic ratios of the offspring?

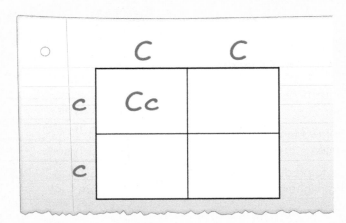

Reading Guide

Key Concepts
ESSENTIAL QUESTIONS

- What is DNA?

- What is the role of RNA in protein production?

- How do changes in the sequence of DNA affect traits?

Vocabulary

DNA p. 426

nucleotide p. 427

replication p. 428

RNA p. 429

transcription p. 429

translation p. 430

mutation p. 431

 Multilingual eGlossary

 8.LS.3, 8.LS.4, 8.LS.6, SEPS.1, SEPS.2, SEPS.4, SEPS.8, 6-8.LST.7.1

DNA and Genetics

Inquiry What is this strand?

What color are your eyes? How tall are you? Traits are controlled by genes. But genes never leave the nucleus of the cell. How does a gene control a trait? This strand and others like it hold the answer to that question.

Science Source

How are codes used to determine traits?

Interpret this code to learn more about how an organism's body cells use codes to determine genetic traits.

1 Analyze the pattern of the simple code shown to the right. For example,
 = DOG

2 In your Science Journal, record the correct letters for the symbols in the code below.

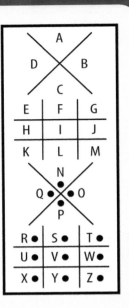

Think About This

1. What do all codes, such as Morse code and Braille, have in common?

2. What do you think might happen if there is a mistake in the code?

3. 🔑 **Key Concept** How do you think an organism's cells might use code to determine its traits?

The Structure of DNA

Have you ever put together a toy or a game for a child? If so, it probably came with directions. Cells put molecules together in much the same way you might assemble a toy. They follow a set of directions.

Genes provide directions for a cell to assemble molecules that express traits such as eye color or seed shape. Recall from Lesson 2 that a gene is a section of a chromosome. Chromosomes are made of proteins and deoxyribonucleic (dee AHK sih ri boh noo klee ihk) acid, or **DNA**–*an organism's genetic material.* A gene is a segment of DNA on a chromosome.

Cells and organisms contain millions of different molecules. Countless numbers of directions are needed to make all those molecules. How do all these directions fit on a few chromosomes? The information, or directions, needed for an organism to grow, maintain itself, and reproduce is contained in DNA. As shown in **Figure 12,** strands of DNA in a chromosome are tightly coiled, like a telephone cord or a coiled spring. This coiling allows more genes to fit in a small space.

🔑 **Key Concept Check** What is DNA?

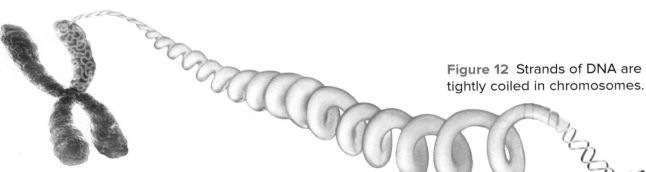

Figure 12 Strands of DNA are tightly coiled in chromosomes.

A Complex Molecule

What's the best way to fold clothes so they will fit into a drawer or a suitcase? Scientists asked a similar question about DNA. What is the shape of the DNA molecule, and how does it fit into a chromosome? The work of several scientists revealed that DNA is like a twisted zipper. This twisted zipper shape is called a double helix. A model of DNA's double helix structure is shown in Figure 13.

How did scientists make this discovery? Rosalind Franklin and Maurice Wilkins were two scientists in London who used X-rays to study DNA. Some of the X-ray data indicated that DNA has a helix shape.

American scientist James Watson visited Franklin and Wilkins and saw one of the DNA X-rays. Watson realized that the X-ray gave valuable clues about DNA's structure. Watson worked with an English scientist, Francis Crick, to build a model of DNA.

Watson and Crick based their work on information from Franklin's and Wilkins's X-rays. They also used chemical information about DNA discovered by another scientist, Erwin Chargaff. After several tries, Watson and Crick built a model that showed how the smaller molecules of DNA bond together and form a double helix.

Four Nucleotides Shape DNA

DNA's twisted-zipper shape is because of molecules called nucleotides. A **nucleotide** is *a molecule made of a nitrogen base, a sugar, and a phosphate group.* Sugar-phosphate groups form the sides of the DNA zipper. The nitrogen bases bond and form the teeth of the zipper. As shown in Figure 13, there are four nitrogen bases: adenine (A), cytosine (C), thymine (T), and guanine (G). A and T always bond together, and C and G always bond together.

 Reading Check What is a nucleotide?

Figure 13 A DNA double helix is made of two strands of DNA. Each strand is a chain of nucleotides.

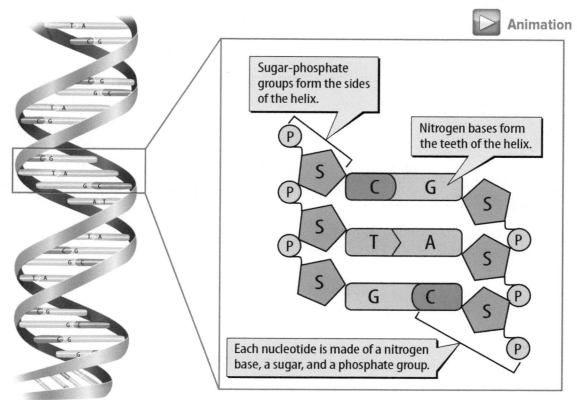

▶ Animation

Sugar-phosphate groups form the sides of the helix.

Nitrogen bases form the teeth of the helix.

Each nucleotide is made of a nitrogen base, a sugar, and a phosphate group.

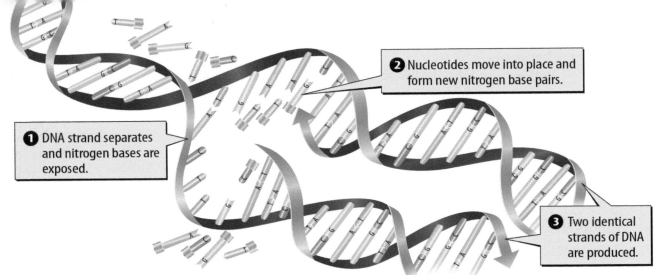

② Nucleotides move into place and form new nitrogen base pairs.

① DNA strand separates and nitrogen bases are exposed.

③ Two identical strands of DNA are produced.

 Animation

Figure 14 Before a cell divides, its DNA is replicated.

How DNA Replicates

Cells contain DNA in chromosomes. So, every time a cell divides, all chromosomes must be copied for the new cell. The new DNA is identical to existing DNA. *The process of copying a DNA molecule to make another DNA molecule is called* **replication.** You can follow the steps of DNA replication in **Figure 14.** First, the strands separate in many places, exposing individual bases. Then nucleotides are added to each exposed base. This produces two identical strands of DNA.

Reading Check What is replication?

 MiniLab   **25 minutes**

How can you model DNA?

Making a model of DNA can help you understand its structure.

① Read and complete a lab safety form.

② Link a **small paper clip** to a **large paper clip.** Repeat four more times, making a chain of 10 paper clips.

③ Choose **four colors of chenille stems.** Each color represents one of the four nitrogen bases. Record the color of each nitrogen base in your Science Journal.

④ Attach a chenille stem to each large paper clip.

⑤ Repeat step 2 and step 4, but this time attach the corresponding chenille-stem nitrogen bases. Connect the nitrogen bases.

⑥ Securely insert one end of your double chain into a **block of styrene foam.**

⑦ Repeat step 6 with the other end of your chain.

⑧ Gently turn the blocks to form a double helix.

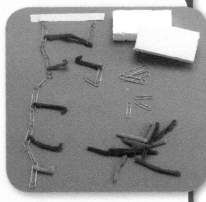

Analyze and Conclude

1. **Explain** which part of a DNA molecule is represented by each material you used.

2. **Predict** what might happen if a mistake were made in creating a nucleotide.

3. **Key Concept** How did making a model of DNA help you understand its structure?

Making Proteins

Recall that proteins are important for every cellular process. The DNA of each cell carries a complete set of genes that provides instructions for making all the proteins a cell requires. Most genes contain instructions for making proteins. Some genes contain instructions for when and how quickly proteins are made.

Junk DNA

As you have learned, all genes are segments of DNA on a chromosome. However, you might be surprised to learn that most of your DNA is not part of any gene. For example, about 97 percent of the DNA on human chromosomes does not form genes. Segments of DNA that are not parts of genes are often called junk DNA. It is not yet known whether junk DNA segments have functions that are important to cells.

The Role of RNA in Making Proteins

How does a cell use the instructions in a gene to make proteins? Proteins are made with the help of ribonucleic acid **(RNA)**—*a type of nucleic acid that carries the code for making proteins from the nucleus to the cytoplasm.* RNA also carries amino acids around inside a cell and forms a part of ribosomes.

RNA, like DNA, is made of nucleotides. However, there are key differences between DNA and RNA. DNA is double-stranded, but RNA is single-stranded. RNA has the nitrogen base uracil (U) instead of thymine (T) and the sugar ribose instead of deoxyribose.

The first step in making a protein is to make mRNA from DNA. *The process of making mRNA from DNA is called* **transcription.** **Figure 15** shows how mRNA is transcribed from DNA.

 Key Concept Check What is the role of RNA in protein production?

Transcription 🔑

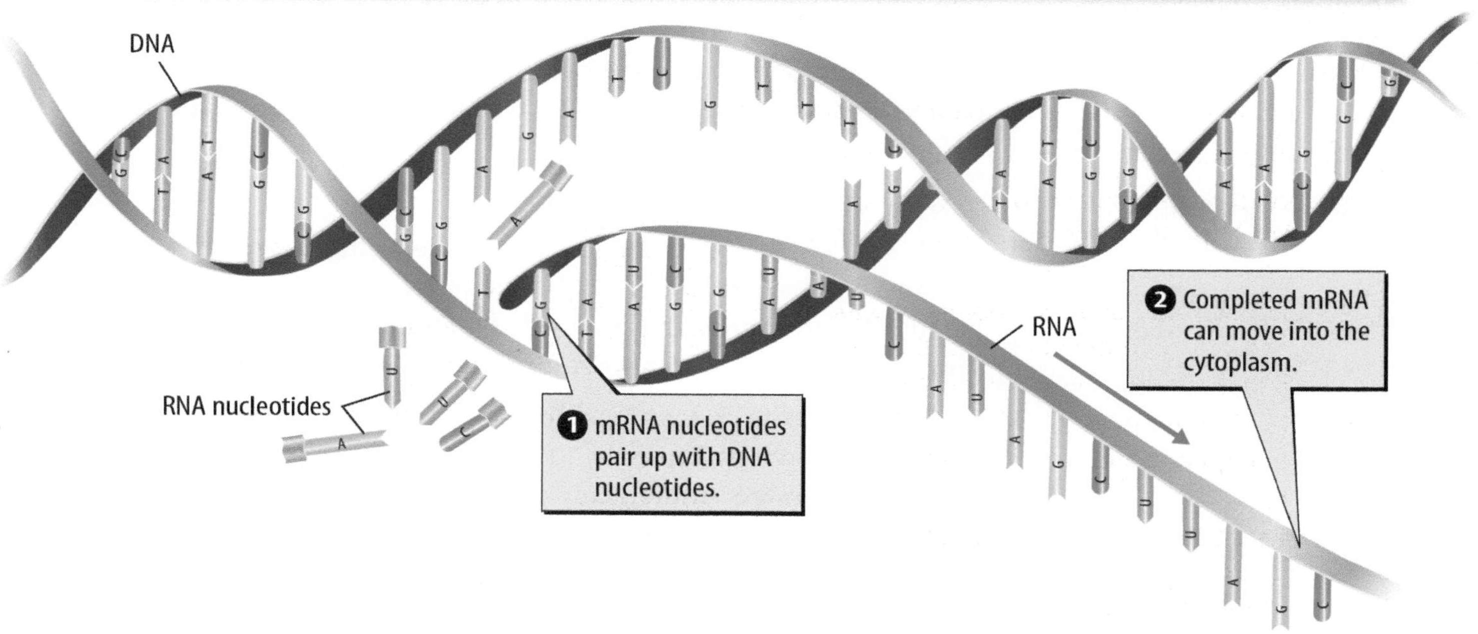

DNA

RNA nucleotides

❶ mRNA nucleotides pair up with DNA nucleotides.

RNA

❷ Completed mRNA can move into the cytoplasm.

Figure 15 Transcription is the first step in making a protein. During transcription, the sequence of nitrogen bases on a gene determines the sequence of bases on mRNA.

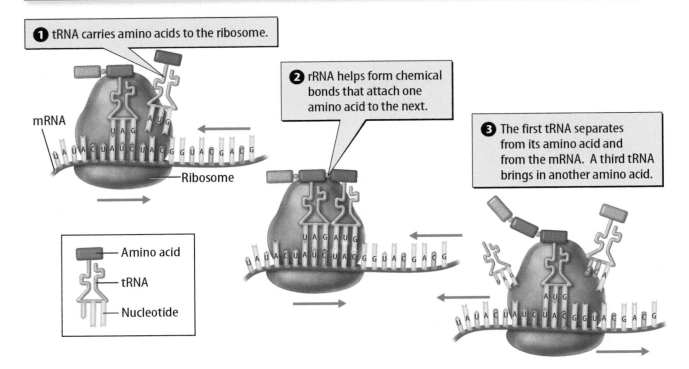

❶ tRNA carries amino acids to the ribosome.

❷ rRNA helps form chemical bonds that attach one amino acid to the next.

❸ The first tRNA separates from its amino acid and from the mRNA. A third tRNA brings in another amino acid.

mRNA

Ribosome

Amino acid

tRNA

Nucleotide

Figure 16 A protein forms as mRNA moves through a ribosome. Different amino acid sequences make different proteins. A complete protein is a folded chain of amino acids.

FOLDABLES

Make a vertical three-tab book and label it as shown. Use your book to record information about the three types of RNA and their functions.

Messenger RNA

Ribosomal RNA

Transfer RNA

Three Types of RNA

On the previous page, you read about messenger RNA (mRNA). There are two other types of RNA, transfer RNA (tRNA) and ribosomal RNA (rRNA). **Figure 16** illustrates how the three work together to make proteins. *The process of making a protein from RNA is called* **translation.** Translation occurs in ribosomes. Recall that ribosomes are cell organelles that are attached to the rough endoplasmic reticulum (rough ER). Ribosomes are also in a cell's cytoplasm.

Translating the RNA Code

Making a protein from mRNA is like using a secret code. Proteins are made of amino acids. The order of the nitrogen bases in mRNA determines the order of the amino acids in a protein. Three nitrogen bases on mRNA form the code for one amino acid.

Each series of three nitrogen bases on mRNA is called a codon. There are 64 codons, but only 20 amino acids. Some of the codons code for the same amino acid. One of the codons codes for an amino acid that is the beginning of a protein. This codon signals that translation should start. Three of the codons do not code for any amino acid. Instead, they code for the end of the protein. They signal that translation should stop.

✓ **Reading Check** What is a codon?

Mutations

You have read that the sequence of nitrogen bases in DNA determines the sequence of nitrogen bases in mRNA, and that the mRNA sequence determines the sequence of amino acids in a protein. You might think these sequences always stay the same, but they can change. *A change in the nucleotide sequence of a gene is called a* **mutation.**

The 46 human chromosomes contain between 20,000 and 25,000 genes that are copied during DNA replication. Sometimes, mistakes can happen during replication. Most mistakes are corrected before replication is completed. A mistake that is not corrected can result in a mutation. Mutations can be triggered by exposure to X-rays, ultraviolet light, radioactive materials, and some kinds of chemicals.

Types of Mutations

There are several types of DNA mutations. Three types are shown in Figure 17. In a deletion mutation, one or more nitrogen bases are left out of the DNA sequence. In an insertion mutation, one or more nitrogen bases are added to the DNA. In a substitution mutation, one nitrogen base is replaced by a different nitrogen base.

Each type of mutation changes the sequence of nitrogen base pairs. This can cause a mutated gene to code for a different protein than a normal gene. Some mutated genes do not code for any protein. For example, a cell might lose the ability to make one of the proteins it needs.

WORD ORIGIN

mutation
from Latin *mutare*, means "to change"

Figure 17 Three types of mutations are substitution, insertion, and deletion.

Visual Check Which base pairs were omitted during replication in the deletion mutation?

Mutations

Original DNA sequence

Substitution
The C-G base pair has been replaced with a T-A pair.

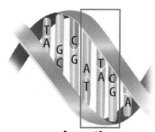

Insertion
Three base pairs have been added.

Deletion
Three base pairs have been removed. Other base pairs will move in to take their place.

Results of a Mutation

The effects of a mutation depend on where in the DNA sequence the mutation happens and the type of mutation. Proteins express traits. Because mutations can change proteins, they can cause traits to change. Some mutations in human DNA cause genetic disorders, such as those described in Table 4.

However, not all mutations have negative effects. Some mutations don't cause changes in proteins, so they don't affect traits. Other mutations might cause a trait to change in a way that benefits the organism.

 Key Concept Check How do changes in the sequence of DNA affect traits?

Scientists still have much to learn about genes and how they determine an organism's traits. Scientists are researching and experimenting to identify all genes that cause specific traits. With this knowledge, we might be one step closer to finding cures and treatments for genetic disorders.

Table 4 Genetic Disorders

Defective Gene or Chromosome	Disorder	Description
Chromosome 12, PAH gene	Phenylketonuria (PKU)	People with defective PAH genes cannot break down the amino acid phenylalanine. If phenylalanine builds up in the blood, it poisons nerve cells.
Chromosome 7, CFTR gene	Cystic fibrosis	In people with defective CFTR genes, salt cannot move in and out of cells normally. Mucus builds up outside cells. The mucus can block airways in lungs and affect digestion.
Chromosome 7, elastin gene	Williams syndrome	People with Williams syndrome are missing part of chromosome 7, including the elastin gene. The protein made from the elastin gene makes blood vessels strong and stretchy.
Chromosome 17, BRCA 1; Chromosome 13, BRCA 2	Breast cancer and ovarian cancer	A defect in BRCA1 and/or BRCA2 does not mean the person will have breast cancer or ovarian cancer. People with defective BRCA1 or BRCA2 genes have an increased risk of developing breast cancer and ovarian cancer.

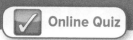
Visual Summary

DNA is a complex molecule that contains the code for an organism's genetic information.

RNA carries the codes for making proteins.

An organism's nucleotide sequence can change through the deletion, insertion, or substitution of nitrogen bases.

FOLDABLES

Use your lesson Foldable to review the lesson. Save your Foldable for the project at the end of the chapter.

What do you think NOW?

You first read the statements below at the beginning of the chapter.

5. Any condition present at birth is genetic.

6. A change in the sequence of an organism's DNA always changes the organism's traits.

Did you change your mind about whether you agree or disagree with the statements? Rewrite any false statements to make them true.

Use Vocabulary

1 **Distinguish** between transcription and translation.

2 **Use the terms** *DNA* and *nucleotide* in a sentence.

3 A change in the sequence of nitrogen bases in a gene is called a(n) _____.

Understand Key Concepts

4 Where does the process of transcription occur?
A. cytoplasm   C. cell nucleus
B. ribosomes   D. outside the cell

5 **Illustrate** Make a drawing that illustrates the process of translation.

6 **Distinguish** between the sides of the DNA double helix and the teeth of the DNA double helix.

Interpret Graphics

7 **Identify** The products of what process are shown in the figure below?

8 **Sequence** Draw a graphic organizer like the one below about important steps in making a protein, beginning with DNA and ending with protein.

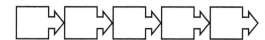

Critical Thinking

9 **Hypothesize** What would happen if a cell were unable to make mRNA?

10 **Assess** What is the importance of DNA replication occurring without any mistakes?

Gummy Bear Genetics

Materials

gummy bears

calculator

paper bag

Safety

Imagine you are on a team of geneticists that is doing "cross-breeding experiments" with gummy bears. Unfortunately, the computer containing your data has crashed. All you have left are six gummy-bear litters that resulted from six sets of parents. But no one can remember which parents produced which litter. You know that gummy-bear traits have either Mendelian inheritance or incomplete dominance. Can you determine which parents produced each set of offspring and how gummy bear traits are inherited?

Ask a Question

What are the genotypes and phenotypes of the parents for each litter?

Make Observations

1. Obtain a bag of gummy bears. Sort the bears by color (phenotype).

   ⚠ *Do not eat the gummy bears.*

2. Count the number (frequency) of bears for each phenotype. Then, calculate the ratio of phenotypes for each litter.

3. Combine data from your litter with those of your classmates using a data table like the one below.

4. As a class, select a letter to represent the alleles for color. Record the possible genotypes for your bears in the class data table.

Gummy Bear Cross Data for Lab Group

Cross #	Phenotype Frequencies	Ratio	Possible Genotypes	Mode of Inheritance	Predicted Parental Genotypes
EXAMPLE	15 green/5 pink	3:1	GG or Gg/gg	Mendelian	Gg x Gg
1.					
2.					
3.					
4.					
5.					

Form a Hypothesis

5 Use the data to form a hypothesis about the probable genotypes and phenotypes of the parents of your litter and the probable type of inheritance.

Test Your Hypothesis

6 Design and complete a Punnett square using the predicted parental genotypes in your hypothesis.

7 Compare your litter's phenotype ratio with the ratio predicted by the Punnett square. Do your data support your hypothesis? If not, revise your hypothesis and repeat steps 5–7.

Analyze and Conclude

8 **Infer** What were the genotypes of the parents? The phenotypes? How do you know?

9 **BIG IDEA** **The Big Idea** Determine the probable modes of inheritance for each phenotype. Explain your reasoning.

10 **Graph** Using the data you collected, draw a bar graph that compares the phenotype frequency for each gummy bear phenotype.

Communicate Your Results

Create a video presentation of the results of your lab. Describe the question you investigated, the steps you took to answer the question, and the data that support your conclusions. Share your video with your classmates.

 **Extension**

Think of a question you have about genetics. For example, can you design a pedigree to trace a Mendelian trait in your family? To investigate your question, design a controlled experiment or an observational study.

6

Reminder

Using Ratios

☑ A ratio is a comparison of two numbers.

☑ A ratio of 15 : 5 can be reduced to 3 : 1.

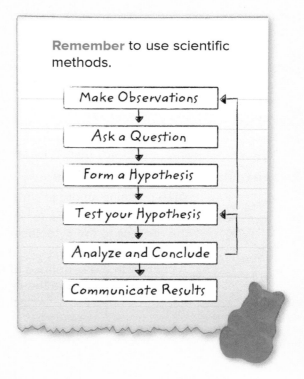

Remember to use scientific methods.

Make Observations

↓

Ask a Question

↓

Form a Hypothesis

↓

Test your Hypothesis

↓

Analyze and Conclude

↓

Communicate Results

THE BIG IDEA

Inherited genes are the basis of an organism's traits.

Key Concepts Summary	Vocabulary
Lesson 1: Mendel and His Peas • Mendel performed cross-pollination experiments to track which traits were produced by specific parental crosses. • Mendel found that two genetic factors—one from a sperm cell and one from an egg cell—control each trait. • **Dominant** traits block the expression of **recessive** traits. Recessive traits are expressed only when two recessive factors are present. ×  →	**heredity** p. 405 **genetics** p. 405 **dominant trait** p. 411 **recessive trait** p. 411
Lesson 2: Understanding Inheritance • **Phenotype** describes how a trait appears. • **Genotype** describes alleles that control a trait. • **Punnett squares** and pedigrees are tools to model patterns of inheritance. • Many patterns of inheritance, such as **codominance** and **polygenic inheritance,** are more complex than Mendel described. 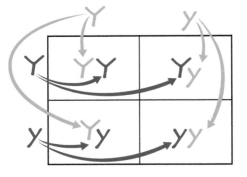	**gene** p. 416 **allele** p. 416 **phenotype** p. 416 **genotype** p. 416 **homozygous** p. 417 **heterozygous** p. 417 **Punnett square** p. 418 **incomplete dominance** p. 420 **codominance** p. 420 **polygenic inheritance** p. 421
Lesson 3: DNA and Genetics  • **DNA** contains an organism's genetic information. • **RNA** carries the codes for making proteins from the nucleus to the cytoplasm. RNA also forms part of ribosomes. • A change in the sequence of DNA, called a **mutation,** can change the traits of an organism.	**DNA** p. 426 **nucleotide** p. 427 **replication** p. 428 **RNA** p. 429 **transcription** p. 429 **translation** p. 430 **mutation** p. 431

FOLDABLES®

Chapter Project

Assemble your lesson Foldables as shown to make a Chapter Project. Use the project to review what you have learned in this chapter.

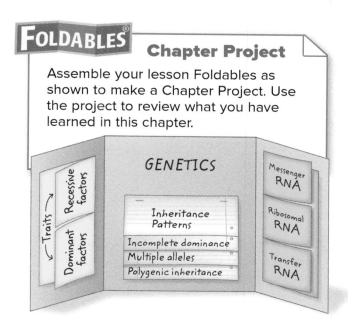

GENETICS

Recessive factors
Dominant factors
Traits

Inheritance Patterns
Incomplete dominance
Multiple alleles
Polygenic inheritance

Messenger RNA
Ribosomal RNA
Transfer RNA

Use Vocabulary

1 The study of how traits are passed from parents to offspring is called _____.

2 The passing of traits from parents to offspring is _____.

3 Human height, weight, and skin color are examples of characteristics determined by _____ _____.

4 A helpful device for predicting the ratios of possible genotypes is a(n) _____.

5 The code for a protein is called a(n) _____.

6 An error made during the copying of DNA is called a(n) _____.

Link Vocabulary and Key Concepts

 Interactive Concept Map

Copy this concept map, and then use vocabulary terms from the previous page to complete the concept map.

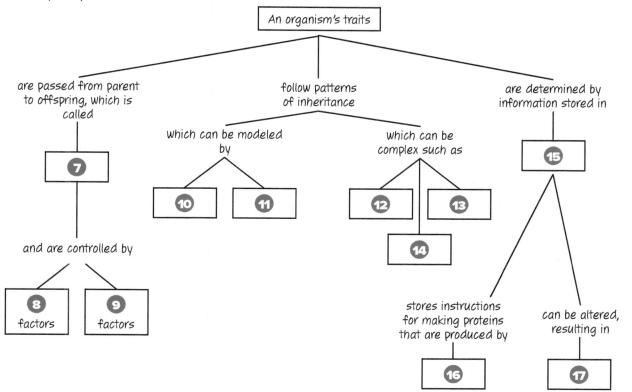

An organism's traits

are passed from parent to offspring, which is called

7

and are controlled by

8 factors

9 factors

follow patterns of inheritance

which can be modeled by

10

11

which can be complex such as

12

13

14

are determined by information stored in

15

stores instructions for making proteins that are produced by

16

can be altered, resulting in

17

Understand Key Concepts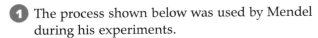

1 The process shown below was used by Mendel during his experiments.

What is the process called?

A. cross-pollination
B. segregation
C. asexual reproduction
D. blending inheritance

2 Which statement best describes Mendel's experiments?

A. He began with hybrid plants.
B. He controlled pollination.
C. He observed only one generation.
D. He used plants that reproduce slowly.

3 Before Mendel's discoveries, which statement describes how people believed traits were inherited?

A. Parental traits blend like colors of paint to produce offspring.
B. Parental traits have no effect on their offspring.
C. Traits from only the female parent are inherited by offspring.
D. Traits from only the male parent are inherited by offspring.

4 Which term describes the offspring of a first-generation cross between parents with different forms of a trait?

A. genotype
B. hybrid
C. phenotype
D. true-breeding

5 Which process makes a copy of a DNA molecule?

A. mutation
B. replication
C. transcription
D. translation

6 Which process uses the code on an RNA molecule to make a protein?

A. mutation
B. replication
C. transcription
D. translation

7 The Punnett square below shows a cross between a pea plant with yellow seeds and a pea plant with green seeds.

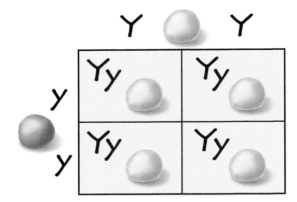

If mating produces 100 offspring, about how many will have yellow seeds?

A. 25
B. 50
C. 75
D. 100

8 Which term describes multiple genes affecting the phenotype of one trait?

A. codominance
B. blending inheritance
C. incomplete dominance
D. polygenic inheritance

Critical Thinking

9 **Compare** heterozygous genotype and homozygous genotype.

10 **Distinguish** between multiple alleles and polygenic inheritance.

11 **Give an example** of how the environment can affect an organism's phenotype.

12 **Predict** In pea plants, the allele for smooth pods is dominant to the allele for bumpy pods. Predict the genotype of a plant with bumpy pods. Can you predict the genotype of a plant with smooth pods? Explain.

13 **Interpret Graphics** In tomato plants, red fruit (*R*) is dominant to yellow fruit (*r*). Interpret the Punnett square below, which shows a cross between a heterozygous red plant and a yellow plant. Include the possible genotypes and corresponding phenotypes.

	R	*r*
r	*Rr*	*rr*
r	*Rr*	*rr*

14 **Compare and contrast** characteristics of replication, transcription, translation, and mutation. Which of these processes takes place only in the nucleus of a cell? Which can take place in both the nucleus and the cytoplasm? How do you know?

Writing in Science

15 **Write** a paragraph contrasting the blending theory of inheritance with the current theory of inheritance. Include a main idea, supporting details, and a concluding sentence.

Keith Szafranski/iStock/360/Getty Images

REVIEW THE BIG IDEA

16 How are traits passed from generation to generation? Explain how dominant and recessive alleles interact to determine the expression of traits.

17 The photo below shows an albino offspring from a non-albino mother. If albinism is a recessive trait, what are the possible genotypes of the mother, the father, and the offspring?

Math Skills ✓ Math Practice

Use Ratios

18 A cross between two heterozygous pea plants with yellow seeds produced 1,719 yellow seeds and 573 green seeds. What is the ratio of yellow to green seeds?

19 A cross between two heterozygous pea plants with smooth green pea pods produced 87 bumpy yellow pea pods, 261 smooth yellow pea pods, 261 bumpy green pea pods, and 783 smooth green pea pods. What is the ratio of bumpy yellow to smooth yellow to bumpy green to smooth green pea pods?

20 A jar contains three red, five green, two blue, and six yellow marbles. What is the ratio of red to green to blue to yellow marbles?

Standardized Test Practice

Record your answers on the answer sheet provided by your teacher or on a sheet of paper.

Multiple Choice

Use the diagram below to answer questions 1 and 2.

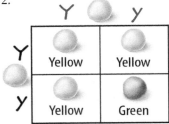

1 Which genotype belongs in the lower right square?

A YY

B Yy

C yY

D yy

2 What percentage of plants from this cross will produce yellow seeds?

A 25 percent

B 50 percent

C 75 percent

D 100 percent

3 When Mendel crossed a true-breeding plant with purple flowers and a true-breeding plant with white flowers, ALL offspring had purple flowers. This is because white flowers are

A dominant.

B heterozygous.

C polygenic.

D recessive.

4 Which process copies an organism's DNA?

A mutation

B replication

C transcription

D translation

Use the chart below to answer question 5.

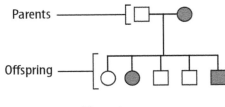

Phenotypes
○ Female, dominant ● Female, recessive
□ Male, dominant ■ Male, recessive

5 Based on the pedigree above, how many offspring from this cross had the recessive phenotype?

A 1

B 2

C 3

D 5

6 Which is NOT true of a hybrid?

A It has one recessive allele.

B It has pairs of chromosomes.

C Its genotype is homozygous.

D Its phenotype is dominant.

7 Alleles are different forms of a

A chromosome.

B gene.

C nucleotide.

D protein.

8 Which is true of an offspring with incomplete dominance?

A Both alleles can be observed in its phenotype.

B Every offspring shows the dominant phenotype.

C Multiple genes determine its phenotype.

D Offspring phenotype is a combination of the parents' phenotypes.

Use the diagrams below to answer question 9.

Before Replication

After Replication

9 The diagrams above show a segment of DNA before and after replication. Which occurred during replication?

A deletion

B insertion

C substitution

D translation

10 Which human characteristic is controlled by polygenic inheritance?

A blood type

B earlobe position

C eye color

D thumb shape

11 Mendel crossed a true-breeding plant with round seeds and a true-breeding plant with wrinkled seeds. Which was true of every offspring of this cross?

A They had the recessive phenotype.

B They showed a combination of traits.

C They were homozygous.

D They were hybrid plants.

Constructed Response

Use the diagram below to answer questions 12 and 13.

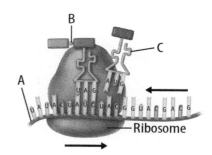

12 Describe what is happening in the phase of translation shown in the diagram.

13 What are the three types of RNA in the diagram? How do these types work together during translation?

14 What is the importance of translation in your body?

15 Mendel began his experiments with true-breeding plants. Why was this important?

16 How did Mendel's experimental methods help him develop his hypotheses on inheritance?

17 What environmental factors affect the phenotypes of organisms other than humans? Provide three examples from nature. What factor, other than genes, affects human phenotype? Give two examples. Why is knowledge of this nongenetic factor helpful?

NEED EXTRA HELP?																	
If You Missed Question...	1	2	3	4	5	6	7	8	9	10	11	12	13	14	15	16	17
Go to Lesson...	2	2	1	3	2	1,2	2	2	3	2	1	3	3	3	1	1	2

The Environment and Change Over Time

THE BIG IDEA

How do species adapt to changing environments over time?

Inquiry **Bees or Flowers?**

A type of orchid plant, called a bee orchid, produces this flower. You might have noticed that the flower looks like a bee.

- What is the advantage to the plant to have flowers that look like bees?

- How did the appearance of the flower develop over time?

- How do species adapt to changing environments over time?

©Zoonar/C.Bosch/age fotostock

Get Ready to Read

What do you think?

Before you read, decide if you agree or disagree with each of these statements. As you read this chapter, see if you change your mind about any of the statements.

 Original tissues can be preserved as fossils.

 Organisms become extinct only in mass extinction events.

 Environmental change causes variations in populations.

 Variations can lead to adaptations.

 Living species contain no evidence that they are related to each other.

 Plants and animals share similar genes.

Your one-stop online resource
connectED.mcgraw-hill.com

LS LearnSmart®

PBL Project-Based Learning Activities

Chapter Resources Files, Reading Essentials, Get Ready to Read, Quick Vocabulary

Lab Manuals, Safety Videos, Virtual Labs & Other Tools

Animations, Videos, Interactive Tables

abc Vocabulary, Multilingual eGlossary, Vocab eGames, Vocab eFlashcards

Self-checks, Quizzes, Tests

Personal Tutors

Fossil Evidence of Evolution

Reading Guide

Key Concepts
ESSENTIAL QUESTIONS

- How do fossils form?
- How do scientists date fossils?
- How are fossils evidence of biological evolution?

Vocabulary

fossil record p. 445

mold p. 447

cast p. 447

trace fossil p. 447

geologic time scale p. 449

extinction p. 450

biological evolution p. 451

abc Multilingual eGlossary

▷ BrainPOP®

Inquiry **What can be learned from fossils?**

When scientists find fossils, they use them as evidence to try to answer questions about past life on Earth. When did this organism live? What did this organism eat? How did it move or grow? How did this organism die? To what other organisms is this one related?

Florida Museum of Natural History photo by Eric Zamora ©2008

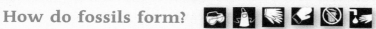
How do fossils form?

Evidence from fossils helps scientists understand how organisms have changed over time. Some fossils form when impressions left by organisms in sand or mud are filled in by sediments that harden.

1. Read and complete a lab safety form.
2. Place a **container of moist sand** on top of **newspaper.** Press a **shell** into the moist sand. Carefully remove the shell. Brush any sand on the shell onto the newspaper.
3. Observe the impression, and record your observations in your Science Journal.
4. Pour **plaster of paris** into the impression. Wait for it to harden.

   ⚠ *The mix gets hot as it sets—do not touch it until it has hardened.*
5. Remove the shell fossil from the sand, and brush it off.
6. Observe the structure of the fossil, and record your observations.

Think About This

1. What effect did the shell have on the sand?

2. 🔑 **Key Concept** What information do you think someone could learn about the shell and the organism that lived inside it by examining the fossil?

The Fossil Record

On your way to school, you might have seen an oak tree or heard a robin. Although these organisms shed leaves or feathers, their characteristics remain the same from day to day. It might seem as if they have been on Earth forever. However, if you were to travel a few million years back in time, you would not see oak trees or robins. You would see different species of trees and birds. That is because species change over time.

You might already know that fossils are the remains or evidence of once-living organisms. *The **fossil record** is made up of all the fossils ever discovered on Earth.* It contains millions of fossils that represent many thousands of species. Most of these species are no longer alive on Earth. The fossil record provides evidence that species have changed over time. Fossils help scientists picture what these species looked like. **Figure 1** shows how scientists think the giant bird *Titanus* might have looked when it was alive. The image is based on fossils that have been discovered and are represented in the photo on the previous page.

The fossil record is enormous, but it is still incomplete. Scientists think it represents only a small fraction of all the organisms that have ever lived on Earth.

Figure 1 Based on fossil evidence, scientists can recreate the physical appearance of species that are no longer alive on Earth.

Hutchings Photography/Digital Light Source

Fossil Formation

If you have ever seen vultures or other animals eating a dead animal, you know they leave little behind. Any soft tissues animals do not eat, bacteria break down. Only the dead animal's hard parts, such as bones, shells, and teeth, remain. In most instances, these hard parts also break down over time. However, under rare conditions, some become fossils. The soft tissues of animals and plants, such as skin, muscles, or leaves, can also become fossils, but these are even more rare. Some of the ways that fossils can form are shown in Table 1.

✔ **Reading Check** Why is it rare for soft tissue to become a fossil?

Mineralization

After an organism dies, its body could be buried under mud, sand, or other sediments in a stream or river. If minerals in the water replace the organism's original material and harden into rock, a fossil forms. This process is called mineralization. Minerals in water also can filter into the small spaces of a dead organism's tissues and become rock. Most mineralized fossils are of shell or bone, but wood can also become a mineralized fossil, as shown in Table 1.

Carbonization

In carbonization, a fossil forms when a dead organism is compressed over time and pressure drives off the organism's liquids and gases. As shown in Table 1, only the carbon outline, or film, of the organism remains.

SCIENCE USE V. COMMON USE

tissue

Science Use similar cells that work together and perform a function

Common Use a piece of soft, absorbent paper

Table 1 Fossils form in several ways.

✔ **Visual Check** What types of organisms or tissues are often preserved as carbon films?

Table 1 How Fossils Form

	Mineralization	Carbonization
Description	Rock-forming minerals, such as calcium carbonate ($CaCO_3$), in water filled in the small spaces in the tissue of these pieces of petrified wood. Water also replaced some of the wood's tissue. Mineralization can preserve the internal structures of an organism.	Fossil films made by carbonization are usually black or dark brown. Fish, insects, and plant leaves, such as this fern frond, are often preserved as carbon films.
Example		

(l)B.A.E. Inc./Alamy, (r)The Natural History Museum/Alamy

446 • Chapter 13
EXPLAIN

Molds and Casts

Sometimes when an organism dies, its shell or bone might make an impression in mud or sand. When the sediment hardens, so does the impression. *The impression of an organism in a rock is called a* **mold.** Sediments can later fill in the mold and harden to form a cast. *A* **cast** *is a fossil copy of an organism in a rock.* A single organism can form both a mold and a cast, as shown in Table 1. Molds and casts show only external features of organisms.

Trace Fossils

Evidence of an organism's movement or behavior–not just its physical structure–also can be preserved in rock. *A* **trace fossil** *is the preserved evidence of the activity of an organism.* For example, an organism might walk across mud. The tracks, such as the ones shown in Table 1, can fossilize if they are filled with sediment that hardens.

Original Material

In rare cases, the original tissues of an organism can be preserved. Examples of original-material fossils include mammoths frozen in ice and saber-toothed cats preserved in tar pits. Fossilized remains of ancient humans have been found in bogs. Most of these fossils are younger than 10,000 years old. However, the insect encased in amber in Table 1 is millions of years old. Scientists also have found original tissue preserved in the bone of a dinosaur that lived 70 million years ago (mya).

 Key Concept Check List the different ways fossils can form.

WORD ORIGIN

fossil
from Latin *fossilis*, means "to obtain by digging"

Molds and Casts	Trace Fossils	Original Material
When sediments hardened around this buried trilobite, a mold formed. Molds are usually of hard parts, such as shells or bone. If a mold is later filled with more sediments that harden, the mold can form a cast.	These footprints were made when a dinosaur walked across mud that later hardened. This trace fossil might provide evidence of the speed and weight of the dinosaur.	If original tissues of organisms are buried in the absence of oxygen for long periods of time, they can fossilize. The insect in this amber became stuck in tree sap that later hardened.

Dating Fossils 🔑

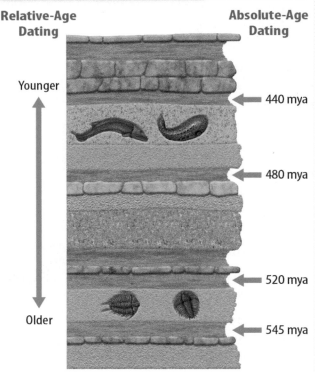

Relative-Age Dating ← (top) → **Absolute-Age Dating**

Younger ↑

← 440 mya

← 480 mya

← 520 mya

Older ↓

← 545 mya

Figure 2 If the age of the igneous layers is known, as shown above, it is possible to estimate the age of the sedimentary layers—and the fossils they contain—between them.

✓ **Visual Check** What is the estimated age of the trilobite fossils (bottom layer of fossils)?

REVIEW VOCABULARY

isotopes
atoms of the same element that have different numbers of neutrons

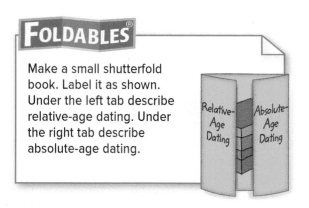

FOLDABLES

Make a small shutterfold book. Label it as shown. Under the left tab describe relative-age dating. Under the right tab describe absolute-age dating.

Relative-Age Dating | Absolute-Age Dating

Determining a Fossil's Age

Scientists cannot date most fossils directly. Instead, they date the rocks the fossils are embedded inside. Rocks erode or are recycled over time. However, scientists can determine ages for most of Earth's rocks.

Relative-Age Dating

How does your age compare to the ages of those around you? You might be younger than a brother but older than a sister. This is your relative age. Similarly, a rock is either older or younger than rocks nearby. In relative-age dating, scientists determine the relative order in which rock layers were deposited. In an undisturbed rock formation, they know that the bottom layers are oldest and the top layers are youngest, as shown in **Figure 2**. Relative-age dating helps scientists determine the relative order in which species have appeared on Earth over time.

 Key Concept Check How does relative-age dating help scientists learn about fossils?

Absolute-Age Dating

Absolute-age dating is more precise than relative-age dating. Scientists take advantage of radioactive decay, a natural clocklike process in rocks, to learn a rock's absolute age, or its age in years. In radioactive decay, unstable **isotopes** in rocks change into stable isotopes over time. Scientists measure the ratio of unstable isotopes to stable isotopes to find the age of a rock. This ratio is best measured in igneous rocks.

Igneous rocks form from volcanic magma. Magma is so hot that it is rare for parts of organisms in it to remain and form fossils. Most fossils form in sediments, which become sedimentary rock. To measure the age of sedimentary rock layers, scientists calculate the ages of igneous layers above and below them. In this way, they can estimate the ages of the fossils embedded within the sedimentary layers, as shown in **Figure 2**.

Fossils over Time

Personal Tutor

How old do you think Earth's oldest fossils are? You might be surprised to learn that evidence of microscopic, unicellular organisms has been found in rocks 3.4 billion years old. The oldest fossils visible to the unaided eye are about 565 million years old.

The Geologic Time Scale

It is hard to keep track of time that is millions and billions of years long. Scientists organize Earth's history into a time line called the geologic time scale. *The **geologic time scale** is a chart that divides Earth's history into different time units.* The longest time units in the geological time scale are eons. As shown in **Figure 3,** Earth's history is divided into four eons. Earth's most recent eon–the Phanerozoic (fa nuh ruh ZOH ihk) eon–is subdivided into three eras, also shown in **Figure 3.**

 Reading Check What is the geologic time scale?

Dividing Time

You might have noticed in **Figure 3** that neither eons nor eras are equal in length. When scientists began developing the geologic time scale in the 1800s, they did not have absolute-age dating methods. To mark time boundaries, they used fossils. Fossils provided an easy way to mark time. Scientists knew that different rock layers contained different types of fossils. Some of the fossils scientists use to mark the time boundaries are shown in **Figure 3.**

Often, a type of fossil found in one rock layer did not appear in layers above it. Even more surprising, entire collections of fossils in one layer were sometimes absent from layers above them. It seemed as if whole communities of organisms had suddenly disappeared.

 Reading Check What do scientists use to mark boundaries in the geologic time scale?

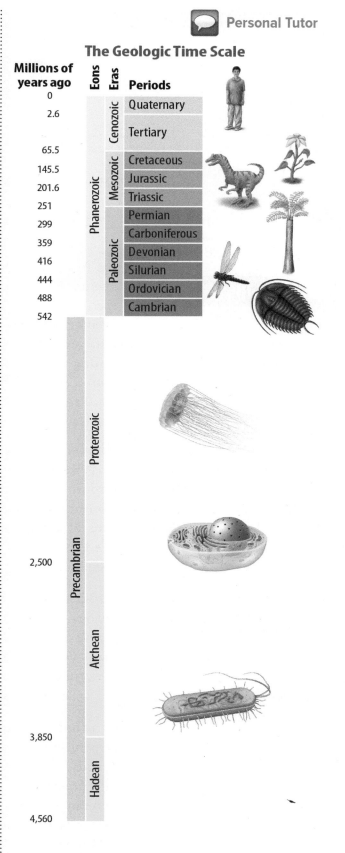

The Geologic Time Scale

Figure 3 The Phanerozoic eon began about 540 million years ago and continues to the present day. It contains most of Earth's fossil record.

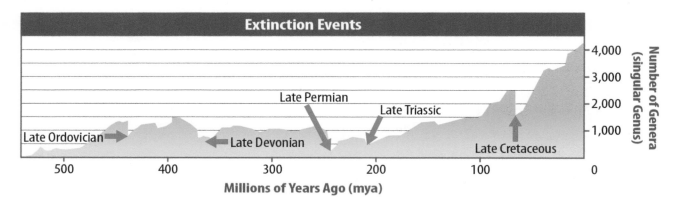

Extinction Events

Number of Genera (singular Genus)

Late Ordovician →

← Late Devonian

Late Permian

Late Triassic

Late Cretaceous

Millions of Years Ago (mya)

Figure 4 Arrows mark the five major extinction events of the Phanerozoic eon.

 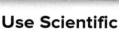

Extinctions

Scientists now understand that sudden disappearances of fossils in rock layers are evidence of extinction (ihk STINGK shun) events. **Extinction** *occurs when the last individual organism of a species dies.* A mass extinction occurs when many species become extinct within a few million years or less. The fossil record contains evidence that five mass extinction events have occurred during the Phanerozoic eon, as shown in **Figure 4.** Extinctions also occur at other times, on smaller scales. Evidence from the fossil record suggests extinctions have been common throughout Earth's history.

Environmental Change

What causes extinctions? Populations of organisms depend on resources in their environment for food and shelter. Sometimes environments change. After a change happens, individual organisms of a species might not be able to find the resources they need to survive. When this happens, the organisms die, and the species becomes extinct.

Sudden Changes Extinctions can occur when environments change quickly. A volcanic eruption or a meteorite impact can throw ash and dust into the atmosphere, blocking sunlight for many years. This can affect global climate and food webs. Scientists hypothesize that the impact of a huge meteorite 65 million years ago contributed to the extinction of dinosaurs.

Gradual Changes Not all environmental change is sudden. Depending on the location, Earth's tectonic plates move between 1 and 15 cm each year. As plates move and collide with each other over time, mountains form and oceans develop. If a mountain range or an ocean isolates a species, the species might become extinct if it cannot find the resources it needs. Species also might become extinct if sea level changes.

Reading Check What is the relationship between extinction and environmental change?

Extinctions and Evolution

The fossil record contains clear evidence of the extinction of species over time. But it also contains evidence of the appearance of many new species. How do new species arise?

Many early scientists thought that each species appeared on Earth independently of every other species. However, as more fossils were discovered, patterns in the fossil record began to emerge. Many fossil species in nearby rock layers had similar body plans and similar structures. It appeared as if they were related. For example, the series of horse fossils in **Figure 5** suggests that the modern horse is related to other extinct species. These species changed over time in what appeared to be a sequence. Change over time is evolution. **Biological evolution** *is the change over time in populations of related organisms.* Charles Darwin developed a theory about how species evolve from other species. You will read about Darwin's theory in the next lesson.

 Key Concept Check How are fossils evidence of biological evolution?

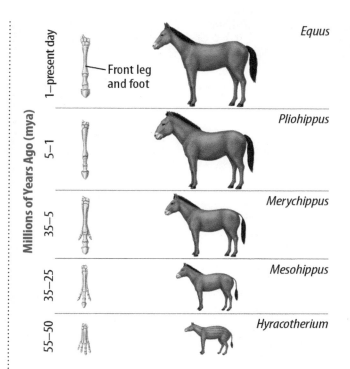

Figure 5 The fossil record is evidence that horses descended from organisms for which only fossils exist today.

Equus

Pliohippus

Merychippus

Mesohippus

Hyracotherium

Millions of Years Ago (mya)

1–present day — Front leg and foot
5–1
35–5
35–25
55–50

MiniLab

20 minutes

How do species change over time?

Over long time periods on Earth, certain individuals within populations of organisms were able to survive better than others.

1. Choose a species from the **Species I.D. Cards.**

2. On **chart paper,** draw six squares in a row and number them 1–6, respectively. Use **colored pencils** and **markers** to make a comic strip showing the ancestral and present-day forms of your species in frames 1 and 6.

3. Use information from the I.D. Card to show what you think would be the progression of changes in the species in frames 2–5.

4. In speech bubbles, explain how each change helped the species to survive.

Analyze and Conclude

1. **Infer** why a scientist would identify a fossil from the species in the first frame of your cartoon as the ancestral form of the present-day species.

2. **Key Concept** How would the fossils of the species at each stage provide evidence of biological change over time?

Lesson 1 Review

☑ Online Quiz

☑ Virtual Lab

Visual Summary

Fossils can consist of the hard parts or soft parts of organisms. Fossils can be an impression of an organism or consist of original tissues.

Scientists determine the age of a fossil through relative-age dating or absolute-age dating.

Scientists use fossils as evidence that species have changed over time.

FOLDABLES

Use your lesson Foldable to review the lesson. Save your Foldable for the project at the end of the chapter.

What do you think NOW?

You first read the statements below at the beginning of the chapter.

1. Original tissues can be preserved as fossils.

2. Organisms become extinct only in mass extinction events.

Did you change your mind about whether you agree or disagree with the statements? Rewrite any false statements to make them true.

Use Vocabulary

1 All of the fossils ever found on Earth make up the _____.

2 When the last individual of a species dies, _____ occurs.

3 **Use the term** *biological evolution* in a sentence.

Understand Key Concepts 🔑

4 Which is the preserved evidence of the activity of an organism?
- **A.** cast
- **B.** mold
- **C.** fossil film
- **D.** trace fossil

5 **Explain** why the hard parts of organisms fossilize more often than soft parts.

6 **Draw and label** a diagram that shows how scientists date sedimentary rock layers.

Interpret Graphics

7 **Identify** Copy and fill in the table below to provide examples of changes that might lead to an extinction event.

Sudden changes	
Gradual changes	

Critical Thinking

8 **Infer** If the rock layers shown below have not been disturbed, what type of dating method would help you determine which layer is oldest? Explain.

Math Skills ✕÷+ ☑ Math Practice

9 Dinosaurs disappeared from Earth about 65,000,000 years ago. Express this number in scientific notation.

Dorling Kindersley/Getty Images

Can you observe changes through time in collections of everyday objects?

Everyday objects that are invented, designed, and manufactured by humans often exhibit changes over time in both structure and function. How have these changes affected the efficiency and/or safety of some common items?

Materials

picture sets of items that have changed over time

Learn It

When scientists **observe** phenomena, they use their senses, such as sight, hearing, touch, and smell. They examine the entire object or situation first, then look carefully for details. After completing their observations, scientists use words or numbers to describe what they saw.

Try It

1. Working with your group members, choose a set of items that you wish to observe, such as telephones, bicycles, or automobiles.

2. Examine the pictures and observe how the item has changed over time.

3. Record your observations in your Science Journal.

4. Observe details of the structure and function of each of the items. Record your observations.

Apply It

5. **Present** your results in the form of an illustrated time line, a consumer magazine article, a role-play of a person-on-the-street interview, a television advertisement, or an idea of your own approved by your teacher.

6. 🔑 **Key Concept** Identify how your product changed over time and in what ways the changes affected the efficiency and/or safety of the product.

Lesson 2

Theory of Evolution by Natural Selection

Reading Guide

Key Concepts

ESSENTIAL QUESTIONS

- Who was Charles Darwin?

- How does Darwin's theory of evolution by natural selection explain how species change over time?

- How are adaptations evidence of natural selection?

Vocabulary

naturalist p. 455

variation p. 457

natural selection p. 458

adaptation p. 459

camouflage p. 460

mimicry p. 460

selective breeding p. 461

 Multilingual eGlossary

 What's Science Got to do With It?

 8.LS.5, SEPS.2, 6-8.LST.7.1

PBL Go to the resource tab in ConnectED to find the PBLs *Spot On* and *Population Probabilities.*

Inquiry Are these exactly the same?

Look closely at these zebras. Are they all exactly the same? How are they different? What accounts for these differences? How do the stripes help these organisms survive in their environment?

©DLILLC/Corbis

Are there variations within your class?

All populations contain variations in some characteristics of their members.

1. Read and complete a lab safety form.
2. Use a **meterstick** to measure the length from your elbow to the tip of your middle finger in centimeters. Record the measurement in your Science Journal.
3. Add your measurement to the class list.
4. Organize all of the measurements from shortest to longest.
5. Break the data into regular increments, such as 31–35 cm, 36–40 cm, and 41–45 cm. Count the number of measurements within each increment.
6. Construct a bar graph using the data. Label each axis and give your graph a title.

Think About This

1. What are the shortest and longest measurements?

2. How much do the shortest and longest lengths vary from each other?

3. 🔑 **Key Concept** Describe how your results provide evidence of variations within your classroom population.

Charles Darwin

How many species of birds can you name? You might think of robins, penguins, or even chickens. Scientists estimate that about 10,000 species of birds live on Earth today. Each bird species has similar characteristics. Each has wings, feathers, and a beak. Scientists hypothesize that all birds evolved from an earlier, or ancestral, population of birdlike organisms. As this population evolved into different species, birds became different sizes and colors. They developed different songs and eating habits, but all retained similar bird characteristics.

How do birds and other species evolve? One scientist who worked to answer this question was Charles Darwin. Darwin was an English naturalist who, in the mid-1800s, developed a theory of how evolution works. *A **naturalist** is a person who studies plants and animals by observing them.* Darwin spent many years observing plants and animals in their natural habitats before developing his theory. Recall that a theory is an explanation of the natural world that is well supported by evidence. Darwin was not the first to develop a theory of evolution, but his theory is the one best supported by evidence today.

🔑 **Key Concept Check** Who was Charles Darwin?

FOLDABLES

Make a small four-door shutterfold book. Use it to investigate the who, what, when, and where of Charles Darwin, the Galápagos Islands, and the theory of evolution by natural selection.

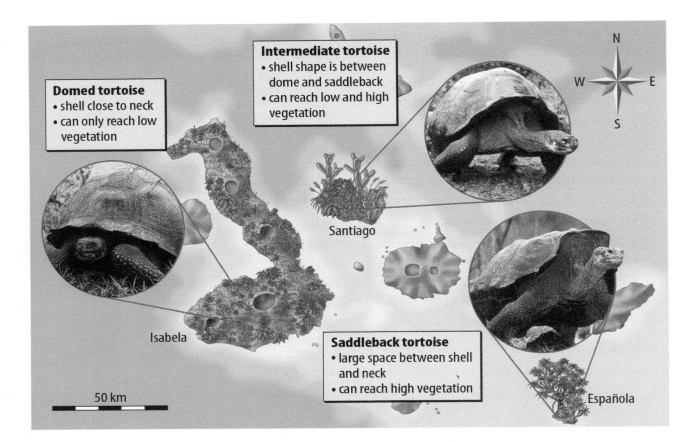

Domed tortoise
• shell close to neck
• can only reach low vegetation

Intermediate tortoise
• shell shape is between dome and saddleback
• can reach low and high vegetation

Santiago

Isabela

Saddleback tortoise
• large space between shell and neck
• can reach high vegetation

Española

50 km

N
W   E
S

Figure 6 Each island in the Galápagos has a different environment. Tortoises look different depending on which island environment they inhabit.

✔ **Visual Check** What type of vegetation do domed tortoises eat?

Voyage of the *Beagle*

Darwin served as a naturalist on the HMS *Beagle,* a survey ship of the British navy. During his voyage around the world, Darwin observed and collected many plants and animals.

The Galápagos Islands

Darwin was especially interested in the organisms he saw on the Galápagos (guh LAH puh gus) Islands. The islands, shown in **Figure 6,** are located 1,000 km off the South American coast in the Pacific Ocean. Darwin saw that each island had a slightly different environment. Some were dry. Some were more humid. Others had mixed environments.

Tortoises Giant tortoises lived on many of the islands. When a resident told him that the tortoises on each island looked different, as shown in **Figure 6,** Darwin became curious.

Mockingbirds and Finches Darwin also became curious about the variety of mockingbirds and finches he saw and collected on the islands. Like the tortoises, different types of mockingbirds and finches lived in different island environments. Later, he was surprised to learn that many of these varieties were different enough to be separate species.

✔ **Reading Check** What made Darwin become curious about the organisms that lived on the Galápagos Islands?

(l)Jeffrey Greenberg/Science Source; (tr)David Hosking/Alamy; (br)©DLILLC/Corbis

Darwin's Theory

Darwin realized there was a relationship between each species and the food sources of the island it lived on. Look again at **Figure 6.** You can see that tortoises with long necks lived on islands that had tall cacti. Their long necks enabled them to reach high to eat the cacti. The tortoises with short necks lived on islands that had plenty of short grass.

Common Ancestors

Darwin became convinced that all the tortoise species were related. He thought they all shared a common ancestor. He suspected that a storm had carried a small ancestral tortoise population to one of the islands from South America millions of years before. Eventually, the tortoises spread to the other islands. Their neck lengths and shell shapes changed to match their islands' food sources. How did this happen?

Variations

Darwin knew that individual members of a species exhibit slight differences, or variations. *A* **variation** *is a slight difference in an inherited trait of individual members of a species.* Even though the snail shells in **Figure 7** are not all exactly the same, they are all from snails of the same species. You can also see variations in the zebras in the photo at the beginning of this lesson. Variations arise naturally in populations. They occur in the offspring as a result of sexual reproduction. You might recall that variations are caused by random mutations, or changes, in genes. Mutations can lead to changes in phenotype. Recall that an organism's phenotype is all of the observable traits and characteristics of the organism. Genetic changes to phenotype can be passed on to future generations.

ACADEMIC VOCABULARY

convince
(*verb*) to overcome
by argument

Project-Based Learning Activity

Spot On Go online to use data to examine the effect of genetic variations on natural selection.

Figure 7 The variations among the shells of a species of tree snail occur naturally within the population.

Visual Check
Describe three variations among these snail shells.

James Carmichael Jr/Newscom

Natural Selection

Darwin did not know about genes. But he realized that variations were the key to the puzzle of how populations of tortoises and other organisms evolved. Darwin understood that food is a limiting resource, which means that the food in each island environment could not support every tortoise that was born. Tortoises had to compete with each other for food. As the tortoises spread to the various islands, some were born with random variations in neck length. If a variation benefited a tortoise, allowing it to compete for food better than other tortoises, the tortoise lived longer. Because it lived longer, it reproduced more. It passed on its variations to its offspring.

This is Darwin's theory of evolution by natural selection. **Natural selection** *is the process by which populations of organisms with variations that help them survive in their environments live longer, compete better, and reproduce more than those that do not have the variations.* Natural selection explains how populations change as their environments change. It explains the process by which Galápagos tortoises became matched to their food sources, as illustrated in **Figure 8.** It also explains the diversity of the Galápagos finches and mockingbirds. Birds with beak variations that help them compete for food live longer and reproduce more.

Key Concept Check What role do variations have in the theory of evolution by natural selection?

Natural Selection

Personal Tutor

① Reproduction
A population of tortoises produces many offspring that inherit its characteristics. More offspring are produced than can survive, which is called overproduction.

② Variation
A tortoise is born with a variation that makes its neck slightly longer.

③ Competition
Due to overproduction and limited resources, not all offspring will survive. An offspring with a longer neck can eat more cacti than other tortoises. It lives longer and produces more offspring.

④ Selection
Over time, the variation is inherited by more and more offspring. Eventually, all tortoises have longer necks.

Figure 8 A beneficial variation in neck length spreads through a tortoise population by natural selection.

Adaptations

Natural selection explains how all species change over time as their environments change. Through natural selection, a helpful variation in one individual can be passed on to future members of a population. As time passes, more variations arise. The accumulation of many similar variations can lead to an adaptation (a dap TAY shun). *An **adaptation** is an inherited trait that increases an organism's chance of surviving and reproducing in its environment.* The long neck of certain species of tortoises is an adaptation to an environment with tall cacti.

 Key Concept Check How do variations lead to adaptations?

Types of Adaptations

Every species has many adaptations. Scientists classify adaptations into three categories: structural, behavioral, and functional. Structural adaptations involve color, shape, and other physical characteristics. The shape of a tortoise's neck is a structural adaptation. Behavioral adaptations involve the way an organism behaves or acts. Hunting at night and moving in herds are examples of behavioral adaptations. Functional adaptations involve internal body systems that affect biochemistry. A drop in body temperature during hibernation is an example of a functional adaptation. **Figure 9** illustrates examples of all three types of adaptations in the desert jackrabbit.

WORD ORIGIN

adaptation
from Latin *adaptare,* means "to fit"

Indiana FYI

What factors affect natural selection? Factors affecting natural selection include competition, genetic variations, environmental changes, and overproduction. Each of these factors affect a species' ability to survive and reproduce.

REVIEW VOCABULARY

biochemistry
the study of chemical processes in living organisms

Figure 9 The desert jackrabbit has structural, behavioral, and functional adaptations. These adaptations enable it to survive in its desert environment.

Structural adaptation The jackrabbit's powerful legs help it run fast to escape from predators.

Behavioral adaptation The jackrabbit stays still during the hottest part of the day, helping it conserve energy.

Functional adaptation The blood vessels in the jackrabbit's ears expand to enable the blood to cool before re-entering the body.

(l)Mark Miller/Photolibrary/Getty Images; (c)Robert Shantz/Alamy; (r)Bryce Flynn/Getty Images

Seahorse

Caterpillar

Pelican

(tl)Paul Sutherland/National Geographic/Getty Images; (tc)Christian Kieffer/Hemera/Getty Images; (tr)©Kay Nietfeld/dpa/Corbis; (b)DARLYNE A. MURAWSKI/National Geographic Creative

▲ Figure 10
Species evolve adaptations as they interact with their environments.

Project-Based Learning Activity

Population Probabilities Go online to learn more about the effect of environmental change on organisms' ability to survive.

Figure 11 This yucca plant and its moth pollinator have evolved so closely together that one cannot exist without the other. The tentacles around the moth's mouth allow it to gather and transfer pollen. ▼

Environmental Interactions

Have you ever wanted to be invisible? Many species have evolved adaptations that make them nearly invisible. The seahorse in Figure 10 is the same color and has a texture similar to the coral it is resting on. This is a structural adaptation called camouflage (KAM uh flahj). **Camouflage** *is an adaptation that enables a species to blend in with its environment.*

Some species have adaptations that draw attention to them. The caterpillar in Figure 10 resembles a snake. Predators see it and are scared away. *The resemblance of one species to another species is* **mimicry** (MIH mih kree). Camouflage and mimicry are adaptations that help species avoid being eaten. Many other adaptations help species eat. The pelican in Figure 10 has a beak and mouth uniquely adapted to its food source–fish.

Reading Check How do camouflage and mimicry differ?

Environments are complex. Species must adapt to an environment's living parts as well as to an environment's nonliving parts. Nonliving things include temperature, water, nutrients in soil, and climate. Deciduous trees shed their leaves due to changes in climate. Camouflage, mimicry, and mouth shape are adaptations mostly to an environment's living parts. An extreme example of two species adapting to each other is shown in Figure 11.

Living and nonliving factors are always changing. Even slight environmental changes affect how species adapt. If a species is unable to adapt, it becomes extinct. The fossil record contains many fossils of species unable to adapt to change.

Artificial Selection

Adaptations provide evidence of how closely Earth's species match their environments. This is exactly what Darwin's theory of evolution by natural selection predicted. Darwin provided many examples of adaptation in *On the Origin of Species,* the book he wrote to explain his theory. Darwin did not write this book until 20 years after he developed his theory. He spent those years collecting more evidence for his theory by studying barnacles, orchids, corals, and earthworms.

Darwin also had a hobby of breeding domestic pigeons. He selectively bred pigeons of different colors and shapes to produce new, fancy varieties. *The breeding of organisms for desired characteristics is called* **selective breeding.** Like many domestic plants and animals produced from selective breeding, pigeons look different from their ancestors, as shown in **Figure 12.** Darwin realized that changes caused by selective breeding were much like changes caused by natural selection. Instead of nature selecting variations, humans selected them. Darwin called this process artificial selection.

Artificial selection explains and supports Darwin's theory. As you will read in Lesson 3, other evidence also supports the idea that species evolve from other species.

Figure 12 The pouter pigeon (bottom left) and the fantail pigeon (bottom right) were derived from the wild rock pigeon (top).

MiniLab
20 minutes

Who survives?

Camouflage helps organisms blend in. This can help them avoid predators or sneak up on prey. Camouflage helps organisms survive in their environments.

1. Read and complete a lab safety form.
2. Choose an area of your classroom where your moth will rest with open wings during the day.
3. Use **scissors, paper, markers,** and a **ruler** to design a moth that measures 2–5 cm in width with open wings and will be camouflaged where it is placed. Write the location where the moth is to be placed. Give the location and your completed moth to your teacher.
4. On the following day, you will have 1 minute to spot as many moths in the room as you can.
5. In your Science Journal, record the location of moths spotted by your team.

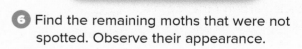

6. Find the remaining moths that were not spotted. Observe their appearance.

Analyze and Conclude

1. **Compare** the appearances and resting places of the moths that were spotted with those that were not spotted.
2.  **Key Concept** Explain how camouflage enables an organism to survive in its environment.

 Online Quiz

Visual Summary

Charles Darwin developed his theory of evolution partly by observing organisms in their natural environments.

Natural selection occurs when organisms with certain variations live longer, compete better, and reproduce more often than organisms that do not have the variations.

Adaptations occur when a beneficial variation is eventually inherited by all members of a population.

FOLDABLES

Use your lesson Foldable to review the lesson. Save your Foldable for the project at the end of the chapter.

What do you think

You first read the statements below at the beginning of the chapter.

3. Environmental change causes variations in populations.

4. Variations can lead to adaptations.

Did you change your mind about whether you agree or disagree with the statements? Rewrite any false statements to make them true.

Use Vocabulary

1 A person who studies plants and animals by observing them is a(n) _____.

2 Through _____, populations of organisms adapt to their environments.

3 Some species blend in to their environments through _____.

Understand Key Concepts

4 The observation that the Galápagos tortoises did not all live in the same environment helped Darwin

A. develop his theory of adaptation.
B. develop his theory of evolution.
C. observe mimicry in nature.
D. practice artificial selection.

5 **Assess** the importance of variations to natural selection.

6 **Compare and contrast** natural selection and artificial selection.

Interpret Graphics

7 **Explain** how the shape of the walking stick at right helps the insect survive in its environment.

8 **Sequence** Copy the graphic organizer below and sequence the steps by which a population of organisms changes by natural selection.

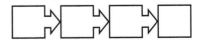

Critical Thinking

9 **Conclude** how Earth's birds developed their diversity through natural selection.

Peter and Rosemary Grant

Observing Natural Selection

Charles Darwin was a naturalist during the mid-1800s. Based on his observations of nature, he developed the theory of evolution by natural selection. Do scientists still work this way—drawing conclusions from observations? Is there information still to be learned about natural selection? The answer to both questions is yes.

Peter and Rosemary Grant are naturalists who have observed finches in the Galápagos Islands for more than 30 years. They have found that variations in the finches' food supply determine which birds will survive and reproduce. They have observed natural selection in action.

The Grants live on Daphne Major, an island in the Galápagos, for part of each year. They observe and take measurements to compare the size and shape of finches' beaks from year to year. They also examine the kinds of seeds and nuts available for the birds to eat. They use this information to relate changes in the birds' food supply to changes in the finch species' beaks.

The island's ecosystem is fragile, so the Grants take great care not to change the environment of Daphne Major as they observe the finches. They carefully plan their diet to avoid introducing new plant species to the island. They bring all the freshwater they need to drink, and they wash in the ocean. For the Grants, it's just part of the job. As naturalists, they try to observe without interfering with the habitat in which they are living.

This large ground finch is one of the kinds of birds studied by the Grants.

©Michael Stubblefield/Alamy

It's Your Turn

RESEARCH AND REPORT Find out more about careers in evolution, ecology, or population biology. What kind of work is done in the laboratory? What kind of work is done in the field? Write a report to explain your findings.

Lesson 3

Reading Guide

Key Concepts
ESSENTIAL QUESTIONS

- What evidence from living species supports the theory that species descended from other species over time?

- How are Earth's organisms related?

Vocabulary

comparative anatomy p. 466

homologous structure p. 466

analogous structure p. 467

vestigial structure p. 467

embryology p. 468

 Multilingual eGlossary

8.LS.5, 8.LS.8, SEPS.6, 6-8.LST.2.1, 6-8.LST.7.1

PBL Go to the resource tab in ConnectED to find the PBL *It's All Relative.*

Biological Evidence of Evolution

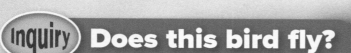 **Does this bird fly?**

Some birds, such as the flightless cormorant above, have wings but cannot fly. Their wings are too small to support their bodies in flight. Why do they still have wings? What can scientists learn about the ancestors of present-day birds that have wings but do not fly?

Joseph Van Os/Getty Images

How is the structure of a spoon related to its function?

Would you eat your morning cereal with a spoon that had holes in it? Is using a teaspoon the most efficient way to serve mashed potatoes and gravy to a large group of people? How about using an extra large spoon, or ladle, to eat soup from a small bowl?

1. Read and complete a lab safety form.

2. In a small group, examine your **set of spoons** and discuss your observations.

3. Sketch or describe the structure of each spoon in your Science Journal. Discuss the purpose that each spoon shape might serve.

4. Label the spoons in your Science Journal with their purposes.

Think About This

1. Describe the similarities and differences among the spoons.

2. If spoons were organisms, what do you think the ancestral spoon would look like?

3. 🔑 **Key Concept** Explain how three of the spoons have different structures and functions, even though they are related by their similarities.

Evidence for Evolution

Recall the sequence of horse fossils from Lesson 1. The sequence might have suggested to you that horses evolved in a straight line—that one species replaced another in a series of orderly steps. Evolution does not occur this way. The diagram in **Figure 13** shows a more realistic version of horse evolution, which looks more like a bush than a straight line. Different horse species were sometimes alive at the same time. They are related to each other because each descended from a common ancestor.

Living species that are closely related share a close common ancestor. The degree to which species are related depends on how closely in time they diverged, or split, from their common ancestor. Although the fossil record is incomplete, it contains many examples of fossil sequences showing close ancestral relationships. Living species show evidence of common ancestry, too.

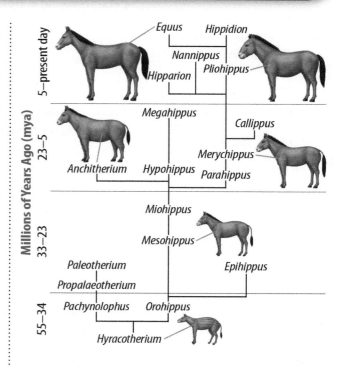

Figure 13 The fossil record indicates that different species of horses often overlapped with each other.

✅ **Visual Check** Which horse is the common ancestor to all horse species in this graph?

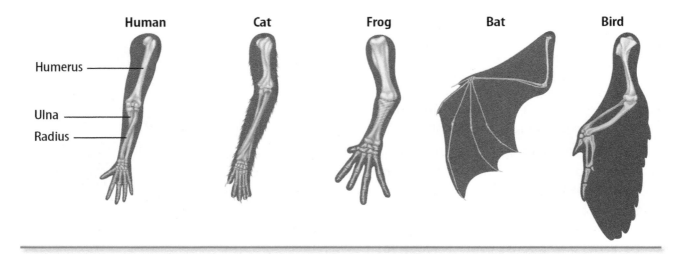

Human   Cat   Frog   Bat   Bird

Humerus

Ulna

Radius

Figure 14 The forelimbs of these species are different sizes, but their placement and structure suggest common ancestry.

 WebQuest

The Origins of Birds Go online to explore and predict the evolutionary relationship between birds and dinosaurs.

FOLDABLES

Make a table with five rows and three columns. Label the rows and columns of the table as shown below. Give your table a title.

	Explanation	Example
Comparative Anatomy		
Vestigial Structures		
Developmental Biology		
Molecular Biology		

Comparative Anatomy

Common ancestry is not difficult to see in many species. For example, it might seem easy to tell that robins, finches, and hawks evolved from a common ancestor. They all have similar features, such as feathers, wings, and beaks. The same is true for tigers, leopards, and house cats. But how are hawks related to cats? How are both hawks and cats related to frogs and bats? Observations of structural and functional similarities and differences in species that do not look alike are possible through comparative anatomy. **Comparative anatomy** *is the study of similarities and differences among structures of living species.*

Homologous Structures Humans, cats, frogs, bats, and birds look different and move in different ways. Humans use their arms for balance and their hands to grasp objects. Cats use their forelimbs to walk, run, and jump. Frogs use their forelimbs to jump. Bats and birds use their forelimbs as wings for flying. However, the forelimb bones of these species exhibit similar patterns, as shown in **Figure 14**. **Homologous** (huh MAH luh gus) **structures** *are body parts of organisms that are similar in structure and position but different in function.*

Homologous structures, such as the forelimbs of humans, cats, frogs, bats, and birds, suggest that these species are related. The more similar two structures are to each other, the more likely it is that the species have evolved from a recent common ancestor.

🔑 **Key Concept Check** How do homologous structures provide evidence for evolution?

Analogous Structures Can you think of a body part in two species that serves the same purpose but differs in structure? How about the wings of birds and flies? Both wings in **Figure 15** are used for flight. But bird wings are covered with feathers. Fly wings are covered with tiny hairs. *Body parts that perform a similar function but differ in structure are* **analogous** (uh NAH luh gus) **structures.** Differences in the structure of bird and fly wings indicate that birds and flies are not closely related.

Vestigial Structures

The bird in the photo at the beginning of this lesson has short, stubby wings. Yet it cannot fly. The bird's wings are an example of vestigial structures. **Vestigial** (veh STIH jee ul) **structures** *are body parts that have lost their original function through evolution.* The best explanation for vestigial structures is that the species with a vestigial structure is related to an ancestral species that used the structure for a specific purpose.

The whale shown in **Figure 16** has tiny pelvic bones. The presence of pelvic bones leads scientists to predict an evolutionary relationship between modern whales and ancestors that used legs for walking on land. The fossil evidence supports this prediction. Many fossilized whale ancestors show a gradual loss of legs over millions of years. They also show that whale ancestors gradually became better adapted to a watery environment.

Key Concept Check How are vestigial structures evidence of descent from ancestral species?

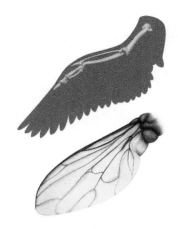

▲ **Figure 15** Though used for the same function—flight—the wings of birds (top) and insects (bottom) are too different in structure to suggest close common ancestry.

Project-Based Learning Activity

It's All Relative Go online to explore the anatomical similarities and differences among modern organisms and fossil organisms.

Figure 16 Present-day whales have vestigial pelvic bones. ▼

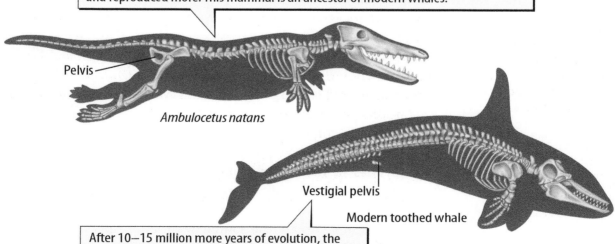

Between 50–40 million years ago, this mammal breathed air and walked clumsily on land. It spent a lot of time in water, but swimming was difficult because of its rear legs. Individuals born with variations that made their rear legs smaller lived longer and reproduced more. This mammal is an ancestor of modern whales.

Pelvis

Ambulocetus natans

Vestigial pelvis

Modern toothed whale

After 10–15 million more years of evolution, the ancestors of modern whales could not walk on land. They were adapted to an aquatic environment. Modern whales have two small vestigial pelvic bones that no longer support legs.

Pharyngeal pouches

Pharyngeal pouches

Pharyngeal pouches

Pharyngeal pouches

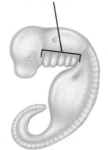

Fish   **Reptile**   **Bird**   **Human**

Figure 17 All vertebrate embryos exhibit pharyngeal pouches at a certain stage of their development. These features, which develop into neck and face parts, suggest relatedness.

WORD ORIGIN

embryology
from Greek *embryon,* means "to swell" and from Greek *logia,* means "study of"

Developmental Biology

You have just read that studying the internal structures of organisms can help scientists learn more about how organisms are related. Studying the development of embryos can also provide scientists with evidence that certain species are related. *The science of the development of embryos from fertilization to birth is called* **embryology** (em bree AH luh jee).

Pharyngeal Pouches Embryos of different species often resemble each other at different stages of their development. For example, all vertebrate embryos have pharyngeal (fuh rihn JEE ul) pouches at one stage, as shown in **Figure 17.** This feature develops into different body parts in each vertebrate. Yet, in all vertebrates, each part is in the face or neck. For example, in reptiles, birds, and humans, part of the pharyngeal pouch develops into a gland in the neck that regulates calcium. In fish, the same part becomes the gills. One function of gills is to regulate calcium. The similarities in function and location of gills and glands suggest a strong evolutionary relationship between fish and other vertebrates.

 Key Concept Check How do pharyngeal pouches provide evidence of relationships among species?

Molecular Biology

Studies of fossils, comparative anatomy, and embryology provide support for Darwin's theory of evolution by natural selection. Molecular biology is the study of gene structure and function. Discoveries in molecular biology have confirmed and extended much of the data already collected about the theory of evolution. Darwin did not know about genes, but scientists today know that mutations in genes are the source of variations upon which natural selection acts. Genes provide powerful support for evolution.

Reading Check What is molecular biology?

Comparing Sequences All organisms on Earth have genes. All genes are made of DNA, and all genes work in similar ways. This supports the idea that all organisms are related. Scientists can study relatedness of organisms by comparing genes and proteins among living species. For example, nearly all organisms contain a gene that codes for cytochrome c, a protein required for cellular respiration. Some species, such as humans and rhesus monkeys, have nearly identical cytochrome c. The more closely related two species are, the more similar their genes and proteins are.

 Key Concept Check How is molecular biology used to determine relationships among species?

Divergence Scientists have found that some stretches of shared DNA mutate at regular, predictable rates. Scientists use this "molecular clock" to estimate at what time in the past living species diverged from common ancestors. For example, as shown in **Figure 18,** molecular data indicate that whales and porpoises are more closely related to hippopotamuses than they are to any other living species.

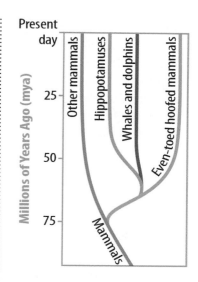

Figure 18 Whales and hippopotamuses share an ancestor that lived 50–60 mya.

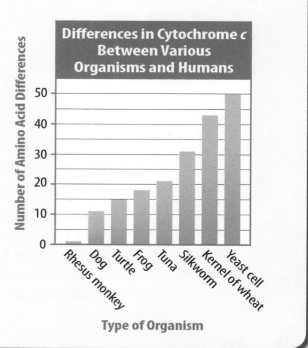

MiniLab

10 minutes

How related are organisms?

Proteins, such as cytochrome c, are made from combinations of just 20 amino acids. The graph below shows the number of amino acid differences in cytochrome c between humans and other organisms.

❶ Use the graph at right to answer the questions below.

Analyze and Conclude

1. **Identify** Which organism has the least difference in the number of amino acids in cytochrome c compared to humans? Which organism has the most difference?

2. **Infer** Which organisms do you think might be more closely related to each other: a dog and a turtle or a dog and a silkworm? Explain your answer.

3. **Key Concept** Notice the differences in the number of amino acids in cytochrome c between each organism and humans. How might these differences explain the relatedness of each organism to humans?

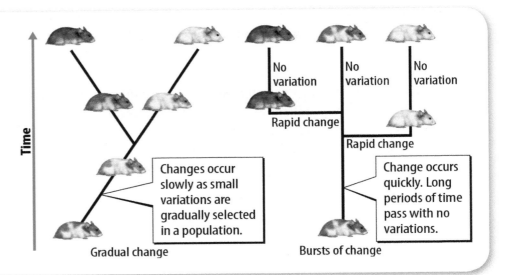

Figure 19 Many scientists think that natural selection produces new species slowly and steadily. Other scientists think species exist stably for long periods, then change occurs in short bursts. ▶

No variation

No variation

No variation

Rapid change

Rapid change

Changes occur slowly as small variations are gradually selected in a population.

Change occurs quickly. Long periods of time pass with no variations.

Gradual change

Bursts of change

Time

Figure 20 *Tiktaalik* lived 385–359 mya. Like amphibians, it had wrists and lungs. Like fish, it had fins, gills, and scales. Scientists think it is an intermediate species linking fish and amphibians. ▼

The Study of Evolution Today

The theory of evolution by natural selection is the cornerstone of modern biology. Since Darwin published his theory, scientists have confirmed, refined, and extended Darwin's work. They have observed natural selection in hundreds of living species. Their studies of fossils, anatomy, embryology, and molecular biology have all provided evidence of relatedness among living and extinct species.

How New Species Form

New evidence supporting the theory of evolution by natural selection is discovered nearly every day. But scientists debate some of the details. Figure 19 shows that scientists have different ideas about the rate at which natural selection produces new species—slowly and gradually or quickly, in bursts. The origin of a species is difficult to study on human time scales. It is also difficult to study in the incomplete fossil record. Yet, new fossils that have features of species that lived both before them and after them are discovered all the time. For example, the *Tiktaalik* fossil shown in Figure 20 has both fish and amphibian features. Further fossil discoveries will help scientists study more details about the origin of new species.

Diversity

How evolution has produced Earth's wide diversity of organisms using the same basic building blocks—genes—is an active area of study in evolutionary biology. Scientists are finding that genes can be reorganized in simple ways and give rise to dramatic changes in organisms. Though scientists now study evolution at the molecular level, the basic principles of Darwin's theory of evolution by natural selection have remained unchanged for over 150 years.

Lesson 3 Review

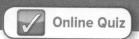

Visual Summary

By comparing the anatomy of organisms and looking for homologous or analogous structures, scientists can determine if organisms had a common ancestor.

Some organisms have vestigial structures, suggesting that they descended from a species that used the structure for a purpose.

Pharyngeal pouches

Human

Scientists use evidence from developmental and molecular biology to help determine if organisms are related.

FOLDABLES

Use your lesson Foldable to review the lesson. Save your Foldable for the project at the end of the chapter.

What do you think NOW?

You first read the statements below at the beginning of the chapter.

5. Living species contain no evidence that they are related to each other.

6. Plants and animals share similar genes.

Did you change your mind about whether you agree or disagree with the statements? Rewrite any false statements to make them true.

Use Vocabulary

1 **Define** *embryology* in your own words.

2 **Distinguish** between a homologous structure and an analogous structure.

3 **Use the term** *vestigial structure* in a complete sentence.

Understand Key Concepts

4 Scientists use molecular biology to determine how two species are related by comparing the genes in one species to genes

  A. in extinct species.   **C.** in related species.
  B. in human species.   **D.** in related fossils.

5 **Discuss** how pharyngeal pouches provide evidence for biological evolution.

6 **Explain** Some blind cave salamanders have eyes. How might this be evidence that cave salamanders evolved from sighted ancestors?

Interpret Graphics

7 **Interpret** The wings of a flightless cormorant are an example of which type of structure?

8 **Assess** Copy and fill in the graphic organizer below to identify four areas of study that provide evidence for evolution.

Evolution

Critical Thinking

9 **Predict** what a fossil that illustrates the evolution of a bird from a reptile might look like.

Materials

clay

colored pencils

colored markers

toothpicks

construction paper

Also needed:
creative construction materials, glue, scissors

Safety

Model Adaptations in an Organism

Conditions on our planet have changed since Earth formed over 4.5 billion years ago. Changes in the concentrations of gases in the atmosphere, temperature, and the amount of precipitation make Earth different today from when it first formed. Other events, such as volcanic eruptions, meteorite strikes, tsunamis, or wildfires, can drastically and rapidly change the conditions in certain environments. As you have read, Earth's fossil record provides evidence that, over millions of years, many organisms developed adaptations that enabled them to survive as Earth's environmental conditions changed.

Ask a Question

How do adaptations enable an organism to survive changes in the environment?

Make Observations

1 Read and complete a lab safety form.

2 Obtain Version 1.0 of the organism you will model from your teacher.

3 Your teacher will describe Event 1 that has occurred on Earth while your organism is alive. Use markers and a piece of construction paper to design adaptations to your organism that would enable it to survive the changing conditions that result from Event 1. Label the adapted organism *Version 1.1*.

Volcanic eruption

4 For each event that your teacher describes, design and draw the adaptations that would enable your organism to survive the changing conditions. Label each new organism *Version 1.X*, filling in the *X* with the appropriate version number.

5 Use the materials provided to make a model of the final version of your organism, showing all of the adaptations.

Predation

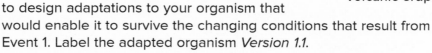

Form a Hypothesis

6 After reviewing and discussing all of the adaptations of your organism, formulate a hypothesis to explain how physical adaptations help an organism survive changes to the environment.

Test Your Hypothesis

7 Research evidence from the fossil record that shows one adaptation that developed and enabled an organism to survive over time under the conditions of one of the environmental events experienced by your model organism.

8 Record the information in your Science Journal.

Analyze and Conclude

9 **Compare** the adaptations that the different groups gave their organisms to survive each event described by your teacher. What kinds of different structures were created to help each organism survive?

10 **The Big Idea** Describe three variations in human populations that would enable some individuals to survive severe environmental changes.

Communicate Your Results

Present your completed organisms to the class and/or judges of "Ultimate Survivor." Explain the adaptations and the reasoning behind them in either an oral presentation or a demonstration, during which classmates and/or judges will review the models.

Inquiry Extension

Examine the traits of individual organisms made by groups in your class. Observe the differences in the adaptations of the organisms. Identify and describe the traits that may give each organism an advantage or disadvantage to survive and reproduce in a stable environment or a changing environment.

Meteorite impact

Lab Tips

☑ Make sure you think of all of the implications of an environmental change event before you decide upon an adaptation.

☑ Decide upon your reasoning for the adaptation before putting the adaptation on your model.

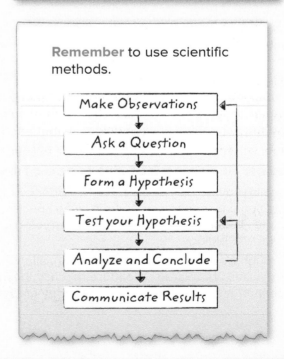

Remember to use scientific methods.

Make Observations
↓
Ask a Question
↓
Form a Hypothesis
↓
Test your Hypothesis
↓
Analyze and Conclude
↓
Communicate Results

 WebQuest

 THE BIG IDEA Through natural selection, species evolve as they adapt to Earth's changing environments.

Key Concepts Summary 🔑

Vocabulary

Lesson 1: Fossil Evidence of Evolution

- Fossils form in many ways, including mineral replacement, carbonization, and impressions in sediment.
- Scientists can learn the ages of fossils by techniques of relative-age dating and absolute-age dating.
- Though incomplete, the **fossil record** contains patterns suggesting the **biological evolution** of related species.

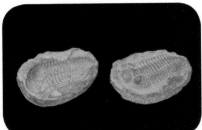

Vocabulary

fossil record p. 445
mold p. 447
cast p. 447
trace fossil p. 447
geologic time scale p. 449
extinction p. 450
biological evolution p. 451

Lesson 2: Theory of Evolution by Natural Selection

- The 19th century **naturalist** Charles Darwin developed a theory of evolution that is still studied today.
- Darwin's theory of evolution by **natural selection** is the process by which populations with **variations** that help them survive in their environments live longer and reproduce more than those without beneficial variations. Over time, beneficial variations spread through populations, and new species that are adapted to their environments evolve.
- **Camouflage, mimicry,** and other **adaptations** are evidence of the close relationships between species and their changing environments.

naturalist p. 455
variation p. 457
natural selection p. 458
adaptation p. 459
camouflage p. 460
mimicry p. 460
selective breeding p. 461

Lesson 3: Biological Evidence of Evolution

- Fossils provide only one source of evidence of evolution. Additional evidence comes from living species, including studies in **comparative anatomy, embryology,** and molecular biology.
- Through evolution by natural selection, all of Earth's organisms are related. The more recently they share a common ancestor, the more closely they are related.

comparative anatomy p. 466
homologous structure p. 466
analogous structure p. 467
vestigial structure p. 467
embryology p. 468

Stan Rohrer/iStock/360/Getty Images

FOLDABLES® Chapter Project

Assemble your lesson Foldables as shown to make a Chapter Project. Use the project to review what you have learned in this chapter.

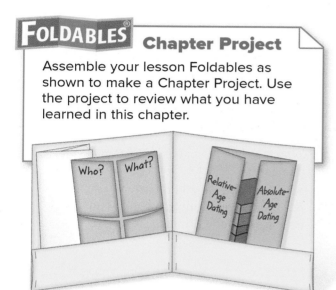

Use Vocabulary

Distinguish between the following terms.

1. *mold* and *cast*
2. *absolute-age dating* and *relative-age dating*
3. *extinction* and *biological evolution*
4. *variations* and *adaptations*
5. *camouflage* and *mimicry*
6. *natural selection* and *selective breeding*
7. *homologous structure* and *analogous structure*
8. *embryology* and *comparative anatomy*
9. *vestigial structure* and *homologous structure*

Link Vocabulary and Key Concepts

 Interactive Concept Map

Copy this concept map, and then use vocabulary terms from the previous page to complete the concept map.

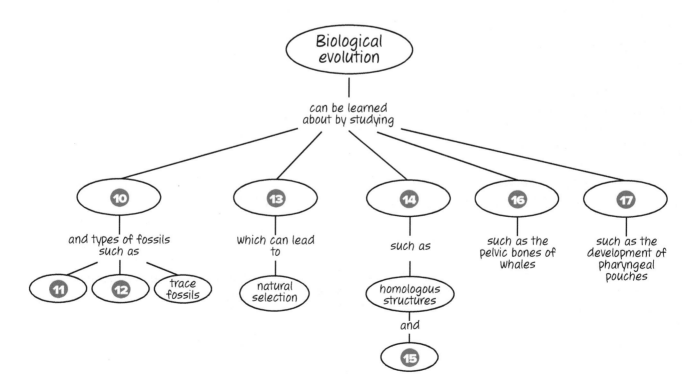

Understand Key Concepts

1 Why do scientists think the fossil record is incomplete?
- A. Fossils decompose over time.
- B. The formation of fossils is rare.
- C. Only organisms with hard parts become fossils.
- D. There are no fossils before the Phanerozoic eon.

2 What do the arrows on the graph below represent?

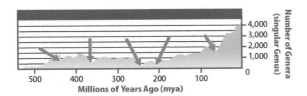

- A. extinction events
- B. meteorite impacts
- C. changes in Earth's temperature
- D. the evolution of a new species

3 What can scientists learn about fossils using techniques of absolute-age dating?
- A. estimated ages of fossils in rock layers
- B. precise ages of fossils in rock layers
- C. causes of fossil disappearances in rock layers
- D. structural similarities to other fossils in rock layers

4 Which is the sequence by which natural selection works?
- A. selection → adaptation → variation
- B. selection → variation → adaptation
- C. variation → adaptation → selection
- D. variation → selection → adaptation

5 Which type of fossil forms through carbonization?
- A. cast
- B. mold
- C. fossil film
- D. trace fossil

6 Which is the source of variations in a population of organisms?
- A. changes in environment
- B. changes in genes
- C. the interaction of genes with an environment
- D. the interaction of individuals with an environment

7 Which is an example of a functional adaptation?
- A. a brightly colored butterfly
- B. birds flying south in the fall
- C. the spray of a skunk
- D. thorns on a rose

8 Which is NOT an example of a vestigial structure?
- A. eyes of a blind salamander
- B. pelvic bones in a whale
- C. thorns on a rose bush
- D. wings on a flightless bird

9 Which do the images below represent?

Human

Cat

- A. analogous structures
- B. embryological structures
- C. homologous structures
- D. vestigial structures

10 Which is an example of a sudden change that could lead to the extinction of species?
- A. a mountain range isolates a species
- B. Earth's tectonic plates move
- C. a volcano erupts
- D. sea level changes

Critical Thinking

11 **Explain** the relationship between fossils and extinction events.

12 **Infer** In 2004, a fossil of an organism that had fins and gills, but also lungs and wrists, was discovered. What might this fossil suggest about evolution?

13 **Summarize** Darwin's theory of natural selection using the Galápagos tortoises or finches as an example.

14 **Assess** how the determination that Earth is 4.6 billion years provided support for the idea that all species evolved from a common ancestor.

15 **Describe** how cytochrome c provides evidence of evolution.

16 **Explain** why the discovery of genes was powerful support for Darwin's theory of natural selection.

17 **Interpret Graphics** The diagram below shows two different methods by which evolution by natural selection might proceed. Discuss how these two methods differ.

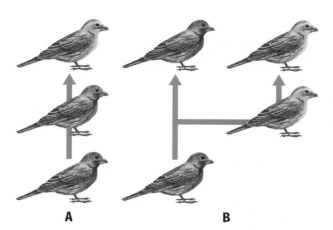

A   B

Writing in Science

18 **Write** a paragraph explaining how each of the following factors affecting natural selection increase or decrease a species' ability to survive and reproduce: competition, genetic variations, environmental changes, and overproduction.

REVIEW THE BIG IDEA

19 How do species adapt to changing environments over time? Explain how evidence from the fossil record and from living species suggests that Earth's species are related. List each type of evidence and provide an example of each.

20 The photo below shows an orchid that looks like a bee. How might this adaptation be evidence of evolution by natural selection?

Math Skills ✓ Math Practice

Use Scientific Notation

21 The earliest fossils appeared about 3,500,000,000 years ago. Express this number in scientific notation.

22 The oldest fossils visible to the unaided eye are about 565,000,000 years old. What is this time in scientific notation?

23 The oldest human fossils are about 1×10^4 years old. Express this as a whole number.

Standardized Test Practice

Record your answers on the answer sheet provided by your teacher or on a sheet of paper.

Multiple Choice

1 Which may form over time from the impression a bird feather makes in mud?

  A cast

  B mold

  C fossil film

  D trace fossil

2 Which is NOT one of the three main categories of adaptations?

  A behavioral

  B functional

  C pharyngeal

  D structural

Use the figure below to answer question 3.

Bat wing   Insect wing

3 The figure shows the wings of a bat and an insect. Which term describes these structures?

  A analogous

  B developmental

  C homologous

  D vestigial

4 What is an adaptation?

  A a body part that has lost its original function through evolution

  B a characteristic that better equips an organism to survive in its environment

  C a feature that appears briefly during early development

  D a slight difference among the individuals in a species

5 What causes variations to arise in a population?

  A changes in the environment

  B competition for limited resources

  C random mutations in genes

  D rapid population increases

Use the image below to answer question 6.

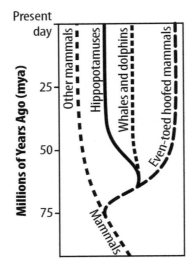

6 The image above shows that even-toed hoofed mammals and other mammals shared a common ancestor. When did this ancestor live?

  A 25–35 million years ago

  B 50–60 million years ago

  C 60–75 million years ago

  D 75 million years ago

7 Which term describes the method Darwin used that resulted in pigeons with desired traits?

  A evolution

  B mimicry

  C natural selection

  D selective breeding

Use the figure below to answer question 8.

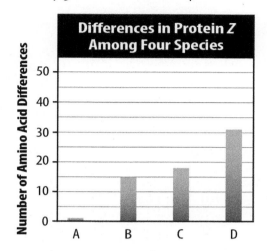

Differences in Protein *Z* Among Four Species

8   The chart shows that species B and C have the fewest amino acid differences for a protein among four species. What does this suggest about their evolutionary relationship?

A They are more closely related to each other than to the other species.

B They evolved at a faster rate when compared to the other species.

C They share a developmental similarity not observed in the other species.

D They do not share a common ancestor with the other species.

9   Which developmental similarity among all vertebrates is evidence that they share a common ancestor?

A analogous structures

B pharyngeal pouches

C variation rates

D vestigial structures

Constructed Response

Use the figure below to answer questions 10 and 11.

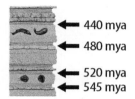

← 440 mya
← 480 mya
← 520 mya
← 545 mya

10   What is the approximate age of the fish fossils (top layer of fossils)? Express your answer as a range, and explain how you derived the answer.

11   What type of material or rock most likely forms the layer that contains the fossils? In your response, explain how these fossils formed.

12   Explain how a sudden and drastic environmental change might lead to the extinction of a species.

13   Darwin formulated his theory of evolution by natural selection based on the observation that food is a limiting resource. What did he mean by that? Use the Galápagos tortoises to explain your answer.

14   Explain how the fossil record provides evidence of biological evolution.

NEED EXTRA HELP?														
If You Missed Question...	1	2	3	4	5	6	7	8	9	10	11	12	13	14
Go to Lesson...	1	2	3	2	2	3	2	3	3	1	1	1	2	1

Chapter 14

Bacteria and Viruses

 What are bacteria and viruses and why are they important?

Color-enhanced TEM Magnification: 63,000×

Inquiry   Are robots attacking?

You might think this photo shows robots landing on another planet. Actually, this is a picture of viruses attacking a type of unicellular organism called a bacterium (plural, bacteria). Many viruses can attach to the surface of one bacterium.

- Do you think the bacterium is harmful? Are the viruses?
- What do you think happens after the viruses attach to the bacterium?
- What are viruses and bacteria and why are they important?

Get Ready to Read

What do you think?

Before you read, decide if you agree or disagree with each of these statements. As you read this chapter, see if you change your mind about any of the statements.

1 A bacterium does not have a nucleus.

2 Bacteria cannot move.

3 All bacteria cause diseases.

4 Bacteria are important for making many types of food.

5 Viruses are the smallest living organisms.

6 Viruses can replicate only inside an organism.

Your one-stop online resource
connectED.mcgraw-hill.com

 LearnSmart®

 Chapter Resources Files, Reading Essentials, Get Ready to Read, Quick Vocabulary

 Animations, Videos, Interactive Tables

 Self-checks, Quizzes, Tests

 Project-Based Learning Activities

 Lab Manuals, Safety Videos, Virtual Labs & Other Tools

 Vocabulary, Multilingual eGlossary, Vocab eGames, Vocab eFlashcards

 Personal Tutors

Reading Guide

Key Concept 🔑

ESSENTIAL QUESTION

• What are bacteria?

Vocabulary

bacterium p. 483

flagellum p. 486

fission p. 486

conjugation p. 486

endospore p. 486

 Multilingual eGlossary

 BrainPOP®

What are bacteria?

Color-enhanced SEM Magnification: 560×

inquiry How clean is this surface?

This photo shows a microscopic view of the point of a needle. The small orange things are bacteria. Bacteria are everywhere, even on surfaces that appear clean. Do you think bacteria are living or nonliving?

Dr. Tony Brain/Science Source

Launch Lab

10 minutes

How small are bacteria?

Bacteria are tiny cells that can be difficult to see, even with a microscope. You might be surprised to learn that bacteria are found all around you, including in the air, on your skin, and in your body. One way of understanding how small bacteria are is to model their size.

1. Read and complete a lab safety form.

2. Examine the size of a **baseball** and a **2.5-gal. bucket.** Estimate how many baseballs you think would fit inside the bucket.

3. As a class, count how many baseballs it takes to fill the bucket.

Think About This

1. How much larger is the bucket than a baseball?

2. If your skin cells were the size of the bucket and bacteria were the size of the baseballs, how many bacterial cells would fit on a skin cell?

3. 🔑 **Key Concept** Why do you think you cannot see bacteria on your skin or on your desk?

Characteristics of Bacteria

Did you know that billions of tiny organisms too small to be seen surround you? These organisms, called bacteria, even live inside your body. **Bacteria** (singular, bacterium) *are microscopic prokaryotes.* You might recall that a prokaryote is a unicellular organism that does not have a nucleus or other membrane-bound organelles.

Bacteria live in almost every habitat on Earth, including the air, glaciers, the ocean floor, and in soil. A teaspoon of soil can contain between 100 million and 1 billion bacteria. Bacteria also live in or on almost every organism, both living and dead. Hundreds of species of bacteria live on your skin. In fact, your body contains more bacterial cells than human cells! The bacteria in your body outnumber human cells by 10 to 1.

🔑 **Key Concept Check** What are bacteria?

Other prokaryotes, called archaea (ar KEE uh; singular, archaean), are similar to bacteria and share many characteristics with them, including the lack of membrane-bound organelles. Archaea can live in places where few other organisms can survive, such as very warm areas or those with little oxygen. Both bacteria and archaea are important to life on Earth.

WORD ORIGIN ···········

bacteria
from Greek *bakterion,* means "small staff"

FOLDABLES®

Make a folded book from a sheet of notebook paper. Label it as shown. Use your book to organize your notes on the characteristics of bacteria.

Characteristics of Bacteria

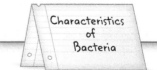

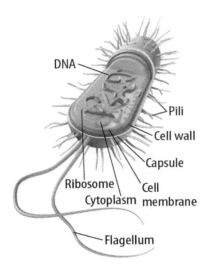

DNA
Pili
Cell wall
Capsule
Ribosome
Cytoplasm
Cell membrane
Flagellum

▲ **Figure 1** Bacteria have a cell membrane and contain cytoplasm.

Structure of Bacteria

A typical bacterium, such as the one shown in **Figure 1**, consists of cytoplasm and DNA surrounded by a cell membrane and a cell wall. The cytoplasm also contains ribosomes. Most bacteria have DNA that is one coiled, circular chromosome. Many bacteria also have one or more small circular pieces of DNA called plasmids that are separate from its other DNA.

Some bacteria have specialized structures that help them survive. For example, the bacterium that causes pneumonia (noo MOH nyuh), an inflammation of the lungs, has a thick covering, or capsule, around its cell wall. The capsule protects the bacterium from drying out. It also prevents white blood cells from surrounding and antibiotics from entering it. Many bacteria have capsules with hairlike structures called pili (PI li) that help the bacteria stick to surfaces.

Size and Shapes of Bacteria

Bacteria are much smaller than plant or animal cells. Bacteria are generally only 1–5 micrometers (μm) (1 m = 1 million μm) wide, while an average eukaryotic cell is 10–100 μm wide. Scientists estimate that as many as 100 bacteria could be lined up across the head of a pin. As shown in **Figure 2**, bacteria generally have one of three basic shapes.

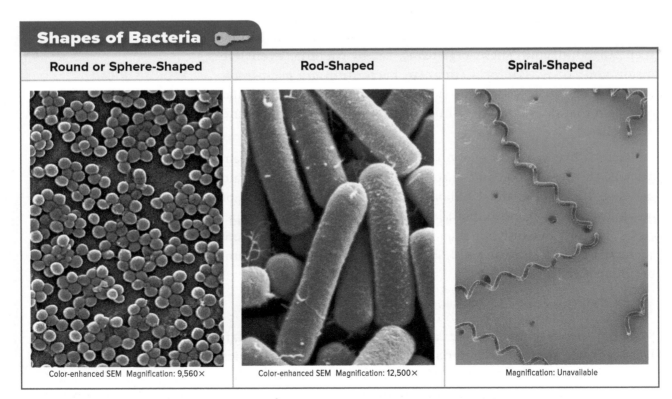

Shapes of Bacteria 🔑

Round or Sphere-Shaped	Rod-Shaped	Spiral-Shaped
Color-enhanced SEM Magnification: 9,560×	Color-enhanced SEM Magnification: 12,500×	Magnification: Unavailable

Figure 2 Bacteria are generally shaped like a sphere, a rod, or a spiral.

✓ **Visual Check** What are the three basic shapes of bacteria?

MiniLab

15 minutes

How does a slime layer work?

Bacteria have a gelatinlike, protective coating called a slime layer on the outside of their cell walls. A slime layer can help a bacterium attach to surfaces or reduce water loss.

1. Read and complete a lab safety form.
2. Cut two 2-cm-wide strips from the long side of a **synthetic kitchen sponge**.
3. Soak both strips in **water**. Remove them from the water and squeeze out the excess water. Both strips should be damp.
4. Completely coat one strip with **hair-styling gel** to simulate a slime layer.
5. Place both strips on a **plate** and let them sit overnight.

Analyze and Conclude

1. **Describe** the appearance of the two strips in your Science Journal. How do they differ?

2. **Key Concept** Explain how a slime layer might be beneficial to a bacterium when moving or finding food.

Obtaining Food and Energy

Bacteria live in many places. Because these environments are very different, bacteria obtain food in various ways. Some bacteria take in food and break it down and obtain energy. Many of these bacteria feed on dead organisms or organic waste, as shown in **Figure 3.** Others take in their nutrients from living hosts. For example, bacteria that cause tooth decay live in dental plaque on teeth and feed on sugars in the foods you eat and the beverages you drink.

Some bacteria make their own food. These bacteria use light energy and make food, like most plants do. These bacteria live where there is a lot of light, such as the surface of lakes and streams. Other bacteria use energy from chemical reactions and make their food. These bacteria live in places where there is no sunlight, such as the dark ocean floor.

Key Concept Check How do bacteria obtain food?

Most organisms, including humans, cannot survive without oxygen. However, certain bacteria do not need oxygen to survive. These bacteria are called anaerobic (a nuh ROH bihk) bacteria. Bacteria that need oxygen are called aerobic (er OH bihk) bacteria. Most bacteria in the environment are aerobic.

Figure 3 This banana is rotting because bacteria are breaking it down to use it for food.

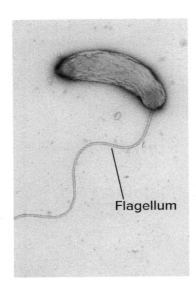

Movement

Some bacteria are able to move around to find the resources that they need to survive. These bacteria have special structures for movement. *Many bacteria have long whiplike structures called* **flagella** (fluh JEH luh; singular, flagellum), as shown in Figure 4. Others twist or spiral as they move. Still other bacteria use their pili like grappling hooks or make threadlike structures that enable them to push away from a surface.

Reproduction

You might recall that organisms reproduce asexually or sexually. Bacteria reproduce asexually by fission. **Fission** *is cell division that forms two genetically identical cells.* Fission can occur quickly—as often as every 20 minutes under ideal conditions.

Bacteria produced by fission are identical to the parent cell. However, genetic variation can be increased by a process called conjugation, shown in Figure 5. *During* **conjugation** (kahn juh GAY shun), *two bacteria of the same species attach to each other and combine their genetic material.* DNA is transferred between the bacteria. This results in new combinations of genes, increasing genetic diversity. New organisms are not produced during conjugation, so the process is not considered reproduction.

Reading Check How does conjugation increase the genetic diversity of bacteria?

▲ Figure 4 Some bacteria move using a flagellum.

Personal Tutor

Conjugation

Figure 5 Conjugation results in genetic diversity by transferring DNA between two bacteria cells.

Visual Check What structure does the donor cell use to connect to the recipient cell?

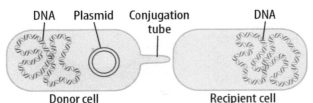

DNA   Plasmid   Conjugation tube   DNA

Donor cell   Recipient cell

❶ The donor cell and recipient cell both have circular chromosomal DNA. The donor cell also has DNA as a plasmid. The donor cell forms a conjugation tube and connects to the recipient cell.

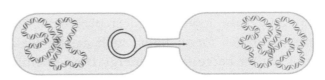

❷ The conjugation tube connects both cells. The plasmid splits in two and one plasmid strand moves through the conjugation tube into the recipient cell.

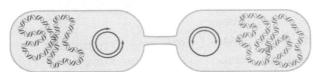

❸ The complimentary strands of the plasmids are completed in both bacteria.

❹ With the new plasmids complete, the bacteria separate from each other. The recipient cell now contains plasmid DNA from the donor cell as well as its own chromosomal DNA.

DNA

Endospore   DNA

Thick wall

❶ Bacterial cells in favorable conditions form without endospores.

❷ As conditions become unfavorable, the cell forms an endospore around some of its DNA.

❸ The cell breaks down, leaving the endospore-protected DNA.

Wet season ⟵

⟶ Dry season

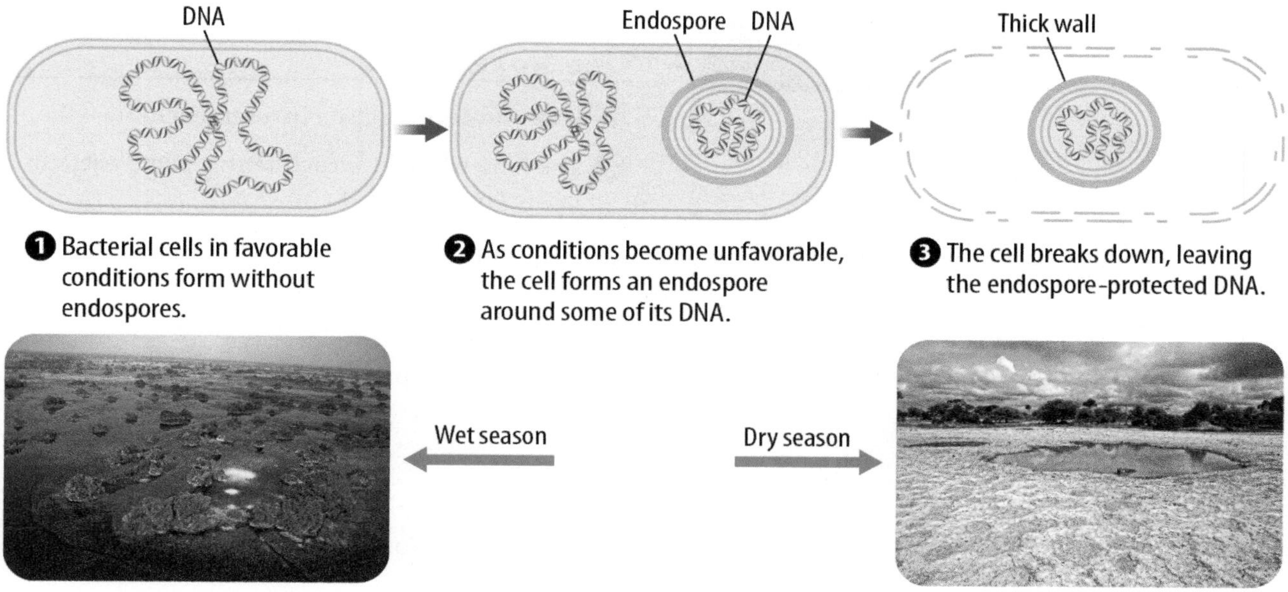

Figure 6 An endospore protects a bacterium.

Endospores

Sometimes environmental conditions are unfavorable for the survival of bacteria. In these cases, some bacteria can form endospores. *An* **endospore** (EN doh spor) *forms when a bacterium builds a thick internal wall around its chromosome and part of the cytoplasm,* as shown in **Figure 6.** An endospore can protect a bacterium from intense heat, cold, or drought. It also enables a bacterium to remain dormant for months or even centuries. The ability to form endospores enables bacteria to survive extreme conditions that would normally kill them.

Archaea

Prokaryotes called archaea were once considered bacteria. Like a bacterium, an archaean has a cell wall and no nucleus or membrane-bound organelles. Its chromosome is also circular, like those in bacteria. However, there are some important differences between archaea and bacteria. The ribosomes of archaea more closely resemble the ribosomes of eukaryotes than those of bacteria. Archaea also contain molecules in their plasma membranes that are not found in any other known organisms. Archaea often live in extreme environments, such as hot springs and salt lakes. Some scientists refer to archaea as extremophiles (ik STREE muh filez)–a term that means "those that love extremes."

Math Skills

Use a Formula

Each time bacteria undergo fission, the population doubles. Use an equation to calculate how many bacteria there are: $n = x \times 2^f$ where n is the final number of bacteria, x is the starting number of bacteria, and f is the number of times that fission occurs.

Example: 100 bacteria undergo fission 3 times.

$f = 3$, so 2^f is 2 multiplied by itself 3 times.
$(2 \times 2 \times 2 = 8)$

$n = 100 \times 8 = 800$ bacteria

Practice

How many bacteria would there be if 1 bacterium underwent fission 10 times?

 Math Practice

 Personal Tutor

(l)©Design Pics Inc./Alamy; (r)Beverly Joubert/National Geographic/Getty Images

Visual Summary

 Bacteria are unicellular prokaryotes.

 Many bacteria feed on dead organic matter.

 Bacteria can increase genetic diversity by sharing DNA through conjugation.

FOLDABLES

Use your lesson Foldable to review the lesson. Save your Foldable for the project at the end of the chapter.

What do you think NOW?

You first read the statements below at the beginning of the chapter.

1. A bacterium does not have a nucleus.

2. Bacteria cannot move.

Did you change your mind about whether you agree or disagree with the statements? Rewrite any false statements to make them true.

Use Vocabulary

1. **Use the term** *bacteria* in a sentence.

2. The long whiplike structure that some bacteria use for movement is a(n) _____.

3. **Define** *conjugation* in your own words.

Understand Key Concepts

4. **Describe** a typical bacterium.

5. Which is NOT a common bacteria shape?
   A. rod
   B. sphere
   C. spiral
   D. square

6. **Contrast** fission and conjugation.

Interpret Graphics

7. **Identify** Copy and complete the table below to identify shapes of bacteria.

Bacterial Shapes	Illustration

Critical Thinking

8. **Describe** how a bacterium's small size could be an advantage or a disadvantage for its survival.

9. **Explain** how bacteria might find food and survive in an environment where few other organisms live.

10. **Analyze** how bacteria that can form endospores would have an advantage over bacteria that cannot form endospores.

Math Skills   Math Practice

11. How many bacteria would there be if fission occurred 4 times with 1,000 bacteria?

Cooking
Bacteria!

How Your Body Is Like Bleach

▼ After cooking, egg proteins become a tangled mass.

When it comes to killing germs, few things work as well as household bleach. How does bleach kill bacteria? Believe it or not, killing bacteria with bleach and boiling an egg involve similar processes.

Eggs are made mostly of proteins. Proteins are complex molecules in all plant and animal tissues. Proteins have specific functions that are dependent on the protein's shape. A protein's function changes if its shape is changed. When you cook an egg, the thermal energy transferred to the egg causes changes to the shape of the egg's proteins. Think of the firm texture of a cooked egg. When the egg's proteins are heated, they become a tangled mass.

▲ Before cooking, the proteins in eggs remain unfolded and change shape easily.

▼ Bacteria also contain proteins that change shape when exposed to heat.

A common ingredient in bleach is also found in your body's immune cells. ▶

Like eggs, bacteria also contain proteins. When bacteria are exposed to high temperatures, their proteins change shape, similar to those in a boiled egg. But what is the connection with bleach? Scientists have discovered that an ingredient in bleach, hypochlorite (hi puh KLOR ite), also causes proteins to change shape. The bacterial proteins that are affected by bleach are needed for the bacteria's growth. When the shape of those proteins changes, they no longer function properly, and the bacteria die.

Scientists also know now that your body's immune cells produce hypochlorite. Your body protects itself with the same chemical you can use to clean your kitchen!

It's Your Turn

RESEARCH AND REPORT A bacterial infection often causes inflammation, or a response to tissue damage that can include swelling and pain. Research and report on what causes inflammation.

Reading Guide

Key Concepts 🔑
ESSENTIAL QUESTIONS

- How can bacteria affect the environment?
- How can bacteria affect health?

Vocabulary

decomposition p. 492

nitrogen fixation p. 492

bioremediation p. 493

pathogen p. 494

antibiotic p. 494

pasteurization p. 495

 Multilingual eGlossary

 What's Science Got to do With It?

Bacteria in Nature

Inquiry Why does this larva glow?

Some bacteria have the ability to glow in the dark. The moth larva shown on this page is filled with many such bacteria. These bacteria produce toxins that can slowly kill the animal. A chemical reaction within each bacterium makes the larva's body appear to glow.

Dante Fenolio/Science Source

How do bacteria affect the environment?

Bacteria are everywhere in your environment. They are in the water, in the air, and even in some foods.

1. Read and complete a lab safety form.
2. Carefully examine the contents of the two **bottles** provided by your teacher.
3. Record your observations in your Science Journal.

Think About This

1. Compare your observations of bottle A to those of bottle B. Which one appears to have more bacteria in it? Support your answer.

2. 🔑 **Key Concept** Based on your observations, how could bacteria affect the environment around you?

Beneficial Bacteria

When you hear about bacteria, you probably think about getting sick. However, only a fraction of all bacteria cause diseases. Most bacteria are beneficial. In fact, many organisms, including humans, depend on bacteria to survive. Some types of bacteria help with digestion and other body processes. For example, one type of bacteria in your intestines makes vitamin K, which helps your blood clot properly. Several others help break down food into smaller particles. Another type of bacteria called *Lactobacillus* lives in your intestines and prevents harmful bacteria from growing.

Animals benefit from bacteria as well. Without bacteria, some organisms, such as the cow pictured in **Figure 7,** wouldn't be able to digest the plants they eat. Bacteria and other microscopic organisms live in a large section of the cow's stomach called the rumen. The bacteria help break down a substance in grass called cellulose into smaller molecules that the cow can use.

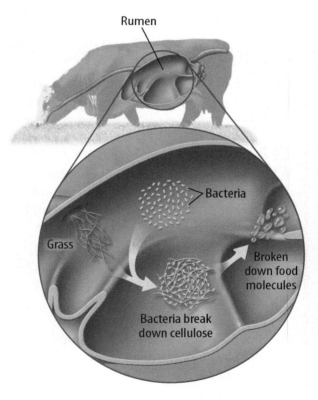

Figure 7 Cows get help digesting the cellulose in plants from the bacteria that live in their rumen—one of four stomach sections.

✔ **Visual Check** What role do bacteria play in a cow's digestion?

(t)Hutchings Photography/Digital Light Source; (b)©David Frazier/Corbis

Decomposition

What do you think would happen if organic waste such as food scraps and dead leaves never decayed? **Decomposition,** *the breaking down of dead organisms and organic waste,* is an important process in nature. When a tree dies, bacteria and other decomposing organisms feed on the dead organic matter. As decomposers break down the tree, they release molecules such as carbon and phosphorus into the soil that other organisms can then take in and use for life processes.

Nitrogen Fixation

Organisms use nitrogen to make proteins. Although about 78 percent of the atmosphere is nitrogen gas, it is in a form that plants and animals cannot use. Some plants can obtain nitrogen from bacteria. These plants have special structures called nodules, shown in **Figure 8,** on their roots. Bacteria in the nodules convert nitrogen from the atmosphere into a form usable to plants. **Nitrogen fixation** *is the conversion of atmospheric nitrogen into nitrogen compounds that are usable by living things.*

 Key Concept Check What are some ways that bacteria are beneficial to the environment?

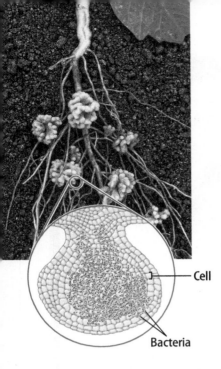

Cell

Bacteria

Figure 8 The roots of some plants have nodules that contain nitrogen-fixing bacteria.

🔬 MiniLab

20 minutes

Can decomposition happen without oxygen?

You have just read that bacteria play an important role as decomposers in the environment. How do you think decomposition differs in aerobic and anaerobic environments?

1. Read and complete a lab safety form.

2. Obtain two **self-sealing plastic bags** from your teacher. Use a **permanent marker** and label one bag *Bag A* and the other *Bag B.*

3. Place a **slice of apple** in bag A. Seal the bag leaving as much air as possible inside of it. Set the bag aside.

4. Place **another slice of apple** in bag B. Carefully squeeze the bag to remove as much air as possible before sealing it. Place both bags in the location specified by your teacher and leave overnight.

5. The next lab day, observe both bags. Note the appearance of the apples. Record your observations in your Science Journal.

6. Carefully dispose of both bags according to your teacher's directions.

Analyze and Conclude

1. **Determine** which apple changed the most. How could you tell? List specific evidence to support your answer.

2. **Draw Conclusions** Does decomposition occur faster, slower, or not at all in environments without oxygen? Justify your answer.

3. 🔑 **Key Concept** Summarize why bacteria are considered important decomposers.

Bioremediation

Can you imagine an organism that eats pollution? Some bacteria do just that. *The use of organisms, such as bacteria, to clean up environmental pollution is called* **bioremediation** (bi oh rih mee dee AY shun). These organisms often break down harmful substances, such as sewage, into less harmful material that can be used as landfill or fertilizers.

Bacteria are commonly used to clean up areas that have been contaminated by oil or harmful plastics. Some kinds of bacteria can even help clean up radioactive waste, such as uranium in the abandoned mine fields shown in **Figure 9.** In many cases, without using bacteria, the substances would take centuries to break down and would contaminate soils and water.

 Reading Check Why might using bacteria to clean up environmental spills be a good option?

FOLDABLES®

Make a four-door book and label it as shown. Use it to summarize the ways bacteria are beneficial to the environment.

| Decomposition | Nitrogen Fixation |
| Bioremediation | Bacteria and Food |

Figure 9 These bacteria clean the environment by removing harmful uranium from the water.

Bacteria and Food

Would you like a side of bacteria with that sandwich? If you have eaten a pickle lately, you might have had some. Some pickles are made when the sugar in cucumbers is converted into an acid by a specific type of bacteria. Pickles are just one of the many food products made with the help of bacteria. Bacteria are used to make foods such as yogurt, cheese, buttermilk, vinegar, and soy sauce. Bacteria are even used in the production of chocolate. They help break down the covering of the cocoa bean during the process of making chocolate. Bacteria are responsible for giving chocolate some of its flavor.

(inset)Eye of Science/Science Source, (bkgd)Debra Reid/AP Images

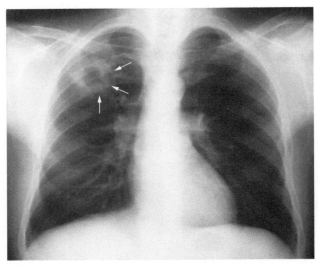

Figure 10 In an X-ray, the lungs of a person with tuberculosis may show pockets or scars where bacterial infection has begun.

✔ **Visual Check** How do you think the bacteria that made this person sick entered his or her body?

Harmful Bacteria

Of the 5,000 known species of bacteria, relatively few are considered **pathogens** (PA thuh junz)—*agents that cause disease.* Some pathogens normally live in your body, but cause illness only when your immune system is weakened. For example, the bacterium *Streptococcus pneumoniae* lives in the throats of most healthy people. However, it can cause pneumonia if a person's immune system is weakened. Other bacterial pathogens can enter your body through a cut, the air you breathe, or the food you eat. Once inside your body, they can reproduce and cause disease.

 Key Concept Check Describe one way that bacteria can be harmful to health.

Bacterial Diseases

Bacteria can harm your body and cause disease in one of two ways. Some bacteria make you sick by damaging tissue. For example, the disease tuberculosis, shown in **Figure 10,** is caused by a bacterium that invades lung tissue and breaks it down for food. Other bacteria cause illness by releasing toxins. For example, the bacterium *Clostridium botulinum* can grow in improperly canned foods and produce toxins. If the contaminated food is eaten, the toxins can cause food poisoning, resulting in paralyzed limbs or even death.

Treating Bacterial Diseases Most bacterial diseases in humans can be treated with antibiotics. **Antibiotics** (an ti bi AH tihks) *are medicines that stop the growth and reproduction of bacteria.* Many antibiotics work by preventing bacteria from building cell walls. Others affect ribosomes in bacteria, interrupting the production of proteins.

Many types of bacteria have become resistant to antibiotics over time. Some diseases, such as tuberculosis, pneumonia, and meningitis, are now more difficult to treat.

Bacterial Resistance How do you think bacteria become resistant to antibiotics? This process, shown in **Figure 11,** can happen over a long or short period of time depending on how quickly the bacteria reproduce. Random mutations occur to a bacterium's DNA that enable it to survive or "resist" a specific antibiotic. If that antibiotic is used as a treatment, only the bacteria with the mutation will survive.

Over time, the resistant bacteria will reproduce and become more common. The antibiotic is no longer effective against that bacterium, and a different antibiotic must be used to fight the disease. Scientists are always working to develop more effective antibiotics to which bacteria have not developed resistances.

 Reading Check How do bacteria develop resistance to antibiotics?

Food Poisoning

All food, unless it has been treated or processed, contains bacteria. Over time these bacteria reproduce and begin breaking down the food, causing it to spoil. As you read on the previous page, eating food contaminated by some bacteria can cause food poisoning. By properly treating or processing food and killing bacteria before the food is stored or eaten, it is easier to avoid food poisoning and other illnesses.

Pasteurization (pas chuh ruh ZAY shun) *is a process of heating food to a temperature that kills most harmful bacteria.* Products such as milk, ice cream, yogurt, and fruit juice are usually pasteurized in factories before they are transported to grocery stores and sold to you. After pasteurization, foods are much safer to eat. Foods do not spoil as quickly once they have been pasteurized. Because of pasteurization, food poisoning is much less common today than it was in the past.

 Key Concept Check How does pasteurization affect human health?

Figure 11 A population of bacteria can develop resistance to antibiotics after being exposed to them over time.

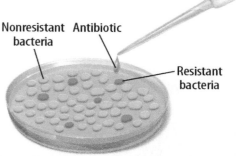

Nonresistant bacteria

Antibiotic

Resistant bacteria

❶ An antibiotic is added to a colony of bacteria. A few of the bacteria have mutations that enable them to resist the antibiotic.

❷ The antibiotic kills most of the nonresistant bacteria. The resistant bacteria survive and reproduce, creating a growing colony of bacteria.

❸ Surviving bacteria are added to another plate containing more of the same antibiotic.

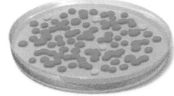

❹ The antibiotic now affects only a small percentage of the bacteria. The surviving bacteria continue to reproduce. Most of the bacteria are resistant to the antibiotic.

Visual Summary

Bacteria can help some organisms, including humans and cows, digest food.

Bacteria can be used to remove harmful substances such as uranium.

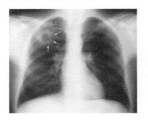

Some bacteria are pathogens, and cause diseases in humans and other organisms.

FOLDABLES

Use your lesson Foldable to review the lesson. Save your Foldable for the project at the end of the chapter.

What do you think **NOW?**

You first read the statements below at the beginning of the chapter.

3. All bacteria cause diseases.

4. Bacteria are important for making many types of food.

Did you change your mind about whether you agree or disagree with the statements? Rewrite any false statements to make them true.

Use Vocabulary

1 **Distinguish** between an antibiotic and a pathogen.

2 **Define** *bioremediation* using your own words.

3 **Use the term** *pasteurization* in a sentence.

Understand Key Concepts 🔑

4 Which of the following is NOT a beneficial use of bacteria?
   A. bioremediation   **C.** food poisoning
   B. decomposition   **D.** nitrogen fixation

5 **Compare** the benefits of nitrogen fixation and decomposition.

6 **Analyze** the importance of bacteria in food production.

Interpret Graphics

7 **Examine** the figure below and describe what would happen if bacteria were not present.

8 **Identify** Copy and complete the graphic organizer below to identify ways that bacteria can be beneficial.

Beneficial Bacteria

Critical Thinking

9 **Evaluate** the effect of all bacteria becoming resistant to antibiotics.

How do lab techniques affect an investigation?

Materials

petri dish

jar with samples

forceps

dissecting microscope

black light

Safety

Pathogens such as bacteria cover almost every surface. When you touch a surface, you transfer particles from that surface to your skin and then to other objects you touch. Your teacher has spread a substance that simulates bacteria on some surfaces in this lab. You will be divided into two groups. Each group will perform the same lab activity but will use slightly different laboratory techniques.

Learn It

In a laboratory it is important to be very careful to keep surfaces as free from contamination as possible. Scientists follow specific **lab techniques** very carefully to prevent contamination that could affect results.

Try It

1. Read and complete a lab safety form.

2. Put on a pair of gloves. Select a Petri dish from the stack. Open the Petri dish and follow the directions on the slip of paper.

3. Go to the station with the jar. Open the jar and use forceps to remove an item. Place the item in your Petri dish. Close the jar. Follow the directions again.

4. Take your Petri dish to the dissecting microscope and examine your object. Sketch the object in your Science Journal.

5. Observe the surfaces in your work area as your teacher shines a black light over them.

Apply It

6. What surfaces light up the most under the black light?

7. What do you see when you use the black light?

8. 🔑 **Key Concept** What difference do you see in the lab areas used by the two groups? Based on your observations, how do you think this difference affects which techniques are used in labs and hospitals?

Lesson 3

Reading Guide

Key Concepts
ESSENTIAL QUESTIONS

- What are viruses?
- How do viruses affect human health?

Vocabulary
virus p. 499
antibody p. 503
vaccine p. 504

 Multilingual eGlossary

SEPS.7, 6-8.LST.5.1, 6-8.LST.5.2

What are viruses?

Inquiry Painted Flowers?

The streaking patterns on the petals of these tulips are not painted on but are caused by a virus. Tulips with these patterns are prized for their beautiful appearance. How do you think a virus could cause this flower's pattern? Do you think all viruses are harmful?

 498 •

Chapter 14
ENGAGE

cstarken/iStock/360/Getty Images

How quickly do viruses replicate?

One characteristic that viruses share is the ability to produce many new viruses from just one virus. In this lab you can use grains of rice to model virus replication. Each grain of rice represents one virus.

Generation	First	Second	Third
Number of "viruses"			

1. Read and complete a lab safety form.
2. Copy the table above into your Science Journal.
3. Estimate the number of **grains of rice** in the **fishbowl** and record this number for the first generation.
4. One student will add the contents of his or her **cup** to the fishbowl. Estimate how many viruses are now in the fishbowl and record your estimate for the second generation.
5. The rest of the class will add the contents of their cups to the fishbowl. Estimate the number of viruses and record that number of viruses for the third generation.

Think About This

1. Recall that bacteria double every generation. How does the number of viruses produced in each generation compare with the number of bacteria produced in each generation?

2. 🔑 **Key Concept** How could the rate at which viruses are produced affect human health?

Characteristics of Viruses

Do chicken pox, mumps, measles, and polio sound familiar? You might have received shots to protect you from these diseases. You might have also received a shot to protect you from influenza, commonly known as the flu. What do these diseases have in common? They are caused by different viruses. *A* **virus** *is a strand of DNA or RNA surrounded by a layer of protein that can infect and replicate in a host cell.* If you have had a cold, you have been infected by a virus.

A virus does not have a cell wall, a nucleus, or any other organelles present in cells. The smallest viruses are between 20 and 100 times smaller than most bacteria. Recall that about 100 bacteria would fit across the head of a pin. Viruses can have different shapes, such as the crystal, cylinder, sphere, and bacteriophage (bak TIHR ee uh fayj) shapes shown in **Figure 12.**

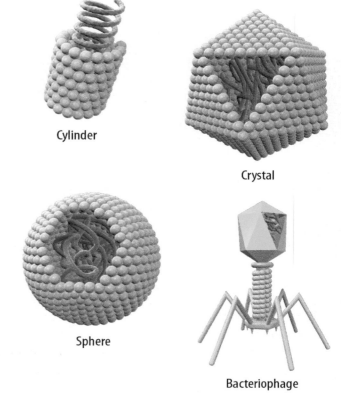

Cylinder

Crystal

Sphere

Bacteriophage

Figure 12 Viruses have a variety of shapes.

Figure 13 A virus infects a cell by inserting its DNA or RNA into the host cell. It then directs the host cell to make new viruses.

Visual Check What occurs when a virus becomes latent?

Dead or Alive?

Do you think that viruses are living things? Scientists do not consider viruses to be alive because they do not have all the characteristics of a living organism. Recall that living things are organized, respond to stimuli, use energy, grow, and reproduce. Viruses cannot do any of these things. A virus can make copies of itself in a process called replication, but it must rely on a living organism to do so.

Key Concept Check Are viruses alive? Explain why or why not.

Viruses and Organisms

Viruses must use organisms to carry on the processes that we usually associate with a living cell. Viruses have no organelles so they are not able to take in nutrients or use energy. They also cannot replicate without using the cellular parts of an organism. Viruses must be inside a cell to replicate. The living cell that a virus infects is called a host cell.

When a virus enters a cell, as shown in **Figure 13,** it can either be active or latent. Latent viruses go through an inactive stage. Their genetic material becomes part of the host cell's genetic material. For a period of time, the virus does not take over the cell to produce more viruses. In some cases, viruses have been known to be inactive for years and years. However, once it becomes active, a virus takes control of the host cell and replicates.

Viral Replication 🔑

 Animation

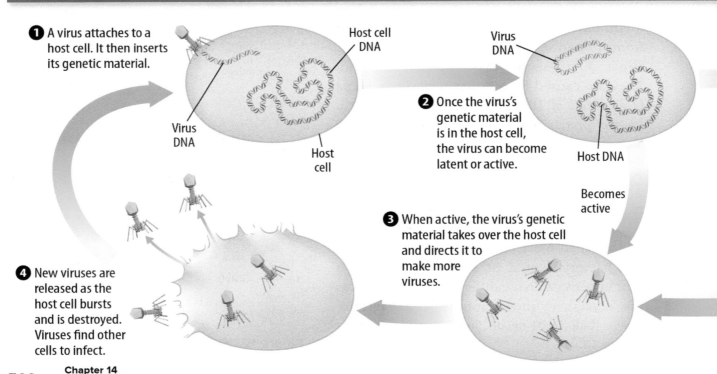

❶ A virus attaches to a host cell. It then inserts its genetic material.

Host cell DNA

Virus DNA

Virus DNA

Host cell

❷ Once the virus's genetic material is in the host cell, the virus can become latent or active.

Host DNA

Becomes active

❸ When active, the virus's genetic material takes over the host cell and directs it to make more viruses.

❹ New viruses are released as the host cell bursts and is destroyed. Viruses find other cells to infect.

Replication

As you read earlier, a virus can make copies of itself in a process called replication, shown in **Figure 13.** A virus cannot infect every cell. A virus can only attach to a host cell with specific molecules on its cell wall or cell membrane. These molecules enable the virus to attach to the host cell. This is similar to the way that only certain electrical plugs can fit into an outlet on a wall. After a virus attaches to the host cell, its DNA or RNA enters the host cell. Once inside, the virus either starts to replicate or becomes latent, also shown in **Figure 13.** After a virus becomes active and replicates in a host cell, it destroys the host cell. Copies of the virus are then released into the host organism, where they can infect other cells.

Mutations

As viruses replicate, their DNA or RNA frequently mutates, or changes. These **mutations** enable viruses to adjust to changes in their host cells. For example, the molecules on the outside of host cells change over time to prevent viruses from attaching to the cell. As viruses mutate, they are able to produce new ways to attach to host cells. These changes happen so rapidly that it can be difficult to cure or prevent viral diseases before they mutate again.

 Reading Check How does mutation enable viruses to continue causing disease?

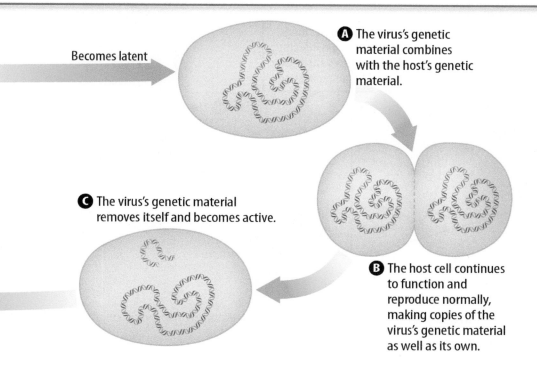

Becomes latent

A The virus's genetic material combines with the host's genetic material.

C The virus's genetic material removes itself and becomes active.

B The host cell continues to function and reproduce normally, making copies of the virus's genetic material as well as its own.

Viral Diseases

You might know that viruses cause many human diseases, such as chicken pox, influenza, some forms of pneumonia, and the common cold. But viruses also infect animals, causing diseases such as rabies and parvo. They can infect plants as well–in some cases causing millions of dollars of damage to crops. The tulips shown at the beginning of this lesson were infected with a virus that caused a streaked appearance on the petals. Most viruses attack and destroy specific cells. This destruction of cells causes the symptoms of the disease.

Some viruses cause symptoms soon after infection. Influenza viruses that cause the flu infect the cells lining your respiratory system, as shown in **Figure 14.** The viruses begin to replicate immediately. Flu symptoms, such as a runny nose and a scratchy throat, usually appear within 2–3 days.

Other viruses might not cause symptoms right away. These viruses are sometimes called latent viruses. Latent viruses continue replicating without damaging the host cell. HIV (human immunodeficiency virus) is one example of a latent virus that might not cause immediate symptoms.

HIV infects white blood cells, which are part of the immune system. Initially, infected cells can function normally, so an HIV-infected person might not appear sick. However, the virus can become active and destroy cells in the body's immune system, making it hard to fight other infections. It can often take a long time for symptoms to appear after infection. People infected with latent viruses might not know for many years that they have been infected.

Reading Check Why is HIV considered a latent virus?

The Flu 🔑

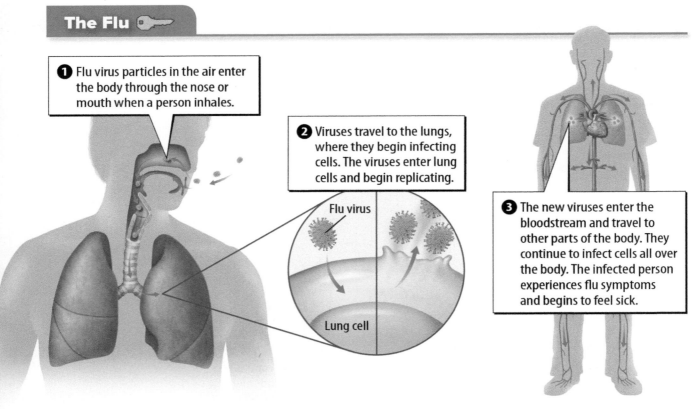

❶ Flu virus particles in the air enter the body through the nose or mouth when a person inhales.

❷ Viruses travel to the lungs, where they begin infecting cells. The viruses enter lung cells and begin replicating.

Flu virus

Lung cell

❸ The new viruses enter the bloodstream and travel to other parts of the body. They continue to infect cells all over the body. The infected person experiences flu symptoms and begins to feel sick.

Figure 14 Viruses that infect the respiratory system usually enter through the nose or mouth.

Visual Check Where do flu viruses replicate?

Treating and Preventing Viral Diseases

Since viruses are constantly changing, viral diseases can be difficult to treat. Antibiotics work only against bacteria, not viruses. Antiviral medicines can be used to treat certain viral diseases or prevent infection. These medicines prevent the virus from entering a cell or stop the virus from replicating. Antiviral medicines are specific to each virus. Like bacteria, viruses can rapidly change and become resistant to medicines.

Health officials use many methods to prevent the spread of viral diseases. One of the best ways to prevent a viral infection is to limit contact with an infected human or animal. The most important way to prevent infections is to practice good hygiene, such as washing your hands.

Immunity

Has anyone you know ever had chicken pox? Did they get it more than once? Most people who became infected with chicken pox develop an immunity to the disease. This is an example of acquired immunity. When a virus infects a person, his or her body begins to make special proteins called antibodies. An **antibody** *is a protein that can attach to a pathogen and make it useless.* Antibodies bind to viruses and other pathogens and prevent them from attaching to a host cell, as shown in Figure 15. The antibodies also target viruses and signal the body to destroy them. These antibodies can multiply quickly if the same pathogen enters the body again, making it easier for the body to fight infection. Another type of immunity, called natural immunity, develops when a mother passes antibodies on to her unborn baby.

WebQuest

Viruses and Bacteria
Go online to investigate how viruses and bacteria affect the human body.

WORD ORIGIN · · · · · · · · · · · ·
immunity
from Latin *immunis*, means "exempt, free"

Antibodies

Figure 15 Antibodies bind to pathogens and prevent them from attaching to cells.

✓ **Visual Check** How does the antibody prevent the virus from attaching to the host cell?

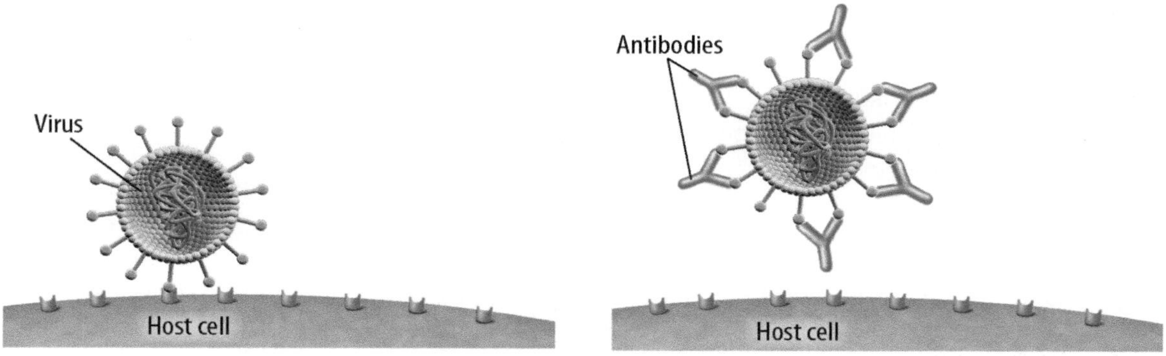

Antibodies

Virus

Host cell

Host cell

How do antibodies work?

When a virus infects a cell it binds to part of that cell called a receptor. The virus and the receptor fit together like puzzle pieces.

1. Read and complete a lab safety form.
2. Cut out two **virus shapes** and two **cell shapes.**
3. Using one virus shape and one cell shape, note how the virus fits against the receptor on the cell. **Tape** the virus and the cell together.
4. Cut out one **antibody shape.** Note how the virus shapes and the antibody shapes attach and tape them together.
5. Try to attach the virus shapes and the antibody shapes you just joined to the cell receptor.

Analyze and Conclude

1. **Observe** whether the virus or the joined virus and antibody were better able to attach to the cell.

2. **Key Concept** Explain how producing more antibodies would be beneficial during a viral infection.

Vaccines

One way to prevent viral diseases is through vaccination. *A **vaccine** is a mixture containing material from one or more deactivated pathogens, such as viruses.* When an organism is given a vaccine for a viral disease, the vaccine triggers the production of antibodies. This is similar to what would happen if the organism became infected with the virus normally. However, because the vaccine contains deactivated pathogens, the organism suffers only mild symptoms or none at all. After being vaccinated against a particular pathogen, the organism will not get as sick if exposed to the pathogen again.

Vaccines can prevent diseases in animals as well as humans. For example, pet owners and farmers get annual rabies vaccinations for their animals. This protects the animals from the disease. Humans are then protected from rabies.

Research with Viruses

Scientists are researching new ways to treat and prevent viral diseases in humans, animals, and plants. Scientists are also studying the link between viruses and cancer. Viruses can cause changes in a host's DNA or RNA, resulting in the formation of tumors or abnormal growth. Because viruses can change very quickly, scientists must always be working on new ways to treat and prevent viral diseases.

You might think that all viruses are harmful. However, scientists have also found beneficial uses for viruses. Viruses may be used to treat genetic disorders and cancer using gene transfer. Scientists use viruses to insert normal genetic information into a specific cell. Scientists hope that gene transfer will eventually be able to treat genetic disorders that are caused by one gene, such as cystic fibrosis or hemophilia.

Key Concept Check How do viruses affect human health?

Visual Summary

A virus is a strand of DNA or RNA surrounded by a layer of protein.

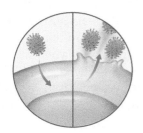

Viruses cause human diseases such as chicken pox and influenza.

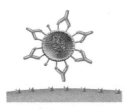

A person's body produces proteins called antibodies that prevent an infection by viruses.

FOLDABLES

Use your lesson Foldable to review the lesson. Save your Foldable for the project at the end of the chapter.

What do you think NOW?

You first read the statements below at the beginning of the chapter.

5. Viruses are the smallest living organisms.

6. Viruses can replicate only inside an organism.

Did you change your mind about whether you agree or disagree with the statements? Rewrite any false statements to make them true.

Use Vocabulary

1 **List** the different shapes a virus can have.

2 **Describe** in your own words how a vaccine works.

3 **Use the term** *antibodies* in a sentence.

Understand Key Concepts

4 **Describe** the structure of a virus.

5 Which is made by the body to fight viruses?
   A. antibody   C. bacteriophage
   B. bacteria   D. proteins

6 **Classify** a virus as a living or nonliving thing. Explain your answer.

7 **Compare** a vaccine and an antibody.

Interpret Graphics

8 **Draw** a graphic organizer like the one below including the steps that occur when a virus infects a cell.

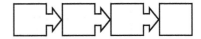

9 **Describe** what happens during this step of viral replication.

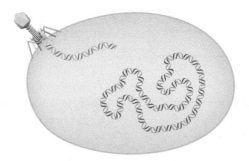

Critical Thinking

10 **Predict** the effect of preventing future mutations of the influenza virus.

11 **Evaluate** the importance of vaccines in keeping people healthy.

Bacterial Growth and Disinfectants

Materials

agar plates

cotton swabs

cellophane tape

permanent marker

hand sanitizer

Safety

Recall that pathogens such as bacteria and viruses are all around you. When studying pathogens, scientists often use agar plates to grow bacteria and other colonies. An agar plate is a Petri dish containing agar, a gel made from seaweed, and nutrients needed for bacteria to grow. When bacteria are transferred to an agar plate, they reproduce. After a few days, you can see colonies of bacteria. Disinfectants are chemicals that deactivate or kill pathogens such as bacteria. In this lab you will test how hand sanitizer, a common disinfectant, affects the growth of bacteria on agar plates.

Ask a Question

What effect does hand sanitizer have on bacterial growth?

Make Observations

1 Read and complete a lab safety form.

2 Set two agar plates on your desk or work area. Turn your agar plates upside down without opening them. With a permanent marker, label one plate *No Treatment* and the other *Disinfected*. Also write your name and the date on the plate. Turn the agar plates right side up.

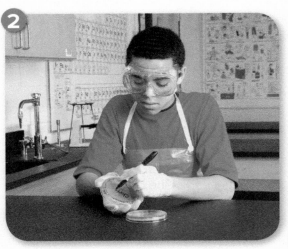

3 Rub the end of a cotton swab across the top of your desk or work area. Open the lid of the agar plate labeled *No Treatment* only enough to stick the swab in. Quickly make several S-shaped streaks on the agar. Close your plate and tape it shut.

4 Carefully clean the top of your desk or work area with hand sanitizer. Repeat step 3 using the agar plate labeled *Disinfected*.

5 Move your plates to an incubation area as directed by your teacher.

(t to b, 2–3, 5–6)Hutchings Photography/Digital Light Source; (4)Ken Karp/McGraw-Hill Education

Form a Hypothesis

6 Using what you know about bacteria and disinfectants, write a hypothesis about how disinfectants affect the growth of bacteria. Make a prediction about how much bacterial growth you expect to see on your two agar plates.

Test Your Hypothesis

7 Check your agar plates after about three days. Record your observations in your Science Journal.

8 Compare the growth of bacteria on your two agar plates. Do your results support your hypothesis?

Analyze and Conclude

9 **Compare** Describe the differences in the amount of bacteria that grew on the two agar plates. Which plate had more?

10 What can you do to decrease the spread of bacteria in school and at home?

11 **Infer** Why didn't your experiment show any evidence of viral replication? How would you study the effect of disinfectants on viruses?

12 **The Big Idea** Why do doctors wash their hands or use hand sanitizer between appointments with different patients?

Communicate Your Results

Make a short video presentation about the results of your lab. Describe the question you investigated, the steps you took to answer your question, and the results that support your conclusions. Show your video to the class.

Inquiry Extension

Think about other situations in which cleanliness is important for preventing disease. Write a procedure in which you could test for bacteria as a comparison. Conduct your experiment and present your results to the class.

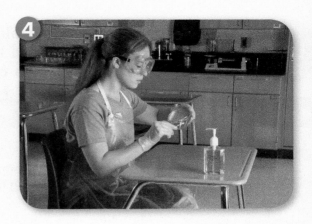

Lab Tips

☑ When streaking bacteria on your plates, use a steady, but light, pressure.

☑ After you disinfect your object, wait for the disinfectant to dry before testing the area.

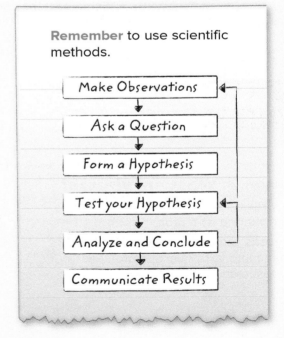

Remember to use scientific methods.

Make Observations

↓

Ask a Question

↓

Form a Hypothesis

↓

Test your Hypothesis

↓

Analyze and Conclude

↓

Communicate Results

 THE BIG IDEA Bacteria are unicellular prokaryotes, and viruses are small pieces of DNA or RNA surrounded by protein. Both bacteria and viruses can cause harmful diseases or can be useful to humans.

Key Concepts Summary	Vocabulary
Lesson 1: What are bacteria? • **Bacteria** and archeans are unicellular organisms without nuclei. They have structures for movement, obtaining food, and reproduction. • Bacteria exchange genetic information in a process called **conjugation.** They reproduce asexually by **fission.**   	**bacterium** p. 483 **flagella** p. 486 **fission** p. 486 **conjugation** p. 486 **endospore** p. 487
 **Lesson 2: Bacteria in Nature** • Bacteria decompose materials, play a role in the nitrogen cycle, clean the environment, and are used in food. • Some bacteria cause disease, while others are used to treat it.	**decomposition** p. 492 **nitrogen fixation** p. 492 **bioremediation** p. 493 **pathogen** p. 494 **antibiotic** p. 494 **pasteurization** p. 495
Lesson 3: What are viruses? • A **virus** is made up of DNA or RNA surrounded by a protein coat. • Viruses can cause disease, can be made into **vaccines,** and are used in research. 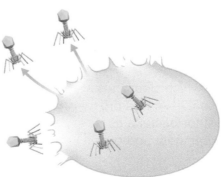	**virus** p. 499 **antibody** p. 503 **vaccine** p. 504

FOLDABLES® Chapter Project

Assemble your lesson Foldables as shown to make a Chapter Project. Use the project to review what you have learned in this chapter.

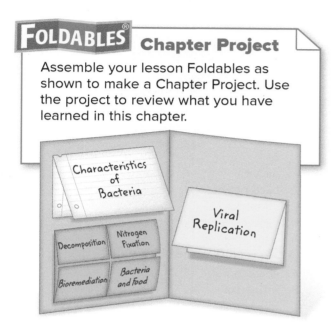

Use Vocabulary

1 Some bacteria have whiplike structures called _____ that are used for movement.

2 Your body produces proteins called _____ in response to infection by a virus.

3 Organisms that cause diseases are known as _____.

4 The process of killing bacteria in a food product by heating it is called _____ .

5 Bacteria can form a(n) _____ to survive when environmental conditions are severe.

6 A(n) _____ is made by using pieces of deactivated viruses or dead pathogens.

Link Vocabulary and Key Concepts

 Interactive Concept Map

Copy this concept map, and then use vocabulary terms from the previous page and other terms from the chapter to complete the concept map.

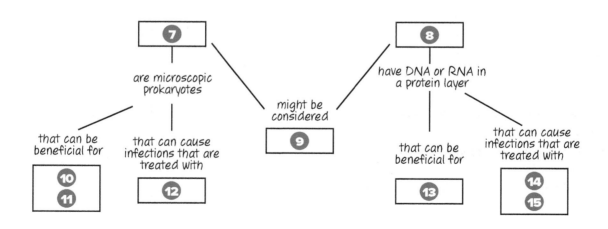

Chapter 14 Review

Understand Key Concepts 🔑

1 Which structure is NOT found in a bacterium?

A. chromosome
B. cytoplasm
C. nucleus
D. ribosome

2 Which structure helps a bacterium move?

A. capsule
B. endospore
C. flagellum
D. plasmid

3 What process is occurring in the illustration below?

A. budding
B. conjugation
C. fission
D. replication

4 Which term describes how bacteria can be used to clean up environmental waste?

A. bioremediation
B. decomposition
C. pasteurization
D. nitrogen fixation

5 Which statement correctly describes pathogens?

A. They are always bacteria.
B. They are in your body only when you are sick.
C. They break down dead organisms.
D. They cause disease.

6 Which statement correctly describes antibiotics?

A. They can kill any kind of bacterium.
B. They help bacteria grow.
C. They stop the growth and reproduction of bacteria.
D. They treat all diseases.

7 What is shown below?

A. bacteria
B. bacteriophage
C. endospore
D. virus

8 Which is NOT caused by a virus?

A. chicken pox
B. influenza
C. rabies
D. tuberculosis

9 What do vaccines stimulate the production of?

A. antibodies
B. DNA or RNA
C. protein
D. ribosomes

10 Scientists hope to be able to use viruses for gene therapy because viruses can

A. become latent for long periods of time.
B. inject genetic material into host cells.
C. make proteins to attack cells.
D. transport themselves throughout the body.

11 Which statement correctly describes viruses?

A. All viruses are latent.
B. All viruses contain DNA.
C. Viruses are considered living things.
D. Viruses do not have organelles.

Critical Thinking

12 **Compare** and **contrast** bacteria and archaea.

13 **Evaluate** the importance of bacterial conjugation.

14 **Model** the life of a bacterium that performs nitrogen fixation in the soil.

15 **Contrast** asexual reproduction in bacteria and replication in viruses. What are some advantages and disadvantages of each?

16 **Organize** the effects of bacteria on health by copying and completing the table below.

Harmful Effects	Beneficial Effects

17 **Analyze** the importance of vaccines in preventing large outbreaks of influenza.

18 **Draw** and label a typical bacterium. Are the features you labeled beneficial for moving, for finding food, or for another purpose? Explain your answer.

19 **Explain** what happens during the process shown below. How does this process eventually create new strains of bacteria that are resistant to antibiotics?

Writing in Science

20 **Summarize** an argument that you could use to encourage all the families in your neighborhood to make sure their pets are vaccinated against rabies.

REVIEW THE BIG IDEA

21 What are bacteria and viruses and why are they important? Include examples of how they are both beneficial and harmful to humans.

22 Describe what is happening in the photo below. Explain what is happening to both the bacterium and the virus.

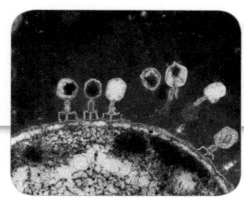

Math Skills

Math Practice

Use a Formula

23 How many bacteria would there be if 100 bacteria underwent fission 8 times?

24 If each fission cycle takes 20 minutes, how many cycles would it take for 100 bacteria to divide into 100,000?

25 A strain of bacteria takes 30 minutes to undergo fission. Starting with 500 bacteria, how many would there be after 4 hours?

Record your answers on the answer sheet provided by your teacher or on a sheet of paper.

Multiple Choice

1 Which is NOT a characteristic of bacteria?

  A They are microscopic.

  B They are unicellular.

  C They can live in many environments.

  D They have a membrane-bound nucleus.

2 Which process increases genetic diversity in bacteria?

  A attachment to a host organism

  B division into two organisms

  C formation of an endospore

  D transfer of plasmid strands

Use the diagram below to answer questions 3 and 4.

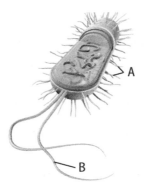

3 The diagram above illustrates a bacterium. What is the function of the structure labeled *A*?

  A attaching to surfaces

  B sensing surroundings

  C stinging prey

  D taking in nutrients

4 The structure labeled *B* helps a bacterium

  A move.

  B protect itself.

  C reproduce.

  D transfer DNA.

5 What beneficial vitamin do some human intestinal bacteria produce?

  A vitamin A

  B vitamin C

  C vitamin D

  D vitamin K

6 Which statement BEST explains why living organisms in an ecosystem depend on bacteria?

  A Bacteria help reduce the number of predators.

  B Bacteria kill weaker members of a species so only the stronger ones survive.

  C Bacteria protect organisms from harmful solar rays.

  D Bacteria release molecules into soil that are used by other organisms.

Use the diagram below to answer question 7.

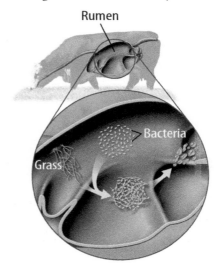

7 What role do bacteria play in the process shown above?

  A They break down cellulose.

  B They convert nitrogen in grass.

  C They prevent viruses from growing.

  D They remove harmful pollutants.

8   In which process do bacteria and other organisms clean up environmental pollution?

   A bioremediation

   B decomposition

   C fixation

   D pasteurization

Use the diagram below to answer question 9.

9   What is pictured in the diagram above?

   A an antibody

   B a bacteriophage

   C a bacterium

   D a plasmid

10   Which BEST explains how mutation benefits a virus?

   A It enables the virus to adjust to changes in its host cell.

   B It enables the virus to reproduce more quickly.

   C It enables the virus to resist antibiotic therapy.

   D It enables the virus to travel from host to host.

Constructed Response

Use the diagrams below to answer questions 11 and 12.

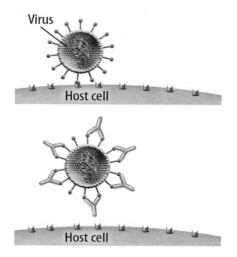

11   Describe how the virus attaches to the host cell in the figure at the top of the diagram.

12   What are the Y-shaped structures on the virus in the figure at the bottom of the diagram? Explain their interaction with the virus.

13   Why can viral infections be more difficult to treat than bacterial infections?

14   What are two methods you can use to prevent a viral infection?

15   What happens to the host cell when a latent virus goes through an inactive stage?

NEED EXTRA HELP?															
If You Missed Question...	1	2	3	4	5	6	7	8	9	10	11	12	13	14	15
Go to Lesson...	1	1	1	1	2	2	2	2	3	3	3	3	3	3	3

Student Resources

For Students and Parents/Guardians

These resources are designed to help you achieve success in science. You will find useful information on laboratory safety, math skills, and science skills. In addition, science reference materials are found in the Reference Handbook. You'll find the information you need to learn and sharpen your skills in these resources.

Table of Contents

Science Skill Handbook **SR-2**

Scientific Methods **SR-2**
    Identify a Question SR-2
    Gather and Organize Information SR-2
    Form a Hypothesis SR-5
    Test the Hypothesis SR-6
    Collect Data SR-6
    Analyze the Data SR-9
    Draw Conclustions SR-10
    Communicate SR-10
Safety Symbols **SR-11**
Safety in the Science Laboratory **SR-12**
    General Safety Rules SR-12
    Prevent Accidents SR-12
    Laboratory Work SR-13
    Laboratory Cleanup SR-13
    Emergencies SR-13

Math Skill Handbook **SR-14**

Math Review **SR-14**
    Use Fractions SR-14
    Use Ratios SR-17
    Use Decimals SR-17
    Use Proportions SR-18
    Use Percentages SR-19
    Solve One-Step Equations SR-19
    Use Statistics SR-20
    Use Geometry SR-21
Science Applications **SR-24**
    Measure in SI SR-24
    Dimensional Analysis SR-24
    Precision and Significant Digits SR-26
    Scientific Notation SR-26
    Make and Use Graphs SR-27

Foldables Handbook **SR-29**

Reference Handbook **SR-40**
    Periodic Table of the Elements SR-40

Glossary G-2

Index I-2

SCIENCE SKILL HANDBOOK

MATH SKILL HANDBOOK

FOLDABLES HANDBOOK

REFERENCE HANDBOOK

GLOSSARY/ GLOSARIO

INDEX

Scientific Methods

Scientists use an orderly approach called the scientific method to solve problems. This includes organizing and recording data so others can understand them. Scientists use many variations in this method when they solve problems.

Identify a Question

The first step in a scientific investigation or experiment is to identify a question to be answered or a problem to be solved. For example, you might ask which gasoline is the most efficient.

Gather and Organize Information

After you have identified your question, begin gathering and organizing information. There are many ways to gather information, such as researching in a library, interviewing those knowledgeable about the subject, and testing and working in the laboratory and field. Fieldwork is investigations and observations done outside of a laboratory.

Researching Information Before moving in a new direction, it is important to gather the information that already is known about the subject. Start by asking yourself questions to determine exactly what you need to know. Then you will look for the information in various reference sources, like the student is doing in **Figure 1.** Some sources may include textbooks, encyclopedias, government documents, professional journals, science magazines, and the Internet. Always list the sources of your information.

Figure 1 The Internet can be a valuable research tool.

Evaluate Sources of Information Not all sources of information are reliable. You should evaluate all of your sources of information, and use only those you know to be dependable. For example, if you are researching ways to make homes more energy efficient, a site written by the U.S. Department of Energy would be more reliable than a site written by a company that is trying to sell a new type of weatherproofing material. Also, remember that research always is changing. Consult the most current resources available to you. For example, a 1985 resource about saving energy would not reflect the most recent findings.

Sometimes scientists use data that they did not collect themselves, or conclusions drawn by other researchers. This data must be evaluated carefully. Ask questions about how the data were obtained, if the investigation was carried out properly, and if it has been duplicated exactly with the same results. Would you reach the same conclusion from the data? Only when you have confidence in the data can you believe it is true and feel comfortable using it.

Interpret Scientific Illustrations As you research a topic in science, you will see drawings, diagrams, and photographs to help you understand what you read. Some illustrations are included to help you understand an idea that you can't see easily by yourself, like the tiny particles in an atom in **Figure 2.** A drawing helps many people to remember details more easily and provides examples that clarify difficult concepts or give additional information about the topic you are studying. Most illustrations have labels or a caption to identify or to provide more information.

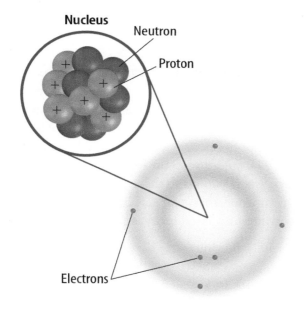

Figure 2 This drawing shows an atom of carbon with its six protons, six neutrons, and six electrons.

Concept Maps One way to organize data is to draw a diagram that shows relationships among ideas (or concepts). A concept map can help make the meanings of ideas and terms more clear, and help you understand and remember what you are studying. Concept maps are useful for breaking large concepts down into smaller parts, making learning easier.

Network Tree A type of concept map that not only shows a relationship, but how the concepts are related is a network tree, shown in **Figure 3.** In a network tree, the words are written in the ovals, while the description of the type of relationship is written across the connecting lines.

When constructing a network tree, write down the topic and all major topics on separate pieces of paper or notecards. Then arrange them in order from general to specific. Branch the related concepts from the major concept and describe the relationship on the connecting line. Continue to more specific concepts until finished.

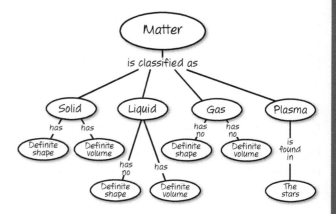

Figure 3 A network tree shows how concepts or objects are related.

Events Chain Another type of concept map is an events chain. Sometimes called a flow chart, it models the order or sequence of items. An events chain can be used to describe a sequence of events, the steps in a procedure, or the stages of a process.

When making an events chain, first find the one event that starts the chain. This event is called the initiating event. Then, find the next event and continue until the outcome is reached, as shown in **Figure 4** on the next page.

SCIENCE SKILL HANDBOOK

MATH SKILL HANDBOOK

FOLDABLES HANDBOOK

REFERENCE HANDBOOK

GLOSSARY/ GLOSARIO

INDEX

SCIENCE SKILL HANDBOOK

MATH SKILL HANDBOOK

FOLDABLES HANDBOOK

REFERENCE HANDBOOK

GLOSSARY/ GLOSARIO

INDEX

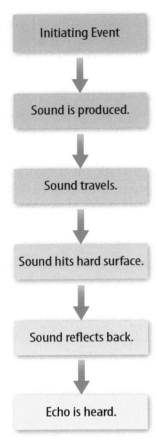

Figure 4 Events-chain concept maps show the order of steps in a process or event. This concept map shows how a sound makes an echo.

Cycle Map A specific type of events chain is a cycle map. It is used when the series of events do not produce a final outcome, but instead relate back to the beginning event, such as in **Figure 5.** Therefore, the cycle repeats itself.

To make a cycle map, first decide what event is the beginning event. This is also called the initiating event. Then list the next events in the order that they occur, with the last event relating back to the initiating event. Words can be written between the events that describe what happens from one event to the next. The number of events in a cycle map can vary, but usually contain three or more events.

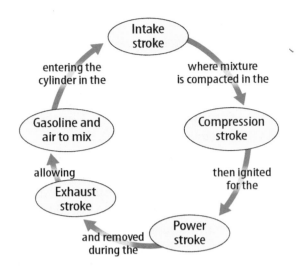

Figure 5 A cycle map shows events that occur in a cycle.

Spider Map A type of concept map that you can use for brainstorming is the spider map. When you have a central idea, you might find that you have a jumble of ideas that relate to it but are not necessarily clearly related to each other. The spider map on sound in **Figure 6** shows that if you write these ideas outside the main concept, then you can begin to separate and group unrelated terms so they become more useful.

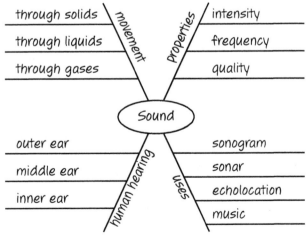

Figure 6 A spider map allows you to list ideas that relate to a central topic but not necessarily to one another.

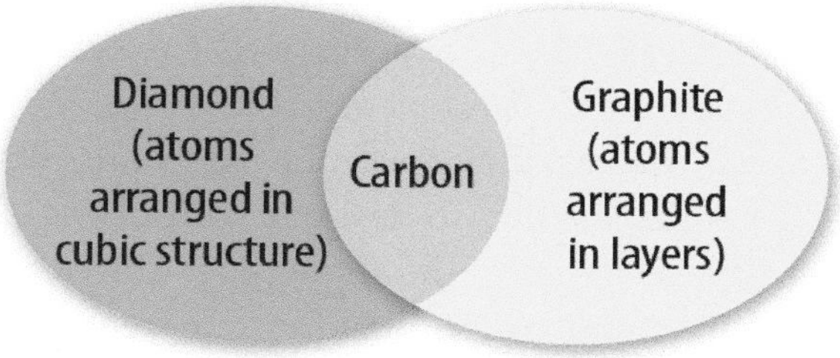

Figure 7 This Venn diagram compares and contrasts two substances made from carbon.

Venn Diagram To illustrate how two subjects compare and contrast you can use a Venn diagram. You can see the characteristics that the subjects have in common and those that they do not, shown in **Figure 7.**

To create a Venn diagram, draw two overlapping ovals that are big enough to write in. List the characteristics unique to one subject in one oval, and the characteristics of the other subject in the other oval. The characteristics in common are listed in the overlapping section.

Make and Use Tables One way to organize information so it is easier to understand is to use a table. Tables can contain numbers, words, or both.

To make a table, list the items to be compared in the first column and the characteristics to be compared in the first row. The title should clearly indicate the content of the table, and the column or row heads should be clear. Notice that in **Table 1** the units are included.

Table 1 Recyclables Collected During Week			
Day of Week	Paper (kg)	Aluminum (kg)	Glass (kg)
Monday	5.0	4.0	12.0
Wednesday	4.0	1.0	10.0
Friday	2.5	2.0	10.0

Make a Model One way to help you better understand the parts of a structure, the way a process works, or to show things too large or small for viewing is to make a model. For example, an atomic model made of a plastic-ball nucleus and chenille stem electron shells can help you visualize how the parts of an atom relate to each other. Other types of models can be devised on a computer or represented by equations.

Form a Hypothesis

A possible explanation based on previous knowledge and observations is called a hypothesis. After researching gasoline types and recalling previous experiences in your family's car, you form a hypothesis—our car runs more efficiently because we use premium gasoline. To be valid, a hypothesis has to be something you can test by using an investigation.

Predict When you apply a hypothesis to a specific situation, you predict something about that situation. A prediction makes a statement in advance, based on prior observation, experience, or scientific reasoning. People use predictions to make everyday decisions. Scientists test predictions by performing investigations. Based on previous observations and experiences, you might form a prediction that cars are more efficient with premium gasoline. The prediction can be tested in an investigation.

Design an Experiment A scientist needs to make many decisions before beginning an investigation. Some of these include: how to carry out the investigation, what steps to follow, how to record the data, and how the investigation will answer the question. It also is important to address any safety concerns.

SCIENCE SKILL HANDBOOK

MATH SKILL HANDBOOK

FOLDABLES HANDBOOK

REFERENCE HANDBOOK

GLOSSARY/ GLOSARIO

INDEX

SCIENCE SKILL HANDBOOK

MATH SKILL HANDBOOK

FOLDABLES HANDBOOK

REFERENCE HANDBOOK

GLOSSARY/ GLOSARIO

INDEX

Test the Hypothesis

Now that you have formed your hypothesis, you need to test it. Using an investigation, you will make observations and collect data, or information. This data might either support or not support your hypothesis. Scientists collect and organize data as numbers and descriptions.

Follow a Procedure In order to know what materials to use, as well as how and in what order to use them, you must follow a procedure. **Figure 8** shows a procedure you might follow to test your hypothesis.

Procedure	
Step 1	Use regular gasoline for two weeks.
Step 2	Record the number of kilometers between fill-ups and the amount of gasoline used.
Step 3	Switch to premium gasoline for two weeks.
Step 4	Record the number of kilometers between fill-ups and the amount of gasoline used.

Figure 8 A procedure tells you what to do step-by-step.

Identify and Manipulate Variables and Controls In any experiment, it is important to keep everything the same except for the item you are testing. The one factor you change is called the independent variable. The change that results is the dependent variable. Make sure you have only one independent variable, to assure yourself of the cause of the changes you observe in the dependent variable. For example, in your gasoline experiment the type of fuel is the independent variable. The dependent variable is the efficiency.

Many experiments also have a control—an individual instance or experimental subject for which the independent variable is not changed. You can then compare the test results to the control results. To design a control you must have two cars of the same type. The control car uses regular gasoline for four weeks. After you are done with the test, you can compare the experimental results to the control results.

Collect Data

Whether you are carrying out an investigation or a short observational experiment, you will collect data, as shown in **Figure 9.** Scientists collect data as numbers and descriptions and organize them in specific ways.

Observe Scientists observe items and events, then record what they see. When they use only words to describe an observation, it is called qualitative data. Scientists' observations also can describe how much there is of something. These observations use numbers, as well as words, in the description and are called quantitative data. For example, if a sample of the element gold is described as being "shiny and very dense" the data are qualitative. Quantitative data on this sample of gold might include "a mass of 30 g and a density of 19.3 g/cm^3."

Figure 9 Collecting data is one way to gather information directly.

Figure 10 Record data neatly and clearly so it is easy to understand.

When you make observations, you should examine the entire object or situation first, and then look carefully for details. It is important to record observations accurately and completely. Always record your notes immediately as you make them, so you do not miss details or make a mistake when recording results from memory. Never put unidentified observations on scraps of paper. Instead they should be recorded in a notebook, like the one in **Figure 10.** Write your data neatly so you can easily read it later. At each point in the experiment, record your observations and label them. That way, you will not have to determine what the figures mean when you look at your notes later. Set up any tables that you will need to use ahead of time, so you can record any observations right away. Remember to avoid bias when collecting data by not including personal thoughts when you record observations. Record only what you observe.

Estimate Scientific work also involves estimating. To estimate is to make a judgment about the size or the number of something without measuring or counting. This is important when the number or size of an object or population is too large or too difficult to accurately count or measure.

Sample Scientists may use a sample or a portion of the total number as a type of estimation. To sample is to take a small, representative portion of the objects or organisms of a population for research. By making careful observations or manipulating variables within that portion of the group, information is discovered and conclusions are drawn that might apply to the whole population. A poorly chosen sample can be unrepresentative of the whole. If you were trying to determine the rainfall in an area, it would not be best to take a rainfall sample from under a tree.

Measure You use measurements every day. Scientists also take measurements when collecting data. When taking measurements, it is important to know how to use measuring tools properly. Accuracy also is important.

Length The SI unit for length is the meter (m). Smaller measurements might be measured in centimeters or millimeters.

Length is measured using a metric ruler or meterstick. When using a metric ruler, line up the 0-cm mark with the end of the object being measured and read the number of the unit where the object ends. Look at the metric ruler shown in **Figure 11.** The centimeter lines are the long, numbered lines, and the shorter lines are millimeter lines. In this instance, the length would be 4.50 cm.

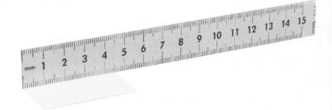

Figure 11 This metric ruler has centimeter and millimeter divisions.

SCIENCE SKILL HANDBOOK

MATH SKILL HANDBOOK

FOLDABLES HANDBOOK

REFERENCE HANDBOOK

GLOSSARY/ GLOSARIO

INDEX

SCIENCE SKILL HANDBOOK

MATH SKILL HANDBOOK

FOLDABLES HANDBOOK

REFERENCE HANDBOOK

GLOSSARY/ GLOSARIO

INDEX

Mass The SI unit for mass is the kilogram (kg). Scientists can measure mass using units formed by adding metric prefixes to the unit gram (g), such as milligram (mg). To measure mass, you might use a triple-beam balance similar to the one shown in **Figure 12.** The balance has a pan on one side and a set of beams on the other side. Each beam has a rider that slides on the beam.

When using a triple-beam balance, place an object on the pan. Slide the largest rider along its beam until the pointer drops below zero. Then move it back one notch. Repeat the process for each rider proceeding from the larger to smaller until the pointer swings an equal distance above and below the zero point. Sum the masses on each beam to find the mass of the object. Move all riders back to zero when finished.

Instead of putting materials directly on the balance, scientists often take a tare of a container. A tare is the mass of a container into which objects or substances are placed for measuring their masses. To find the mass of objects or substances, find the mass of a clean container. Remove the container from the pan, and place the object or substances in the container. Find the mass of the container with the materials in it. Subtract the mass of the empty container from the mass of the filled container to find the mass of the materials you are using.

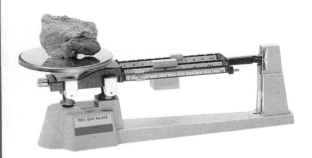

Figure 12 A triple-beam balance is used to determine the mass of an object.

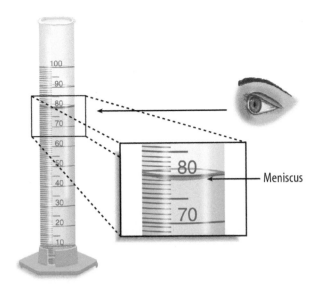

Figure 13 Graduated cylinders measure liquid volume.

Liquid Volume The SI unit for measuring liquids is the liter (l). When a smaller unit is needed, scientists might use a milliliter. Because a milliliter takes up the volume of a cube measuring 1 cm on each side it also can be called a cubic centimeter ($cm^3 = cm \times cm \times cm$).

You can use beakers and graduated cylinders to measure liquid volume. A graduated cylinder, shown in **Figure 13,** is marked from bottom to top in milliliters. In lab, you might use a 10-mL graduated cylinder or a 100-mL graduated cylinder. When measuring liquids, notice that the liquid has a curved surface. Look at the surface at eye level, and measure the bottom of the curve. This is called the meniscus. The graduated cylinder in **Figure 13** contains 79.0 mL, or 79.0 cm^3, of a liquid.

Temperature Scientists often measure temperature using the Celsius scale. Pure water has a freezing point of 0°C and boiling point of 100°C. The unit of measurement is degrees Celsius. Two other scales often used are the Fahrenheit and Kelvin scales.

Figure 14 A thermometer measures the temperature of an object.

Scientists use a thermometer to measure temperature. Most thermometers in a laboratory are glass tubes with a bulb at the bottom end containing a liquid such as colored alcohol. The liquid rises or falls with a change in temperature. To read a glass thermometer like the thermometer in **Figure 14,** rotate it slowly until a red line appears. Read the temperature where the red line ends.

Form Operational Definitions
An operational definition defines an object by how it functions, works, or behaves. For example, when you are playing hide and seek and a tree is home base, you have created an operational definition for a tree.

Objects can have more than one operational definition. For example, a ruler can be defined as a tool that measures the length of an object (how it is used). It can also be a tool with a series of marks used as a standard when measuring (how it works).

Analyze the Data

To determine the meaning of your observations and investigation results, you will need to look for patterns in the data. Then you must think critically to determine what the data mean. Scientists use several approaches when they analyze the data they have collected and recorded. Each approach is useful for identifying specific patterns.

Interpret Data The word *interpret* means "to explain the meaning of something." When analyzing data from an experiment, try to find out what the data show. Identify the control group and the test group to see whether changes in the independent variable have had an effect. Look for differences in the dependent variable between the control and test groups.

Classify Sorting objects or events into groups based on common features is called classifying. When classifying, first observe the objects or events to be classified. Then select one feature that is shared by some members in the group, but not by all. Place those members that share that feature in a subgroup. You can classify members into smaller and smaller subgroups based on characteristics. Remember that when you classify, you are grouping objects or events for a purpose. Keep your purpose in mind as you select the features to form groups and subgroups.

Compare and Contrast Observations can be analyzed by noting the similarities and differences between two or more objects or events that you observe. When you look at objects or events to see how they are similar, you are comparing them. Contrasting is looking for differences in objects or events.

SCIENCE SKILL HANDBOOK

MATH SKILL HANDBOOK

FOLDABLES HANDBOOK

REFERENCE HANDBOOK

GLOSSARY/ GLOSARIO

INDEX

SCIENCE SKILL HANDBOOK

MATH SKILL HANDBOOK

FOLDABLES HANDBOOK

REFERENCE HANDBOOK

GLOSSARY/ GLOSARIO

INDEX

Recognize Cause and Effect A cause is a reason for an action or condition. The effect is that action or condition. When two events happen together, it is not necessarily true that one event caused the other. Scientists must design a controlled investigation to recognize the exact cause and effect.

Draw Conclusions

When scientists have analyzed the data they collected, they proceed to draw conclusions about the data. These conclusions are sometimes stated in words similar to the hypothesis that you formed earlier. They may confirm a hypothesis, or lead you to a new hypothesis.

Infer Scientists often make inferences based on their observations. An inference is an attempt to explain observations or to indicate a cause. An inference is not a fact, but a logical conclusion that needs further investigation. For example, you may infer that a fire has caused smoke. Until you investigate, however, you do not know for sure.

Apply When you draw a conclusion, you must apply those conclusions to determine whether the data supports the hypothesis. If your data do not support your hypothesis, it does not mean that the hypothesis is wrong. It means only that the result of the investigation did not support the hypothesis. Maybe the experiment needs to be redesigned, or some of the initial observations on which the hypothesis was based were incomplete or biased. Perhaps more observation or research is needed to refine your hypothesis. A successful investigation does not always come out the way you originally predicted.

Avoid Bias Sometimes a scientific investigation involves making judgments. When you make a judgment, you form an opinion. It is important to be honest and not to allow any expectations of results to bias your judgments. This is important throughout the entire investigation, from researching to collecting data to drawing conclusions.

Communicate

The communication of ideas is an important part of the work of scientists. A discovery that is not reported will not advance the scientific community's understanding or knowledge. Communication among scientists also is important as a way of improving their investigations.

Scientists communicate in many ways, from writing articles in journals and magazines that explain their investigations and experiments, to announcing important discoveries on television and radio. Scientists also share ideas with colleagues on the Internet or present them as lectures, like the student is doing in **Figure 15.**

Figure 15 A student communicates to his peers about his investigation.

These safety symbols are used in laboratory and field investigations in this book to indicate possible hazards. Learn the meaning of each symbol and refer to this page often. *Remember to wash your hands thoroughly after completing lab procedures.*

PROTECTIVE EQUIPMENT   Do not begin any lab without the proper protection equipment.

 GOGGLES Proper eye protection must be worn when performing or observing science activities that involve items or conditions as listed below.

 APRON Wear an approved apron when using substances that could stain, wet, or destroy cloth.

 SOAP Wash hands with soap and water before removing goggles and after all lab activities.

 GLOVES Wear gloves when working with biological materials, chemicals, animals, or materials that can stain or irritate hands.

LABORATORY HAZARDS

Symbols	Potential Hazards	Precaution	Response
DISPOSAL	contamination of classroom or environment due to improper disposal of materials such as chemicals and live specimens	• DO NOT dispose of hazardous materials in the sink or trash can. • Dispose of wastes as directed by your teacher.	• If hazardous materials are disposed of improperly, notify your teacher immediately.
EXTREME TEMPERATURE	skin burns due to extremely hot or cold materials such as hot glass, liquids, or metals; liquid nitrogen; dry ice	• Use proper protective equipment, such as hot mitts and/or tongs, when handling objects with extreme temperatures.	• If injury occurs, notify your teacher immediately.
SHARP OBJECTS	punctures or cuts from sharp objects such as razor blades, pins, scalpels, and broken glass	• Handle glassware carefully to avoid breakage. • Walk with sharp objects pointed downward, away from you and others.	• If broken glass or injury occurs, notify your teacher immediately.
ELECTRICAL	electric shock or skin burn due to improper grounding, short circuits, liquid spills, or exposed wires	• Check condition of wires and apparatus for fraying or uninsulated wires, and broken or cracked equipment. • Use only GFCI-protected outlets	• DO NOT attempt to fix electrical problems. Notify your teacher immediately.
CHEMICAL	skin irritation or burns, breathing difficulty, and/or poisoning due to touching, swallowing, or inhalation of chemicals such as acids, bases, bleach, metal compounds, iodine, poinsettias, pollen, ammonia, acetone, nail polish remover, heated chemicals, mothballs, and any other chemicals labeled or known to be dangerous	• Wear proper protective equipment such as goggles, apron, and gloves when using chemicals. • Ensure proper room ventilation or use a fume hood when using materials that produce fumes. • NEVER smell fumes directly. • NEVER taste or eat any material in the laboratory.	• If contact occurs, immediately flush affected area with water and notify your teacher. • If a spill occurs, leave the area immediately and notify your teacher.
FLAMMABLE	unexpected fire due to liquids or gases that ignite easily such as rubbing alcohol	• Avoid open flames, sparks, or heat when flammable liquids are present.	• If a fire occurs, leave the area immediately and notify your teacher.
OPEN FLAME	burns or fire due to open flame from matches, Bunsen burners, or burning materials	• Tie back loose hair and clothing. • Keep flame away from all materials. • Follow teacher instructions when lighting and extinguishing flames. • Use proper protection, such as hot mitts or tongs, when handling hot objects.	• If a fire occurs, leave the area immediately and notify your teacher.
ANIMAL SAFETY	injury to or from laboratory animals	• Wear proper protective equipment such as gloves, apron, and goggles when working with animals. • Wash hands after handling animals.	• If injury occurs, notify your teacher immediately.
BIOLOGICAL	infection or adverse reaction due to contact with organisms such as bacteria, fungi, and biological materials such as blood, animal or plant materials	• Wear proper protective equipment such as gloves, goggles, and apron when working with biological materials. • Avoid skin contact with an organism or any part of the organism. • Wash hands after handling organisms.	• If contact occurs, wash the affected area and notify your teacher immediately.
FUME	breathing difficulties from inhalation of fumes from substances such as ammonia, acetone, nail polish remover, heated chemicals, and mothballs	• Wear goggles, apron, and gloves. • Ensure proper room ventilation or use a fume hood when using substances that produce fumes. • NEVER smell fumes directly.	• If a spill occurs, leave area and notify your teacher immediately.
IRRITANT	irritation of skin, mucous membranes, or respiratory tract due to materials such as acids, bases, bleach, pollen, mothballs, steel wool, and potassium permanganate	• Wear goggles, apron, and gloves. • Wear a dust mask to protect against fine particles.	• If skin contact occurs, immediately flush the affected area with water and notify your teacher.
RADIOACTIVE	excessive exposure from alpha, beta, and gamma particles	• Remove gloves and wash hands with soap and water before removing remainder of protective equipment.	• If cracks or holes are found in the container, notify your teacher immediately.

SCIENCE SKILL HANDBOOK

MATH SKILL HANDBOOK

FOLDABLES HANDBOOK

REFERENCE HANDBOOK

GLOSSARY/ GLOSARIO

INDEX

Safety in the Science Laboratory

SCIENCE SKILL HANDBOOK

MATH SKILL HANDBOOK

FOLDABLES HANDBOOK

REFERENCE HANDBOOK

GLOSSARY/ GLOSARIO

INDEX

Introduction to Science Safety

The science laboratory is a safe place to work if you follow standard safety procedures. Being responsible for your own safety helps to make the entire laboratory a safer place for everyone. When performing any lab, read and apply the caution statements and safety symbol listed at the beginning of the lab.

General Safety Rules

1. Complete the *Lab Safety Form* or other safety contract BEFORE starting any science lab.

2. Study the procedure. Ask your teacher any questions. Be sure you understand safety symbols shown on the page.

3. Notify your teacher about allergies or other health conditions that can affect your participation in a lab.

4. Learn and follow use and safety procedures for your equipment. If unsure, ask your teacher.

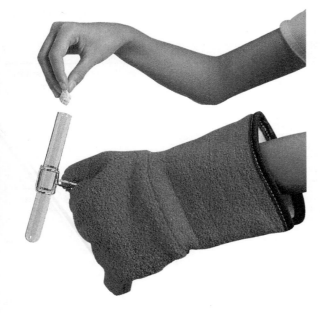

5. Never eat, drink, chew gum, apply cosmetics, or do any personal grooming in the lab. Never use lab glassware as food or drink containers. Keep your hands away from your face and mouth.

6. Know the location and proper use of the safety shower, eye wash, fire blanket, and fire alarm.

Prevent Accidents

1. Use the safety equipment provided to you. Goggles and a safety apron should be worn during investigations.

2. Do NOT use hair spray, mousse, or other flammable hair products. Tie back long hair and tie down loose clothing.

3. Do NOT wear sandals or other open-toed shoes in the lab.

4. Remove jewelry on hands and wrists. Loose jewelry, such as chains and long necklaces, should be removed to prevent them from getting caught in equipment.

5. Do not taste any substances or draw any material into a tube with your mouth.

6. Proper behavior is expected in the lab. Practical jokes and fooling around can lead to accidents and injury.

7. Keep your work area uncluttered.

Laboratory Work

1. Collect and carry all equipment and materials to your work area before beginning a lab.

2. Remain in your own work area unless given permission by your teacher to leave it.

3. Always slant test tubes away from yourself and others when heating them, adding substances to them, or rinsing them.

4. If instructed to smell a substance in a container, hold the container a short distance away and fan vapors toward your nose.

5. Do NOT substitute other chemicals/substances for those in the materials list unless instructed to do so by your teacher.

6. Do NOT take any materials or chemicals outside of the laboratory.

7. Stay out of storage areas unless instructed to be there and supervised by your teacher.

Laboratory Cleanup

1. Turn off all burners, water, and gas, and disconnect all electrical devices.

2. Clean all pieces of equipment and return all materials to their proper places.

3. Dispose of chemicals and other materials as directed by your teacher. Place broken glass and solid substances in the proper containers. Never discard materials in the sink.

4. Clean your work area.

5. Wash your hands with soap and water thoroughly BEFORE removing your goggles.

Emergencies

1. Report any fire, electrical shock, glassware breakage, spill, or injury, no matter how small, to your teacher immediately. Follow his or her instructions.

2. If your clothing should catch fire, STOP, DROP, and ROLL. If possible, smother it with the fire blanket or get under a safety shower. NEVER RUN.

3. If a fire should occur, turn off all gas and leave the room according to established procedures.

4. In most instances, your teacher will clean up spills. Do NOT attempt to clean up spills unless you are given permission and instructions to do so.

5. If chemicals come into contact with your eyes or skin, notify your teacher immediately. Use the eyewash, or flush your skin or eyes with large quantities of water.

6. The fire extinguisher and first-aid kit should only be used by your teacher unless it is an extreme emergency and you have been given permission.

7. If someone is injured or becomes ill, only a professional medical provider or someone certified in first aid should perform first-aid procedures.

SCIENCE SKILL HANDBOOK

MATH SKILL HANDBOOK

FOLDABLES HANDBOOK

REFERENCE HANDBOOK

GLOSSARY/ GLOSARIO

INDEX

Use Fractions

A fraction compares a part to a whole. In the fraction $\frac{2}{3}$, the 2 represents the part and is the numerator. The 3 represents the whole and is the denominator.

Reduce Fractions To reduce a fraction, you must find the largest factor that is common to both the numerator and the denominator, the greatest common factor (GCF). Divide both numbers by the GCF. The fraction has then been reduced, or it is in its simplest form.

Example

Twelve of the 20 chemicals in the science lab are in powder form. What fraction of the chemicals used in the lab are in powder form?

Step 1   Write the fraction.

$$\frac{part}{whole} = \frac{12}{20}$$

Step 2   To find the GCF of the numerator and denominator, list all of the factors of each number.

Factors of 12: 1, 2, 3, 4, 6, 12 (the numbers that divide evenly into 12)

Factors of 20: 1, 2, 4, 5, 10, 20 (the numbers that divide evenly into 20)

Step 3   List the common factors.

1, 2, 4

Step 4   Choose the greatest factor in the list. The GCF of 12 and 20 is 4.

Step 5   Divide the numerator and denominator by the GCF.

$$\frac{12 \div 4}{20 \div 4} = \frac{3}{5}$$

In the lab, $\frac{3}{5}$ of the chemicals are in powder form.

Practice Problem At an amusement park, 66 of 90 rides have a height restriction. What fraction of the rides, in its simplest form, has a height restriction?

Add and Subtract Fractions with Like Denominators To add or subtract fractions with the same denominator, add or subtract the numerators and write the sum or difference over the denominator. After finding the sum or difference, find the simplest form for your fraction.

Example 1

In the forest outside your house, $\frac{1}{8}$ of the animals are rabbits, $\frac{3}{8}$ are squirrels, and the remainder are birds and insects. How many are mammals?

Step 1   Add the numerators.

$$\frac{1}{8} + \frac{3}{8} = \frac{(1+3)}{8} = \frac{4}{8}$$

Step 2   Find the GCF.

$\frac{4}{8}$ (GCF, 4)

Step 3   Divide the numerator and denominator by the GCF.

$$\frac{4 \div 4}{8 \div 4} = \frac{1}{2}$$

$\frac{1}{2}$ of the animals are mammals.

Example 2

If $\frac{7}{16}$ of the Earth is covered by freshwater, and $\frac{1}{16}$ of that is in glaciers, how much freshwater is not frozen?

Step 1   Subtract the numerators.

$$\frac{7}{16} - \frac{1}{16} = \frac{(7-1)}{16} = \frac{6}{16}$$

Step 2   Find the GCF.

$\frac{6}{16}$ (GCF, 2)

Step 3   Divide the numerator and denominator by the GCF.

$$\frac{6 \div 2}{16 \div 2} = \frac{3}{8}$$

$\frac{3}{8}$ of the freshwater is not frozen.

Practice Problem A bicycle rider is riding at a rate of 15 km/h for $\frac{4}{9}$ of his ride, 10 km/h for $\frac{2}{9}$ of his ride, and 8 km/h for the remainder of the ride. How much of his ride is he riding at a rate greater than 8 km/h?

SCIENCE SKILL HANDBOOK

MATH SKILL HANDBOOK

FOLDABLES HANDBOOK

REFERENCE HANDBOOK

GLOSSARY/ GLOSARI

INDEX

Add and Subtract Fractions with Unlike Denominators To add or subtract fractions with unlike denominators, first find the least common denominator (LCD). This is the smallest number that is a common multiple of both denominators. Rename each fraction with the LCD, and then add or subtract. Find the simplest form if necessary.

Example 1

A chemist makes a paste that is $\frac{1}{2}$ table salt (NaCl), $\frac{1}{3}$ sugar ($C_6H_{12}O_6$), and the remainder is water (H_2O). How much of the paste is a solid?

Step 1   Find the LCD of the fractions.

$\frac{1}{2} + \frac{1}{3}$ (LCD, 6)

Step 2   Rename each numerator and each denominator with the LCD.

Step 3   Add the numerators.

$\frac{3}{6} + \frac{2}{6} = \frac{(3+2)}{6} = \frac{5}{6}$

$\frac{5}{6}$ of the paste is a solid.

Example 2

The average precipitation in Grand Junction, CO, is $\frac{7}{10}$ inch in November, and $\frac{3}{5}$ inch in December. What is the total average precipitation?

Step 1   Find the LCD of the fractions.

$\frac{7}{10} + \frac{3}{5}$ (LCD, 10)

Step 2   Rename each numerator and each denominator with the LCD.

Step 3   Add the numerators.

$\frac{7}{10} + \frac{6}{10} = \frac{(7+6)}{10} = \frac{13}{10}$

$\frac{13}{10}$ inches total precipitation, or $1\frac{3}{10}$ inches.

Practice Problem On an electric bill, about $\frac{1}{8}$ of the energy is from solar energy and about $\frac{1}{10}$ is from wind power. How much of the total bill is from solar energy and wind power combined?

Example 3

In your body, $\frac{7}{10}$ of your muscle contractions are involuntary (cardiac and smooth muscle tissue). Smooth muscle makes $\frac{3}{15}$ of your muscle contractions. How many of your muscle contractions are made by cardiac muscle?

Step 1   Find the LCD of the fractions.

$\frac{7}{10} - \frac{3}{15}$ (LCD, 30)

Step 2   Rename each numerator and each denominator with the LCD.

$\frac{7 \times 3}{10 \times 3} = \frac{21}{30}$

$\frac{3 \times 2}{15 \times 2} = \frac{6}{30}$

Step 3   Subtract the numerators.

$\frac{21}{30} - \frac{6}{30} = \frac{(21-6)}{30} = \frac{15}{30}$

Step 4   Find the GCF.

$\frac{15}{30}$ (GCF, 15)

$\frac{1}{2}$

$\frac{1}{2}$ of all muscle contractions are cardiac muscle.

Example 4

Tony wants to make cookies that call for $\frac{3}{4}$ of a cup of flour, but he only has $\frac{1}{3}$ of a cup. How much more flour does he need?

Step 1   Find the LCD of the fractions.

$\frac{3}{4} - \frac{1}{3}$ (LCD, 12)

Step 2   Rename each numerator and each denominator with the LCD.

$\frac{3 \times 3}{4 \times 3} = \frac{9}{12}$

$\frac{1 \times 4}{3 \times 4} = \frac{4}{12}$

Step 3   Subtract the numerators.

$\frac{9}{12} - \frac{4}{12} = \frac{(9-4)}{12} = \frac{5}{12}$

$\frac{5}{12}$ of a cup of flour

Practice Problem Using the information provided to you in Example 3 above, determine how many muscle contractions are voluntary (skeletal muscle).

SCIENCE SKILL HANDBOOK

MATH SKILL HANDBOOK

FOLDABLES HANDBOOK

REFERENCE HANDBOOK

GLOSSARY/ GLOSARIO

INDEX

SCIENCE SKILL HANDBOOK

MATH SKILL HANDBOOK

FOLDABLES HANDBOOK

REFERENCE HANDBOOK

GLOSSARY/ GLOSARIO

INDEX

Multiply Fractions To multiply with fractions, multiply the numerators and multiply the denominators. Find the simplest form if necessary.

Example

Multiply $\frac{3}{5}$ by $\frac{1}{3}$.

Step 1 Multiply the numerators and denominators.

$$\frac{3}{5} \times \frac{1}{3} = \frac{(3 \times 1)}{(5 \times 3)}\ \frac{3}{15}$$

Step 2 Find the GCF.

$$\frac{3}{15} \text{ (GCF, 3)}$$

Step 3 Divide the numerator and denominator by the GCF.

$$\frac{3 \div 3}{15 \div 3} = \frac{1}{5}$$

$\frac{3}{5}$ multiplied by $\frac{1}{3}$ is $\frac{1}{5}$.

Practice Problem Multiply $\frac{3}{14}$ by $\frac{5}{16}$.

Find a Reciprocal Two numbers whose product is 1 are called multiplicative inverses, or reciprocals.

Example

Find the reciprocal of $\frac{3}{8}$.

Step 1 Inverse the fraction by putting the denominator on top and the numerator on the bottom.

$$\frac{8}{3}$$

The reciprocal of $\frac{3}{8}$ is $\frac{8}{3}$.

Practice Problem Find the reciprocal of $\frac{4}{9}$.

Divide Fractions To divide one fraction by another fraction, multiply the dividend by the reciprocal of the divisor. Find the simplest form if necessary.

Example 1

Divide $\frac{1}{9}$ by $\frac{1}{3}$.

Step 1 Find the reciprocal of the divisor. The reciprocal of $\frac{1}{3}$ is $\frac{3}{1}$.

Step 2 Multiply the dividend by the reciprocal of the divisor.

$$\frac{\frac{1}{9}}{\frac{1}{3}} = \frac{1}{9} \times \frac{3}{1} = \frac{(1 \times 3)}{(9 \times 1)} = \frac{3}{9}$$

Step 3 Find the GCF.

$$\frac{3}{9} \text{ (GCF, 3)}$$

Step 4 Divide the numerator and denominator by the GCF.

$$\frac{3 \div 3}{9 \div 3} = \frac{1}{3}$$

$\frac{1}{9}$ divided by $\frac{1}{3}$ is $\frac{1}{3}$.

Example 2

Divide $\frac{3}{5}$ by $\frac{1}{4}$.

Step 1 Find the reciprocal of the divisor. The reciprocal of $\frac{1}{4}$ is $\frac{4}{1}$.

Step 2 Multiply the dividend by the reciprocal of the divisor.

$$\frac{\frac{3}{5}}{\frac{1}{4}} = \frac{3}{5} \times \frac{4}{1} = \frac{(3 \times 4)}{(5 \times 1)} = \frac{12}{5}$$

$\frac{3}{5}$ divided by $\frac{1}{4}$ is $\frac{12}{5}$ or $2\frac{2}{5}$.

Practice Problem Divide $\frac{3}{11}$ by $\frac{7}{10}$.

Use Ratios

When you compare two numbers by division, you are using a ratio. Ratios can be written 3 to 5, 3:5, or $\frac{3}{5}$. Ratios, like fractions, also can be written in simplest form.

Ratios can represent one type of probability, called odds. This is a ratio that compares the number of ways a certain outcome occurs to the number of possible outcomes. For example, if you flip a coin 100 times, what are the odds that it will come up heads? There are two possible outcomes, heads or tails, so the odds of coming up heads are 50:100. Another way to say this is that 50 out of 100 times the coin will come up heads. In its simplest form, the ratio is 1:2.

Example 1

A chemical solution contains 40 g of salt and 64 g of baking soda. What is the ratio of salt to baking soda as a fraction in simplest form?

Step 1 Write the ratio as a fraction.
$$\frac{\text{salt}}{\text{baking soda}} = \frac{40}{64}$$

Step 2 Express the fraction in simplest form. The GCF of 40 and 64 is 8.
$$\frac{40}{64} = \frac{40 \div 8}{64 \div 8} = \frac{5}{8}$$

The ratio of salt to baking soda in the chemical solution is 5:8.

Example 2

Sean rolls a 6-sided die 6 times. What are the odds that the side with a 3 will show?

Step 1 Write the ratio as a fraction.
$$\frac{\text{number of sides with a 3}}{\text{number of possible sides}} = \frac{1}{6}$$

Step 2 Multiply by the number of attempts.
$$\frac{1}{6} \times 6 \text{ attempts} = \frac{6}{6} \text{ attempts} = 1 \text{ attempt}$$

1 attempt out of 6 will show a 3.

Practice Problem Two metal rods measure 100 cm and 144 cm in length. What is the ratio of their lengths in simplest form?

Use Decimals

A fraction with a denominator that is a power of ten can be written as a decimal. For example, 0.27 means $\frac{27}{100}$. The decimal point separates the ones place from the tenths place.

Any fraction can be written as a decimal using division. For example, the fraction $\frac{5}{8}$ can be written as a decimal by dividing 5 by 8. Written as a decimal, it is 0.625.

Add or Subtract Decimals When adding and subtracting decimals, line up the decimal points before carrying out the operation.

Example 1

Find the sum of 47.68 and 7.80.

Step 1 Line up the decimal places when you write the numbers.

```
  47.68
+  7.80
```

Step 2 Add the decimals.

```
  ¹¹
  47.68
+  7.80
  55.48
```

The sum of 47.68 and 7.80 is 55.48.

Example 2

Find the difference of 42.17 and 15.85.

Step 1 Line up the decimal places when you write the number.

```
  42.17
− 15.85
```

Step 2 Subtract the decimals.

```
  ³¹¹
  42.17
− 15.85
  26.32
```

The difference of 42.17 and 15.85 is 26.32.

Practice Problem Find the sum of 1.245 and 3.842.

SCIENCE SKILL HANDBOOK

MATH SKILL HANDBOOK

FOLDABLES HANDBOOK

REFERENCE HANDBOOK

GLOSSARY/ GLOSARIO

INDEX

SCIENCE SKILL HANDBOOK

MATH SKILL HANDBOOK

FOLDABLES HANDBOOK

REFERENCE HANDBOOK

GLOSSARY/ GLOSARIO

INDEX

Multiply Decimals To multiply decimals, multiply the numbers like numbers without decimal points. Count the decimal places in each factor. The product will have the same number of decimal places as the sum of the decimal places in the factors.

Example

Multiply 2.4 by 5.9.

Step 1 Multiply the factors like two whole numbers.

$24 \times 59 = 1416$

Step 2 Find the sum of the number of decimal places in the factors. Each factor has one decimal place, for a sum of two decimal places.

Step 3 The product will have two decimal places.

14.16

The product of 2.4 and 5.9 is 14.16.

Practice Problem Multiply 4.6 by 2.2.

Divide Decimals When dividing decimals, change the divisor to a whole number. To do this, multiply both the divisor and the dividend by the same power of ten. Then place the decimal point in the quotient directly above the decimal point in the dividend. Then divide as you do with whole numbers.

Example

Divide 8.84 by 3.4.

Step 1 Multiply both factors by 10.

$3.4 \times 10 = 34,\ 8.84 \times 10 = 88.4$

Step 2 Divide 88.4 by 34.

$$
\begin{array}{r}
2.6 \\
34\overline{)88.4} \\
-68 \\
\hline
204 \\
-204 \\
\hline
0
\end{array}
$$

8.84 divided by 3.4 is 2.6.

Practice Problem Divide 75.6 by 3.6.

Use Proportions

An equation that shows that two ratios are equivalent is a proportion. The ratios $\frac{2}{4}$ and $\frac{5}{10}$ are equivalent, so they can be written as $\frac{2}{4} = \frac{5}{10}$. This equation is a proportion.

When two ratios form a proportion, the cross products are equal. To find the cross products in the proportion $\frac{2}{4} = \frac{5}{10}$, multiply the 2 and the 10, and the 4 and the 5. Therefore $2 \times 10 = 4 \times 5$, or $20 = 20$.

Because you know that both ratios are equal, you can use cross products to find a missing term in a proportion. This is known as solving the proportion.

Example

The heights of a tree and a pole are proportional to the lengths of their shadows. The tree casts a shadow of 24 m when a 6-m pole casts a shadow of 4 m. What is the height of the tree?

Step 1 Write a proportion.

$$\frac{\text{height of tree}}{\text{height of pole}} = \frac{\text{length of tree's shadow}}{\text{length of pole's shadow}}$$

Step 2 Substitute the known values into the proportion. Let h represent the unknown value, the height of the tree.

$$\frac{h}{6} \times \frac{24}{4}$$

Step 3 Find the cross products.

$h \times 4 = 6 \times 24$

Step 4 Simplify the equation.

$4h = 144$

Step 5 Divide each side by 4.

$$\frac{4h}{4} = \frac{144}{4}$$

$h = 36$

The height of the tree is 36 m.

Practice Problem The ratios of the weights of two objects on the Moon and on Earth are in proportion. A rock weighing 3 N on the Moon weighs 18 N on Earth. How much would a rock that weighs 5 N on the Moon weigh on Earth?

Use Percentages

The word *percent* means "out of one hundred." It is a ratio that compares a number to 100. Suppose you read that 77 percent of Earth's surface is covered by water. That is the same as reading that the fraction of Earth's surface covered by water is $\frac{77}{100}$. To express a fraction as a percent, first find the equivalent decimal for the fraction. Then, multiply the decimal by 100 and add the percent symbol.

Example 1

Express $\frac{13}{20}$ as a percent.

Step 1   Find the equivalent decimal for the fraction.

$$\begin{array}{r} 0.65 \\ 20\overline{)13.00} \\ \underline{12\,0} \\ 1\,00 \\ \underline{1\,00} \\ 0 \end{array}$$

Step 2   Rewrite the fraction $\frac{13}{20}$ as 0.65.

Step 3   Multiply 0.65 by 100 and add the % symbol.

$0.65 \times 100 = 65 = 65\%$

So, $\frac{13}{20} = 65\%$.

This also can be solved as a proportion.

Example 2

Express $\frac{13}{20}$ as a percent.

Step 1   Write a proportion.

$\frac{13}{20} = \frac{x}{100}$

Step 2   Find the cross products.

$1300 = 20x$

Step 3   Divide each side by 20.

$\frac{1300}{20} = \frac{20x}{20}$

$65\% = x$

$65 = x = 65\%$

So, $\frac{13}{20} = 65\%$

Practice Problem In one year, 73 of 365 days were rainy in one city. What percent of the days in that city were rainy?

Solve One-Step Equations

A statement that two expressions are equal is an equation. For example, $A = B$ is an equation that states that A is equal to B.

An equation is solved when a variable is replaced with a value that makes both sides of the equation equal. To make both sides equal the inverse operation is used. Addition and subtraction are inverses, and multiplication and division are inverses.

Example 1

Solve the equation $x - 10 = 35$.

Step 1   Find the solution by adding 10 to each side of the equation.

$$x - 10 = 35$$
$$x - 10 + 10 = 35 + 10$$
$$x = 45$$

Step 2   Check the solution.

$$x - 10 = 35$$
$$45 - 10 = 35$$
$$35 = 35$$

Both sides of the equation are equal, so $x = 45$.

Example 2

In the formula $a = bc$, find the value of c if $a = 20$ and $b = 2$.

Step 1   Rearrange the formula so the unknown value is by itself on one side of the equation by dividing both sides by b.

$$a = bc$$
$$\frac{a}{b} = \frac{bc}{b}$$
$$\frac{a}{b} = c$$

Step 2   Replace the variables a and b with the values that are given.

$$\frac{a}{b} = c$$
$$\frac{20}{2} = c$$
$$10 = c$$

Step 3   Check the solution.

$$a = bc$$
$$20 = 2 \times 10$$
$$20 = 20$$

Both sides of the equation are equal, so $c = 10$ is the solution when $a = 20$ and $b = 2$.

Practice Problem In the formula $h = gd$, find the value of d if $g = 12.3$ and $h = 17.4$.

SCIENCE SKILL HANDBOOK

MATH SKILL HANDBOOK

FOLDABLES HANDBOOK

REFERENCE HANDBOOK

GLOSSARY/ GLOSARIO

INDEX

Use Statistics

The branch of mathematics that deals with collecting, analyzing, and presenting data is statistics. In statistics, there are three common ways to summarize data with a single number—the mean, the median, and the mode.

The **mean** of a set of data is the arithmetic average. It is found by adding the numbers in the data set and dividing by the number of items in the set.

The **median** is the middle number in a set of data when the data are arranged in numerical order. If there were an even number of data points, the median would be the mean of the two middle numbers.

The **mode** of a set of data is the number or item that appears most often.

Another number that often is used to describe a set of data is the range. The **range** is the difference between the largest number and the smallest number in a set of data.

Example

The speeds (in m/s) for a race car during five different time trials are 39, 37, 44, 36, and 44.

To find the mean:

Step 1 Find the sum of the numbers.

39 + 37 + 44 + 36 + 44 = 200

Step 2 Divide the sum by the number of items, which is 5.

200 ÷ 5 = 40

The mean is 40 m/s.

To find the median:

Step 1 Arrange the measures from least to greatest.

36, 37, 39, 44, 44

Step 2 Determine the middle measure.

36, 37, 39, 44, 44

The median is 39 m/s.

To find the mode:

Step 1 Group the numbers that are the same together.

44, 44, 36, 37, 39

Step 2 Determine the number that occurs most in the set.

44, 44, 36, 37, 39

The mode is 44 m/s.

To find the range:

Step 1 Arrange the measures from greatest to least.

44, 44, 39, 37, 36

Step 2 Determine the greatest and least measures in the set.

44, 44, 39, 37, 36

Step 3 Find the difference between the greatest and least measures.

44 − 36 = 8

The range is 8 m/s.

Practice Problem Find the mean, median, mode, and range for the data set 8, 4, 12, 8, 11, 14, 16.

A **frequency table** shows how many times each piece of data occurs, usually in a survey. **Table 1** below shows the results of a student survey on favorite color.

Table 1 Student Color Choice		
Color	Tally	Frequency
red	IIII	4
blue	THL	5
black	II	2
green	III	3
purple	THL II	7
yellow	THL I	6

Based on the frequency table data, which color is the favorite?

Use Geometry

The branch of mathematics that deals with the measurement, properties, and relationships of points, lines, angles, surfaces, and solids is called geometry.

Perimeter The **perimeter** (P) is the distance around a geometric figure. To find the perimeter of a rectangle, add the length and width and multiply that sum by two, or $2(l + w)$. To find perimeters of irregular figures, add the length of all the sides.

Example 1

Find the perimeter of a rectangle that is 3 m long and 5 m wide.

Step 1 You know that the perimeter is 2 times the sum of the width and length.

$P = 2(3 \text{ m} + 5 \text{ m})$

Step 2 Find the sum of the width and length.

$P = 2(8 \text{ m})$

Step 3 Multiply by 2.

$P = 16 \text{ m}$

The perimeter is 16 m.

Example 2

Find the perimeter of a shape with sides measuring 2 cm, 5 cm, 6 cm, 3 cm.

Step 1 You know that the perimeter is the sum of all the sides.

$P = 2 + 5 + 6 + 3$

Step 2 Find the sum of the sides.

$P = 2 + 5 + 6 + 3$

$P = 16$

The perimeter is 16 cm.

Practice Problem Find the perimeter of a rectangle with a length of 18 m and a width of 7 m.

Practice Problem Find the perimeter of a triangle measuring 1.6 cm by 2.4 cm by 2.4 cm.

Area of a Rectangle The **area** (A) is the number of square units needed to cover a surface. To find the area of a rectangle, multiply the length times the width, or $l \times w$. When finding area, the units also are multiplied. Area is given in square units.

Example

Find the area of a rectangle with a length of 1 cm and a width of 10 cm.

Step 1 You know that the area is the length multiplied by the width.

$A = (1 \text{ cm} \times 10 \text{ cm})$

Step 2 Multiply the length by the width. Also multiply the units.

$A = 10 \text{ cm}^2$

The area is 10 cm².

Practice Problem Find the area of a square whose sides measure 4 m.

Area of a Triangle To find the area of a triangle, use the formula:

$A = \frac{1}{2}(\text{base} \times \text{height})$

The base of a triangle can be any of its sides. The height is the perpendicular distance from a base to the opposite endpoint, or vertex.

Example

Find the area of a triangle with a base of 18 m and a height of 7 m.

Step 1 You know that the area is $\frac{1}{2}$ the base times the height.

$A = \frac{1}{2}(18 \text{ m} \times 7 \text{ m})$

Step 2 Multiply $\frac{1}{2}$ by the product of 18×7. Multiply the units.

$A = \frac{1}{2}(126 \text{ m}^2)$

$A = 63 \text{ m}^2$

The area is 63 m².

Practice Problem Find the area of a triangle with a base of 27 cm and a height of 17 cm.

SCIENCE SKILL HANDBOOK

MATH SKILL HANDBOOK

FOLDABLES HANDBOOK

REFERENCE HANDBOOK

GLOSSARY/ GLOSARIO

INDEX

SCIENCE SKILL HANDBOOK

MATH SKILL HANDBOOK

FOLDABLES HANDBOOK

REFERENCE HANDBOOK

GLOSSARY/ GLOSARIO

INDEX

Circumference of a Circle The **diameter** (d) of a circle is the distance across the circle through its center, and the **radius** (r) is the distance from the center to any point on the circle. The radius is half of the diameter. The distance around the circle is called the **circumference** (C). The formula for finding the circumference is:

$$C = 2\pi r \ \text{ or } \ C = \pi d$$

The circumference divided by the diameter is always equal to 3.1415926... This nonterminating and nonrepeating number is represented by the Greek letter π (pi). An approximation often used for π is 3.14.

Example 1

Find the circumference of a circle with a radius of 3 m.

Step 1 You know the formula for the circumference is 2 times the radius times π.

$$C = 2\pi(3)$$

Step 2 Multiply 2 times the radius.

$$C = 6\pi$$

Step 3 Multiply by π.

$$C \approx 19 \text{ m}$$

The circumference is about 19 m.

Example 2

Find the circumference of a circle with a diameter of 24.0 cm.

Step 1 You know the formula for the circumference is the diameter times π.

$$C = \pi(24.0)$$

Step 2 Multiply the diameter by π.

$$C \approx 75.4 \text{ cm}$$

The circumference is about 75.4 cm.

Practice Problem Find the circumference of a circle with a radius of 19 cm.

Area of a Circle The formula for the area of a circle is: $A = \pi r^2$

Example 1

Find the area of a circle with a radius of 4.0 cm.

Step 1 $A = \pi(4.0)^2$

Step 2 Find the square of the radius.

$$A = 16\pi$$

Step 3 Multiply the square of the radius by π.

$$A \approx 50 \text{ cm}^2$$

The area of the circle is about 50 cm².

Example 2

Find the area of a circle with a radius of 225 m.

Step 1 $A = \pi(225)^2$

Step 2 Find the square of the radius.

$$A = 50625\pi$$

Step 3 Multiply the square of the radius by π.

$$A \approx 159043.1$$

The area of the circle is about 159043.1 m².

Example 3

Find the area of a circle whose diameter is 20.0 mm.

Step 1 Remember that the radius is half of the diameter.

$$A = \pi\left(\frac{20.0}{2}\right)^2$$

Step 2 Find the radius.

$$A = \pi(10.0)^2$$

Step 3 Find the square of the radius.

$$A = 100\pi$$

Step 4 Multiply the square of the radius by π.

$$A \approx 314 \text{ mm}^2$$

The area of the circle is about 314 mm².

Practice Problem Find the area of a circle with a radius of 16 m.

Volume The measure of space occupied by a solid is the **volume** (V). To find the volume of a rectangular solid, multiply the length times width times height, or $V = l \times w \times h$. It is measured in cubic units, such as cubic centimeters (cm^3).

Example

Find the volume of a rectangular solid with a length of 2.0 m, a width of 4.0 m, and a height of 3.0 m.

Step 1 You know the formula for volume is the length times the width times the height.

$$V = 2.0 \text{ m} \times 4.0 \text{ m} \times 3.0 \text{ m}$$

Step 2 Multiply the length times the width times the height.

$$V = 24 \text{ m}^3$$

The volume is 24 m³.

Practice Problem Find the volume of a rectangular solid that is 8 m long, 4 m wide, and 4 m high.

To find the volume of other solids, multiply the area of the base times the height.

Example 1

Find the volume of a solid that has a triangular base with a length of 8.0 m and a height of 7.0 m. The height of the entire solid is 15.0 m.

Step 1 You know that the base is a triangle, and the area of a triangle is $\frac{1}{2}$ the base times the height, and the volume is the area of the base times the height.

$$V = \left[\frac{1}{2}(b \times h)\right] \times 15$$

Step 2 Find the area of the base.

$$V = \left[\frac{1}{2}(8 \times 7)\right] \times 15$$

$$V = \left(\frac{1}{2} \times 56\right) \times 15$$

Step 3 Multiply the area of the base by the height of the solid.

$$V = 28 \times 15$$

$$V = 420 \text{ m}^3$$

The volume is 420 m³.

Example 2

Find the volume of a cylinder that has a base with a radius of 12.0 cm, and a height of 21.0 cm.

Step 1 You know that the base is a circle, and the area of a circle is the square of the radius times π, and the volume is the area of the base times the height.

$$V = (\pi r^2) \times 21$$

$$V = (\pi 12^2) \times 21$$

Step 2 Find the area of the base.

$$V = 144\pi \times 21$$

$$V = 452 \times 21$$

Step 3 Multiply the area of the base by the height of the solid.

$$V \approx 9{,}500 \text{ cm}^3$$

The volume is about 9,500 cm³.

Example 3

Find the volume of a cylinder that has a diameter of 15 mm and a height of 4.8 mm.

Step 1 You know that the base is a circle with an area equal to the square of the radius times π. The radius is one-half the diameter. The volume is the area of the base times the height.

$$V = (\pi r^2) \times 4.8$$

$$V = \left[\pi\left(\frac{1}{2} \times 15\right)^2\right] \times 4.8$$

$$V = (\pi 7.5^2) \times 4.8$$

Step 2 Find the area of the base.

$$V = 56.25\pi \times 4.8$$

$$V \approx 176.71 \times 4.8$$

Step 3 Multiply the area of the base by the height of the solid.

$$V \approx 848.2$$

The volume is about 848.2 mm³.

Practice Problem Find the volume of a cylinder with a diameter of 7 cm in the base and a height of 16 cm.

SCIENCE SKILL HANDBOOK

MATH SKILL HANDBOOK

FOLDABLES HANDBOOK

REFERENCE HANDBOOK

GLOSSARY/ GLOSARIO

INDEX

Science Applications

SCIENCE SKILL HANDBOOK

MATH SKILL HANDBOOK

FOLDABLES HANDBOOK

REFERENCE HANDBOOK

GLOSSARY/ GLOSARIO

INDEX

Measure in SI

The metric system of measurement was developed in 1795. A modern form of the metric system, called the International System (SI), was adopted in 1960 and provides the standard measurements that all scientists around the world can understand.

The SI system is convenient because unit sizes vary by powers of 10. Prefixes are used to name units. Look at **Table 2** for some common SI prefixes and their meanings.

Table 2 Common SI Prefixes			
Prefix	Symbol	Meaning	
kilo–	k	1,000	thousandth
hecto–	h	100	hundred
deka–	da	10	ten
deci–	d	0.1	tenth
centi–	c	0.01	hundreth
milli–	m	0.001	thousandth

Example

How many grams equal one kilogram?

Step 1 Find the prefix *kilo–* in **Table 2.**

Step 2 Using **Table 2,** determine the meaning of *kilo–*. According to the table, it means 1,000. When the prefix *kilo–* is added to a unit, it means that there are 1,000 of the units in a "kilounit."

Step 3 Apply the prefix to the units in the question. The units in the question are grams. There are 1,000 grams in a kilogram.

Practice Problem Is a milligram larger or smaller than a gram? How many of the smaller units equal one larger unit? What fraction of the larger unit does one smaller unit represent?

Dimensional Analysis

Convert SI Units In science, quantities such as length, mass, and time sometimes are measured using different units. A process called dimensional analysis can be used to change one unit of measure to another. This process involves multiplying your starting quantity and units by one or more conversion factors. A conversion factor is a ratio equal to one and can be made from any two equal quantities with different units. If 1,000 mL equal 1 L then two ratios can be made.

$$\frac{1,000 \text{ mL}}{1 \text{ L}} = \frac{1 \text{ L}}{1,000 \text{ mL}} = 1$$

One can convert between units in the SI system by using the equivalents in **Table 2** to make conversion factors.

Example

How many cm are in 4 m?

Step 1 Write conversion factors for the units given. From **Table 2,** you know that 100 cm = 1 m. The conversion factors are

$$\frac{100 \text{ cm}}{1 \text{ m}} \text{ and } \frac{1 \text{ m}}{100 \text{ cm}}$$

Step 2 Decide which conversion factor to use. Select the factor that has the units you are converting from (m) in the denominator and the units you are converting to (cm) in the numerator.

$$\frac{100 \text{ cm}}{1 \text{ m}}$$

Step 3 Multiply the starting quantity and units by the conversion factor. Cancel the starting units with the units in the denominator. There are 400 cm in 4 m.

$$4 \cancel{\text{ m}} = \frac{100 \text{ cm}}{1 \cancel{\text{ m}}} = 400 \text{ cm}$$

Practice Problem How many milligrams are in one kilogram? (Hint: You will need to use two conversion factors from **Table 2.**)

Table 3 Unit System Equivalents

Type of Measurement	Equivalent
Length	1 in = 2.54 cm 1 yd = 0.91 m 1 mi = 1.61 km
Mass and weight*	1 oz = 28.35 g 1 lb = 0.45 kg 1 ton (short) = 0.91 tonnes (metric tons) 1 lb = 4.45 N
Volume	$1 \text{ in}^3 = 16.39 \text{ cm}^3$ 1 qt = 0.95 L 1 gal = 3.78 L
Area	$1 \text{ in}^2 = 6.45 \text{ cm}^2$ $1 \text{ yd}^2 = 0.83 \text{ m}^2$ $1 \text{ mi}^2 = 2.59 \text{ km}^2$ 1 acre = 0.40 hectares
Temperature	$°C = \dfrac{(°F - 32)}{1.8}$ $K = °C + 273$

*Weight is measured in standard Earth gravity.

Convert Between Unit Systems **Table 3** gives a list of equivalents that can be used to convert between English and SI units.

Example

If a meterstick has a length of 100 cm, how long is the meterstick in inches?

Step 1 Write the conversion factors for the units given. From **Table 3,** 1 in = 2.54 cm.

$$\frac{1 \text{ in}}{2.54 \text{ cm}} \text{ and } \frac{2.54 \text{ cm}}{1 \text{ in}}$$

Step 2 Determine which conversion factor to use. You are converting from cm to in. Use the conversion factor with cm on the bottom.

$$\frac{1 \text{ in}}{2.54 \text{ cm}}$$

Step 3 Multiply the starting quantity and units by the conversion factor. Cancel the starting units with the units in the denominator. Round your answer to the nearest tenth.

$$100 \text{ cm} \times \frac{1 \text{ in}}{2.54 \text{ cm}} = 39.37 \text{ in}$$

The meterstick is about 39.4 in long.

Practice Problem 1 A book has a mass of 5 lb. What is the mass of the book in kg?

Practice Problem 2 Use the equivalent for in and cm (1 in = 2.54 cm) to show how $1 \text{ in}^3 \approx 16.39 \text{ cm}^3$.

SCIENCE SKILL HANDBOOK

MATH SKILL HANDBOOK

FOLDABLES HANDBOOK

REFERENCE HANDBOOK

GLOSSARY/ GLOSARIO

INDEX

SCIENCE SKILL HANDBOOK

MATH SKILL HANDBOOK

FOLDABLES HANDBOOK

REFERENCE HANDBOOK

GLOSSARY/ GLOSARIO

INDEX

Precision and Significant Digits

When you make a measurement, the value you record depends on the precision of the measuring instrument. This precision is represented by the number of significant digits recorded in the measurement. When counting the number of significant digits, all digits are counted except zeros at the end of a number with no decimal point such as 2,050, and zeros at the beginning of a decimal such as 0.03020. When adding or subtracting numbers with different precision, round the answer to the smallest number of decimal places of any number in the sum or difference. When multiplying or dividing, the answer is rounded to the smallest number of significant digits of any number being multiplied or divided.

Example

The lengths 5.28 and 5.2 are measured in meters. Find the sum of these lengths and record your answer using the correct number of significant digits.

Step 1 Find the sum.

5.28 m	2 digits after the decimal
+ 5.2 m	1 digit after the decimal
10.48 m	

Step 2 Round to one digit after the decimal because the least number of digits after the decimal of the numbers being added is 1.

The sum is 10.5 m.

Practice Problem 1 How many significant digits are in the measurement 7,071,301 m? How many significant digits are in the measurement 0.003010 g?

Practice Problem 2 Multiply 5.28 and 5.2 using the rule for multiplying and dividing. Record the answer using the correct number of significant digits.

Scientific Notation

Many times numbers used in science are very small or very large. Because these numbers are difficult to work with scientists use scientific notation. To write numbers in scientific notation, move the decimal point until only one non-zero digit remains on the left. Then count the number of places you moved the decimal point and use that number as a power of ten. For example, the average distance from the Sun to Mars is 227,800,000,000 m. In scientific notation, this distance is 2.278×10^{11} m. Because you moved the decimal point to the left, the number is a positive power of ten.

The mass of an electron is about 0.000 000 000 000 000 000 000 000 000 000 911 kg. Expressed in scientific notation, this mass is 9.11×10^{-31} kg. Because the decimal point was moved to the right, the number is a negative power of ten.

Example

Earth is 149,600,000 km from the Sun. Express this in scientific notation.

Step 1 Move the decimal point until one non-zero digit remains on the left.

1.496 000 00

Step 2 Count the number of decimal places you have moved. In this case, eight.

Step 2 Show that number as a power of ten, 10^8.

Earth is 1.496×10^8 km from the Sun.

Practice Problem 1 How many significant digits are in 149,600,000 km? How many significant digits are in 1.496×10^8 km?

Practice Problem 2 Parts used in a high performance car must be measured to 7×10^{-6} m. Express this number as a decimal.

Practice Problem 3 A CD is spinning at 539 revolutions per minute. Express this number in scientific notation.

Make and Use Graphs

Data in tables can be displayed in a graph—a visual representation of data. Common graph types include line graphs, bar graphs, and circle graphs.

Line Graph A line graph shows a relationship between two variables that change continuously. The independent variable is changed and is plotted on the *x*-axis. The dependent variable is observed, and is plotted on the *y*-axis.

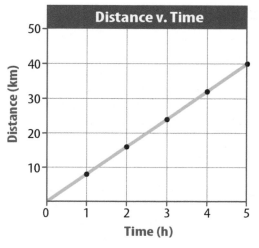

Figure 8 This line graph shows the relationship between distance and time during a bicycle ride.

Practice Problem A puppy's shoulder height is measured during the first year of her life. The following measurements were collected: (3 mo, 52 cm), (6 mo, 72 cm), (9 mo, 83 cm), (12 mo, 86 cm). Graph this data.

Find a Slope The slope of a straight line is the ratio of the vertical change, rise, to the horizontal change, run.

$$\text{Slope} = \frac{\text{vertical change (rise)}}{\text{horizontal change (run)}} = \frac{\text{change in } y}{\text{change in } x}$$

Example

Draw a line graph of the data below from a cyclist in a long-distance race.

Table 4 Bicycle Race Data

Time (h)	Distance (km)
0	0
1	8
2	16
3	24
4	32
5	40

Step 1 Determine the *x*-axis and *y*-axis variables. Time varies independently of distance and is plotted on the *x*-axis. Distance is dependent on time and is plotted on the *y*-axis.

Step 2 Determine the scale of each axis. The *x*-axis data ranges from 0 to 5. The *y*-axis data ranges from 0 to 50.

Step 3 Using graph paper, draw and label the axes. Include units in the labels.

Step 4 Draw a point at the intersection of the time value on the *x*-axis and corresponding distance value on the *y*-axis. Connect the points and label the graph with a title, as shown in **Figure 8.**

Example

Find the slope of the graph in **Figure 8**.

Step 1 You know that the slope is the change in *y* divided by the change in *x*.

$$\text{Slope} = \frac{\text{change in } y}{\text{change in } x}$$

Step 2 Determine the data points you will be using. For a straight line, choose the two sets of points that are the farthest apart.

$$\text{Slope} = \frac{(40 - 0) \text{ km}}{(5 - 0) \text{ h}}$$

Step 3 Find the change in *y* and *x*.

$$\text{Slope} = \frac{40 \text{ km}}{5 \text{ h}}$$

Step 4 Divide the change in *y* by the change in *x*.

$$\text{Slope} = \frac{8 \text{ km}}{\text{h}}$$

The slope of the graph is 8 km/h.

SCIENCE SKILL HANDBOOK

MATH SKILL HANDBOOK

FOLDABLES HANDBOOK

REFERENCE HANDBOOK

GLOSSARY/ GLOSARIO

INDEX

SCIENCE SKILL HANDBOOK

MATH SKILL HANDBOOK

FOLDABLES HANDBOOK

REFERENCE HANDBOOK

GLOSSARY/ GLOSARIO

INDEX

Bar Graph To compare data that does not change continuously you might choose a bar graph. A bar graph uses bars to show the relationships between variables. The *x*-axis variable is divided into parts. The parts can be numbers such as years, or a category such as a type of animal. The *y*-axis is a number and increases continuously along the axis.

Example

A recycling center collects 4.0 kg of aluminum on Monday, 1.0 kg on Wednesday, and 2.0 kg on Friday. Create a bar graph of this data.

Step 1 Select the *x*-axis and *y*-axis variables. The measured numbers (the masses of aluminum) should be placed on the *y*-axis. The variable divided into parts (collection days) is placed on the *x*-axis.

Step 2 Create a graph grid like you would for a line graph. Include labels and units.

Step 3 For each measured number, draw a vertical bar above the *x*-axis value up to the *y*-axis value. For the first data point, draw a vertical bar above Monday up to 4.0 kg.

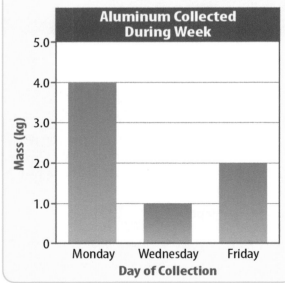

Practice Problem Draw a bar graph of the gases in air: 78% nitrogen, 21% oxygen, 1% other gases.

Circle Graph To display data as parts of a whole, you might use a circle graph. A circle graph is a circle divided into sections that represent the relative size of each piece of data. The entire circle represents 100%, half represents 50%, and so on.

Example

Air is made up of 78% nitrogen, 21% oxygen, and 1% other gases. Display the composition of air in a circle graph.

Step 1 Multiply each percent by 360° and divide by 100 to find the angle of each section in the circle.

$$78\% \times \frac{360°}{100} = 280.8°$$

$$21\% \times \frac{360°}{100} = 75.6°$$

$$1\% \times \frac{360°}{100} = 3.6°$$

Step 2 Use a compass to draw a circle and to mark the center of the circle. Draw a straight line from the center to the edge of the circle.

Step 3 Use a protractor and the angles you calculated to divide the circle into parts. Place the center of the protractor over the center of the circle and line the base of the protractor over the straight line.

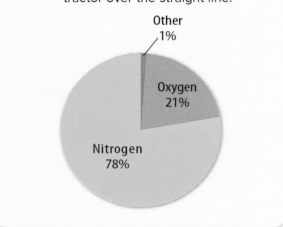

Practice Problem Draw a circle graph to represent the amount of aluminum collected during the week shown in the bar graph to the left.

Student Study Guides & Instructions
By Dinah Zike

1. You will find suggestions for Study Guides, also known as Foldables or books, in each chapter lesson and as a final project. Look at the end of the chapter to determine the project format and glue the Foldables in place as you progress through the chapter lessons.

2. Creating the Foldables or books is simple and easy to do by using copy paper, art paper, and internet printouts. Photocopies of maps, diagrams, or your own illustrations may also be used for some of the Foldables. Notebook paper is the most common source of material for study guides and 83% of all Foldables are created from it. When folded to make books, notebook paper Foldables easily fit into 11" × 17" or 12" × 18" chapter projects with space left over. Foldables made using photocopy paper are slightly larger and they fit into Projects, but snugly. Use the least amount of glue, tape, and staples needed to assemble the Foldables.

3. Seven of the Foldables can be made using either small or large paper. When 11" × 17" or 12" × 18" paper is used, these become projects for housing smaller Foldables. Project format boxes are located within the instructions to remind you of this option.

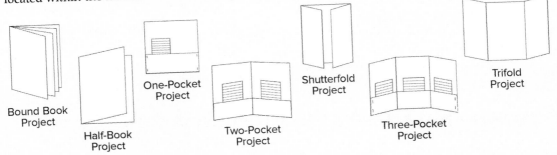

Bound Book Project

Half-Book Project

One-Pocket Project

Two-Pocket Project

Shutterfold Project

Three-Pocket Project

Trifold Project

4. Use one-gallon self-locking plastic bags to store your projects. Place strips of two-inch clear tape along the left, long side of the bag and punch holes through the taped edge. Cut the bottom corners off the bag so it will not hold air. Store this Project Portfolio inside a three-hole binder. To store a large collection of project bags, use a giant laundry-soap box. Holes can be punched in some of the Foldable Projects so they can be stored in a three-hole binder without using a plastic bag. Punch holes in the pocket books before gluing or stapling the pocket.

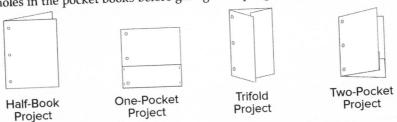

Half-Book Project

One-Pocket Project

Trifold Project

Two-Pocket Project

5. Maximize the use of the projects by collecting additional information and placing it on the back of the project and other unused spaces of the large Foldables.

SCIENCE SKILL HANDBOOK

MATH SKILL HANDBOOK

FOLDABLES HANDBOOK

REFERENCE HANDBOOK

GLOSSARY/ GLOSARIO

INDEX

Half-Book Foldable® By Dinah Zike

Step 1 Fold a sheet of notebook or copy paper in half.

Label the exterior tab and use the inside space to write information.

PROJECT FORMAT
Use 11" × 17" or 12" × 18" paper on the horizontal axis to make a large project book.

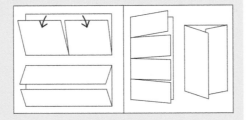

Variations

Paper can be folded horizontally, like a *hamburger* or vertically, like a *hot dog*.

A

B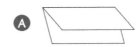

C Half-books can be folded so that one side is ½ inch longer than the other side. A title or question can be written on the extended tab.

Worksheet Foldable or Folded Book® By Dinah Zike

Step 1 Make a half-book (see above) using work sheets, internet printouts, diagrams, or maps.

Step 2 Fold it in half again.

Variations

A This folded sheet as a small book with two pages can be used for comparing and contrasting, cause and effect, or other skills.

B When the sheet of paper is open, the four sections can be used separately or used collectively to show sequences or steps.

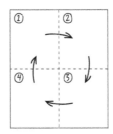

SCIENCE SKILL HANDBOOK

MATH SKILL HANDBOOK

FOLDABLES HANDBOOK

REFERENCE HANDBOOK

GLOSSARY/ GLOSARIO

INDEX

Two-Tab and Concept-Map Foldable® By Dinah Zike

Step 1 Fold a sheet of notebook or copy paper in half vertically or horizontally.

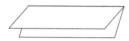

Step 2 Fold it in half again, as shown.

Step 3 Unfold once and cut along the fold line or valley of the top flap to make two flaps.

Variations

A Concept maps can be made by leaving a ½ inch tab at the top when folding the paper in half. Use arrows and labels to relate topics to the primary concept.

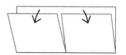

B Use two sheets of paper to make multiple page tab books. Glue or staple books together at the top fold.

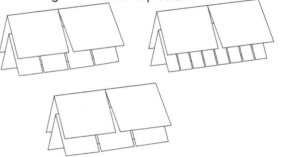

Three-Quarter Foldable® By Dinah Zike

Step 1 Make a two-tab book (see above) and cut the left tab off at the top of the fold line.

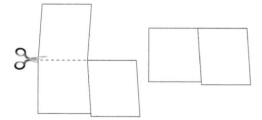

Variations

A Use this book to draw a diagram or a map on the exposed left tab. Write questions about the illustration on the top right tab and provide complete answers on the space under the tab.

B Compose a self-test using multiple choice answers for your questions. Include the correct answer with three wrong responses. The correct answers can be written on the back of the book or upside down on the bottom of the inside page.

SCIENCE SKILL HANDBOOK

MATH SKILL HANDBOOK

FOLDABLES HANDBOOK

REFERENCE HANDBOOK

GLOSSARY/ GLOSARIO

INDEX

Three-Tab Foldable® By Dinah Zike

Step 1 Fold a sheet of paper in half horizontally.

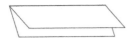

Step 2 Fold into thirds.

Step 3 Unfold and cut along the folds of the top flap to make three sections.

Variations

A Before cutting the three tabs draw a Venn diagram across the front of the book.

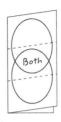

B Make a space to use for titles or concept maps by leaving a ½ inch tab at the top when folding the paper in half.

Four-Tab Foldable® By Dinah Zike

Step 1 Fold a sheet of paper in half horizontally.

Step 2 Fold in half and then fold each half as shown below.

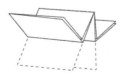

Step 3 Unfold and cut along the fold lines of the top flap to make four tabs.

Variations

A Make a space to use for titles or concept maps by leaving a ½ inch tab at the top when folding the paper in half.

B Use the book on the vertical axis, with or without an extended tab.

SCIENCE SKILL HANDBOOK

MATH SKILL HANDBOOK

FOLDABLES HANDBOOK

REFERENCE HANDBOOK

GLOSSARY/ GLOSARIO

INDEX

Folding Fifths for a Foldable® By Dinah Zike

Step 1 Fold a sheet of paper in half horizontally.

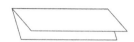

Step 2 Fold again so one-third of the paper is exposed and two-thirds are covered.

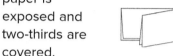

Step 3 Fold the two-thirds section in half.

Step 4 Fold the one-third section, a single thickness, backward to make a fold line.

Variations

A Unfold and cut along the fold lines to make five tabs.

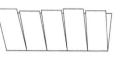

B Make a five-tab book with a ½ inch tab at the top (see two-tab instructions).

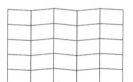

C Use 11" × 17" or 12" × 18" paper and fold into fifths for a five-column and/ or row table or chart.

- -

Folded Table or Chart, and Trifold Foldable® By Dinah Zike

Step 1 Fold a sheet of paper in the required number of vertical columns for the table or chart.

Step 2 Fold the horizontal rows needed for the table or chart.

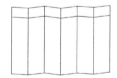

PROJECT FORMAT
Use 11" × 17" or 12" × 18" paper and fold it to make a large trifold project book or larger tables and charts.

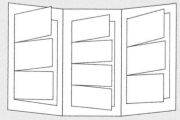

Variations

A Make a trifold by folding the paper into thirds vertically or horizontally.

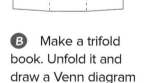

B Make a trifold book. Unfold it and draw a Venn diagram on the inside.

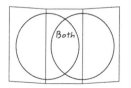

SCIENCE SKILL HANDBOOK

MATH SKILL HANDBOOK

FOLDABLES HANDBOOK

REFERENCE HANDBOOK

GLOSSARY/ GLOSARIO

INDEX

Two or Three-Pockets Foldable® By Dinah Zike

Step 1 Fold up the long side of a horizontal sheet of paper about 5 cm.

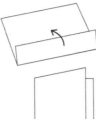

Step 2 Fold the paper in half.

Step 3 Open the paper and glue or staple the outer edges to make two compartments.

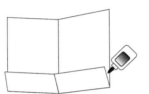

Variations

A Make a multi-page booklet by gluing several pocket books together.

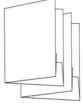

B Make a three-pocket book by using a trifold (see previous instructions).

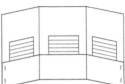

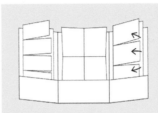

PROJECT FORMAT
Use 11" × 17" or 12" × 18" paper and fold it horizontally to make a large multi-pocket project.

Matchbook Foldable® By Dinah Zike

Step 1 Fold a sheet of paper almost in half and make the back edge about 1–2 cm longer than the front edge.

Step 2 Find the midpoint of the shorter flap.

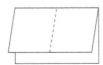

Step 3 Open the paper and cut the short side along the midpoint making two tabs.

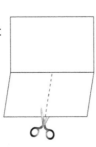

Step 4 Close the book and fold the tab over the short side.

Variations

A Make a single-tab matchbook by skipping Steps 2 and 3.

B Make two smaller matchbooks by cutting the single-tab matchbook in half.

Shutterfold Foldable® By Dinah Zike

Step 1 Begin as if you were folding a vertical sheet of paper in half, but instead of creasing the paper, pinch it to show the midpoint.

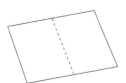

PROJECT FORMAT
Use 11" × 17" or 12" × 18" paper and fold it to make a large shutterfold project.

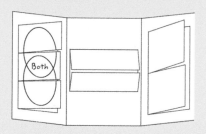

Step 2 Fold the top and bottom to the middle and crease the folds.

Variations

A Use the shutterfold on the horizontal axis.

B Create a center tab by leaving .5–2 cm between the flaps in Step 2.

- -

Four-Door Foldable® By Dinah Zike

Step 1 Make a shutterfold (see above).

Step 2 Fold the sheet of paper in half.

Step 3 Open the last fold and cut along the inside fold lines to make four tabs.

Variations

A Use the four-door book on the opposite axis.

B Create a center tab by leaving .5–2 cm between the flaps in Step 1.

SCIENCE SKILL HANDBOOK

MATH SKILL HANDBOOK

FOLDABLES HANDBOOK

REFERENCE HANDBOOK

GLOSSARY/ GLOSARIO

INDEX

SCIENCE SKILL HANDBOOK

MATH SKILL HANDBOOK

FOLDABLES HANDBOOK

REFERENCE HANDBOOK

GLOSSARY/ GLOSARIO

INDEX

Bound Book Foldable® By Dinah Zike

Step 1 Fold three sheets of paper in half. Place the papers in a stack, leaving about .5 cm between each top fold. Mark all three sheets about 3 cm from the outer edges.

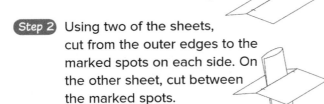

Step 2 Using two of the sheets, cut from the outer edges to the marked spots on each side. On the other sheet, cut between the marked spots.

Step 3 Take the two sheets from Step 1 and slide them through the cut in the third sheet to make a 12-page book.

Step 4 Fold the bound pages in half to form a book.

Variation

A Use two sheets of paper to make an eight-page book, or increase the number of pages by using more than three sheets.

PROJECT FORMAT
Use two or more sheets of 11" × 17" or 12" × 18" paper and fold it to make a large bound book project.

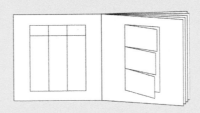

- -

Accordion Foldable® By Dinah Zike

Step 1 Fold the selected paper in half vertically, like a *hamburger*.

Step 2 Cut each sheet of folded paper in half along the fold lines.

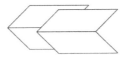

Step 3 Fold each half-sheet almost in half, leaving a 2 cm tab at the top.

Step 4 Fold the top tab over the short side, then fold it in the opposite direction.

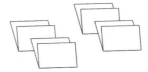

Variations

A Glue the straight edge of one paper inside the tab of another sheet. Leave a tab at the end of the book to add more pages.

B Tape the straight edge of one paper to the tab of another sheet, or just tape the straight edges of nonfolded paper end to end to make an accordion.

C Use whole sheets of paper to make a large accordion.

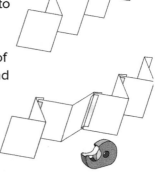

Layered Foldable® By Dinah Zike

Step 1 Stack two sheets of paper about 1–2 cm apart. Keep the right and left edges even.

Step 2 Fold up the bottom edges to form four tabs. Crease the fold to hold the tabs in place.

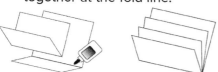

Step 3 Staple along the folded edge, or open and glue the papers together at the fold line.

Variations

A Rotate the book so the fold is at the top or to the side.

B Extend the book by using more than two sheets of paper.

Envelope Foldable® By Dinah Zike

Step 1 Fold a sheet of paper into a *taco*. Cut off the tab at the top.

Step 2 Open the *taco* and fold it the opposite way making another *taco* and an X-fold pattern on the sheet of paper.

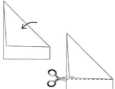

Step 3 Cut a map, illustration, or diagram to fit the inside of the envelope.

Step 4 Use the outside tabs for labels and inside tabs for writing information.

Variations

A Use 11" × 17" or 12" × 18" paper to make a large envelope.

B Cut off the points of the four tabs to make a window in the middle of the book.

SCIENCE SKILL HANDBOOK

MATH SKILL HANDBOOK

FOLDABLES HANDBOOK

REFERENCE HANDBOOK

GLOSSARY/ GLOSARIO

INDEX

Sentence Strip Foldable® By Dinah Zike

Step 1 Fold two sheets of paper in half vertically, like a *hamburger*.

Step 2 Unfold and cut along fold lines making four half sheets.

Step 3 Fold each half sheet in half horizontally, like a *hot dog*.

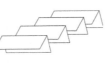

Step 4 Stack folded horizontal sheets evenly and staple together on the left side.

Step 5 Open the top flap of the first sentence strip and make a cut about 2 cm from the stapled edge to the fold line. This forms a flap that can be raised and lowered. Repeat this step for each sentence strip.

Variations

A Expand this book by using more than two sheets of paper.

B Use whole sheets of paper to make large books.

- -

Pyramid Foldable® By Dinah Zike

Step 1 Fold a sheet of paper into a *taco*. Crease the fold line, but do not cut it off.

Step 2 Open the folded sheet and refold it like a *taco* in the opposite direction to create an X-fold pattern.

Step 3 Cut one fold line as shown, stopping at the center of the X-fold to make a flap.

Step 4 Outline the fold lines of the X-fold. Label the three front sections and use the inside spaces for notes. Use the tab for the title.

Step 5 Glue the tab into a project book or notebook. Use the space under the pyramid for other information.

Step 6 To display the pyramid, fold the flap under and secure with a paper clip, if needed.

SCIENCE SKILL HANDBOOK

MATH SKILL HANDBOOK

FOLDABLES HANDBOOK

REFERENCE HANDBOOK

GLOSSARY/ GLOSARIO

INDEX

Single-Pocket or One-Pocket Foldable® By Dinah Zike

Step 1 Using a large piece of paper on a vertical axis, fold the bottom edge of the paper upwards, about 5 cm.

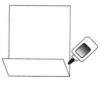

Step 2 Glue or staple the outer edges to make a large pocket.

PROJECT FORMAT
Use 11" × 17" or 12" × 18" paper and fold it vertically or horizontally to make a large pocket project.

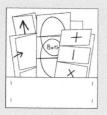

Variations

A Make the one-pocket project using the paper on the horizontal axis.

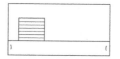

B To store materials securely inside, fold the top of the paper almost to the center, leaving about 2–4 cm between the paper edges. Slip the Foldables through the opening and under the top and bottom pockets.

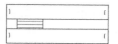

Multi-Tab Foldable® By Dinah Zike

Step 1 Fold a sheet of notebook paper in half like a *hot dog*.

Step 2 Open the paper and on one side cut every third line. This makes ten tabs on wide ruled notebook paper and twelve tabs on college ruled.

Step 3 Label the tabs on the front side and use the inside space for definitions or other information.

Variation

A Make a tab for a title by folding the paper so the holes remain uncovered. This allows the notebook Foldable to be stored in a three-hole binder.

SCIENCE SKILL HANDBOOK

MATH SKILL HANDBOOK

FOLDABLES HANDBOOK

REFERENCE HANDBOOK

GLOSSARY/ GLOSARIO

INDEX

PERIODIC TABLE OF THE ELEMENTS

Element — Hydrogen
Atomic number — 1
Symbol — **H**
Atomic mass — 1.01
State of matter

- Gas
- Liquid
- Solid
- Synthetic

A column in the periodic table is called a **group.**

A row in the periodic table is called a **period.**

1

Hydrogen
1
H
1.01

2
Lithium
3
Li
6.94

Beryllium
4
Be
9.01

Sodium
11
Na
22.99

Magnesium
12
Mg
24.31

3

4

5

6

7

8

9

Potassium
19
K
39.10

Calcium
20
Ca
40.08

Scandium
21
Sc
44.96

Titanium
22
Ti
47.87

Vanadium
23
V
50.94

Chromium
24
Cr
52.00

Manganese
25
Mn
54.94

Iron
26
Fe
55.85

Cobalt
27
Co
58.93

Rubidium
37
Rb
85.47

Strontium
38
Sr
87.62

Yttrium
39
Y
88.91

Zirconium
40
Zr
91.22

Niobium
41
Nb
92.91

Molybdenum
42
Mo
95.96

Technetium
43
Tc
(98)

Ruthenium
44
Ru
101.07

Rhodium
45
Rh
102.91

Cesium
55
Cs
132.91

Barium
56
Ba
137.33

Lanthanum
57
La
138.91

Hafnium
72
Hf
178.49

Tantalum
73
Ta
180.95

Tungsten
74
W
183.84

Rhenium
75
Re
186.21

Osmium
76
Os
190.23

Iridium
77
Ir
192.22

Francium
87
Fr
(223)

Radium
88
Ra
(226)

Actinium
89
Ac
(227)

Rutherfordium
104
Rf
(267)

Dubnium
105
Db
(268)

Seaborgium
106
Sg
(271)

Bohrium
107
Bh
(272)

Hassium
108
Hs
(270)

Meitnerium
109
Mt
(276)

The number in parentheses is the mass number of the longest lived isotope for that element.

Lanthanide series

Cerium
58
Ce
140.12

Praseodymium
59
Pr
140.91

Neodymium
60
Nd
144.24

Promethium
61
Pm
(145)

Samarium
62
Sm
150.36

Europium
63
Eu
151.96

Actinide series

Thorium
90
Th
232.04

Protactinium
91
Pa
231.04

Uranium
92
U
238.03

Neptunium
93
Np
(237)

Plutonium
94
Pu
(244)

Americium
95
Am
(243)

Metal

Metalloid

Nonmetal

Recently discovered

												18

	13	**14**	**15**	**16**	**17**	Helium 2 **He** 4.00

Boron 5 **B** 10.81	Carbon 6 **C** 12.01	Nitrogen 7 **N** 14.01	Oxygen 8 **O** 16.00	Fluorine 9 **F** 19.00	Neon 10 **Ne** 20.18

	10	**11**	**12**	Aluminum 13 **Al** 26.98	Silicon 14 **Si** 28.09	Phosphorus 15 **P** 30.97	Sulfur 16 **S** 32.07	Chlorine 17 **Cl** 35.45	Argon 18 **Ar** 39.95

Nickel 28 **Ni** 58.69	Copper 29 **Cu** 63.55	Zinc 30 **Zn** 65.38	Gallium 31 **Ga** 69.72	Germanium 32 **Ge** 72.64	Arsenic 33 **As** 74.92	Selenium 34 **Se** 78.96	Bromine 35 **Br** 79.90	Krypton 36 **Kr** 83.80

Palladium 46 **Pd** 106.42	Silver 47 **Ag** 107.87	Cadmium 48 **Cd** 112.41	Indium 49 **In** 114.82	Tin 50 **Sn** 118.71	Antimony 51 **Sb** 121.76	Tellurium 52 **Te** 127.60	Iodine 53 **I** 126.90	Xenon 54 **Xe** 131.29

Platinum 78 **Pt** 195.08	Gold 79 **Au** 196.97	Mercury 80 **Hg** 200.59	Thallium 81 **Tl** 204.38	Lead 82 **Pb** 207.20	Bismuth 83 **Bi** 208.98	Polonium 84 **Po** (209)	Astatine 85 **At** (210)	Radon 86 **Rn** (222)

Darmstadtium 110 **Ds** (281)	Roentgenium 111 **Rg** (280)	Copernicium 112 **Cn** (285)	* Ununtrium 113 **Uut** (284)	Flerovium 114 **Fl** (289)	* Ununpentium 115 **Uup** (288)	Livermorium 116 **Lv** (293)	* Ununseptium 117 **Uus** (294)	* Ununoctium 118 **Uuo** (294)

* The names and symbols for elements 113, 115, 117, and 118 are temporary. Final names will be approved by IUPAC (International Union of Pure and Applied Chemistry).

Gadolinium 64 **Gd** 157.25	Terbium 65 **Tb** 158.93	Dysprosium 66 **Dy** 162.50	Holmium 67 **Ho** 164.93	Erbium 68 **Er** 167.26	Thulium 69 **Tm** 168.93	Ytterbium 70 **Yb** 173.05	Lutetium 71 **Lu** 174.97

Curium 96 **Cm** (247)	Berkelium 97 **Bk** (247)	Californium 98 **Cf** (251)	Einsteinium 99 **Es** (252)	Fermium 100 **Fm** (257)	Mendelevium 101 **Md** (258)	Nobelium 102 **No** (259)	Lawrencium 103 **Lr** (262)

SCIENCE SKILL HANDBOOK

MATH SKILL HANDBOOK

FOLDABLES HANDBOOK

REFERENCE HANDBOOK

GLOSSARY/ GLOSARIO

INDEX

Glossary/Glosario

Cómo usar el glosario en español:
1. Busca el término en inglés que desees encontrar.
2. El término en español, junto con la definición, se encuentran en la columna de la derecha.

Pronunciation Key

Use the following key to help you sound out words in the glossary:

a	back (BAK)	ew	food (FEWD)
ay	day (DAY)	yoo	pure (PYOOR)
ah	father (FAH thur)	yew	few (FYEW)
ow	flower (FLOW ur)	uh	comma (CAH muh)
ar	car (CAR)	u (+ con)	rub (RUB)
e	less (LES)	sh	shelf (SHELF)
ee	leaf (LEEF)	ch	nature (NAY chur)
ih	trip (TRIHP)	g	gift (GIHFT)
i (i + con + e)	idea (i DEE uh)	j	gem (JEM)
oh	go (GOH)	ing	sing (SING)
aw	soft (SAWFT)	zh	vision (VIH zhun)
or	orbit (OR buht)	k	cake (KAYK)
oy	coin (COYN)	s	seed, cent (SEED, SENT)
oo	foot (FOOT)	z	zone, raise (ZOHN, RAYZ)

English	Ⓐ	Español

acid precipitation/air pressure   **precipitación ácida/presión del aire**

acid precipitation: precipitation that has a lower pH than that of normal rainwater (pH 5.6). (p. 324)

activation energy: the minimum amount of energy needed to start a chemical reaction. (p. 172)

adaptation (a dap TAY shun): an inherited trait that increases an organism's chance of surviving and reproducing in a particular environment. (p. 459)

adhesion: the attraction among molecules that are not alike. (p. 275)

air mass: a large area of air that has uniform temperature, humidity, and pressure. (p. 200)

air pressure: the force that a column of air applies on the air or a surface below it. (p. 192)

precipitación ácida: precipitación que tiene un pH más bajo que el del agua de la lluvia normal (pH 5.6). (pág. 324)

energía de activación: cantidad mínima de energía necesaria para iniciar una reacción química. (pág. 172)

adaptación: rasgo heredado que aumenta la oportunidad de un organismo de sobrevivir y reproducirse en su medioambiente. (pág. 459)

adhesión: atracción entre moléculas que son diferentes. (pág. 275)

masa de aire: amplia zona de aire que tiene uniforme de temperatura, humedad y presión. (pág. 200)

presión del aire: presión que una columna de aire ejerce sobre el aire o sobre la superficie debajo de ella. (pág. 192)

SCIENCE SKILL HANDBOOK
MATH SKILL HANDBOOK
FOLDABLES HANDBOOK
REFERENCE HANDBOOK
GLOSSARY/GLOSARIO
INDEX

Air Quality Index (AQI): a scale that ranks levels of ozone and other air pollutants. (p. 327)

alkali (AL kuh li) metal: an element in group 1 on the periodic table. (p. 95)

alkaline (AL kuh lun) earth metal: an element in group 2 on the periodic table. (p. 95)

allele (uh LEEL): a different form of a gene. (p. 416)

analogous (uh NAH luh gus) structures: body parts that perform a similar function but differ in structure. (p. 467)

antibiotic (an ti bi AH tihk): a medicine that stops the growth and reproduction of bacteria. (p. 494)

antibody: a protein that can attach to a pathogen and make it useless. (p. 503)

asexual reproduction: a type of reproduction in which one parent organism produces offspring without meiosis and fertilization. (p. 385)

atom: the smallest piece of an element that still represents that element. (p. 53)

atomic number: the number of protons in an atom of an element. (p. 65)

autotroph (AW tuh trohf): an organism that converts light energy to usable energy. (p. 348)

average atomic mass: the average mass of the element's isotopes, weighted according to the abundance of each isotope. (p. 67)

Índice de calidad del aire (ICA): escala que clasifica los niveles de ozono y de otros contaminantes del aire. (pág. 327)

metal alcalino: elemento del grupo 1 de la tabla periódica. (pág. 95)

metal alcalinotérreo: elemento del grupo 2 de la tabla periódica. (pág. 95)

alelo: forma diferente de un gen. (pág. 416)

estructuras análogas: partes del cuerpo que ejecutan una función similar pero tienen una estructura distinta. (pág. 467)

antibiótico: medicina que detiene el crecimiento y reproducción de las bacterias. (pág. 494)

anticuerpo: proteína que se adhiere a un patógeno y lo hace inútil. (pág. 503)

reproducción asexual: tipo de reproducción en la cual un organismo parental produce crías sin mitosis ni fertilización. (pág. 385)

átomo: parte más pequeña de un elemento que mantiene la identidad de dicho elemento. (pág. 53)

número atómico: número de protones en el átomo de un elemento. (pág. 65)

autótrofo: organismo que convierte la energía lumínica en energía útil. (pág. 348)

masa atómica promedio: masa atómica promedio de los isótopos de un elemento, ponderado según la abundancia de cada isótopo. (pág. 67)

B

bacterium: a microscopic prokaryote. (p. 483)

binomial nomenclature (bi NOH mee ul • NOH mun klay chur): a naming system that gives each organism a two-word scientific name. (p. 350)

bioindicator: an organism that is sensitive to environmental conditions and is one of the first to respond to changes. (p. 286)

biological evolution: the change over time in populations of related organisms. (p. 451)

bioremediation (bi oh rih mee dee AY shun): the use of organisms, such as bacteria, to clean up environmental pollution. (p. 493)

blizzard: a violent winter storm characterized by freezing temperatures, strong winds, and blowing snow. (p. 207)

budding: the process during which a new organism grows by mitosis and cell division on the body of its parent. (p. 387)

bacteria: procariota microscópica. (pág. 483)

nomenclatura binomial: sistema de nombrar que le da a cada organismo un nombre científico de dos palabras. (pág. 350)

bioindicador: organismo que es sensible a las condiciones medioambientales y es uno de los primeros en responder a los cambios. (pág. 286)

evolución biológica: cambio a través del tiempo en las poblaciones de organismos relacionados. (pág. 451)

biorremediación: uso de microorganismos, como bacterias, para limpiar la contaminación del medioambiente. (pág. 493)

ventisca: tormenta violenta de invierno caracterizada por temperaturas heladas, vientos fuertes, y nieve que sopla. (pág. 207)

germinación: proceso durante el cual un organismo nuevo crece por medio de mitosis y división celular en el cuerpo de su progenitor. (pág. 387)

SCIENCE SKILL HANDBOOK

MATH SKILL HANDBOOK

FOLDABLES HANDBOOK

REFERENCE HANDBOOK

GLOSSARY/ GLOSARIO

INDEX

C

camouflage (KAM uh flahj): an adaptation that enables a species to blend in with its environment. (p. 460)

carrying capacity: the largest number of individuals of one species that an ecosystem can support over time. (p. 300)

cast: a fossil copy of an organism made when a mold of the organism is filled with sediment or mineral deposits. (p. 447)

catalyst: a substance that increases reaction rate by lowering the activation energy of a reaction. (p. 174)

chemical bond: a force that holds two or more atoms together. (p. 120)

chemical change: a change in matter in which the substances that make up the matter change into other substances with different chemical and physical properties. (p. 35)

chemical equation: a description of a reaction using element symbols and chemical formulas. (p. 156)

chemical formula: a group of chemical symbols and numbers that represent the elements and the number of atoms of each element that make up a compound. (p. 132)

chemical property: the ability or inability of a substance to combine with or change into one or more new substances. (p. 34)

chemical reaction: a process in which atoms of one or more substances rearrange to form one or more new substances. (p. 153)

climate: the long-term average weather conditions that occur in a particular region. (p. 227)

cloning: a type of asexual reproduction performed in a laboratory that produces identical individuals from a cell or a cluster of cells taken from a multicellular organism. (p. 390)

codominance: an inheritance pattern in which both alleles can be observed in a phenotype. (p. 420)

coefficient: a number placed in front of an element symbol or chemical formula in an equation. (p. 160)

camuflaje: adaptación que permite a las especies mezclarse con su medioambiente. (pág. 460)

capacidad de carga: número mayor de individuos de una especie que un medioambiente puede mantener. (pág. 300)

contramolde: copia fósil de un organismo compuesto en un molde de el organismo está lleno de sedimentos o los depósitos de minerales. (pág. 447)

catalizador: sustancia que aumenta la velocidad de reacción al disminuir la energía de activación de una reacción. (pág. 174)

enlace químico: fuerza que mantiene unidos dos o más átomos. (pág. 120)

cambio químico: cambio de la materia en el cual las sustancias que componen la materia se transforman en otras sustancias con propiedades químicas y físicas diferentes. (pág. 35)

ecuación química: descripción de una reacción con símbolos de los elementos y fórmulas químicas. (pág. 156)

fórmula química: grupo de símbolos químicos y números que representan los elementos y el número de átomos de cada elemento que forman un compuesto. (pág. 132)

propiedad química: capacidad o incapacidad de una sustancia para combinarse con o transformarse en una o más sustancias. (pág. 34)

reacción química: proceso en el cual átomos de una o más sustancias se acomodan para formar una o más sustancias nuevas. (pág. 153)

clima: promedio a largo plazo de las condiciones del tiempo atmosférico de una región en particular. (pág. 227)

clonación: tipo de reproducción asexual realizada en un laboratorio que produce individuos idénticos a partir de una célula o grupo de células tomadas de un organismo pluricelular. (pág. 390)

condominante: patrón heredado en el cual los dos alelos se observan en un fenotipo. (pág. 420)

coeficiente: número colocado en frente del símbolo de un elemento o de una fórmula química en una ecuación. (pág. 160)

cohesion: the attraction among molecules that are alike. (p. 275)

combustion: a chemical reaction in which a substance combines with oxygen and releases energy. (p. 166)

comparative anatomy: the study of similarities and differences among structures of living species. (p. 466)

compound: a substance containing atoms of two or more different elements chemically bonded together. (p. 12)

computer model: detailed computer programs that solve a set of complex mathematical formulas. (p. 214)

concentration: the amount of a particular solute in a given amount of solution. (p. 38)

condensation: the process by which a gas changes to a liquid. (p. 267)

conjugation (kahn juh GAY shun): a process during which two bacteria of the same species attach to each other and combine their genetic material. (p. 486)

constants: the factors in an experiment that remain the same. (p. NOS 27)

control group: the part of a controlled experiment that contains the same factors as the experimental group, but the independent variable is not changed. (p. NOS 27)

covalent bond: a chemical bond formed when two atoms share one or more pairs of valence electrons. (p. 129)

critical thinking: comparing what you already know with information you are given in order to decide whether you agree with it. (p. NOS 10)

cytoplasm: the liquid part of a cell inside the cell membrane; contains salts and other molecules. (p. 358)

cohesión: atracción entre moléculas que son parecidas. (pág. 275)

combustión: reacción química en la cual una sustancia se combina con oxígeno y libera energía. (pág. 166)

anatomía comparativa: estudio de las similitudes y diferencias entre las estructuras de las especies vivas. (pág. 466)

compuesto: sustancia que contiene átomos de dos o más elementos diferentes unidos químicamente. (pág. 12)

modelo de computadora: programas de computadora que resuelven un conjunto de fórmulas matemáticas complejas. (pág. 214)

concentración: cantidad de cierto soluto en una cantidad dada de solución. (pág. 38)

condensación: proceso por el cual un organismo cambia a líquido. (pág. 267)

conjugación: proceso durante el cual dos bacterias de la misma especie se adhieren una a la otra y combinan sus material genético. (pág. 486)

constantes: factores que no cambian en un experimento. (pág. NOS 27)

grupo de control: parte de un experimento controlado que contiene los mismos factores que el grupo experimental, pero la variable independiente no se cambia. (pág. NOS 27)

enlace covalente: enlace químico formado cuando dos átomos comparten uno o más pares de electrones de valencia. (pág. 129)

pensamiento crítico: comparación que se hace cuando se sabe algo acerca de información nueva, y se decide si se está o no de acuerdo con ella. (pág. NOS 10)

citoplasma: fluido en el interior de una célula que contiene sales y otras moléculas. (pág. 358)

D

---

decomposition: a type of chemical reaction in which one compound breaks down and forms two or more substances. (p. 165)

decomposition: the breaking down of dead organisms and organic waste. (p. 492)

deforestation: the removal of large areas of forests for human purposes. (p. 305)

descomposición: tipo de reacción química en la que un compuesto se descompone y forma dos o más sustancias. (pág. 165)

descomposición: degradación de organismos muertos y desecho orgánico. (pág. 492)

deforestación: eliminación de grandes áreas de bosques con propósitos humanos. (pág. 305)

SCIENCE SKILL HANDBOOK

MATH SKILL HANDBOOK

FOLDABLES HANDBOOK

REFERENCE HANDBOOK

GLOSSARY/ GLOSARIO

INDEX

deforestation: the removal of large areas of forests for human purposes. (p. 247)

density: the mass per unit volume of a substance. (p. 27)

dependent variable: the factor a scientist observes or measures during an experiment. (p. NOS 27)

description: a spoken or written summary of an observation. (p. NOS 18)

desertification: the development of desertlike conditions due to human activities and/or climate change. (p. 306)

dew point: temperature at which air is saturated and condensation can occur. (p. 193)

diploid: a cell that has pairs of chromosomes. (p. 374)

dissolve: to form a solution by mixing evenly. (p. 13)

DNA: the abbreviation for deoxyribonucleic (dee AHK sih ri boh noo klee ihk) acid, an organism's genetic material. (p. 426)

dominant (DAH muh nunt) trait: a genetic factor that blocks another genetic factor. (p. 411)

Doppler radar: a specialized type of radar that can detect precipitation as well as the movement of small particles, which can be used to approximate wind speed. (p. 212)

double-replacement reaction: a type of chemical reaction in which the negative ions in two compounds switch places, forming two new compounds. (p. 166)

drought: a period of below-average precipitation. (p. 241)

ductility (duk TIH luh tee): the ability to be pulled into thin wires. (p. 94)

deforestación: eliminación de grandes áreas de bosques con propósitos humanos. (pág. 247)

densidad: cantidad de masa por unidad de volumen de una sustancia. (pág. 27)

variable dependiente: factor que el científico observa o mide durante un experimento. (pág. NOS 27)

descripción: resumen oral o escrito de una observación. (pág. NOS 18)

desertificación: desarrollo de condiciones parecidas a las del desierto debido a actividades humanas y/o al cambio en el clima. (pág. 306)

punto de rocío: temperatura en la cual el aire está saturado y occure la condensación. (pág. 193)

diploide: célula que tiene pares de cromosomas. (pág. 374)

disolver: preparar una solución mezclando de manera homogénea. (pág. 13)

ADN: abreviatura para ácido desoxirribonucleico, material genético de un organismo. (pág. 426)

rasgo dominante: factor genético que bloquea otro factor genético. (pág. 411)

radar Doppler: tipo de radar especializado que detecta tanto la precipitación como el movimiento de partículas pequeñas, que se pueden usar para determinar la velocidad aproximada del viento. (pág. 212)

reacción de sustitución doble: tipo de reacción química en la que los iones negativos de dos compuestos intercambian lugares, para formar dos compuestos nuevos. (pág. 166)

sequía: período de bajo promedio de precipitación. (pág. 241)

ductilidad: capacidad para formar alambres delgados. (pág. 94)

E

egg: the female reproductive, or sex, cell; forms in an ovary (p. 373)

El Niño/Southern Oscillation: the combined ocean and atmospheric cycle that results in weakened trade winds across the Pacific Ocean. (p. 240)

electron cloud: the region surrounding an atom's nucleus where one or more electrons are most likely to be found. (p. 60)

óvulo: célula reproductiva femenina o sexual; forma en un ovario. (pág. 373)

El Niño/Oscilación meridional: ciclo atmosférico y oceánico combinado que produce el debilitamiento de los vientos alisios en el Océano Pacífico. (pág. 240)

nube de electrones: región que rodea el núcleo de un átomo en donde es más probable encontrar uno o más electrones. (pág. 60)

SCIENCE SKILL HANDBOOK

MATH SKILL HANDBOOK

FOLDABLES HANDBOOK

REFERENCE HANDBOOK

GLOSSARY/ GLOSARIO

INDEX

electron dot diagram: a model that represents valence electrons in an atom as dots around the element's chemical symbol. (p. 123)

electron: a negatively charged particle that occupies the space in an atom outside the nucleus. (p. 55)

element: a substance that consists of only one type of atom. (p. 11)

embryology (em bree AH luh jee): the science of the development of embryos from fertilization to birth. (p. 468)

endospore (EN doh spor): a thick internal wall that a bacterium builds around its chromosome and part of its cytoplasm. (p. 487)

endothermic reaction: a chemical reaction that absorbs thermal energy. (p. 171)

enzyme: a catalyst that speeds up chemical reactions in living cells. (p. 174)

eukaryotic (yew ker ee AH tihk) cell: a cell that has a nucleus and other membrane-bound organelles. (p. 356)

evaporation: the process of a liquid changing to a gas at the surface of the liquid. (p. 267)

exothermic reaction: a chemical reaction that releases thermal energy. (p. 171)

experimental group: the part of the controlled experiment used to study relationships among variables. (p. NOS 27)

explanation: an interpretation of observations. (p. NOS 18)

extinction (ihk STINGK shun): event that occurs when the last individual organism of a species dies. (p. 450)

diagrama de puntos de Lewis: modelo que representa electrones de valencia en un átomo a manera de puntos alrededor del símbolo químico del elemento. (pág. 123)

electrón: partícula cargada negativamente que ocupa el espacio por fuera del núcleo de un átomo. (pág. 55)

elemento: sustancia que consiste de un sólo tipo de átomo. (pág. 11)

embriología: ciencia que trata el desarrollo de embriones desde la fertilización hasta el nacimiento. (pág. 468)

endospora: pared interna gruesa que una bacteria produce alrededor del cromosoma y parte del citoplasma. (pág. 487)

reacción endotérmica: reacción química que absorbe energía térmica. (pág. 171)

enzima: catalizador que acelera reacciones químicas en las células vivas. (pág. 174)

célula eucariótica: célula que tiene un núcleo y otros organelos limitados por una membrana. (pág. 356)

evaporación: proceso por el cual un líquido cambia a gas en la superficie de un líquido. (pág. 267)

reacción exotérmica: reacción química que libera energía térmica. (pág. 171)

grupo experimental: parte del experimento controlado que se usa para estudiar las relaciones entre las variables. (pág. NOS 27)

explicación: interpretación de las observaciones. (pág. NOS 18)

extinción: evento que ocurre cuando el último organismo individual de una especie muere. (pág. 450)

F

fertilization (fur tuh luh ZAY shun): a reproductive process in which a sperm joins with an egg. (p. 373)

fission: cell division that forms two genetically identical cells. (pp. 386, 486)

flagellum (fluh JEH lum): a long whiplike structure on many bacteria. (p. 486)

fossil record: record of all the fossils ever discovered on Earth. (p. 445)

front: a boundary between two air masses. (p. 202)

fertilización: proceso reproductivo en el cual un espermatozoide se une con un óvulo. (pág. 373)

fisión: división celular que forma dos células genéticamente idénticas. (pág. 386, 486)

flagelo: estructura larga similar a un látigo que tienen muchas bacterias. (pág. 486)

registro fósil: registro de todos los fósiles descubiertos en la Tierra. (pág. 445)

frente: límite entre dos masas de aire. (pág. 202)

SCIENCE SKILL HANDBOOK

MATH SKILL HANDBOOK

FOLDABLES HANDBOOK

REFERENCE HANDBOOK

GLOSSARY/ GLOSARIO

INDEX

G

gene (JEEN): a section of DNA on a chromosome that has genetic information for one trait. (p. 416)

genetics: the study of how traits are passed from parents to offspring. (p. 405)

genotype (JEE nuh tipe): the alleles of all the genes on an organism's chromosomes; controls an organism's phenotype. (p. 416)

geologic time scale: a chart that divides Earth's history into different time units based on changes in the rocks and fossils. (p. 449)

global climate model: a set of complex equations used to predict future climates. (p. 249)

global warming: an increase in the average temperature of Earth's surface. (pp. 246, 325)

greenhouse effect: the natural process that occurs when certain gases in the atmosphere absorb and reradiate thermal energy from the Sun. (p. 326)

greenhouse gas: a gas in the atmosphere that absorbs Earth's outgoing infrared radiation. (p. 246)

group: a column on the periodic table. (p. 88)

gen: parte del ADN en un cromosoma que contiene información genética para un rasgo. (pág. 416)

genética: estudio de cómo los rasgos pasan de los padres a los hijos. (pág. 405)

genotipo: de los alelos de todos los genes en los cromosomas de un organismo, los controles de fenotipo de un organismo. (pág. 416)

escala de tiempo geológico: tabla que divide la historia de la Tierra en diferentes unidades de tiempo, basado en los cambios en las rocas y fósiles de. (pág. 449)

modelo de clima global: conjunto de ecuaciones complejas para predecir climas futuros. (pág. 249)

calentamiento global: incremento en la temperatura promedio de la superficie de la Tierra. (pág. 246, 325)

efecto invernadero: proceso natural que ocurre cuando ciertos gases en la atmósfera absorben y vuelven a irradiar la energía térmica del Sol. (pág. 326)

gas de invernadero: gas en la atmósfera que absorbe la salida de radiación infrarroja de la Tierra. (pág. 246)

grupo: columna en la tabla periódica. (pág. 88)

H

habitat: the place within an ecosystem where an organism lives; provides the biotic and abiotic factors an organism needs to survive and reproduce. (p. 349)

halogen (HA luh jun): an element in group 17 on the periodic table. (p. 103)

haploid: a cell that has only one chromosome from each pair. (p. 375)

heredity (huh REH duh tee): the passing of traits from parents to offspring. (p. 405)

heterogeneous mixture: a mixture in which substances are not evenly mixed. (p. 13)

heterotroph (HE tuh roh trohf): an organism that obtains energy from other organisms. (p. 348)

heterozygous (he tuh roh ZI gus): a genotype in which the two alleles of a gene are different. (p. 417)

hábitat: lugar en un ecosistema donde vive un organismo; proporciona los factores bióticos y abióticos de un organismo necesita para sobrevivir y reproducirse. (pág. 349)

halógeno: elemento del grupo 17 de la tabla periódica. (pág. 103)

haploide: célula que tiene solamente un cromosoma de cada par. (pág. 375)

herencia: paso de rasgos de los padres a los hijos. (pág. 405)

mezcla heterogénea: mezcla en la cual las sustancias no están mezcladas de manera uniforme. (pág. 13)

heterótrofo: organismo que obtiene energía de otros organismos. (pág. 348)

heterocigoto: genotipo en el cual los dos alelos de un gen son diferentes. (pág. 417)

high-pressure system: a large body of circulating air with high pressure at its center and lower pressure outside of the system. (p. 199)

homogeneous mixture: a mixture in which two or more substances are evenly mixed but not bonded together. (p. 13)

homologous (huh MAH luh gus) chromosomes: pairs of chromosomes that have genes for the same traits arranged in the same order. (p. 374)

homologous (huh MAH luh gus) structures: body parts of organisms that are similar in structure and position but different in function. (p. 466)

homozygous (hoh muh ZI gus): a genotype in which the two alleles of a gene are the same. (p. 417)

humidity (hyew MIH duh tee): the amount of water vapor in the air. (p. 192)

hurricane: an intense tropical storm with winds exceeding 119 km/h. (p. 206)

hydrosphere: the system containing all Earth's water. (p. 266)

hypothesis: a possible explanation for an observation that can be tested by scientific investigations. (p. NOS 4)

sistema de alta presión: gran cuerpo de aire circulante con presión alta en el centro y presión más baja fuera del sistema. (pág. 199)

mezcla homogénea: mezcla en la cual dos o más sustancias están mezcladas de manera uniforme, pero no están unidas químicamente. (pág. 13)

cromosomas homólogos: pares de cromosomas que tienen genes de iguales rasgos dispuestos en el mismo orden. (pág. 374)

estructuras homólogas: partes del cuerpo de los organismos que son similares en estructura y posición pero diferentes en función. (pág. 466)

homocigoto: genotipo en el cual los dos alelos de un gen son iguales. (pág. 417)

humedad: cantidad de vapor de agua en el aire. (pág. 192)

huracán: tormenta tropical intensa con vientos que exceden los 119 km/h. (pág. 206)

hidrosfera: sistema que contiene toda el agua de la Tierra. (pág. 266)

hipótesis: explicación posible para una observación que puede ponerse a prueba en investigaciones científicas. (pág. NOS 4)

I

ice age: a period of time when a large portion of Earth's surface is covered by glaciers. (p. 236)

incomplete dominance: an inheritance pattern in which an offspring's phenotype is a combination of the parents' phenotypes. (p. 420)

independent variable: the factor that is changed by the investigator to observe how it affects a dependent variable. (p. NOS 27)

inference: a logical explanation of an observation that is drawn from prior knowledge or experience. (p. NOS 6)

inhibitor: a substance that slows, or even stops, a chemical reaction. (p. 174)

interglacial: a warm period that occurs during an ice age or between ice ages. (p. 236)

International System of Units (SI): the internationally accepted system of measurement. (p. NOS 10)

ion (I ahn): an atom that is no longer neutral because it has lost or gained valence electrons. (pp. 70, 136)

era del hielo: período de tiempo cuando los glaciares cubren una gran porción de la superficie de la Tierra. (pág. 236)

dominancia incompleta: patrón heredado en el cual el fenotipo de un hijo es una combinación de los fenotipos de los padres. (pág. 420)

variable independiente: factor que el investigador cambia para observar cómo afecta la variable dependiente. (pág. NOS 27)

inferencia: explicación lógica de una observación que se obtiene a partir de conocimiento previo o experiencia. (pág. NOS 6)

inhibidor: sustancia que disminuye, o incluso detiene, una reacción química. (pág. 174)

interglacial: período tibio que ocurre durante una era del hielo o entre las eras del hielo. (pág. 236)

Sistema Internacional de Unidades (SI): sistema de medidas aceptado internacionalmente. (pág. NOS 10)

ión: átomo que no es neutro porque ha ganado o perdido electrones de valencia. (pág. 70, 136)

SCIENCE SKILL HANDBOOK

MATH SKILL HANDBOOK

FOLDABLES HANDBOOK

REFERENCE HANDBOOK

GLOSSARY/GLOSARIO

INDEX

ionic bond: the attraction between positively and negatively charged ions in an ionic compound. (p. 138)

isobar: lines that connect all places on a map where pressure has the same value. (p. 213)

isotopes: atoms of the same element that have different numbers of neutrons. (p. 66)

enlace iónico: atracción entre iones cargados positiva y negativamente en un compuesto iónico. (pág. 138)

isobara: línea que conectan todos los lugares en un mapa donde la presión tiene el mismo valor. (pág. 213)

isótopos: átomos del mismo elemento que tienen diferente número de neutrones. (pág. 66)

L

law of conservation of mass: law that states that the total mass of the reactants before a chemical reaction is the same as the total mass of the products after the chemical reaction. (p. 158)

lens: a transparent object with at least one curved side that causes light to change direction.

low-pressure system: a large body of circulating air with low pressure at its center and higher pressure outside of the system. (p. 199)

luster: the way a mineral reflects or absorbs light at its surface. (p. 93)

ley de la conservación de la masa: ley que plantea que la masa total de los reactivos antes de una reacción química es la misma que la masa total de los productos después de la reacción química. (pág. 158)

lente: un objeto transparente con al menos un lado curvo que hace que la luz para cambiar de dirección.

sistema baja presión: gran cuerpo de aire circulante con presión baja en el centro y presión más alta fuera del sistema. (pág. 199)

brillo: forma en que un mineral refleja o absorbe la luz en su superficie. (pág. 93)

M

malleability (ma lee uh BIH luh tee): the ability of a substance to be hammered or rolled into sheets. (p. 94)

mass number: the sum of the number of protons and neutrons in an atom. (p. 66)

mass: the amount of matter in an object. (p. 20)

matter: anything that has mass and takes up space. (p. 9)

meiosis: a process in which one diploid cell divides to make four haploid sex cells. (p. 375)

metal: an element that is generally shiny, is easily pulled into wires or hammered into thin sheets, and is a good conductor of electricity and thermal energy. (p. 93)

metallic bond: a bond formed when many metal atoms share their pooled valence electrons. (p. 139)

metalloid (MEH tul oyd): an element that has physical and chemical properties of both metals and nonmetals. (p. 105)

maleabilidad: capacidad de una sustancia de martillarse o laminarse para formar hojas. (pág. 94)

número de masa: suma del número de protones y neutrones de un átomo. (pág. 66)

masa: cantidad de materia en un objeto. (pág. 20)

materia: cualquier cosa que tiene masa y ocupa espacio. (pág. 9)

meiosis: proceso en el cual una célula diploide se divide para constituir cuatro células sexuales haploides. (pág. 375)

metal: elemento que generalmente es brillante, fácilmente puede estirarse para formar alambres o martillarse para formar hojas delgadas y es buen conductor de electricidad y energía térmica. (pág. 93)

enlace metálico: enlace formado cuando muchos átomos metálicos comparten su banco de electrones de valencia. (pág. 139)

metaloide: elemento que tiene las propiedades físicas y químicas de metales y no metales. (pág. 105)

SCIENCE SKILL HANDBOOK

MATH SKILL HANDBOOK

FOLDABLES HANDBOOK

REFERENCE HANDBOOK

GLOSSARY/ GLOSARIO

INDEX

microclimate: a localized climate that is different from the climate of the larger area surrounding it. (p. 231)

mimicry (MIH mih kree): an adaptation in which one species looks like another species. (p. 460)

mitochondrion (mi tuh KAHN dree ahn): an organelle that breaks down food and releases energy. (p. 359)

mixture: matter that can vary in composition. (p. 12)

mold: the impression of an organism in a rock. (p. 447)

molecule (MAH lih kyewl): two or more atoms that are held together by covalent bonds and act as a unit. (p. 130)

monsoon: a wind circulation pattern that changes direction with the seasons. (p. 241)

mutation: a permanent change in the sequence of DNA, or the nucleotides, in a gene or a chromosome. (p. 431)

microclima: clima localizado que es diferente del clima de área más extensa que lo rodea. (pág. 231)

mimetismo: una adaptación en el cual una especie se parece a otra especie. (pág. 460)

mitocondria: organelo que descompone el alimento y libera energía. (pág. 359)

mezcla: materia cuya composición puede variar. (pág. 12)

molde: impresión de un organismo en una roca. (pág. 447)

molécula: dos o más átomos que están unidos mediante enlaces covalentes y actúan como una unidad. (pág. 130)

monsón: patrón de viento circulante que cambia de dirección con las estaciones. (pág. 241)

mutación: cambio permanente en la secuencia de ADN, de los nucleótidos, en un gen o en un cromosoma. (pág. 431)

N

natural selection: the process by which organisms with variations that help them survive in their environment live longer, compete better, and reproduce more than those that do not have the variations. (p. 458)

naturalist: a person who studies plants and animals by observing them. (p. 455)

neutron: a neutral particle in the nucleus of an atom. (p. 59)

nitrate: a nitrogen-based compound often used in fertilizers. (p. 285)

nitrogen fixation (NI truh jun • fihk SAY shun): the process that changes atmospheric nitrogen into nitrogen compounds that are usable by living things. (p. 492)

noble gas: an element in group 18 on the periodic table. (p. 104)

nonmetal: an element that has no metallic properties. (p. 101)

nonpoint-source pollution: pollution from several widespread sources that cannot be traced back to a single location. (pp. 283, 317)

selección natural: proceso por el cual los organismos con variaciones que las ayudan a sobrevivir en sus medioambientes viven más, compiten mejor y se reproducen más que aquellas que no tienen esas variaciones. (pág. 458)

naturalista: persona que estudia las plantas y los animales por medio de la observación. (pág. 455)

neutrón: partícula neutra en el núcleo de un átomo. (pág. 59)

nitrato: compuesto con base en nitrógeno usado en los fertilizantes. (pág. 285)

fijación del nitrógeno: proceso que cambia el nitrógeno atmosférico en componentes de nitrógeno útiles para los seres vivos. (pág. 492)

gas noble: elemento del grupo 18 de la tabla periódica. (pág. 104)

no metal: elemento que tiene propiedades no metálicas. (pág. 101)

contaminación de fuente no puntual: contaminación de varias fuentes apartadas que no se pueden rastrear hasta una sola ubicación. (pág. 283, 317)

SCIENCE SKILL HANDBOOK

MATH SKILL HANDBOOK

FOLDABLES HANDBOOK

REFERENCE HANDBOOK

GLOSSARY/ GLOSARIO

INDEX

nuclear decay: a process that occurs when an unstable atomic nucleus changes into another more stable nucleus by emitting radiation. (p. 69)

nucleotide: a molecule made of a nitrogen base, a sugar, and a phosphate group. (p. 427)

nucleus: the region in the center of an atom where most of an atom's mass and positive charge are concentrated. (p. 58)

desintegración nuclear: proceso que ocurre cuando un núcleo atómico inestable cambia a otro núcleo atómico más estable mediante emisión de radiación. (pág. 69)

nucelótido: molécula constituida de una base de nitrógeno, azúcar y un grupo de fosfato. (pág. 427)

núcleo: región en el centro de un átomo donde se concentra la mayor cantidad de masa y las cargas positivas. (pág. 58)

observation: the act of using one or more of your senses to gather information and take note of what occurs. (p. NOS 6)

observación: acción de usar uno o más sentidos para reunir información y tomar notar de lo que ocurre. (pág. NOS 6)

particulate matter: the mix of both solid and liquid particles in the air. (p. 324)

pasteurization (pas chuh ruh ZAY shun): a process of heating food or liquid to a temperature that kills most harmful bacteria. (p. 495)

pathogen (PA thuh jun): an agent that causes disease. (p. 494)

percent error: the expression of error as a percentage of the accepted value. (p. NOS 21)

period: a row on the periodic table. (p. 88)

periodic table: a chart of the elements arranged into rows and columns according to their physical and chemical properties. (p. 83)

phenotype (FEE nuh tipe): how a trait appears or is expressed. (p. 416)

photochemical smog: air pollution that forms from the interaction between chemicals in the air and sunlight. (p. 323)

physical change: a change in the size, shape, form, or state of matter that does not change the matter's identity. (p. 27)

physical property: a characteristic of matter that you can observe or measure without changing the identity of the matter. (p. 18)

point-source pollution: pollution from a single source that can be identified. (pp. 283, 316)

polar molecule: a molecule with a slight negative charge in one area and a slight positive charge in another area. (p. 131)

partículas en suspensión: mezcla de partículas sólidas y líquidas en el aire. (pág. 324)

pasteurización: proceso en el cual se calientan los alimentos o líquidos para matar la mayoría de bacterias dañinas. (pág. 495)

patógeno: agente que causa enfermedad. (pág. 494)

error porcentual: expresión del error como porcentaje del valor aceptado. (pág. NOS 21)

periodo: hilera en la tabla periódica. (pág. 88)

tabla periódica: cuadro en que los elementos están organizados en hileras y columnas según sus propiedades físicas y químicas. (pág. 83)

fenotipo: forma como aparece o se expresa un rasgo. (pág. 416)

smog fotoquímico: polución del aire que se forma de la interacción entre los químicos en el aire y la luz solar. (pág. 323)

cambio físico: cambio en el tamaño, la forma o el estado de la materia en el que no cambia la identidad de la materia. (pág. 27)

propiedad física: característica de la materia que puede observarse o medirse sin cambiar la identidad de la materia. (pág. 18)

contaminación de fuente puntual: contaminación de una sola fuente que se puede identificar. (pág. 283, 316)

molécula polar: molécula con carga ligeramente negativa en una parte y ligeramente positiva en otra. (pág. 131)

SCIENCE SKILL HANDBOOK

MATH SKILL HANDBOOK

FOLDABLES HANDBOOK

REFERENCE HANDBOOK

GLOSSARY/GLOSARIO

INDEX

polarity: a condition in which opposite ends of a molecule have slightly opposite charges, but the overall charge of the molecule is neutral. (p. 274)

polygenic inheritance: an inheritance pattern in which multiple genes determine the phenotype of a trait. (p. 421)

population: all the organisms of the same species that live in the same area at the same time. (p. 299)

precipitation: water, in liquid or solid form, that falls from the atmosphere. (p. 195)

prediction: a statement of what will happen next in a sequence of events. (p. NOS 6)

product: a substance produced by a chemical reaction. (p. 157)

prokaryotic (pro kayr ee AH tihk) cell: a cell that does not have a nucleus or other membrane-bound organelles. (p. 356)

proton: positively charged particle in the nucleus of an atom. (p. 58)

Punnett square: a model that is used to show the probability of all possible genotypes and phenotypes of offspring. (p. 418)

polaridad: condición en la cual los extremos opuestos de una molécula tienen cargas ligeramente opuestas, pero la carga completa de la molécula es neutra. (pág. 274)

herencia poligénica: patrón de herencia en el cual genes múltiples determinan el fenotipo de un rasgo. (pág. 421)

población: todos los organismos de la misma especie que viven en la misma área al mismo tiempo. (pág. 299)

precipitación: agua, de forma líquida o sólida, que cae de la atmósfera. (pág. 195)

predicción: afirmación de lo que ocurrirá después en una secuencia de eventos. (pág. NOS 6)

producto: sustancia producida por una reacción química. (pág. 157)

célula procariota: célula que no tiene núcleo ni otros organelos limitados por una membrana. (pág. 356)

protón: partícula cargada positivamente en el núcleo de un átomo. (pág. 58)

cuadro de Punnett: modelo que se utiliza para demostrar la probabilidad de que todos los genotipos y fenotipos posibles de cría. (pág. 418)

Q

qualitative data: the use of words to describe what is observed in an experiment. (p. NOS 27)

quantitative data: the use of numbers to describe what is observed in an experiment. (p. NOS 27)

datos cualitativos: uso de palabras para describir lo que se observa en un experimento. (pág. NOS 27)

datos cuantitativos: uso de números para describir lo que se observa en un experimento. (pág. NOS 27)

R

radioactive: any element that spontaneously emits radiation. (p. 68)

rain shadow: an area of low rainfall on the downwind slope of a mountain. (p. 229)

reactant: a starting substance in a chemical reaction. (p. 157)

recessive (rih SE sihv) trait: a genetic factor that is blocked by the presence of a dominant factor. (p. 411)

reclamation: a process in which mined land must be recovered with soil and replanted with vegetation. (p. 310)

radiactivo: cualquier elemento que emite radiación de manera espontánea. (pág. 68)

sombra de lluvia: área de baja precipitación en la ladera de sotavento de una montaña. (pág. 229)

reactivo: sustancia inicial en una reacción química. (pág. 157)

rasgo recesivo: factor genético boqueado por la presencia de un factor dominante. (pág. 411)

recuperación: proceso por el cual las tierras explotadas se deben recubrir con suelo y se deben replantar con vegetación. (pág. 310)

SCIENCE SKILL HANDBOOK

MATH SKILL HANDBOOK

FOLDABLES HANDBOOK

REFERENCE HANDBOOK

GLOSSARY/ GLOSARIO

INDEX

reforestation: process of planting trees to replace trees that have been cut or burned down. (p. 310)

regeneration: a type of asexual reproduction that occurs when an offspring grows from a piece of its parent. (p. 388)

relative humidity: the amount of water vapor present in the air compared to the maximum amount of water vapor the air could contain at that temperature. (p. 193)

remote sensing: the process of collecting information about an area without coming into contact with it. (p. 281)

replication: the process of copying a DNA molecule to make another DNA molecule. (p. 428)

RNA: ribonucleic acid, a type of nucleic acid that carries the code for making proteins from the nucleus to the cytoplasm. (p. 429)

reforestación: proceso de siembra de árboles para reemplazar los árboles que se han cortado o quemado. (pág. 310)

regeneración: tipo de reproducción asexual que ocurre cuando un organismo se origina de una parte de su progenitor. (pág. 388)

humedad relativa: cantidad de vapor de agua presente en el aire comparada con la cantidad máxima de vapor de agua que el aire podría contener en esa temperatura. (pág. 193)

teledetección: proceso de recolectar información sobre un área sin entrar en contacto con ella. (pág. 281)

replicación: proceso por el cual se copia una molécula de ADN para hacer otra molécula de ADN. (pág. 428)

ARN: ácido ribonucleico, un tipo de ácido nucléico que contiene el código para hacer proteínas del núcleo para el citoplasma. (pág. 429)

S

science: the investigation and exploration of natural events and of the new information that results from those investigations. (p. NOS 4)

scientific law: a rule that describes a pattern in nature. (p. NOS 9)

scientific notation: a method of writing or displaying very small or very large values in a short form. (p. NOS 21)

scientific theory: an explanation of observations or events that is based on knowledge gained from many observations and investigations. (p. NOS 9)

selective breeding: the selection and breeding of organisms for desired traits. (p. 461)

semiconductor: a substance that conducts electricity at high temperatures but not at low temperatures. (p. 105)

sexual reproduction: type of reproduction in which the genetic material from two different cells—a sperm and an egg—combine, producing an offspring. (p. 373)

single-replacement reaction: a type of chemical reaction in which one element replaces another element in a compound. (p. 166)

ciencia: investigación y exploración de eventos naturales y la información nueva que resulta de dichas investigaciones. (pág. NOS 4)

ley científica: regla que describe un patrón en la naturaleza. (pág. NOS 9)

notación científica: método para escribir o expresar números muy pequeños o muy grandes en una forma corta. (pág. NOS 21)

teoría científica: explicación de las observaciones y los eventos basada en conocimiento obtenido en muchas observaciones e investigaciones. (pág. NOS 9)

cría selectiva: selección y la cría de organismos para las características deseadas. (pág. 461)

semiconductor: sustancia que conduce electricidad a altas temperaturas, pero no a bajas temperaturas. (pág. 105)

reproducción sexual: tipo de reproducción en la cual el material genético de dos células diferentes de un espermatozoide y un óvulo se combinan, produciendo una cría. (pág. 373)

reacción de sustitución sencilla: tipo de reacción química en la que un elemento reemplaza a otro en un compuesto. (pág. 166)

SCIENCE SKILL HANDBOOK

MATH SKILL HANDBOOK

FOLDABLES HANDBOOK

REFERENCE HANDBOOK

GLOSSARY/ GLOSARIO

INDEX

solubility (sahl yuh BIH luh tee): the maximum amount of solute that can dissolve in a given amount of solvent at a given temperature and pressure. (p. 22)

specific heat: the amount of thermal energy (joules) needed to raise the temperature of 1 kg of material 1°C. (pp. 229, 265)

sperm: a male reproductive, or sex, cell; forms in a testis (p. 373)

substance: matter with a composition that is always the same. (p. 11)

surface report: a description of a set of weather measurements made on Earth's surface. (p. 211)

synthesis (SIHN thuh sus): a type of chemical reaction in which two or more substances combine and form one compound. (p. 165)

solubilidad: cantidad máxima de soluto que puede disolverse en una cantidad dada de solvente a temperatura y presión dadas. (pág. 22)

calor específico: cantidad de energía (julios) térmica requerida para subir la temperatura de 1 kg de materia a 1°C. (pág. 229, 265)

esperma: célula reproductora masculina o sexual; forma en un testículo. (pág. 373)

sustancia: materia cuya composición es siempre la misma. (pág. 11)

informe de superficie: descripción de un conjunto de mediciones del tiempo realizadas en la superficie de la Tierra. (pág. 211)

síntesis: tipo de reacción química en el que dos o más sustancias se combinan y forman un compuesto. (pág. 165)

T

taxon: a group of organisms. (p. 351)

technology: the practical use of scientific knowledge, especially for industrial or commercial use. (p. NOS 9)

tornado: a violent, whirling column of air in contact with the ground. (p. 205)

trace fossil: the preserved evidence of the activity of an organism. (p. 447)

transcription: the process of making mRNA from DNA. (p. 429)

transition element: an element in groups 3–12 on the periodic table. (p. 96)

translation: the process of making a protein from RNA. (p. 430)

transpiration: the process by which plants release water vapor through their leaves. (p. 269)

turbidity (tur BIH duh tee): a measure of the cloudiness of water from sediments, microscopic organisms, or pollutants. (p. 285)

taxón: grupo de organismos. (pág. 351)

tecnología: uso práctico del conocimiento científico, especialmente para empleo industrial o comercial. (pág. NOS 9)

tornado: columna de aire violenta y rotativa en contacto con el suelo. (pág. 205)

traza fósil: evidencia conservada de la actividad de un organismo. (pág. 447)

transcripción: proceso por el cual se hace mARN de ADN. (pág. 429)

elemento de transición: elemento de los grupos 3–12 de la tabla periódica. (pág. 96)

traslación: proceso por el cual se hacen proteínas a partir de ARN. (pág. 430)

transpiración: proceso por el cual las plantas liberan vapor de agua por medio de las hojas. (pág. 269)

turbidez: medida de la turbiedad del agua debido a sedimentos, organismos microscópicos o contaminantes. (pág. 285)

U

upper-air report: a description of wind, temperature, and humidity conditions above Earth's surface. (p. 211)

urban sprawl: the development of land for houses and other buildings near a city. (p. 308)

informe del aire superior: descripción de las condiciones del viento, de la temperatura y de la humedad por encima de la superficie de la Tierra. (pág. 211)

expansión urbana: urbanización de tierra para viviendas y otras construcciones cerca de la ciudad. (pág. 308)

SCIENCE SKILL HANDBOOK

MATH SKILL HANDBOOK

FOLDABLES HANDBOOK

REFERENCE HANDBOOK

GLOSSARY/ GLOSARIO

INDEX

V

vaccine: a mixture containing material from one or more deactivated pathogens, such as viruses. (p. 504)

valence electron: the outermost electron of an atom that participates in chemical bonding. (p. 122)

variable: any factor that can have more than one value. (p. NOS 27)

variation: a slight difference in an inherited trait among individual members of a species. (p. 457)

vegetative reproduction: a form of asexual reproduction in which offspring grow from a part of a parent plant. (p. 389)

vestigial (veh STIH jee ul) structure: body part that has lost its original function through evolution. (p. 467)

virus: a strand of DNA or RNA surrounded by a layer of protein that can infect and replicate in a host cell. (p. 499)

vacuna: mezcla que contiene material de uno o más patógenos desactivados, como los virus. (pág. 504)

electrón de valencia: electrón más externo de un átomo que participa en el enlace químico. (pág. 122)

variable: cualquier factor que tenga más de un valor. (pág. NOS 27)

variación: ligera diferencia en un rasgo hereditario entre los miembros individuales de una especie. (pág. 457)

reproducción vegetativa: forma de reproducción asexual en la cual el organismo se origina a partir de una planta parental. (pág. 389)

estructura vestigial: Parte del cuerpo que a través de la evolución perdió la función original. (pág. 467)

virus: filamento de ADN o de ARN rodeado por una capa de proteína que puede infectar una célula huésped y replicarse en ella. (pág. 499)

W

water cycle: the series of natural processes by which water continually moves throughout the hydrosphere. (pp. 195, 268)

water quality: the chemical, biological, and physical status of a body of water. (p. 282)

weather: the atmospheric conditions, along with short-term changes, of a certain place at a certain time. (p. 191)

ciclo del agua: serie de procesos naturales mediante la cual el agua se mueve continuamente en toda la hidrosfera. (pág. 195, 268)

calidad del agua: estado químico, biológico y físico de un cuerpo de agua. (pág. 282)

tiempo atmosférico: condiciones atmosféricas, junto con cambios a corto plazo, de un lugar determinado a una hora determinada. (pág. 191)

Z

zygote (ZI goht): the new cell that forms when a sperm cell fertilizes an egg cell (p. 373)

zigoto: Célula nueva que se forma cuando un espermatozoide fertiliza un óvulo. (pág. 373)

Index

| *Italic numbers* = illustration/photo | **Bold numbers** = vocabulary term |
| *lab* = indicates entry is used in a lab on this page | |

A

ABO blood types, 421, *421*
Absolute-age dating, 448, *448*
Academic Vocabulary, 104, 140, 204, 240, 276, 346, 388, 421, 457. *See also* **Vocabulary**
Acidity, 285
Acid precipitation, 324, 328
Actinide series, 97
Active viruses, 500
Adaptations
    environmental, 460, 472–473 *lab*
    explanation of, **459**
    types of, 459, *459*
Adenine, 427
Adhesion, *275,* **275**
Aerobic bacteria, 485
Aerosols, 247
Agriculture
    environmental impact of, 306
    nitrogen cycle and, 306, *306*
Air masses
    Antarctic air masses, 200
    Arctic air masses, 200, 201
    classification of, *200,* 200–201
    explanation of, **200**
Air pollution. *See also* **Pollution**
    actions to reduce, 328, *328*
    explanation of, 322
    health effects of, 326, *326*
    types of, *323,* 323–324, *324*
Air pressure
    explanation of, *192,* **192**
    observation of, 201 *lab*
Air Quality Index (AQI), 327, *327*
Airships, 126
Air temperature
    explanation of, 192
    pressure and, 199, 199 *lab*
    water vapor and, 193, *193*
Albedo, 234
Algae, 321, *321*
    decay of, 284, 285
    overgrowth of, 284–286, *285,* 286
Algal blooms, 285, *285,* 321, *321*
Alkali metals, 95, **95**
Alkaline earth metals, 95
Alleles
    dominant and recessive, 417, *417,* 418, 419
    explanation of, **416,** *416*
    multiple, 421
Altitude
    temperature and, 227, 228, *228*
Amino acids
    proteins made from, 430, *430*
Amoeba
    reproduction in, 387, *387*

Amoebas, 346
Anaerobic bacteria, 485
Analogous structures, 467
Anaphase, 376, *376,* 377, *377*
Anatomy, comparative, 466–467
Ancestry, 466
Anemometer, 192, *192*
Animal cloning, 391, *391*
Animal regeneration, 388, *388*
Animals
    adaptations to climate by, 232
    bacteria living in, 491, *491*
Antarctica
    temperature in, 227
Antibiotics
    explanation of, **494,** 503, **503**
    function of, 504 *lab*
    resistance to, 494–495, *495*
Arachnologists, 383
Araschnia levana, 422
Archaea, 483, 487
Argon, 104, 123
Arizona, 241
Artificial selection, 461
Asexual reproduction
    advantages of, 392
    animal regeneration as, 388, *388*
    budding as, 387, *387*
    cloning as, 390, 390–391, *391*
    disadvantages of, 392
    explanation of, 347, **385,** 396, 486
    fission as, 386, *386*
    mitotic cell division as, 387, *387*
    vegetative, 389, *389,* 389 *lab*
Atomic number, 85
Atoms
    electrons in, *120,* 120–123, *121–123*
    explanation of, 120
    of polar and nonpolar molecules, 131, *131*
    stable and unstable, 124, *124*
ATP (adenosine triphosphate), 359
Autotrophs, *348,* **348,** *348,* **348**

B

Bacteria
    aerobic, 485
    affecting investigations, 497
    anaerobic, 485
    antibiotic resistance and, 494–495
    archaea v., 487
    beneficial, *491,* 491–493, *492, 493*
    characteristics of, 355 *lab*
    as chemoautotrophs, 348
    effect of disinfectants on, 506–507 *lab*
    endospores and, 487, *487*
    explanation of, 346, 356
    in environment, 491 *lab*

    explanation of, **483**
    food and, 493
    function of, 485
    harmful, *494,* 494–495, *495*
    method to kill, 489
    movement of, 486, *486*
    reproduction in, 386, 486, *486*
    size and shape of, 483 *lab,* 484, *484*
    slime layer in, 485 *lab*
    structure of, 484
Barium, as alkaline earth metal, 95
Barometers, *192*
Barometric pressure, 192
Bateson, William, 413
Behavioral adaptations, 459, *459*
Beryllium, 95
Big Idea, 110, 144
    Review, 113, 147
Binomial nomenclature, 350, *350*
Bioindicators, 286
Biological evolution, 451
Bioremediation, 493
Birds
    species of, 455
Bjerknes, Jacob, 202
Blending inheritance, 405
Blizzards, *207,* **207**
Body temperature, 264 *See also* **Temperature**
Bohr, Neils, *89*
Boiling point, 84
Bonds, 128. *See also* **Chemical bonds**
Breast cancer, *432*
Bromine
    properties of, 103, *103*
Budding, 387, *387*
Butane
    Cadmium, 85, *85*

C

Calcium, 95
Camouflage, 460, 461 *lab*
Cancer
    breast, *432*
    ovarian, *432*
    research on, 504
Canis, 351
Carbohydrates
    in cells, 356
    energy from, 348
    explanation of, 346
    produced by photosynthesis, 359
Carbon cycle, 325, *325*
Carbon dioxide
    in atmosphere, 264
    chemical formula for, 132, *132*
    deforestation and, 305
    greenhouse effect and, 326

as greenhouse gas, 246, *246*
sources of, 247
vehicle emissions of, 249 *lab*
Carbonization, 446, *446*
Carbon monoxide, 324, 328
Carbon. *See also* **Hydrocarbons**
Organic compounds
in human body, 101, *101*
properties of, *102*, 103
Careers in Science, 243, 271, 353, 383, 463
Casts, *447*, **447**
Cell membrane, 357, *357*
Cells
activities of, 358
cytoplasm in, 358
explanation of, 347, 355
macromolecules in, 346, 356
molecules in, 426
storage in, 360, *360*
substances in, 356, 358
types of, 356
Cell wall, 357, *357*
Centromere, 376
Cesium, 95
CFCs
efforts to phase out use of, 328
explanation of, 324
Chapter Review, 112–113, 146–147, 220–221, 256–257, 292–293, 334–335, 366–367, 398–399, 438–439, 476–477, 510–511
Chargaff, Erwin, 427
Chase, Martha, 413
Chemical bonds
covalent, *129*, 129–130, *130*
explanation of, **120**, 121–124, **128**
Chemical energy
light energy converted to, 348
Chemical formulas, *132*, **132**
Chemicals, 319
Chemoautotrophs, 348
Cherrapunji, India, 241
Chlorine
properties of, 103, *103*
Chloroplasts, 359
Chromosomes
composition of, 426
DNA in, *426*, 426–428
explanation of, 374, *374*
genetic information in, 415, 416, *416*
homologous, 374
human, *415*, 429, 431
Mendel's laws of inheritance and, 413
in sex cells, 375, 378
Classes, 351
Clean Air Act (1970), 328
Clean Water Act, 319
Climate change. *See also* **Global**
warming
environmental impact of, 248
human impact on, 246–247
methods to predict, 249–250
methods to reduce, 250
regional and global, 245, *245*
sources of information on, 236, *236*, 243

Climate cycles
causes of long-term, 237, *237*
explanation of, 236
ice ages and, 236, 237
short-term, 238–241
Climate. *See also* **Temperature**
Weather
adaptations to, 232, *232*
comparison of, 227 *lab*
effect of albedo on, 234
explanation of, **227**
factors affecting, 227–229, 245 *lab*
methods to classify, 230, *231*
microclimates, 230
Cloning
animal, 391, *391*
explanation of, **390**
human, 391
plant, 390, *390*
Clostridium botulinum, 494
Clouds
cumulus, 204, *204*
effect on climate, 247, *247*
explanation of, 194, 266
formation of, 191 *lab*, 194, 195
water cycle and, 195
Coastlines
climate on, 227, 229
Codominance, *420*, **420**
Codons, 430
Cohesion, *275*, **275**
Cold fronts, 202, *202*
Cold waves, 241
Comparative anatomy
analogous structures and, 467
explanation of, **466**
homologous structures and, 466
Compost, 311, *311*
Compounds. *See also* **Organic**
Compounds
containing metals, 99
covalent, 130, 131
elements that make up, 128, 128 *lab*
explanation of, **120**
formation of, 132 *lab*
halogens in, 103
ionic, 138, 139
method to model, 134
Conclude, 421
Condensation
explanation of, **267**, *268–269*, 269
in water cycle, 195
Conduct, 140
Conjugation, *486*, **486**
Construct, 104
Continental climate, *231*, 232
Continental polar air masses, 201
Continental tropical air masses, 201
Convince, 457
Copper
on periodic table, 85, *85*
uses for, 93
Coral bleaching, 284
Coral
information from fossilized, 271
Covalent bonds
double and triple, 130, *130*

electron sharing and, 129
explanation of, **129**, *140*
Covalent compounds
chemical compounds and, 132
explanation of, 130
molecule as unit of, 130
nonpolar molecules and, 131, *131*
polar molecules and, 131, *131*
Cows, 491, *491*
Crabgrass, 392, *392*
Crabs, 388
Crick, Francis, 413, 427
Critical thinking, 90, 98, 107, 113, 125, 133, 141, 147
Cross-pollination
experiments in, *407*, 407–409, *408, 409*
explanation of, 406
Culture, *390*, **390**
Cumulus clouds, *194*, 204
Cuyahoga River, 318, *318*
Cystic fibrosis
explanation of, *432*
research on, 504
Cytokinesis, 375, 387
Cytoplasm
in bacteria, 484, *484*
explanation of, **358**
in meiosis, 375, 376, *376*, 377, *377*
in mitosis, 375, 387
proteins in, 359, 360
Cytosine, 427

D

Darwin, Charles
background of, 455
on HMS *Beagle,* 456
theory of evolution, 457–458, 461, 463, 470
Dead zones, 321, *321*
Deciduous trees, 232
Decomposition
in aerobic and anaerobic environments, 492 *lab*
explanation of, **492**
Deforestation, 246, 247, **247**, **305**, *305*
Deletion mutation, 431, *431*
Density, **94**
explanation of, 276
water, *276*, 276–278, *277, 278*
Desertification, **306**
Developmental biology, 468
Dew point, **193**, 193 *lab*
Dichotomous key, 351, 351 *lab*
Diploid cells
chromosomes of, 374, 375
explanation of, **374**
meiosis in, 375, 375 *lab*, 378, *378*
Disease
bacterial, *494*, 494–495, *495*
viral, 499, *502*, 502–504, 503
Disinfectants, 506–507 *lab*
Dispose, 309
Divergence, 469
Diversity, 470

DNA
in bacteria, 484, 486, *486*
explanation of, 346, 358, 362, **380, 426,** *426 lab*
function of, 469
junk, 429
making mRNA from, 429, *429*
modeling of, 428 *lab*
mutations and, *431,* 431–432
in prokaryotes, 386
replication of, 428, *428*
research on, 413
sexual reproduction and, 380, 385
structure of, 427, *427,* 429
in viruses, 499, 501
Dolly (sheep), 391, *391*
Domains, 351
Dominance, 420, *420*
Dominant alleles, *417,* 417–419
Dominant traits, 411, 411 *lab*
Dominate, 204
Doppler radar, 212
Downdrafts, 204
Down syndrome, 374
Drought, 241, 248
Dry climate, *231,* 232, *232*
Ductility, 94

E

Earth
curved surface of, 228
effect of orbit and tilt of axis on climate of, 236 *lab,* 237, *237,* 238, *238*
revolution of, *239,* 239
water on, 266, *266*
Earth
surface temperature of, 325, 326
Eastern chipmunk, 350, *350*
E. coli
reproduction in, 386
Ecosystems. *See also* **Biomes**
effect of global warming on, 325
Egg cells, 406
Eggs
explanation of, **373**
Electron dot diagrams
explanation of, **123,** *123,* 124
function of, 134
Electron pooling, 139
Electrons
bonding and, 121
energy and, 121, *121*
noble gases and, 124, *124,* 129
number and arrangement of, 120, *121*
shared, 129
valence, 122, *122,* 124, 129, 130, *130,* 139
Elements. *See also specific elements*
in periodic table, 83–88, *84, 85, 86–88*
synthetic, 89
transition, *96,* 96–97
El Niño, 240
El Niño/Southern Oscillation (ENSO), 240
Embryology, 468

Endangered species. *See also* **Species**
cloning of, 391
Endoplasmic reticulum, 360
Endospores, *487,* **487**
Energy
electrons and, 121, *121*
Energy resources, 328
Energy. *See also* **Nonrenewable energy resources**
Renewable energy resources
for cells, 359
Energy use, 348, *348*
Environment
adaptations based on, 460
Environmental impact, 248, 301, *301*
Environmental protection, 250, *250*
Environmental Protection Agency (EPA), 309, 327
Environment
effect of air pollution on, 326, *326*
impact of daily actions on, 301, *301,* 303
for living things, 348
positive actions to protect, *310,* 310–311, *311*
Eons, 449
Equator
solar energy and, 228
temperature near, 227
Equinox
explanation of, 239, *239*
Eras, 449, *449*
Ethical issues, 391
Eukaryotes
explanation of, 356, 359
proteins in, 360
reproduction in, 387
Eukaryotic cells
explanation of, **356,** *356*
RNA in, 358
Evaporation
explanation of, *267,* **267**
in water cycle, 195
of water from plants, 269
Evolution
biological, 451
contemporary research on, 470
Darwin's theory of, 455, 457–458, 461, 463, 470
evidence for, 465–469, *467, 468, 469*
explanation of, 451, *451*
Extinction
causes of, 450
evolution and, 451, *451*
explanation of, **450**
Extremophiles, 487

F

Families, 351
Fertilization
explanation of, **373,** *373*
Fertilizers, 285, 306, 321
Finches, 456, 458, 463
Fireworks, 99
Fission, *386,* **386, 486**
Flagella, 486, *486*

Fluorine
properties of, 103, *103*
Fog, 194
Foldables, 85, 94, 103, 111, 121, 129, 136, 145, 194, 200, 212, 219, 230, 238, 245, 255, 268, 275, 283, 291, 300, 309, 317, 324, 333, 349, 358, 365, 374, 385, 397, 411, 420, 430, 437, 448, 455, 466, 475, 483, 493, 500, 509
Food, 349
Food poisoning, 495
Foods. *See also* **Healthful eating**
bacteria and, 493
Forests
protection of, 310
Fossil fuels, 247
air pollution from burning, 323
CO_2 levels and, 423
disadvantages of, 363
Fossil record, 445, 465
Fossils
evidence of extinction by studying, *445,* 450, *450*
evidence of new species by studying, 451, *451*
explanation of, 445
formation of, 445 *lab,* 446, *446–447*
methods to date, 448, *448*
time scale for, 449, *449*
trace, 447, *447*
Francium, 95
Franklin, Rosalind, 427
Freshwater
density of, *277,* 278, *278*
distribution of, 266, *266*
Fronts
cold, 202, *202*
explanation of, **202**
occluded, 203, *203*
stationary, 203, *203*
warm, *202,* 203
Frostbite, 207
Fujita, Ted, 205
Functional adaptations, 459, *459*
Fungi
reproduction in, 385
Fungus, 345

G

Galápagos Islands, 456–458
Gases, noble, 104, 124, *124,* 267
g/cm³ 455
Genera, 351
Genes
environment and, 422, *422*
explanation of, **416,** 426, 429
Genetic disorders
DNA mutations and, 432, *432*
viruses to treat, 504
Genetics. *See also* **Inheritance**
DNA and, *426,* 426–432, *427, 428, 429*
experimentation with, 434–435 *lab*
explanation of, **405**
pioneers in, 405, 413
Genetic variation, 380, *380,* 392

Gene transfer, 504
Genotypes. *See also* **Inheritance**
  explanation of, **416**
  inferred from phenotypes, 417 *lab*
  prediction of, 418, *418*, 419
  symbols for, 417, *417*
Genus, 351
Geologic time scale, 449
Geologists, 243, 271
Geothermal energy, 328
Germanium, 106
Glaciers
  ice layers in, 236
Global climate model (GCM), 249
Global warming, 325, *325*, 326. *See also Climate* **change**
  explanation of, **246**
  hurricanes and, 197
Glucose, 359
Gold
  on periodic table, 85, *85*
  properties of, 94
  uses for, 93, *94*
Golgi, 360
Grant, Peter, 463
Grant, Rosemary, 463
Great Lakes, 318, *318*
Green buildings, *250*
Green city design, 330–331 *lab*
Greenhouse effect. *See also* **Climate change**
  explanation of, 246, 264, *264, 326,* **326**
  modeling of, 252–253 lab
Greenhouse gases. *See also* **Climate change**
  in atmosphere, 264
  explanation of, **246**
  methods to reduce, 250, *250*
  sources of, 247
Greenland, 271
Green Science, 126, 321
Green spaces
  design of, 330–331 *lab*
  explanation of, 311, *311*
Groundwater
  explanation of, 266
Groups, in periodic table, **88,** 119, *120*
Guanine, 427
Gulf of Mexico, 321
Gulf Stream
  explanation of, 229
Gunpowder, 99

H

Habitats, 308, 310
  explanation of, **349**
Hail, 195. *See also* **Precipitation**
Halogens, 103, *103*
Haploid cells, 375
Harmful algal blooms, 285, *285*
Hazardous waste, 309, 319
Health
  air pollution and, 326
Heat waves, 241, 248
Helium airships, 126

Helium
  atoms of, 123
  electron structure of, 124
  on periodic table, 87, *87*
Hemophilia, 504
Heredity
  explanation of, **405**
  Mendel's experiments on, *406, 406–411, 407, 408, 409, 410*
Hershey, Alfred, 413
Heterotrophs, 348
Heterozygous, 417, *417*
High-pressure system, *199,* **199,** 200
Hindenburg, 126, *126*
HIV. *See also* **Human immunodeficiency virus,** 502
HMS Beagle, 456
Holocene epoch, 237
Homologous structures, 466
Homo sapiens, 350. *See also* **Humans**
Homozygous, 417, *417*
How It Works, 489
Human beings
  population of, 299, 300, *300*
Human cloning, 391
Human immunodeficiency virus (HIV), 502
Human population growth, 250, *250*
Humans, 101, *101*
  blood types in, 421, *421*
  chromosomes in, *415,* 415, 429, 431
  healthful lifestyle choices by, 422
  impact on climate change, 246–247
Humidity, 192, 193
Hurricane Floyd, 286, *286*
Hurricane Katrina
  global warming and, 197
Hurricanes
  explanation of, **206**
  formation of, 206, *206*
  global warming and, 197
Hybrid, 409
Hybrid cars, 328, *328*
Hybrid plants
  cross-pollination of, 408, 409, *409, 410*
  explanation of, **409**
Hydra, 387, *387,* 388
Hydrangeas, *422*
Hydrogen airships, 126, *126*
Hydrogen
  atoms of, 123, 131
  in human body, 101, *101*
  properties of, 104
  in universe, *104*
Hydrogen molecules, 131
Hydrosphere, 266, 267
Hypochlorite, 489
Hypothermia, 207

I

Ice ages, 236, 237
Ice cores
  analysis of, 243
  explanation of, 236, *236*
  method to collect, 243

Ice
  density of, 277, *277,* 278, 280
  formation of, 266
Ice sheets
  formation of, 236
  melting of, 271
  in most recent ice age, 237
Ice storms, 207
Igneous rock, 448
Iguana, 349, *349*
Immunity
  explanation of, **503**
Incomplete dominance, 420, *420*
Influenza, 502, *502*
Infrared satellite images, 212, *212*
Inheritance. *See also* **Genetics Genotypes; Traits**
  blending, 405
  complex patterns of, *420, 420–421, 421*
  Mendel's experiments on, *406, 406–411, 407, 408, 409, 410*
  modeling, *418,* 418–419, *419,* 424
  polygenic, 421
Insertion mutation, 431, *431*
Interglacials, 236, 237
Intergovernmental Panel on Climate Change (IPCC), 246
Interphase, 376
Interpret Graphics, 90, 98, 107, 125, 133, 141
Iodine
  properties of, 103, *103*
Ionic bonds, 138, 138, *140*
Ionic compounds, 138, 139
Ions
  determining charge of, 138
  explanation of, **136**
  gaining valence electrons and, 137, *137*
  losing valence electrons and, 137, *137*
  in solution, 142–143 *lab*
Isobars, 213
Isotherms, 213
Isotopes, 448

J

Jellyfish, 263, *263*
Junk DNA, 429

K

Key, 351
Key Concepts, 82, 92, 100, 118, 127, 135
  Check, 85, 88, 93, 94, 102, 105, 121, 124, 128, 130, 131, 138, 139
  Summary, 110, 144
  Understand, 90, 98, 107, 125, 133, 141, 146
Kinetic energy, 192
Kingdoms, 351
Köppen, Wladimir, 230
Krypton, as noble gas, 104

L

Lab, 108–109, 142–143, 216–217, 252–253, 288–289, 330–331, 362–363, 394–395, 434–435, 472–473, 506–507. *See also* **Launch Lab**
Launch Lab
MiniLab
MiniLab
Skill Practice
Skill Practice
Lactobacillus, 491
Ladybugs, 347, *347*
Landfills, 309, 313
Land resources
actions to protect, *310,* 310–311, *311*
environmental impact on, *305,* 305–308, *306, 307, 308*
La Niña, 241 *lab*
Lanthanide series, 97
Latitude
temperature and, 227, 228, *228,* 238
Launch Lab, 83, 93, 101, 119, 128, 136, 191, 199, 211, 227, 236, 245, 263, 273, 282, 305, 315, 323, 345, 355, 373, 385, 405, 415, 426, 445, 455, 465, 483, 491, 499
Lava
density of, 276
Leeches, 353, *353*
Lesson Review, 90, 98, 107, 125, 133, 141, 196, 208, 215, 233, 242, 251, 270, 279, 287, 302, 312, 320, 329, 352, 361, 382, 393, 412, 423, 433, 452, 462, 471, 488, 496, 505
Lewis, Gilbert, 123
Light energy
converted to chemical energy, 348
Linnaeus, Carolus, 350, 351
Lipids, 346, 357
Liquids
explanation of, 267
Lithium, 95, *95*
Little Ice Age, 237
Living things
characteristics of, 345, 345 *lab*
classification of, *350,* 350–351, 362–363 *lab*
effects of stimuli on, 348, *348*
energy sources for, 348, *348*
food and water requirements for, 349, *349*
growth, development and reproduc- tion in, 347, *347*
habitats for, 349
multicellular, 347, *347*
organization of, 346
unicellular, 346, *346*
Loma Prieta earthquake (1989)
Low-pressure system, *199,* **199**
Luster, **93**

M

Macromolecules
in cells, 358
explanation of, **346,** 356

Magma, 448
Magnesium, 95
Malleability, **94,** 97
Map butterfly, *422*
Maritime polar air masses, 201
Maritime tropical air masses, 201
Math Skills, 88, 90, 138, 141, 147, 201, 208, 221, 248, 251, 257, 265, 270, 293, 308, 312, 335, 350, 352, 367, 379, 382, 399, 410, 439, 450, 452, 477, 487, 488, 511
Mating, 383
Meiosis
characteristics of, *379*
chromosome movement during, 394–395 *lab*
diploid cells and, 375, 375 *lab,* 378, *378*
explanation of, **375,** 396
haploid cells and, 375, 375 *lab,* 378, 379
importance of, 378, *378*
mitosis v., 379, *379*
phases of, 375–377, *376, 377*
Meiosis I, 375, 376, *376*
Meiosis II, 375, 377, *377*
Melting point, 84, *84*
Mendel, Gregor
background of, 405, 413
conclusions reached by, 411, 416, 421
experimental methods used by, *406,* 406–407, *407,* 420
results of experiments by, *408,* 408–410, *409, 410,* 419
Mendeleev, Dimitri, 84, 85, 104
Mercury, *85*
Meristems, 390
Metallic bonds, **139,** *140*
Metalloids
explanation of, **105**
in periodic table, 88, 120
properties and uses of, 106
as semiconductors, 105
Metals
alkali, 95, *95*
alkaline earth, 95
chemical properties of, 94
explanation of, **93**
patterns in properties of, 97, *97*
in periodic table, 88, 93, 120
physical properties of, 93–94, *94*
as transition elements, *96,* 96–97
uses of, 93 *lab*
Metaphase, 376, *376,* 377, *377*
Meteorologists, 191, 212, 214 *lab*
Methane, 326
in atmosphere, 264
as greenhouse gas, 246
Mettner, Lise, 89
Microclimates, *230,* 232 *lab*
Microscopes, 355, *355,* 358 *lab*
Mild climate, *231*
Mimicry, 460
Mineralization, 446, *446*
MiniLab, 89, 97, 106, 124, 132, 139, 193, 201, 214, 232, 241, 249, 267, 277, 284, 307, 318, 327, 351, 358, 375, 389, 411, 417, 428, 451, 461, 469,

485, 492, 504. *See also* Lab
Lab
Mining
environmental impact of, 301, 307, *307*
process of, 307 *lab*
Mitochondria, **359**
Mitochondrion, **358**
Mitosis
characteristics of, *379*
chromosome movement during, 394–395 *lab*
explanation of, 375
meiosis v., 379, *379*
Mitotic cell division, *387,* 387
Mockingbirds, 456, 458
Mold, 345, *345*
Molds, *447,* **447**
Molecular biology, 468–469
Molecular models, 132, *132*
Molecules
explanation of, **130**
nonpolar, 131, *131*
polar, 131, *131*
Monsoon, **241**
Montreal Protocol, 328
Moseley, Henry, 85
Motor vehicles, 249 *lab,* 250
energy-efficient technologies for, 328, *328*
Mountains
rain shadows on, 229, *229*
weather in, 227
mRNA, 429, *429,* 430, *430,* 431
Muhs, *Daniel,* 271
Multicellular organisms, 347, *347*
Mustard plant, 381, *381*
Mutations
explanation of, 392, **431, 501**
function of, 457
results of, 432, *432*
types of, 431, *431*

N

National Human Genome Research Institute (NHGRI), 413
Naturalists, **455**
Natural selection
explanation of, **458,** *458,* 461
theory of evolution by, 461, 463, 470
Neon
electron structure of, 124, *124*
as noble gas, 104
Nerve cells, 348
Neutrons, 120, *120*
Newts, 388
NGC 3603, **283**
Nitrates, *285*
Nitrogen
air pollution from, 323, 324
compounds with, 103
explanation of, 306
in human body, 101, *101*
in runoff, 321, *321*
Nitrogen cycle, 306, *306*
Nitrogen fixation
explanation of, *492,* **492**

Noble gases
electron arrangement in, 129
explanation of, **104**, 124, *124*
Nonmetals
explanation of, **101**
metals v., *102*, 102–103, *103*
in periodic table, 88, 103, 120
properties of, 101 *lab*, 102, *102*
Nonpoint-source pollution, 283, *283,* **317**
Nonpolar molecules, 131, *131*
North Atlantic Oscillation (NAO), 240
North Pole
solar energy and, 228, *228*
Nucleic acids, 346, 356, 358
Nucleotides
changes in, 431
DNA and, 427, *427*
explanation of, **427,** *427*
RNA and, 429, *429*
Nucleus, 120, *120*
cell, 358

Observation
of change, 453
Occluded fronts, 203
Ocean currents
climate and, 229
Oceans. *See also* **Seafloor**
dead zones in, 321, *321*
Seawater
warming of, 197
Octopus, 348, *348*
Offspring
in asexual reproduction, 385, 388, 391, 392
genetic makeup of, 378, 380
physical characteristics in, 373 *lab*
in sexual reproduction, 380, 385
On the Origin of Species (Darwin), 461
Orders, 351
Organelles, 356, 358
Organisms. *See also* **Living things Multicellular organisms Unicellular organisms**
adaptations in, 472–473 *lab*
diversity of, 470
relatedness of, 469, 469 *lab*
Organ systems, 347
Ovarian cancer, *432*
Oxygen
atoms of, 129
compounds with, 103
dissolved, 284, 284 lab
in human body, 101, *101*
Ozone
effects of, 327
effects to reduce levels of, 328
explanation of, 323
Ozone layer, 324

Pamlico Sound, 286, *286*
Paramecia, 346
Particulate matter, *324*

Pasteurization, 495
Pathogens
affecting investigations, 497
explanation of, **494**
Paupae, 347, *347*
Pea plants, *406,* 406–410, *407, 408, 409, 410,* 420
Pedigrees, 419, *419*
Pedipalps, 383
Periodic, 84
Periodic table. *See also* specific *elements*
arrangement of, 91
development of, *84,* 84–85, *85*
element key in, 87, *87*
explanation of, **83,** 84
groups in, 88, *88,* 119, *120*
illustration of, *86–87*
modeling procedure used to develop, 108–109 *lab*
organization of, 119 *lab,* 120
periods in, 88, *88,* 119, *120*
use by scientists of, 89
Periods, in periodic table, **88,** 119, *120*
Permafrost, 232
Phanerozoic eon, 449, *449*
Pharyngeal pouches, 468, *468*
Phenomenon, 240
Phenotypes. *See also* **Inheritance**
environment and, 422, *422*
explanation of, **416,** *417,* 457
to infer genotypes, 417 *lab*
Phenylketonuria (PKU), 432
pH
of rainwater, 324
Phosphorous, 321, *321*
Phosphorus
compounds with, 103
in human body, 101
properties of, *102*
Photochemical smog, *323,* **323**
Photosynthesis
explanation of, 264, 358
process of, 247
Phyla, 351
Pigeons, 461, *461*
Planarians, 388, *388*
Plant cells
storage in, 360, *360*
Plant cloning, 390, *390*
Plants
hybrid, *408,* 409, *409,* 410
true-breeding, 407, 408, *408*
Plasmodial, 346, *346*
Platnick, Norman, 383
Plutonium, 97
Pneumonia, 484
Point-source pollution, 283, 316
Polar, 274
Polar climate, *231*
Polarity
explanation of, **274**
of water molecules, 274, *274*
Polar molecules, 131, *131*
Polar regions, 228
Pollination, 406, *406*
Pollution, 493. *See also* **Air pollution Water pollution**
actions to reduce, *318,* 318–319,

319, 328, *328*
explanation of, **316**
methods to reduce, 250, *250*
nonpoint-source, 283
point-source, 283
Polygenic inheritance, 421
Population
explanation of, *299,* **299**
human, 299, 300, *300*
resources to support, 300
size increase of, 299 *lab*
Potassium
as alkali metal, 95, *95*
properties of, 97
Potassium nitrate, 99
Potential, 388
Precipitation, acid, 324
Precipitation. *See also* **Rain**
climate change and, 248
effects of, 269
explanation of, **194, 195, 229,** *268,* 269
types of, *195*
water cycle and, 195
Pressure systems, 199
Prokaryotes, 356, 359, 360
archaea as, 487
bacteria as, 483
cell division in, 386
Prokaryotic cells, 356, *356,* 358
Prophase, 376, *376,* 377, *377*
Proteins
in cells, 356, 358, 359, 360
explanation of, 346
production of, *429,* 429–430, *430*
Protons, 120, *120*
Punnett squares
analysis of, 418, *418*
explanation of, **418**
use of, 419, 424

Radar, 212
Radium, 95
Radon, 104
Rain forests
deforestation in, 305
Rain. *See also* **Precipitation**
adaptations to, 232
explanation of, 195, 269
freezing, 207
Rain shadows, *229,* **229**
Reading Check, 84, 89, 95, 97, 101, 103, 104, 106, 119, 120, 123, 132, 136, 137, 140
Recessive alleles, *417,* 417–419
Recessive traits, 411
Reclamation, 310
Recreation, 308
Recycling, 250
benefits of, 311, *311*
Reforestation, 310
Regeneration, 388, *388*
Relative-age dating, 448, *448*
Relative humidity, 193
Remote sensing
explanation of, **286**
Renewable energy resources, 328

SCIENCE SKILL HANDBOOK

MATH SKILL HANDBOOK

FOLDABLES HANDBOOK

REFERENCE HANDBOOK

GLOSSARY/ GLOSARIO

INDEX

Replication
explanation of, **428**
of viruses, 499 *lab,* 500, *500–502,*
501
Reproduction
asexual, 347
sexual, 347
Reproduction. *See also* **Asexual**
reproduction
Sexual reproduction
asexual, 385–392, *386, 387, 388,*
389, 390, 391, 392, 396
in bacteria, 486
sexual, *373,* 373–381, *374, 376,*
377, 378, 379, 380, 381, 396
Reservoirs, 269
Resistant, 494, 495, *495*
Resources
consumption of, 301
explanation of, **301**
use of land, *305,* 305–307, *306,*
307
Review Vocabulary, 94, 120, 191, 192,
229, 276, 307, 346, 380, 406, 448,
501. *See also* **Vocabulary**
Revolution
explanation of, **239**
Ribosomes, 360
of archaea, 487
in cytoplasm, 484
RNA, 358
explanation of, 429
protein production and, 429–430,
430
types of, 430
in viruses, 499, 501, 504
Roadways, 308
rRNA, 430
Rubidium, 95
Runoff
effects of, 269
environmental impact of, 308, 321
explanation of, **307,** 316
from fertilizers, 285
of sediment, 286, *286*

Safe Drinking Water Act, 319
Sahara, 227
Saltpeter, 99
Satellite images
weather information from, 212, *212*
Science and Society, 413
Science Methods, 109, 143, 217, 253,
289, 331, 363, 395, 435, 473, 507
Science & Society, 99, 197
Science Use v. Common Use, 86, 128,
202, 239, 274, 301, 351, 390, 409,
446, 494. *See also* Vocabulary
Vocabulary
Seaborg, Glen T., *89*
Sea cucumbers, 388
Sea level
melting of ice sheets and, 271
Seasons
explanation of, 238
monsoon winds and, 241, *241*
Sea stars, 388

Sea urchins, 388
Sedimentary rock, 448
Sediment
in water, 282 *lab*
Selective breeding, 381, *381,* 461
Selenium, 103
Self-pollination, 406, *406,* 407
Semiconductors, 105
Sex cells
explanation of, 373, 374
formation of, 375–378, *376, 377,*
381
variations in, 378
Sexual reproduction
advantages of, *380,* 380–381, *381*
disadvantages of, 381
explanation of, 347, **373,** 385, 396
meiosis and, 379
in spiders, 383
Sheep, 391, *391*
Siamese cats, *422*
Siddall, Mark, 353
Silicon
explanation of, 105
uses of, 105, *105,* 106
Silver, 85, *85*
Skill Practice, 91, 134, 209, 234, 280,
303, 313, 424, 453, 497. *See also*
Lab; **Lab**
Sleet, 195. *See also* **Precipitation**
Smog, 323, *323*
Snow. *See also* **Precipitation**
albedo of, 234
as driving hazard, 207
explanation of, 195
Sodium, 95, *95*
Sodium chloride, 274
Soil, 305
Solar cars, 328, *328*
Solar energy
climate cycles and, 237, 238, *238*
reflected back into atmosphere,
234
temperatures and, 227, 228, *228*
Solid state, 267
Solstice
explanation of, 239, *239*
Solvents, water as, 274
South Pole, 228, *228*
Species, 351
Species
adaptations made by, *459,*
459–460
change in, 451 *lab*
endangered, 391
formation of new, 470
relationships and variations within,
457
Specific heat, 229, 265
Sperm
explanation of, **373, 406**
Spiders, 383
Sponges, 388
Standardized Test Practice, 114–115,
148–149, 222–223, 258–259,
294–295, 336–337, 368–369,
400–401, 440–441, 478–479,
512–513
Stationary fronts, 203

Station model, 213, *213,* 214 *lab*
Stimuli
explanation of, 348, *348*
Stolons, 389, 389
Stoneflies, 286
Strawberry plants, 389, *389*
Streptococcus pneumoniae, 494
Strip mines, 307, *307*
Strontium, 95
Structural adaptations, 459, *459*
Study Guide, 110–111, 144–145,
218–219, 254–255, 290–291,
332–333, 364–365, 396–397,
436–437, 474–475, 508–509
Substitution mutation, 431, *431*
Suburbs, 308
Sugar, 130, 131
Sulfur
in human body, 101
properties of, 103, 106
Sun
reflection of rays from, 234
Surface reports, 211
Sutton, Walter, 413

Tadpoles, 388
Tamias striatus, 350
Taxon, 351
Taxonomy, 351
Telophase, 376, *376,* 377, *377*
Temperature. *See also* **Body**
tempera- ture Climate Weather
adaptations to, 232
of air, 192, 193, *193,* 199 *lab*
changes in water, 284
effect of greenhouse gases on,
246
effect of increasing, 248–249
stability of Earth's, 265
states of water and, 267, *267 lab*
trends in, 245, *245*
variations in, 227, 228, *228*
water density and, 277, *277,* 278,
278, 288–289 *lab*
Thermal energy
conduction of, 97 *lab,* 106 *lab*
effects of, 316
Thermal energy. *See also* **Heat**
effects of, 232
effects on water, 267
explanation of, 265
in ocean water, 229
from Sun, 264
Thompson, Lonnie, 243
Thunderstorms
explanation of, 204, *204, 205*
safety precautions during, 207
Thymine, 427
Tiktaalik fossil, 470, *470*
Tissues
explanation of, **446**
Titanus, 445, *445*
Tornado Alley, 205
Tornadoes, 205, *205*
Tortoises, *456,* 456–458
Trace fossils, *447,* **447**
Trade winds, 240

Traits. *See also* **Inheritance**
codes used to determine, 426 *lab*
cross-pollination experiments and, *410*
dominant, 411
factors that control, *415,* 415–417, *416*
mutations and, 432
prediction of, *418,* 418–419
uniqueness of, 405 *lab*
variations in, 415 *lab*
Transcription, 429, *429*
Transition elements, *96,* **96**
Translation, 430, *430*
Transpiration, 269
tRNA, 430
Tropical climate, *231*
Tropical cyclones, 206
Tropical rain forests, 305
Tuberculosis, 494, *494*
Turbidity, *285,* **285**
Typhoons, 206

U

Unicellular organisms
explanation of, 346, *346,* 355 *lab*
growth of, 347
types of, 356
Unique, 346
United States
water use in, 315, *315*
Updrafts
explanation of, 204, *205*
tornado formation and, 205
Upper-air reports, 211
Upwelling
explanation of, 240
Uracil, 429
Uranium, 493, *493*
Urban areas
population growth projections for, 250
temperatures in, 227, *231*
Urban heat island, 231, *231*
Urban sprawl, 308
U.S. National Weather Service, 207

V

Vaccinations
explanation of, **505**
Vacuoles, 360, *360*
Valence electrons
covalent bond and, 130, *130*
explanation of, 122, *122,* 124, 139
metallic bonds and, 139
shared electrons as, 129
Variable, 191
Variations, 457, **457,** 458
Vegetation
adaptations to climate by, 232
classifying climate by native, 230
in mountains, 229

Vegetative reproduction, 389, 389 *lab*
Vehicle emissions, 249 *lab,* 250
Vesicles, 360
Vestigial structures, *467,* **467**
Viral diseases
explanation of, 502, *502*
immunity to, 503, *503*
medications to treat, 503
types of, 499, 502
vaccines to prevent, 504
Viruses
beneficial, 504
explanation of, **499,** 501
latent, 500
mutations in, 501
organisms and, 500
replication of, 499 *lab,* 500, *500–501,* 501
research with, 504
shapes of, 499, *499*
Visible light satellite images, 212, *212*
Visual Check, 87, 94, 102, 103, 122, 130
Vocabulary, 81, 82, 92, 100, 110, 117, 118, 127, 135, 144. *See also*
Academic Vocabulary
Review Vocabulary
Science Use v. Common Use
Word Origin
Use, 90, 98, 107, 111, 125, 133, 141, 145

W

Warm fronts, *202,* 203
Waste management, 309, *309*
Water
biological functions of, 263–264, *265*
cloudy, 282 lab
on Earth, 266, *266*
importance of, 263, *265*
properties of, 273, 273 lab, 274–276
as resource, 315
specific heat of, 229, 265
states of, 267–269
Water bodies, 227, 229–230
Water conservation, 319
Water cycle, 316
explanation of, *195,* **195,** 268
paths in, *268,* 268–269, *269*
storage areas and, 269
Water density
explanation of, 276
features of, *276,* 278, 280
temperature and, 277, *277,* 278, *278,* 288–289 lab
Water filters, 315 *lab*
Water molecule, 131, *131*
adhesion among, 275, *275*
cohesion among, 275, *275*
forces between, 273, *273*
polarity of, 274, *274*

as solvent, 274
Water pollution, 283, *283. See also*
Pollution
actions to reduce, *318,* 318–319, *319*
sources of, 316–317, *316–317*
Water quality
acidity and, 285
bioindicators for, 286
dissolved oxygen and, 284
explanation of, **282**
human effects on, 282
nitrates and, 285, *285*
turbidity and, 285, *285*
water temperature and, 284
Water vapor, 316, 326
air temperature and, 193, *193*
in atmosphere, 264
condensation of, 269, *269*
distribution of, 266
explanation of, 267
as greenhouse gas, 246
temperature of, 265
water cycle and, 195
Watson, James, 413, 427
Weather forecasts
explanation of, 211
methods for, 216–217 lab
satellite and radar images for, 212
station models used for, 213, 214 lab
surface reports as, 211
understanding, 211 lab
upper-air reports as, 211
use of technology in, 212, 214, *214*
Weather maps, 212–213, *213*
Weather. *See also* **Climate;**
Temperature
cycles of, 236–241
explanation of, **191,** 227
reasons for change in, 209
safety precautions during severe, 207
types of severe, *204,* 204–207, *205–207*
variables related to, 191–195, *192–195*
water cycle and, 195, *195*
Well water, 318 *lab*
What do you think?, 81, 90, 98, 107, 117, 125, 133, 141
Wilkins, Maurice, 427
Williams syndrome, 432
Windchill, 207
Wind
explanation of, 192
measurement of, 192, *192*
monsoon, 241
pressure systems and, 199
Winter storms, 207
Word Origin, 85, 94, 103, 105, 122, 131, 194, 206, 213, 230, 237, 246, 266, 275, 285, 310, 316, 324, 349, 359, 375, 386, 416, 431, 447, 459, 468, 483, 494, 503. *See also*
Vocabulary
Writing In Science, 147, 221, 257, 293, 335, 367, 439, 477, 511

SCIENCE SKILL HANDBOOK

MATH SKILL HANDBOOK

FOLDABLES HANDBOOK

REFERENCE HANDBOOK

GLOSSARY/ GLOSARIO

INDEX

X

Xenon, 104

Y

Yeast
reproduction in, 385 *lab,* 387
Yellowstone National Park, 310, *310*

Z

Zebra fish, 388
Zinc, 85, *85*
Zygotes
chromosomes and, 374
explanation of, *373,* **373**

PERIODIC TABLE OF THE ELEMENTS

Gas
Liquid
Solid
Synthetic

Element — Hydrogen
Atomic number — 1
Symbol — H
Atomic mass — 1.01
State of matter

A column in the periodic table is called a **group.**

A row in the periodic table is called a **period.**

1	2	3	4	5	6	7	8	9
Hydrogen 1 **H** 1.01								
Lithium 3 **Li** 6.94	Beryllium 4 **Be** 9.01							
Sodium 11 **Na** 22.99	Magnesium 12 **Mg** 24.31							
Potassium 19 **K** 39.10	Calcium 20 **Ca** 40.08	Scandium 21 **Sc** 44.96	Titanium 22 **Ti** 47.87	Vanadium 23 **V** 50.94	Chromium 24 **Cr** 52.00	Manganese 25 **Mn** 54.94	Iron 26 **Fe** 55.85	Cobalt 27 **Co** 58.93
Rubidium 37 **Rb** 85.47	Strontium 38 **Sr** 87.62	Yttrium 39 **Y** 88.91	Zirconium 40 **Zr** 91.22	Niobium 41 **Nb** 92.91	Molybdenum 42 **Mo** 95.96	Technetium 43 **Tc** (98)	Ruthenium 44 **Ru** 101.07	Rhodium 45 **Rh** 102.91
Cesium 55 **Cs** 132.91	Barium 56 **Ba** 137.33	Lanthanum 57 **La** 138.91	Hafnium 72 **Hf** 178.49	Tantalum 73 **Ta** 180.95	Tungsten 74 **W** 183.84	Rhenium 75 **Re** 186.21	Osmium 76 **Os** 190.23	Iridium 77 **Ir** 192.22
Francium 87 **Fr** (223)	Radium 88 **Ra** (226)	Actinium 89 **Ac** (227)	Rutherfordium 104 **Rf** (267)	Dubnium 105 **Db** (268)	Seaborgium 106 **Sg** (271)	Bohrium 107 **Bh** (272)	Hassium 108 **Hs** (270)	Meitnerium 109 **Mt** (276)

The number in parentheses is the mass number of the longest lived isotope for that element.

Lanthanide series

Cerium 58 **Ce** 140.12	Praseodymium 59 **Pr** 140.91	Neodymium 60 **Nd** 144.24	Promethium 61 **Pm** (145)	Samarium 62 **Sm** 150.36	Europium 63 **Eu** 151.96

Actinide series

Thorium 90 **Th** 232.04	Protactinium 91 **Pa** 231.04	Uranium 92 **U** 238.03	Neptunium 93 **Np** (237)	Plutonium 94 **Pu** (244)	Americium 95 **Am** (243)